THE
CURRICULUM
AND
SMALL GROUP
RESOURCE GUIDE

DR. JUDY HAMLIN

NAVPRESS
A MINISTRY OF THE NAVIGATORS
P.O. BOX 6000, COLORADO SPRINGS, COLORADO 80934

The Navigators is an international Christian organization. Jesus Christ gave His followers the Great Commission to go and make disciples (Matthew 28:19). The aim of The Navigators is to help fulfill that commission by multiplying laborers for Christ in every nation.

NavPress is the publishing ministry of The Navigators. NavPress publications are tools to help Christians grow. Although publications alone cannot make disciples or change lives, they can help believers learn biblical discipleship, and apply what they learn to their lives and ministries.

Scripture in this publication is from the *New American Standard Bible* (NASB), © The Lockman Foundation 1960, 1962, 1963, 1968, 1971, 1972, 1973, 1975, 1977; *The Living Bible* © 1971 owned by assignment by the Illinois Regional Bank N.A. (as trustee), used by permission of Tyndale House Publishers, Inc., Wheaton, IL 60189; and the *Good News Bible: Today's English Version* (TEV), copyright © American Bible Society 1966, 1971, 1976.

Printed in the United States of America

To Newt Hamlin,
my editor, friend, and husband;
and to my son, Andrew.
Both are truly gifts from God.

CONTENTS

TO THE USER

I am pleased to present a tool I believe will benefit Christians as they direct others' study paths, introducing them to Christ or helping them mature in their faith.

This reference tool is designed to make your selection of materials both efficient and effective. There are so many curriculum and small-group products in print that without such a tool it is impossible to tap the wealth of resources available.

Each publisher represented here has provided a philosophy statement. Christian publishers have gone virtually unnoticed by many Christians, and I pray this directory will promote knowledge and appreciation of their past, present, and future efforts.

I commend NavPress, which accepted the challenge of publishing this work, for its desire to help people begin small groups and spread the Word of Jesus Christ.

This directory will be updated as the market requires. I hope you will inform others of its existence, so it will be used fully, and so other publishers will add to the wealth of resources.

—JUDY HAMLIN, PH.D.
President, Small Group Services

INTRODUCTION

PURPOSE

This directory will help laypeople, coordinators of small groups, ministers of education, bookstore personnel, and librarians become familiar with publishers of small group curricula. They can then use that curricula to the best advantage in building community, studying God's Word, and reaching out to others with the good news of Jesus Christ. The available software stands alone and provides a more interactive source of materials. Resources will be updated as the market requires.

SCOPE

Since no directory can possibly cover a whole field and meet everyone's needs, only curricula on the open market are covered, including junior high, senior high, young adult, and adult materials. No attempt was made to gather denominational materials. No attempt was made to censor any information.

Forty-seven publishers are listed. Seventeen have only one or two books included, and in most cases these are small group resource materials. Of the remaining thirty, eight have three to nine entries, two have thirteen, and the remaining twenty have from twenty-four to over 150 entries each. Over 1100 entries are included.

PRICE

Prices are noted for all curricula. Where an accompanying leader's guide is indicated, the price is not given. Prices for student material are given, since budgetary considerations sometimes are equally as important as selection.

ACQUISITION OF MATERIALS

Materials were acquired from each publisher, along with catalogs, promotional materials, and current price sheets. In all but approximately thirty cases, the actual resource was used for the evaluation. The other resources are not yet on the market, and were evaluated based on promotional materials and with the assistance of the publisher.

If you publish or distribute curricula or materials you wish to include in an update of this directory, send them to:

Judy Hamlin, President
Small Group Services
17207 Townsley Court
Dallas, TX 75248
(214) 380-2884

HOW TO USE
THIS REFERENCE TOOL

1. Before examining the curricula, describe the target user group, including:

   a. Age
   b. Stage in life
   c. Stage in spiritual walk
   d. Time available for group meeting
   e. Number of weeks willing to commit
   f. Felt needs and/or areas of interest

2. Decide which index will be most helpful in finding the type of curriculum you are interested in. For example, if you want something that deals with grace, turn to the subject index and look under "Grace." Each entry in the subject index includes the name of the publisher, which may help you narrow your choice of possible resources. Each entry also includes a location number at the end that directs you to the corresponding main entry, which includes detailed information about the resources in which you are interested.

3. Examine the following information in the main entry as you look for a match:

   a. Scope of curriculum as indicated in title
   b. Author's name
   c. Author's previous materials
   d. Series
   e. Publisher
   f. Date of publication. If you are dealing with a certain segment of the population (i.e., baby boomers) more recent, contemporary curricula might be desirable.

4. Scan the basic information:

   a. Number of lessons in a study
   b. Time parameters
   c. Number of pages in the study
   d. Average number of questions
   e. Audience
   f. Format. A workbook format may be more desirable than one requiring an additional notebook, especially in an evangelistic study.
   g. Type of study. A topical study may be preferable to a book, for an evangelistic group.

5. Examine the features.

    a. Thirty-six features are possible for each entry. For a new leader, leader's notes may be important. Many recent curricula include prayer helps.
    b. Personal application
    c. Relationship building
    d. Preparation time
    e. Leader's guide availability (separate book)
    f. ISBN
    g. Size

6. Familiarize yourself with the subjects listed in the subject index on page 29.

7. Read the "comment" section to assure a study meets the needs of a given group, or to clarify that the title describes the content.

8. Maintain records on curricula used. This can help later when you want to recommend successful materials. The following "Curricula Tracking Form" can facilitate this process. Have each leader complete and file the form for reference.

CURRICULA TRACKING FORM

SMALL GROUP PROFILE

Name _____ Leader/Host/Hostess

Address of Group Meeting (Host/Hostess)

_____

City, State, Zip _____

Phone (Host/Hostess) _____ Home _____ Work

Phone (Leader) _____ Home _____ Work

Day of Meeting _____ Time of Meeting _____

Group Type   ❏ Married/Young Children   ❏ Married/Teens

          ❏ Single Parent/Young Children   ❏ Single/Teens

          ❏ Business Persons   ❏ Empty Nesters

          ❏ Newly Married   ❏ Homemakers

CURRICULUM TITLE: _____

Author _____ Date of Publication _____

Publisher _____ Series Title _____

Outside Study Time _____ In Group Time _____

Number of Pages _____ Number of Lessons _____ ISBN _____

Average Number of Questions per Lesson _____ Price _____

Level of Difficulty   ❏ Low   ❏ Moderate   ❏ High

I Would Recommend This Study   ❏ Yes   ❏ No

Why, or why not?

EXPLANATION OF INFORMATION

The largest section of this guide is the list of main entries, which details the features of each curriculum item. (A sample entry appears below.) These main entries are listed alphabetically by *the author's last name*. Entries in which no author is named are alphabetized by *title* and are listed at the beginning of the main entry section.

In addition, each entry is listed in indexes sorted by title, publisher, series, subject, and book of the Bible. The heads in the first four indexes are alphabetical. The Old and New Testament index is in the order of books in the Bible. The entries in the title index are also in alphabetical order. The entries in the subject index, the Old and New Testament index, the publisher index, and the series index are in order based on the location number.

Author: Briscoe, Jill   **157**
Series: Jill Briscoe Bible Study
Title: *Heaven and Hell: A Study of the Promise and the Peril*
          of Eternity
Publisher: Victor Books, 1990

Num. Sess.	Group Time	Num. Pgs.	Avg. Qst.	Price	Audience	Format	Bible Study
8	60-90	95	18	5.99	New Christian	Workbk	Topical

Features: Intro to Leading a Study, Intro to Study, Prayer Helps, Scrpt Memory Helps, Digging Deeper Quest, Follow Up
  ★★★ Personal Application   Preparation Time: Med   ISBN: 0-89693-768-2
  ★★★ Relationship Building Ldr. Guide Avail.: No   Size: 6.0 x 9.0
Subjects: Devotionals, Eschatology, Heaven/Hell
Comments: This study concerns the promise and peril of eternity. Participants will find various responses to questions about afterlife, such as: What are Heaven and hell like? Where are they? Are they physical places or states of mind? and, Where will we spend eternity? Each lesson provides a devotional narrative, suggestions for group discussion and prayer, and a Bible study for more advanced study. A notebook is recommended for recording thoughts, discoveries, and prayer requests.

AUTHOR
Name of author(s) is given. When an entry has more than two authors, an et al. designation is given after the listing of first author.

SERIES
The publisher series title is abbreviated when necessary.

TITLE
The title of the entry is listed. Entries beginning with "A" or "The" are listed according to the first important word. Subtitles are given, space permitting.

PUBLISHER
Name of the publisher, or in some cases the distributor, is listed, followed by the earliest printing date.

NUMBER OF SESSIONS—Num Sess.
The number of sessions in the curriculum is indicated. When entry is for Bible Study Resources, total number of chapters is given.

GROUP TIME
A time range—from minimum to maximum number of minutes, depending on time spent in fellowship and prayer—is provided.

NUMBER OF PAGES—Num Pgs.
The last numbered page in the item is indicated. When blank pages at the end are counted by the publishers, the catalog publisher count is given.

AVERAGE NUMBER QUESTIONS—Avg Qst.
An average number of questions per chapter is given. When the range is too great to provide a meaningful number, a

"vry" designation has been given. When there are no questions a "not applicable (N/A)" designation is given.

PRICE
Current catalog prices (for early 1991) are listed and are subject to change.

AUDIENCE
Three categories are possible: beginner, new Christian, and mature Christian. A "beginner" audience is anyone who is open to Christian study (a commitment to Christ is not assumed). "Beginner" does not necessarily imply that mature believers would not enjoy or benefit from the study. A "new Christian" audience has exceeded beginner level and assumed a commitment to Christ. A "mature Christian" audience is asked to commit itself to homework and a longer period of time. At this level, personal application and relationship building are not primary features but byproducts; a designation of mature Christian with a 1 rating in Personal Application and a 1 rating in Relationship Building is common. It does not in any way reflect a poor study. On the contrary, this is probably desirable.

FORMAT
Options include book, workbook, video, and audio. "Book" is designated when the entry is in a book format and no questions are provided, or they're provided at the end of a chapter. The designation also applies to Bible studies in book format but with no space for response to questions. "Workbook" is the designation for studies that provide room for response to questions. "Video" is used when the entry is a video kit. "Audio" means the entry is an audio kit. This category is not used often. Usually audio tapes may be ordered to supplement a printed Bible study. For example, for a Chuck Swindoll entry, audio is indicated as a feature.

BIBLE STUDY
Options are topical, book, character, and no. A topical study treats a subject from a scriptural basis (*Divorce Recovery*). A book study deals with a book of the Bible (*Letters to Timothy*). A character study deals with a Bible book character (*Nehemiah, Succeeding by Serving*). "No" indicates the study is not a Bible study, but includes Bible study resources (*The Small Group Leaders' Training Course*).

FEATURES
A list of enhancements is mentioned for each entry. Possible features include the following: introduction to leading a study, introduction to the study, objectives, bibliography, prayer helps, scripture memory, worship helps, study overview, no group questions, prediscussion questions, digging deeper questions, follow-up, summary, scripture printed leader's notes, drawings, cartoons, photos, handouts, personal study questions, charts, transparency masters, glossary, maps, agenda, index, cross-references, topical index, appendix, cassettes available, exam, word study, publicity ideas, book inc., video study guide, book available. Only the features of the book to be studied are listed. If a curriculum is

evaluated and an accompanying leader's guide includes additional features, they are not listed under "Features." If space permits, those features are given in the comments section.

PERSONAL APPLICATION
This rating is based on the inclusion of personal application questions and the presence of certain features such as introduction, follow-up, summary, personal study questions, drawings, cartoons, photos, prayer helps, and format of the entry. The subject and how it is treated by the author is taken into consideration, as is, in some cases, the amount of Scripture used to support the study.

RELATIONSHIP BUILDING
This rating is based on the inclusion of the following: features like an introduction, agenda, prayer helps, and worship helps; the presence of a warm-up or icebreaker section; and in some cases contemporary treatment when it is important. A low rating in this category does not imply that a group won't build strong relationships while using the given entry. Any leader or group members can build relationships if they choose. A low rating simply means that the printed or taped material does not include much overt help in building relationships. Such a product leaves relationship building up to the leader and members.

PREPARATION TIME
None—no homework required; Low—up to one hour; Med—from one to three hours; High—over three hours.

LEADER'S GUIDE—Ldr. Guide Avail.
A "yes" indicates a leader's guide is available; a "no" indicates one is not available.

ISBN
The International Standard Book number assigned to each entry by the Library of Congress is listed; for video kits the number from the video kit is given.

SIZE
The size of each entry from left to right then top to bottom is listed. This information is useful for library shelf placement and for group leaders who have a particular size in mind. For example, one might want a study that fits inside a Bible.

SUBJECTS
See page 29 for a complete listing. At least one subject is given for each entry.

COMMENTS
A brief overview of each entry outlines the contents and benefits of that particular study.

LOCATION NUMBER
Entries are numbered consecutively from 1 to 1195. Each entry in the indexes includes a location number so that you can quickly find the resource in the main entry list.

PUBLISHER PHILOSOPHY STATEMENTS

The philosophy statements presented here will help acquaint you with the publishers of small group curriculum.

AGLOW PUBLICATIONS

Aglow Publications is a ministry of Women's Aglow Fellowship, International. Women all over the world are finding support in the pages of Aglow Publications. A dedicated team of writers, editors, and artists create quality materials to equip women for the challenges of today and the opportunities of tomorrow. Through books, Bible studies, evangelistic literature, and the bimonthly Aglow magazine, Aglow Publications has been equipping women for over twenty years.

Women Aglow Fellowship is an international, interdenominational organization of renewed Christian women. In 1967, four women in Seattle, Washington, began to pray for a way Spirit-filled women might fellowship together. From an initial luncheon meeting, Women's Aglow Fellowship has grown into an international organization of over 2,500 fellowships in 103 nations on six continents.

Women's Aglow Fellowship provides support, education, training, and ministry opportunities to help women worldwide discover their true identity in Jesus Christ through the power of the Holy Spirit. We believe that:

- All women and men are created equal in the image of God, each with dignity and value.
- God has a unique purpose for each of us, and equips us for that purpose.
- We can reach our full potential only after finding identity and restoration in Jesus Christ.

AUGSBURG FORTRESS PUBLISHERS

Augsburg Fortress Publishers produce resources to help proclaim God's saving gospel of justification by grace for Christ's sake through faith alone, according to the apostolic witness in the Holy Scripture, preserving and transmitting the gospel faithfully to future generations.

Resources reflect the work of authors, writers, and editors who:

- confess the Triune God, Father, Son, and Holy Spirit;
- confess Jesus Christ as Lord and Savior and the gospel as the power of God for the salvation of all who believe;
- accept the canonical Scriptures of the Old and New Testaments as the inspired Word of God and the authoritative source and norm of faith and life.

BETHANY HOUSE PUBLISHERS

Bethany House Publishers' most significant curriculum effort is the Building Books Young Adult Curriculum. This series of eight student books and teacher's guides provides young adults with a strongly biblical-oriented lesson that can be used for Bible classes, small group studies, or individual devotional study. Each book presents thirty-four lessons essential for Christian growth and covers the practical themes of developing Bible study skills, Christian character, commitment, confidence, discipline, relationships, values, and defending the gospel against cults. These books meet a need for groups looking for a straight biblical study without denominational affiliation.

Bethany also offers curriculum related either to best-selling books or audio tape series from best-selling authors for which a study guide was designed. In both cases the curriculum was designed to accompany and enhance the message of the original product.

CHURCH DEVELOPMENT RESOURCES

Church Development Resources, which provides the Men's Life and women's Coffee Break programs and materials, is a service organization committed to helping churches be vital and growing. Our aim is to provide attractive, up-to-date Bible study materials that are biblically sound, strategically accurate, and culturally relevant. Leadership training, consultation, and support services are also available through a network of regional personnel.

GOSPEL LIGHT PUBLICATIONS/REGAL BOOKS

The mission of Gospel Light is to know Christ and make Him know; to provide His church with effective Bible teaching and learning resources for use in making disciples, empowering them for godly living, equipping them for ministry and the evangelization of the world.

Gospel Light affirms: We believe the Bible to be the divinely inspired and authoritative Word of God, the only infallible rule of faith and practice.

We believe in one God, creator and sustainer of the universe, who eternally exists in three persons: Father, Son, and Holy Spirit.

We believe in the Lord Jesus Christ, who being fully God became fully man, was born of a virgin, lived a sinless life, died on a cross, was raised bodily, is exalted to God's right hand, and will personally come again.

We believe that all have sinned and are guilty before God,a nd, as a result, all, both individually and corporately, suffer the consequences of the fall and are under condemnation.

We believe that because of His love God sent His Son, Jesus Christ, who inaugurated His kingdom, provided an atonement for sin, conquered the principalities and powers, is reconciling the world to Himself, and will consummate His kingdom in righteousness, power, and glory.

We believe that all those who repent and believe in Christ are delivered from the judgment of God and are born again into life eternal, and are called to be instruments of God's righteousness and reconciliation in human society.

We believe in the Holy Spirit who glorifies Jesus Christ, works in all peoples to bring them to faith and obedience, and dwells in believers equipping and empowering them for lives of holiness and fruitful service.

We believe that the Church, the Body of Christ, consists of all believers and exists to fulfill Christ's mission, making disciples of all nations and bringing healing and justice to human society, all to the glory of God.

We believe in the resurrection of the body, the everlasting punishment of unbelievers and the everlasting blessedness of believers in the presence of Christ.

GROUP PUBLISHING, INC.

Group's mission statement: To encourage Christian growth in children, youth, and those who nurture them.

Doctrinal statement: We believe the Bible is the inspired, authoritative Word of God. We believe there is one God, eternally existent in three persons: Father, Son, and Holy Spirit. We believe in the deity of Jesus Christ, in His virgin birth, in His sinless life, in His shed blood, in His bodily resurrection, in His ascension to the right hand of the Father, and in His personal return.

Group's active (experiential) learning philosophy: All Group curricula and teaching resources are based on active learning. Where young people learn by doing—through experiences. With active learning, young people will grow in wisdom, maturity, and faith. Active learning is a discovery process that helps learning stick. It's the opposite of passive learning where a teacher tells students what to think and believe. The active (experiential) learning process involves: *Action*—when students do something. It can be a direct experience, game simulation or role play. *Reflection*—when students talk about how they felt about the experience. Everyone shares. *Interpretation*—when students discover a message from the experience. Here's when teenagers discover the relevancy of the Bible—to their own lives today. *Application*—helps apply the teaching to each young person's everyday life—with a commitment to change. These active learning experiences can be applied to groups of any size—from small to large.

Group is: *Interdenominational*—our products and services are used by people of all Christian denominations. Group is in no way connected with nor subject to any particular denominational body, but rather serves them all. *Innovative*—Group stays on the cutting edge of youth and children's ministry by providing the largest single collection of youth and family ministry resources in the world. *Independent*—Group is a privately held Colorado corporation and is not connected with any other company or organization.

HERE'S LIFE PUBLISHERS, INC.

We believe that everyone who does not know Jesus Christ personally is a target of God's love. Our goal is to introduce these people to God's love, demonstrated in Christ's death and resurrection, and then disciple them until they themselves are bringing others to Christ. Some, however, are bound by emotional chains acquired through childhood or adolescent abuse, through spousal abuse, or addictive habits—and we need to help them get rid of those chains before they can be truly productive disciples of Jesus Christ.

The small group is one way Jesus ministered. Thus as the publishing arm of Campus Crusade for Christ, Here's Life Publishers provides evangelism and follow-up materials for small group use. Evangelistic studies, like [How to Get Better Grades and Have More Fun and *How to Achieve Your Potential and Enjoy Life* have been extremely successful in smaller group studies on campuses. *Vision-Driven Leadership* represents a small group study tool for business people who wan tot lead others to Christ through study of a high felt need topic, using Christian role models.

For follow up of new believers, small group studies like *The Ten Basic Steps* and *The Transferable Concepts* have helped people gain not only a broad knowledge of the Bible but also what it means to live the Spirit-filled life.

INTERVARSITY PRESS

The goals and purpose of InterVarsity Press are to serve the university, the church, and the world by creating quality products and services that communicate the lordship of Christ over all of life. As the publishing arm of InterVarsity Christian Fellowship, our books are consistent with the IVCF statement of faith.

In all of our publishing we believe that it crucial to communicate effectively to the intended audience through books that exhibit high standards of quality and have integrity. We also want to publish books that develop people in Christlikeness and are responsibly biblical.

IVCF small groups include four basic components: study, worship, community, and mission. InterVarsity Press small group books and Bible study guides explore these aspects of small group life from a variety of perspectives.

LAY ACTION MINISTRY PROGRAM, INC.

Lay Action Ministry Program, Inc. (LAMP) believes that the central command of our Lord to His Church is to "make disciples." LAMP helps churches fulfill this command by providing a curriculum of lay training courses and a design for using them.

Some LAMP courses *ground* new and untaught Christians in discipleship and Bible knowledge. Other courses help them *grow* in awareness of their call and gifts for ministry. Still other courses equip them to *go* into any of a variety of ministries.

The LAMP book, *Design For Lay Ministry* explains how to put this ministry philosophy into operation in your church.

LIGONIER MINISTRIES

Hearing and doing the Word of God in all of life, this is the passion of Dr. R. C. Sproul, chairman of Ligonier Ministries. Watch his videos, read his books, listen to his tapes, experience his seminars and you see, hear, and experience passion. Passion for truth and knowledge; passion for transformation and reformation; but more than anything, passion for Jesus Christ.

R. C.'s credentials include degrees from Westminster College, Pittsburgh Theological Seminary, and the Free University of Amsterdam. He is the author of twenty-five books and scores of magazine articles for evangelical publications. He is also J. D. Trimble Professor of Systematic Theology at the Orlando campus of Reformed Theological Seminary, and has taught at Westminster College, Gordon College, and Gordon-Conwell Theological Seminary.

In 1971, R. C. helped establish Ligonier Ministries, a ministry designed to fill the gap in Christian education between Sunday school and formal seminary education. R. C.'s goal for Ligonier is "to flood society with articulate, well-equipped Christians who will minister to the pain of our world. "To achieve this, Ligonier offers a wide range of resources for adult Christian education, resources not just for restricted use in the classroom, but for frequent and practical applications in everyday situations. These resources are available on audio and video tapes on subjects such as apologetics, theology, ethics, culture, and Bible study. Ligonier's ministry also includes R. C.'s books, Tabletalk magazine, conferences, and curricula that accompanies many of the audio and video series.

MOODY PRESS

The mission of Moody Press is to educate and edify the Christian and to evangelize the non-Christian by ethically publishing conservative, evangelical Christian literature and other media for all ages, around the world. Moody Press has earned a reputation for publishing books that draw solid solutions from Scripture. Answers that really work in the world. To help you delve more deeply in Scripture on your own. To help you reach your own conclusions about the issues you face. So you can engage your culture, and change it for Christ.

NAVPRESS

We believe that people exist to know and glorify God, and that we are in the world in order to draw the lost to know Christ. We also believe that spiritual growth is primarily a relationship with Christ and with others; that prayer, scripture study, etc., are means toward the end of knowing Christ; and that believers will draw the lost to Christ to the extent that they incarnate the gospel. That is, the Word of God needs to become flesh in believers' lives, and those believers need to dwell among the lost.

Small groups, we think, are integral to this growth in incarnating the gospel. Therefore, NavPress small group materials will support the church in equipping ordinary people in this process. They will help group members, leaders, and coordinators deal with the complex issues of contemporary society in the light of Who Christ is. They will serve believers from a range of traditions and a variety of group types. They will foster fun and productive group relationships, be rooted in biblical truth, and be culturally relevant.

RAPHA PUBLISHING

Rapha's mission statement: *To attain* national leadership in the field of Christ-centered counseling. *To promote* biblical and spiritual solutions to persons with psychiatric and substance abuse problems. *To provide* excellence in mental health care. *To glorify* God and share our commitment to the lordship of Jesus Christ with a needy nation. *To generate* measurable benefits for: the patient; the Christian community; supportive ministries; the company; the employee; the local church.

ROPER PRESS

We at Roper Press are committed to the Word of God. We know its impact on the hearts and lives of people and, by God's grace, will continue to produce Bible study materials that are true to the Word of God, that honor and glorify the Lord Jesus Christ, and that minister to the needs of believers.

Roper Press is known for its rich heritage and commitment to evangelical bible study. Our materials are widely used and respected wherever Bible teaching has priority. Whether for Sunday school, vacation Bible school, Christian school, youth conference, or home Bible study, we are committed to focusing on God's Word as the answer for the twentieth-century man.

We realize that commitment, character, and credentials, while essential, are not sufficient apart from the ministry of the Holy Spirit in individual lives. Author, editor, teacher, and student alike must come before God with an attitude of submissiveness and expectancy, knowing that personal response to the Word of God is absolutely essential. God can and will bring about changes in our lives that will honor and glorify the Lord Jesus Christ. This is our ultimate goal.

SERENDIPITY HOUSE

Serendipity is a philosophy of ministry that includes small groups at the heart and center of the church; it is a movement of many like-minded people who have a passion for seeing the church renewed; it is an institution that trains pastors and church leaders in this philosophy of ministry and to be used by those that have been trained.

Serendipity did not grow up in the academic world but instead came out of the trenches of daily contact with nonchurched and counter-cultural ministry, our concepts for small groups, "which we call strategies," are quite different from any other ministry organization that employs small groups. For instance, we believe that every church must have at least five different models: (1) discipleship groups, (2) covenant groups, (3) support groups, (4) recovery groups, and (5) task/mission groups. A church that is only one of these models is by definition limiting the scope of its small group program.

The preceding strategies are the reasons why we feel it is important that groups follow a progressive, ever-deepening approach to Bible study. In the first seven weeks, when the group should focus on group building, we strongly recommend Bible stories that allow you to share your own personal story through the stories in the Bible. In the second phase, when the need is a spiritual formation, we recommend a deeper form of Bible study often called inductive Bible study, in which the emphasis is upon cognitive material.

Serendipity has a very clear statement of purpose. Our objective is to see an effective small group ministry in every church in the United States by the year 2000. We are intentional about this objective with training for pastors, church leaders, and small group leaders. Our curricula are essential to this training, but are never intended to stand alone.

SERVANT PUBLICATIONS

Since Servant Publications opened its doors in 1972, our aim has never been to build the biggest, the brightest,or the most successful Christian publishing company. Instead, we have tried in a small way to publish books that will introduce men and women to the gospel, strengthen Christians in their life with God, and help people sort out light from darkness in an age of confusion.

We believe that God is asking us to build bridges among all our brothers and sisters in Christ. So, for most of our history, we've made it our mission to publish for Protestant and Catholic readers. Such a strategy doesn't always make sense in the marketplace, but it works out pretty well in the kingdom of God, where Jesus prays for our unity.

HAROLD SHAW PUBLISHERS

God's people need each other as they live out their faith in this world. Small groups provide ideal settings for outreach and growth as people discover God's Word for themselves and encourage one another to put it into practice. Being in a small group of caring people opens up a whole new dimension of growing that can't take place individually or in large groups.

Shaw Publishers is committed to providing materials that will promote spiritual growth as people study and apply God's Word together. Inductive questions lead to responsible interpretation of Scripture. In the interactive, personal environment of a small group, Scripture, and prayer can be tied to life specifically and individually. Shaw study guides are designed to help groups interact with the Bible in life-changing ways. They challenge seekers and Christians from a diverse range of backgrounds to investigate Scripture and live out its truth.

SHEPHERD MINISTRIES

We believe America's teenagers are facing greater struggles and possess fewer biblical values than at any time in the history of our nation. Therefore our mission is defined to be:

- Creating opportunities to present biblical values and spiritual solutions to both churched and unchurched teenagers through conferences, crusades, and media.
- Arranging for these teenagers to receive spiritual counseling and appropriate resource materials.
- Motivating, mobilizing, and training youth workers and parents to understand and become involved in the rescue, nurture, and discipleship of American's teenagers.

STANDARD PUBLISHING

Our philosophy: To teach God's Word with excitement. To study the whole Bible systematically. To build each lesson upon specific learning objectives. To use a variety of the most effective teaching methods. To involve students actively in the learning process. To ensure that lessons change students' lives. To give special emphasis to such basic bible doctrines as the creation of the world and man by direct act of God; the deity of Jesus Christ, His virgin birth, His miracles, His atoning death, His bodily resurrection, and His return.

TYNDALE HOUSE PUBLISHERS

Our corporate purpose is to minister to the spiritual needs of people, primarily through literature consistent with biblical principles.

VICTOR BOOKS

Victor Books seeks to equip learners and educators for ministries in and outside the church. Our corporate mission statement reflects their goals: "Called by God and committed to produce excellent, Bible-based, life-related curriculum, books, and Christian education products that will be used to reach and teach people for Christ."

As Bible study moves beyond Sunday school into weekday slots, Victor Books realizes that one product or format will not meet all the needs of those involved in various types of small groups. Therefore, Victor Books is committed to developing a complete line of quality books for use in a variety of settings. Our intention is to provide small group members and their leaders with solid biblical principles, relevancy, and flexibility in methods and topics.

If a small group is more comfortable with a traditional teacher/student situation, we recommend our Electives/Leader's Guide Available products as well as our Inductive Bible Studies.

However, more and more church leaders are stressing a strong relational emphasis in small groups to help meet the isolation and interpersonal needs of people within our large, often impersonal society who are felling the need to belong to an intimate community. If a small group is looking for something other than the traditional teacher/student format, we recommend GroupBuilder Resources, a new line of books specifically geared to help baby boomer small group member (1) build relationships by sharing their lives and experiences, (2) find direction in God's Word, and (3) practice the truths they learn in the context of their small group.

For children and youth, we provide SonPower High School Small Group Studies, High School and Junior High Electives, Inductive and Discipleship studies, and KidBuilder's programming materials.

WORD, INC.

Small groups are a vital part of the growth and vitality of the local church. It is in these non-threatening, fellowship laboratories of learning that most Christians find their greatest source of spiritual growth. Love, acceptance, and security are combined with the power of prayer, Scripture study, and worship to provide a fertile ground for the Holy Spirit's work of sanctification.

Word is committed to providing the most effective resources for these small groups. Our programs offer a wide variety of designs, formats, and approaches. Audio, video, and print are often combined to meet a stated goal. Each program is unique. Target age groups play a vital part in design as well as the gifts and talents of the speaker or writer.

Theologically, Word's small group resources can be trusted to uphold the highest view of spiritual authority and maintain a thoroughly evangelical perspective. Men and women of integrity share their insight from a variety of denominational backgrounds but with the one goal of glorifying Christ and equipping the believer for the work of the kingdom.

ZONDERVAN PUBLISHING HOUSE

Zondervan small group materials are written with one goal in mind, to allow the Spirit of God to use the Word of God to strengthen us in Christ. To accomplish that goal, all of Zondervan's newer study guides have several key features:

- The questions help you discover what the Bible says rather than simply telling you the answers. This teaches people how to feed themselves from Scripture rather than always relying on the insights of "experts."
- The questions are opened ended, encouraging more than one answer. This makes your group discussions more lively and allows people to hear several perspectives.
- The studies are personal, helping you to apply the passage to your everyday situations. We believe this is the ultimate goal of Bible study.
- Most studies focus on only one or two passages. This allows you to see Scripture in its context, avoiding the temptation of prooftexting and the frustration of "Bible hopscotch" (jumping from verse to verse).
- Every study guide contains leader's notes. These provide additional insights into the questions, give tips on group dynamics, and provide helpful background information about the passage. With these notes, almost anyone can lead an effective study.

Whether used by small groups, Sunday-school classes, neighborhood Bible studies, or by individuals in their quiet times, all Zondervan Bible studies are designed to allow the Scriptures to renew our minds so that we can be transformed by the Spirit of God.

PUBLISHER ADDRESSES
AND CUSTOMER SERVICE PHONE NUMBERS

Abingdon Press
P. O. Box 801
Nashville, TN 37202
(800) 251-3320

Aglow Publications
P. O. Box 1548
Lynnwood, WA 98046-1558
(206) 775-7282

Augsburg Fortress Publishers
426 South Fifth Street
Box 1209
Minneapolis, MN 55440
(800) 328-4648

Baker Book House
P. O. Box 6287
Grand Rapids, MI 49516-6287
(800) 877-2665

Bethany House Publishers
6820 Auto Club Road
Minneapolis, MN 55438
(800) 328-6109

Bridge Publishing, Inc.
2500 Hamilton Boulevard
South Plainfield, NJ 07080
(800) 631-5802

Broadman Press
127 Ninth Avenue, North
Nashville, TN 37234
(800) 251-3225

Campus Crusade for Christ, Inc.
Arrowhead Springs
San Bernardino, CA 92414
(714) 886-5224

Christian Literature Crusade
P. O. Box 1449
Fort Washington, PA 19034
(800) 659-1240

Church Development Resources
2850 Kalamazoo Avenue
Grand Rapids, MI 49560
(800) 777-7270

Church Growth
2640 South Myrtle Avenue, Suite A-3
Monrovia, CA 91016
(800) 423-4844

Cokesbury
Box 801
Nashville, TN 37202
(615) 749-6123

David C. Cook Publishers
850 North Grove Avenue
Elgin, IL 60120
(800) 323-7543

Faith at Work
11065 Little Patuxent Parkway
Columbia, MD 21044
(301) 730-3690

Gospel Films, Inc.
P. O. Box 455
Muskegon, MI 49443-0455
(800) 253-0413

Gospel Light Publications
2300 Knoll Drive
Ventura, CA 93003
(800) 446-7735

Group Publishing, Inc.
2890 North Monroe Avenue
Box 481
Loveland, CO 80539
(800) 747-6060

Here's Life Publishers, Inc.
2700 Little Mountain Drive
P. O. 15761
San Bernardino, CA 92402-1572
(800) 950-1457

Holt, Rinehart, Winston, Inc.
6277 Sea Harbor Drive
Orlando, FL 32821
(800) 782-4479

InterVarsity Press
5206 Main Street
P. O. Box 1400
Downers Grove, IL 60515
(800) 843-7225

Lay Action Ministry Program, Inc.
5827 South Rapp Street
Littleton, CO 80120
(303) 730-8340

Ligonier Ministries
Box 7500
Orlando, FL 32854
(800) 435-4343

Loizeaux Brothers, Inc.
P. O. Box 277
Neptune, NJ 07754-0277
(800) 526-2796

Macmillan Publishing Co.
866 Third Avenue
New York, NY 10022
(800) 257-5755

Maranatha Publications
P. O. Box 1799
Gainesville, FL 32602
(904) 375-6000

Moody Press
820 North LaSalle Drive
Chicago, IL 60610
(800) 621-7105

Multnomah Press
10209 Southeast Division Street
Portland, OR 97266
(800) 547-5890

NavPress
P. O. Box 35001
Colorado Springs, CO 80935
(800) 366-7788

Prentice-Hall, Inc.
200 Old Tappan Road
Old Tappan, NJ 07675
(800) 922-0579

Rapha Publishing
Box 580355
Houston, TX 77258
(800) 992-4673

Recovery Publications, Inc.
1201 Knoxville Street
San Diego, CA 92110
(800) 873-8384

Regal Books, Division of Gospel Light
2300 Knoll Drive
Ventura, CA 93003
(800) 446-7735

Roper Press, Inc.
915 Dragon Street
Dallas, TX 75207
(800) 284-0158

Scripture Press Publications, Inc.
1825 College Avenue
Wheaton, IL 60187
(800) 323-9409

Serendipity House, Inc.
P. O. Box 1012
Littleton, CO 80160
(800) 525-9563

Servant Publications
840 Airport Boulevard
P. O. Box 8617
Ann Arbor, MI 48107
(313) 761-8505

Harold Shaw Publishers
388 Gundersen Drive
P. O. Box 567
Wheaton, IL 60189
(800) 742-9782

Shepherd Ministries
2845 West Airport Freeway, Suite 137
Irving, TX 75062
(214) 570-7599

Standard Publishing
8121 Hamilton Avenue
Cincinnati, OH 45231
(800) 543-1301

Stephen Ministries
1325 Baland
Saint Louis, MO 63117
(314) 645-5511

Tyndale House Publishers
336 Gundersen Drive
P. O. Box 80
Wheaton, IL 60189
(800) 323-9400

University Associates, Inc.
8517 Production Avenue
San Diego, CA 92121
(619) 578-5900

Victor Books
1825 College Avenue
Wheaton, IL 60187
(800) 323-2608

Warner Press
1200 East Fifth Street
P. O. Box 2499
Anderson, IN 46018
(800) 347-6468

The Westminister Press
100 Witherspoon Street
Louisville, KY 40202-1396
(800) 523-1631

Word, Inc.
5221 North O'Connor Boulevard, Suite 1000
Irving, TX 75039
(800) 299-9673

Zondervan Publishing House
1415 Lake Drive, Southeast
Grand Rapids, MI 49506
(800) 444-4012

INDEXES

Subject Headings

Abortion
Accountability
Addictions
Angels
Apocalyptic
Apologetics
Baptism
Beliefs
Bible Personalities
Bible Study
Caring
Charismatic Interest
Christian Life
Christian Living
Church Life
Commitments
Counseling
Cults
Decision Making
Devotionals
Discipleship
Divorce
Emotions
Eschatology
Ethics
Evangelism
Failure
Faith
False Teachers
Family
Fasting
Forgiveness
Friendships
Fruit of the Spirit
God
God's Promises
Gospels
Grace
Grief
Heaven/Hell
Holiness
Holy Spirit
Holy Week
Hope

Integrity
Jesus: Life/Teaching
Joy
Leadership
Loneliness
Love
Major Prophets
Marriage
Medical Issues
Men's Issues
Minor Prophets
Miracles
Missions
Money
Morals
New Testament
Obedience
Occult
Old Testament
Parables
Parenting
Pastoral Epistles
Prayer
Prison Epistles
Prophecy
Psychology
Reconciliation
Relationships
Remarriage
Renewal
Repentance
Revival
Satan
Self-esteem
Self-help
Senior Adults
Sermon on the Mount
Service
Sexual Issues
Singles Issues
Small Group Resources
Social Issues
Spiritual Gifts
Stewardship

Stress
Success
Suffering
Support
Teens: Bible/Personalities
   Bible Study
   Christian Living
   Cults
   Decisions
   Devotionals
   Discipleship
   Drugs/Drinking
   Emotions
   Ethics
   Evangelism
   Family
   Friends
   Jesus' Life
   Junior High
   Music
   New Testament
   Occult
   Old Testament
   Peer Pressure
   Prayer
   Psychology
   Relationships
   Self-esteem
   Self-image
   Senior High
   Sexuality
   Theology
   Youth Life
Ten Commandments
Theology
Time
Victorious Living
Wholeness
Wisdom
Women's Issues
Work
Worship
Young Marrieds
Youth Life

SUBJECT INDEX

Christian Living

False Teachers

Family

Leadership

Loneliness

Love

Major Prophets

Prophecy

Psychology

Reconciliation

Relationships

Old and New Testament Headings

Genesis
Exodus
Leviticus
Numbers/Deuteronomy
Joshua
Judges
Ruth
1 & 2 Samuel
Kings/Chronicles
Ezra/Nehemiah
Esther
Job
Psalms
Proverbs

Ecclesiastes
Song of Solomon
Major Prophets
Isaiah/Jeremiah
Lamentations
Ezekiel
Daniel
Jonah
Minor Prophets
Matthew
Mark
Luke
John
Acts

Romans
1 Corinthians
2 Corinthians
Galatians
Ephesians
Philippians
Colossians/Philemon
1 & 2 Thessalonians
1 & 2 Timothy/Titus
Hebrews
James
1 & 2 Peter
1, 2, & 3 John/Jude
Revelation

OLD AND NEW TESTAMENT INDEX

TITLE INDEX

PUBLISHER INDEX

Discover: The Gospel of Mark—Part 2, $2.10, 352

Discover: The Gospel of Mark—Part 1, $2.10, 353

Discover: 1 John, $1.10, 354

Discover: Genesis, $1.80, 901

Discover: Genesis—Abraham and Sarah, $2.10, 902

Discover: God in the Psalms, $1.25, 903

Discover: Ephesians, $1.95, 934

Discover: Galatians, $1.35, 935

Discover Luke: Jesus' Parables and Miracles, $1.50, 936

Discover Luke: Jesus' Last Days, $1.50, 937

Discover: The Sermon on the Mount, $1.35, 938

Discover: Prayer, $1.35, 1120

Church Growth

Growing in Love, $198.00, 73

Cokesbury

2 Corinthians—Volumes 1 & 2, $29.95, 307

Exodus—Volumes 1-3, $29.95, 332

Gospel of Mark, The—Volumes 1-3, $29.95, 333

More Than Conquerors—Volumes 1-3, $29.95, 334

Twelve Parables of Jesus—Volumes 1-3, $29.95, 335

Gospel of John, The: Volume 1 & 2, $29.95, 486

Matthew: Volume 1 & 2, $29.95, 587

1 Corinthians—Volumes 1-3, $29.95, 773

Acts—Volumes 1 & 2, $29.95, 1177

David C. Cook Publishing Co.

Balancing Your Priorities, $3.95, 774

Getting Along with People You Love, $3.95, 775

Getting Your Act Together, $3.95, 776

Living in Harmony, $3.95, 777

Faith at Work, Inc.

Making Peace with the Pieces of My Life, $2.50, 34

Great Biblical Themes, $2.50, 492

Group Encounters with the Bible, $2.00, 493

Journeying in the Spirit, $2.00, 494

Lessons in the Life of Faith, $2.50, 495

Gospel Films, Inc.

Divorce Recovery Workshop: Rebuilding the Castle That Has Come Down, $149.95, 374

Whatever Happened to the Human Race?, $149.95, 926

One Is a Whole Number, $129.95, 979

Gospel Light Publications

Christ B. C., $13.95, 8

Christ B. C.—Youth Edition, $13.95, 9

Complete Junior High Bible Study Resource Book #10, The, $14.95, 360

Complete Junior High Bible Study Resource Book #3, The, $14.95, 361

Complete Junior High Bible Study Resource Book #11, The, $14.95, 362

Complete Junior High Bible Study Resource Book #12, The, $14.95, 363

Complete Junior High Bible Study Resource Book #5, The, $14.95, 364

Complete Junior High Bible Study Resource Book #1, The, $14.95, 365

Complete Junior High Bible Study Resource Book #6, The, $14.95, 366

Complete Junior High Bible Study Resource Book #7, The, $14.95, 367

Complete Junior High Bible Study Resource Book #9, The, $14.95, 368

Complete Junior High Bible Study Resource Book #2, The, $14.95, 369

Complete Junior High Bible Study Resource Book #8, The, $14.95, 370

Group Publishing, Inc.

Active Meetings on Basic Christianity, $10.95, 2

Group's Best Junior High Meetings—Volume 2, $15.95, 21

Group's Best Junior High Meetings—Volume 1, $18.95, 22

Headline News Discussion Starters, $8.95, 26

Worry, Worry, Worry: School, War and Other Scary Stuff—Student Book, $3.95, 55

Gospel of John, The: Jesus' Teachings, $6.95, 57

Dennis Benson's Creative Bible Studies: Matthew—Acts, $19.95, 93

Dennis Benson's Creative Bible Studies: Romans—Revelation, $12.95, 94

Getting Along with Parents, $6.95, 97

Peer Pressure, $6.95, 225

Faith for Tough Times, $6.95, 228

Joy of Serving, The, $6.95, 232

Money: A Christian Perspective, $6.95, 250

Your Life as a Disciple, $6.95, 324

Drugs, God, and Me, $9.95, 346

Fun Old Testament Bible Studies, $12.95, 414

Making Good Decisions, $6.95, 415

Youth & Parents Together: Facing Life's Struggles—Participants Book, $3.95, 416

Boosting Self-Esteem, $6.95, 419

Knowing God's Will, $6.95, 440

Jesus' Death and Resurrection, $6.95, 442

Making Parents Proud, $6.95, 453

Clear-Headed Choices in a Sexually Confused World, $11.95, 460

Evil and the Occult, $6.95, 649

Sex: A Christian Perspective, $6.95, 726

Becoming Responsible, $6.95, 748

Controversial Topics for Youth Groups, $13.95, 755

Hazardous to Your Health, $6.95, 756

Today's Music: Good or Bad?, $6.95, 823

Prayer, $6.95, 845

Creating Quality Relationships in a Fast-Paced World—Study Guide, $4.50, 913

Creative Bible Studies for Young Adults, $11.95, 914

Is Marriage in Your Future?, $6.95, 939

School Struggles, $6.95, 999

Genesis: The Beginnings, $6.95, 1039

Guys & Girls: Understanding Each Other, $6.95, 1091

Drugs & Drinking, $6.95, 1121

Is God Unfair?, $6.95, 1122

Dealing with Death, $6.95, 1175

Applying the Bible to Life, $6.95, 1184

What's a Christian?, $6.95, 1185

Responding to Injustice, $6.95, 1193

Telling Your Friends About Christ, $6.95, 1194

Here's Life

Action Group—Book 3, $3.25, 1

Discipleship Group—Book 2, $3.25, 14

Discovery Group—Book 1, $3.50, 16

Christian Adventure, The—Step 1, $2.25, 132

Christian and Obedience, The—Step 6, $2.25, 133

Christian and the Holy Spirit, The—Step 3, $2.25, 134

Christian and the Bible, The—Step 5, $2.25, 135

Christian and Witnessing, The—Step 7, $2.25, 136

Christian and Prayer, The—Step 4, $2.25, 137

Christian and the Abundant Life, The—Step 2, $2.25, 138

Christian and Stewardship, The—Step 8, $2.25, 139

Handbook for Christian Maturity, A, $8.95, 140

New Testament Highlights—Step 10, $2.25, 146

Old Testament Highlights—Step 9, $2.25, 147

Uniqueness of Jesus, The: Introduction, $2.25, 148

Being a Woman of God, $4.25, 394

Acts, $7.95, 519

David: A Man After God's Own Heart, $4.95, 522

General Epistles: James, Peter, John, Jude, $7.95, 530

Hebrews: And the Pastoral Epistles, $7.95, 534

John, $7.95, 538

Luke, $7.95, 544

Mark, $7.95, 546

Matthew, $7.95, 548

Prison Epistles: 1 and 2 Thessalonians, $7.95, 554

Psalms, $7.95, 556

Revelation, $7.95, 558

Romans, $7.95, 560

Ruth & Mary: Women of Courage, $4.95, 562

1 Corinthians, $7.95, 563

2 Corinthians/Galatians, $7.95, 570

Holt, Rinehart and Winston

Looking Out, Looking In, $19.90, 60

InterVarsity

Good Things Come in Small Groups, $8.95, 20

Leadership in the 21st Century, $4.95, 61

Joshua: The Power of God's Promises, $3.95, 83

Philippians: Jesus Our Joy, $3.95, 84

John's Letters: Discovering Genuine Christianity, $3.95, 98

Multi-Ethnicity, $4.95, 224

Urbanization, $4.95, 227

Daniel: Spiritual Living in a Secular World, $3.95, 286

John: The Way to True Life, $3.95, 287

Christian Beliefs, $3.95, 357

Matthew: Being Discipled by Jesus, $3.95, 358

People and Technology, $4.95, 373

Meeting Jesus, $3.95, 379

Disciple-Makers' Handbook, $8.95, 390

Handbook for Engaged Couples, A, $4.95, 391

Handbook for Married Couples, A, $4.95, 392

Spiritual Conflict, $4.95, 418

Getting Together, $9.95, 432

Healing for Broken People, $4.95, 445

Jonah, Joel & Amos: Seek the Lord and Live, $3.95, 446

Making of a Leader, The, $7.95, 467

Mark: Follow Me, $3.95, 491

Genesis: God's Creative Call, $3.95, 498

Spiritual Gifts, $3.95, 499

Loving Justice, $3.95, 501

Women of the Old Testament, $3.95, 509

Fundamentalistic Religion, $4.95, 518

David: A Heart for God, $3.95, 609

Galatians: Why God Accepts Us, $3.95, 610

Romans: Becoming New in Christ, $3.95, 612

Self-Esteem: Seeing Ourselves As God Sees Us, $3.95, 614

Ephesians: Wholeness for a Broken World, $3.95, 651

James: Faith That Works, $3.95, 652

One Plus One Equals One, $6.95, 653

Caring for Emotional Needs, $3.95, 654

Caring for People in Grief, $3.95, 655

Caring for People in Conflict, $3.95, 656

Declaring His Deity: John—Part 2—Youth, $4.50, 873

Disruption and Dispersion: 1 Kings 9–2 Chronicles—Youth, $4.50, 874

Disruption, Dispersion & Restoration: 1 Kings 9–Job, $4.50, 875

God Leads His People: Exodus 19–Deuteronomy—Youth, $4.50, 876

God Leads His People: Exodus 19–Deuteronomy, $4.50, 877

God's Salvation and Grace: Romans–Galatians—Youth, $4.50, 878

God's Salvation and Grace: Romans–Galatians, $4.50, 879

Golden Years of the Kingdom, The: 1 Samuel 13–1 Kings 8—Youth, $4.50, 880

In the Beginning God: Genesis–Exodus 18, $4.50, 881

In the Beginning God: Genesis–Exodus 18—Youth, $4.50, 882

Jesus Christ the Son of God: Matthew thru Luke (Part 2), Youth, $4.50, 883

Jesus Christ the Son of God: Matthew thru Luke (Part 1), Youth, $4.50, 884

Jesus Christ the Son of God: Matthew thru Luke (Part 1), $4.50, 885

Jesus Christ the Son of God: Matthew thru Luke (Part 2), $4.50, 886

Land and the Kingdom, The: Joshua–1 Kings 8, $4.50, 887

Letters To Believers: Ephesians–Titus—Youth, $4.50, 888

Letters to Believers: Ephesians–Titus, $4.50, 889

Let the Wicked Be Warned: Joel–Malachi—Youth, $4.50, 890

Let the Wicked Be Warned: Lamentations–Malachi, $4.50, 891

Occupying the Land: Joshua–1 Samuel 12—Youth, $4.50, 892

Predictions of Judgment and Glory: Isaiah–Jeremiah—Youth, $4.50, 893

Prophecy out of Captivity: Lamentations–Hosea—Youth, $4.50, 894

Return and Restoration: Ezra–Job—Youth, $4.50, 895

Songs, Sayings and Searches: Psalms–Song of Solomon—Youth, $4.50, 896

Wisdom and Prophecy: Psalms–Jeremiah, $4.50, 897

Explore the Word, $6.95, 1147

Scripture Union Books

Growing Christians in Small Groups, $14.95, 725

Serendipity House

Serendipity Bible for Groups, $19.95, 42

Serendipity New Testament for Groups, $9.95, 43

Newly Married: How to Have a Great First Year, $5.45, 182

All the Way: On Discipleship, $2.95, 258

Beginning a Basic Group: Six Sessions to Examine Your Faith, $2.95, 259

Beginning a Serendipity Group: Six Sessions to Get Acquainted, $2.95, 260

Belonging: What's a Friend, $2.95, 261

Choices: On Morality, $2.95, 262

Dear Me: On My Identity, $2.95, 263

Ephesians, $5.95, 264

Go for It: On Becoming a Christian, $2.95, 265

Gospel of Mark: Exploring the Life of Jesus, $4.95, 266

Hassles: On Relationships, $2.95, 267

James, $5.95, 268

Philippians, $5.95, 269

Philippians/Ephesians: Becoming a Caring Community, $4.95, 270

Revelation: Looking at the End of Time, $4.95, 271

Romans, $5.95, 272

Romans: Discovering God's Plan for the World, $4.95, 273

Torn Between: On My Lifestyle, $2.95, 274

Up Front: On Tough Issues, $2.95, 275

Youth Ministry Encyclopedia, $19.95, 276

1 Corinthians, $5.95, 277

1 Corinthians: Taking On the Tough Issues, $4.95, 278

1 John/Galatians: Exposing Religious Counterfeits, $4.95, 279

1 Peter, $5.95, 280

1 Peter/James: Living Through Difficult Times, $4.95, 281

1 & 2 Timothy, $5.95, 282

1 & 2 Timothy & Titus: Learning to Thrive in a Hostile World, $4.95, 283

Blended Families: Yours, Mine, Ours, $5.45, 303

Dealing with Grief & Loss: Hope in the Midst of Pain, $5.45, 304

Parenting Adolescents: Easing the Way to Adulthood, $5.45, 305

Single Parents: Flying Solo, $5.45, 306

Infertility: Coping With the Pain of Childlessness, $5.45, 490

Career: Take This Job and Love It, $4.95, 759

Family: Living Under the Same Leaky Roof, $4.95, 760

Lifestyles: Going In Style, $4.95, 761

Mid Life: The Crisis That Brings Renewal, $5.45, 762

Money: Handling the Bucks, $4.95, 763

Singles: Looking Out for Number One, $4.95, 764

Stressed-Out: Keeping It Together When It's Falling Apart, $4.95, 765

Success: Does the One with the Most Toys Win?, $4.95, 766

Transitions: Savoring the Seasons of Life, $4.95, 767

Wholeness: Putting the Pieces Together, $4.95, 768

1 John, $5.95, 826

12 Steps: The Path to Wholeness, $5.45, 827

Compassion Fatigue: Worn Out from Caring, $5.45, 855

Unemployed Unfulfilled: Down but Not Out, $5.45, 1178

Servant Publications

Faith: A Guide to Following God, $4.95, 313

Against the Night: Study Guide, $4.95, 667

Praying the Scriptures: A Guide to Talking with God, $4.95, 727

Repentance: A Guide to Receiving God's Forgiveness, $4.95, 922

Catholic Bible Study Workbook, The: A Guide to the Gospel of John, $8.95, 930

Intercession: A Guide to Effective Prayer, $4.95, 969

Shaw

Get Wise: Studies in Proverbs, $2.95, 56

Women Like Us: Wisdom for Today's Issues, $3.95, 89

Ephesians: Living in God's Household, $3.95, 90

Ecclesiastes: God's Wisdom for Evangelism, $3.95, 119

Examining the Claims of Jesus, $3.95, 120

How Should a Christian Live? 1, 2 & 3 John, $3.95, 122

Proverbs & Parables: God's Wisdom for Living, $3.95, 123

Building Your House on the Lord: Marriage & Parenthood, $3.95, 124

Friendship: Portraits in God's Family Album, $3.95, 125

Higher Ground: Steps Toward Christian Maturity, $3.95, 126

1 & 2 Peter, Jude: Called for a Purpose, $3.95, 127

David: Man After God's Own Heart—Volume 2, $3.95, 229

David: Man After God's Own Heart—Volume 1, $3.95, 230

Elijah: Obedience in a Threatening World, $3.95, 231

Acts 1-12: God Moves in the Early Church, $3.95, 236

James: Faith in Action, $3.95, 237

Mark: God in Action, $3.95, 238

Paul: Thirteenth Apostle, $3.95, 239

Women Who Achieved for God, $3.95, 240

Women Who Believed God, $3.95, 241

Wholly Single, $3.50, 329

Church, The: Pictures of Christ's Body, $3.95, 338

Personal Integrity, $3.50, 341

Redeeming Time, $3.50, 342

Who Am I?: A Look in the Mirror, $2.95, 375

Acts: Mission Accomplished, $2.95, 382

Genesis: Walking with God (Revised Edition), $3.95, 383

Jonah, Habakkuk & Malachi: Living Responsibly, $3.95, 384

Let's Pray Together, $3.95, 385

Letters to the Thessalonians, $3.95, 386

Letters to Timothy: Discipleship in Action, $3.95, 387

Joshua: Promises to Keep, $2.95, 427

Men Like Us: Ordinary Men, Extraordinary God, $3.95, 455

1 Corinthians: Problems & Solutions in a Growing Church, $3.95, 500

God Who Understands Me, The: Sermon on the Mount, $3.95, 502

Hebrews: From Shadows to Reality, $3.95, 503

John: Eyewitness, $3.95, 504

Relationships, $3.95, 505

Revelation: The Lamb Who Is the Lion, $3.95, 506

Romans: Made Righteous by Faith, $3.95, 507

Stories Jesus Told, $3.95, 508

Encouraging Others: Biblical Models for Caring, $3.95, 575

Luke: Following Jesus, $3.95, 586

Job: God's Answer to Suffering, $3.95, 593

Philippians: Be Glad!, $2.95, 594

Philippians: God's Guide to Joy, $3.95, 595

Psalms: A Guide to Prayer & Praise, $3.95, 596

Real Questions, The: Searching the Psalms for Answers, $2.95, 597

One Body, One Spirit, $3.95, 639

Tending Creation, $3.50, 640

Forgiveness: No Guilt, No Grudges, $2.95, 642

Galatians: Free At Last, $2.95, 644

Joseph: Non-Stop Faith, $2.95, 645

Running the Race: Keeping the Faith, $2.95, 646

Mark: God on the Move, $2.95, 796

Relationships: Face to Face, $2.95, 798

Romans: Christianity on Trial, $3.95, 799

Sexuality: God's Good Idea, $2.95, 800

Great Passages of the Bible, $3.95, 835

Great People of the Bible, $3.95, 836
Great Prayers of the Bible, $3.95, 837
Pilgrims in Progress, $7.95, 838
Strengthened to Serve: 2 Corinthians, $3.95, 839
Discipleship: The Growing Christian's Lifestyle, $3.95, 848
Romans: The Christian Story, $3.95, 851
Friendship Evangelism, $3.50, 866
Servant Leadership, $3.50, 931
Colossians: Focus on Christ, $3.95, 967
Matthew: People of the Kingdom, $3.95, 970
Meeting Jesus, $3.95, 972
Guidance & God's Will, $3.95, 1022
Satisfying Work: Christian Living from Nine to Five, $3.95, 1031
Fulfilling Work, $3.50, 1034
Marriage: Learning from Couples in Scripture, $3.95, 1035
Ruth & Daniel: God's People in an Alien Society, $3.95, 1037
Lifestyle Priorities, $3.50, 1143

Shepherd Ministries
Discussion Manual for Student Relationships—Volume 2, $8.75, 730
Discussion Manual for Student Relationships—Volume 1, $8.75, 731
Discussion Manual for Student Relationships—Volume 3, $8.75, 732
Discussion Manual for Student Discipleship—Volume 2, $8.50, 733
Discussion Manual for Student Discipleship—Volume 1, $8.50, 734
Preparing Your Teenager for Sexuality, $6.95, 736
Search for Significance: Youth Edition, $7.95, 737
Walk with Christ Through the Resurrection, A, $8.95, 739
Walk with Christ to the Cross, A, $8.95, 740
Who Are You, God? and What Are You Like?, $7.95, 741
Who Are You Jesus?, $7.95, 742
You, God, and Your Sexuality, $3.95, 743

Standard Publishing
Second Corinthians, $3.50, 149
Revelation, $3.50, 454
Hebrews, $3.50, 745
Galatians/Ephesians, $3.50, 746
John, $3.50, 840
This Is the Thanks I Get? A Guide to Raising Teenagers, $5.99, 860
What Should I Do Now? A Guide to Raising Children, $5.99, 861
Colossians, $4.99, 1001
Philippians, $4.99, 1002
2 Corinthians, $4.99, 1003
Acts, $3.50, 1102
Luke, $3.50, 1103
First Corinthians, $3.50, 1104
Matthew, $3.50, 1105

Stephen Ministries
Stephen Ministry at Work, $8.50, 46

The Westminster Press
Using the Bible in Groups, $7.95, 466

Tyndale House
How Come It's Taking Me So Long?: Steps to Spiritual Maturity, $6.95, 59
When a Woman Takes God at His Word, $6.95, 85

God in Three Persons, $7.95, 92
Building People Through a Caring, Sharing Fellowship, $7.95, 184
Convinced: New Directions for Active People from John, $3.50, 185
Encouraged: New Directions for Active People from Psalms, $2.95, 186
Equipped: New Directions for Active People from Ephesians, $2.95, 187
Informed: New Directions for Active People from Luke, $3.50, 188
Motivated: New Directions for Active People from Acts, $3.50, 189
Energized: New Directions for Active People on Personal Growth, $2.95, 190
Proverbs: Practical Directions for Living, $5.95, 322
Daniel, $4.95, 398
Mark, $4.95, 399
1, 2 Timothy & Titus, $4.95, 400
Acts, $2.95, 615
Bible Leaders Who Coped with Stress, $2.95, 616
Coming of the Lord, The, $2.95, 617
Courage to Cope, $2.95, 618
Four Men of God: Abraham, Joseph, Moses, David, $3.95, 619
Genesis, $2.95, 620
Hebrews, $3.95, 621
How to Start a Neighborhood Bible Study, $3.95, 622
Isaiah, $2.95, 623
John—Book 1, $3.95, 624
John—Book 2, $3.50, 625
Mark, $2.95, 626
Matthew—Book 1, $3.95, 627
Philippians & Colossians: Letters from Prison, $2.95, 628
Promises from God, $2.95, 629
Psalms & Proverbs, $2.95, 630
Romans, $2.95, 631
They Met Jesus, $3.95, 632
1 John & James, $3.95, 633
1 & 2 Peter: Letters to People in Trouble, $3.95, 634
2 Corinthians and Galatians, $2.95, 635
Spirit-Controlled Temperament, $6.95, 636
Philippians & Colossians, $4.95, 806
Romans, $4.95, 807
Ten Commandments, The, $4.95, 821
Basic Bible Studies, $3.95, 927
Revelation, $4.95, 932
Becoming God's Woman, $2.95, 982
Becoming the Parent Your Child Needs, $2.95, 983
Celebration of Womanhood, $3.95, 984
Coping with Life and Its Problems, $3.95, 985
Dating, Love, & Sex, $2.95, 986
Esther: A Woman of Courage, $3.95, 987
Fulfillment, $2.95, 988
Giants, Lions, & Fire, $2.95, 989
Growing in Faith, $2.95, 990
Growing Through Life's Challenges: Studies in 2 Corinthians, $3.95, 991
Learning to Talk with God, $2.95, 992
Ruth, A Woman of Worth, $3.95, 993
Significance of Jesus, The, $2.95, 994
Spiritual Living, $3.95, 995
Understanding Your Emotions, $3.95, 996
Walking in the Light, $2.95, 997
Woman's Priorities, A, $3.95, 998
Famous Couples of the Bible, $5.95, 1042
Marriage Is for Love, $5.95, 1043
Ruth & Esther, $4.95, 1092
John, $4.95, 1099
Acts, $4.95, 1114

His Name Is Wonderful, $7.95, 1171
Genesis, $4.95, 1179
Hosea & Jonah, $4.95, 1180
Joshua, $4.95, 1181
Discover Your Spiritual Gift and Use It, $5.95, 1192

University Associates, Inc.
Groups: Leadership and Group Development, $29.95, 314

Victor Books
Thirst for Wholeness, A, $7.99, 58
Mother's Time, A: A Realistic Approach to Time Management for Mothers, $7.99, 74
Mother's Touch, A, $7.99, 75
God of Second Chances, The: The Remaking of Moses, $6.99, 82
What Did Jesus Say About That?, $6.99, 86
Gift of Gender, The, $5.99, 87
Encounters with Jesus, $7.99, 88
I'm Glad You Asked, $9.99, 108
Ordinary Men Called by God: Abraham, Moses & David, $7.99, 110
Any Old Time—Book 5, $9.99, 113
Know the Marks of Cults, $6.99, 118
Friendships of Women, The, $6.99, 121
Before You Say "Amen": Spending Time with God Through Prayer, $5.99, 150
Body Language: When Our Actions Speak Louder Than Our Words, $5.99, 151
Evergrowing, Evergreen: Getting to Know God in the Psalms, $5.99, 153
Faith Enough to Finish, $5.99, 154
God's Name, God's Nature, $5.99, 155
Grace to Go On, $5.99, 156
Heaven and Hell: A Study of the Promise and the Peril of Eternity, $5.99, 157
"Here Am I—Send Aaron!", $7.99, 158
Starlight, $5.99, 159
Women in the Life of Jesus, $5.99, 160
Women Who Changed Their World: How God Uses Women to Make a Difference, $5.99, 161
David: A Heart for God, $6.99, 162
What Works When Life Doesn't, $7.99, 163
Making Sense of Your Faith: Believing in an Age of Doubt, $6.99, 183
Breaking Down the Walls, $5.99, 193
Joshua: Leader Under Fire, $7.99, 200
Judges: Leaders in Crisis Times, $6.99, 201
How to Really Love Your Child, $6.99, 202
Good News to Go—Book 2, $6.99, 203
Home at Last—Book 4, $6.99, 204
Priority Mail—Book 3, $6.99, 205
When God Left Footprints—Book 1, $6.99, 206
Staying Positive in a Negative World, $6.99, 207
How to Really Love Your Teenager, $6.99, 208
Any Old Time—Book 4, $9.99, 209
Any Old Time—Book 3, $9.99, 210
Fighters & Writers—Book 3, $5.99, 211
From the Desk of the Apostle Paul—Book 7, $5.99, 212
Growing Pains: The Church Hits the Road—Book 6, $5.99, 213
Higher Love—Leader's Book, $12.99, 214
Jesus: God Undercover—Book 5, $5.99, 215
Nobody Like Me—Leader's Book, $12.99, 216
Saga Begins, The—Book 1, $5.99, 217
Saga Never Ends, The—Book 8, $5.99, 218
That's the Way the Kingdom Crumbles—Book 2, $5.99, 219
What's This World Coming To?—Book 4, $5.99, 220
Power Delusion, The: A Serious Call to Consider Jesus' Approach to Powe, $7.99, 221

Preeminent Person of Christ, The: A Study of Hebrews 1-10, $4.99, 1077

Prophecy, $3.99, 1078

Questions Christians Ask, $3.99, 1079

Relating to Others in Love: A Study of Romans 12-16, $3.99, 1080

Solomon, $3.99, 1081

Spiritual Gifts, $3.99, 1082

Steadfast Christianity: A Study of Second Thessalonians, $3.99, 1083

Stones of Remembrance, $3.99, 1084

Strengthening Your Grip: Essentials in an Aimless World, $4.99, 1085

Strengthening Your Grip, $179.99, 1086

Strong Reproofs for a Scandalous Church: A Study of 1 Corinthians, $3.99, 1087

You and Your Child, $3.99, 1088

You and Your Problems, $4.99, 1089

Maximum Marriage, $159.99, 1095

Zondervan

Behold Your God: Studies on the Attributes of God, $5.95, 62

Loving & Obeying God: Studies on 1 Samuel, $4.95, 63

Workshop on Self-Giving, A, $6.95, 65

Beloved Unbeliever: Loving Your Husband into the Faith, $6.95, 95

Growing Godly: Studies on Bible Women, $4.95, 99

Workshop on Bible Marriages, A, $4.50, 100

Workshop on the Beatitudes, A, $4.50, 101

Workshop on the Book of Job, A, $3.95, 102

Workshop on the Book of Proverbs, A, $4.95, 103

Workshop on the Sermon on the Mount, A, $5.95, 104

Heart Trouble: Studies on Christian Character, $5.95, 191

Mastering Motherhood, $6.95, 192

Hebrews, $7.95, 308

Portraits of Christ in Genesis, $7.95, 309

Growth Groups, $9.95, 312

Holiness for Ordinary People, $6.95, 323

Faithfulness: The Foundation of True Friendship, $3.95, 356

Patience: The Benefits of Waiting, $3.95, 359

Believing the Bible, $5.95, 371

Resurrection Evidences: A Bible Study, $1.95, 372

Workshop on the Book of Philippians, A, $4.95, 388

Workshop on the Book of Colossians, A, $5.95, 389

Talking with God: Studies on Prayer, $6.95, 417

Faith: Studies on Living the Christian Life, $4.95, 488

Workshop on the Book of Ephesians, A, $5.95, 489

Peace: Overcoming Anxiety and Conflict, $3.95, 611

Self-Control: Mastering Our Passions, $3.95, 613

Gentleness: The Strength of Being Tender, $3.95, 660

Joy: How to Rejoice in Any Situation, $3.95, 662

Kindness: Reaching Out to Others, $3.95, 663

Designed by God: Studies on Healing & Wholeness, $6.95, 779

Forgiveness, $6.95, 780

People in Turmoil: A Woman's Workshop on 1 Corinthians, $2.95, 797

Workshop on David and His Psalms, A, $6.95, 801

Workshop on the Christian Faith, A, $4.95, 802

Workshop on the Book of John, A, $6.95, 803

Workshop on the Book of James, A, $5.95, 804

Workshop on the Book of Romans, A, $5.95, 805

Creative Personal Bible Study, $7.95, 858

99 Ways to Start a Study Group and Keep It Growing, $6.95, 859

Workshop on Time Management, A, $4.95, 864

Love: Building Healthy Relationships, $3.95, 923

Open Up Your Life: A Woman's Workshop on Hospitality, $5.95, 958

Time, Talents, Things: A Woman's Workshop on Christian Stewardship, $4.95, 959

Greater Love: Studies on Friendship, $4.95, 966

Decide to Love, $29.95, 974

Decide to Love: A Couple's Workshop, $4.95, 975

Perfect in His Eyes: Studies on Self-esteem, $4.95, 1044

Fruit of the Spirit, The: Studies on Galatians 5:22-23, $6.95, 1046

Methodical Bible Study, $15.95, 1097

Faith for the Journey, $5.95, 1134

Let's Listen to Jesus, $5.95, 1135

Open Secret of Strength, The, $5.95, 1136

Our Freedom in Christ, $5.95, 1137

Brand Name Christians: A Bible-Study Devotional for Junior Highers, $6.95, 1186

Finding Freedom from Fear, $7.95, 1187

Wisdom as a Lifestyle: Building Biblical Life-Codes, $7.95, 1188

Students Guide to the Bible, The, $4.95, 1191

SERIES INDEX

MAIN ENTRIES
BY AUTHOR

Author: 1
Series: Discipleship Series
Title: *Action Group (Book 3)*
Publisher: Here's Life, 1983

Num. Sess.	Group Time	Num. Pgs.	Avg. Qst.	Price	Audience	Format	Bible Study
9	45-60	52	Vry	3.25	New Christian	Workbk	Topical

Features: Charts
★★★Personal Application   Preparation Time: Low   ISBN: 0-86605-132-5
★★Relationship Building Ldr. Guide Avail.: No   Size: 5.0 x 8.0
Subjects: Discipleship, Obedience, Service
Comments: This study, the final step in a three-part discipleship series, helps participants teach others biblical philosophy as well as methods for starting their own discovery and discipleship groups. Topics covered include God's will, obedience, servant leadership, the Great Commission, and other related topics.

Author: 2
Series:
Title: *Active Meetings on Basic Christianity*
Publisher: Group Publishing, 1991

Num. Sess.	Group Time	Num. Pgs.	Avg. Qst.	Price	Audience	Format	Bible Study
13	45-60	100	Vry	10.95	New Christian	Book	Topical

Features: Intro to Study, Objectives, Prayer Helps, Drawings, Handouts
★★★★Personal Application   Preparation Time: None ISBN: 1-559-45060-6
★★★★Relationship Building Ldr. Guide Avail.: No   Size: 7.0 x 10.0
Subjects: Teens: Jesus' Life, Teens: Theology
Comments: This resource provides thirteen meetings for grounding young people in the basics of Christian faith. Each meeting focuses on Jesus and is good for Sunday school or religious education classes, youth group meetings, and confirmation and new-believer classes. The meetings strengthen teenagers' faith through topics like "Who is God?" "Who is Jesus?" "The Bible," "Faith Commitment," and more. Step-by-step meeting plans, photocopiable handouts, and discussion questions are provided.

Author: 3
Series: Discover Life
Title: *Be a Winner*
Publisher: Church Development Resources, 1986

Num. Sess.	Group Time	Num. Pgs.	Avg. Qst.	Price	Audience	Format	Bible Study
7	45-60	16	6	2.35	Beginner	Workbk	Topical

Features: Intro to Study, Follow Up, Full Scrpt Printed
★★★Personal Application   Preparation Time: None ISBN:
★★Relationship Building Ldr. Guide Avail.: Yes   Size: 8.50 x 11.0
Subjects: Emotions, Evangelism, Men's Issues, Self-esteem
Comments: This seven-week study explores winning over worry, discouragement, anger, guilt, low self-esteem, busyness, and temptation. Old and New Testament scriptures are included. Accompanying materials are designed for nonChristians and the nonchurched, and homework is not required. Lessons are distributed prior to each study. Bible passages are printed, eliminating student embarrassment over inability to find passages, or bringing a Bible to a public place.

Author: 4
Series: Studies in Christian Living
Title: *Beginning a New Life (Book 2)*
Publisher: NavPress, 1964

Num. Sess.	Group Time	Num. Pgs.	Avg. Qst.	Price	Audience	Format	Bible Study
4	45-60	27	Vry	2.50	New Christian	Workbk	Topical

Features: Intro to Study
★★Personal Application   Preparation Time: Low   ISBN: 0-89109-078-9
★★Relationship Building Ldr. Guide Avail.: No   Size: 5.50 x 8.50
Subjects: Discipleship, Teens: Devotionals, Teens: Discipleship, Teens: Jesus' Life
Comments: This four-lesson study for new believers fifteen years old and older is used by many churches for basic discipleship follow-up. Book two includes these topics: "New Life," "The Lordship of Christ," "The Devotional Life," and "Witnessing for Christ." This series of six studies helps new Christians establish personal Bible study and learn and practice the essentials of Christian life. This series could be used as a small group study aid for new believers.

Author: 5
Series:
Title: *Bible Visual, The: Resource Book*
Publisher: Regal Books, 1989

Num. Sess.	Group Time	Num. Pgs.	Avg. Qst.	Price	Audience	Format	Bible Study
15	-	290	N/A	19.95		Book	No

Features: Intro to Study, Drawings, Charts, Maps
Personal Application   Preparation Time: ISBN: 0-8307-1368-9
Relationship Building Ldr. Guide Avail.:   Size: 8.50 x 11.25
Subjects: Bible Study, Small Group Resource
Comments: This book provides a wide variety of reproducible resources for individual or group Bible study. Visual aids include: maps, to place scriptural events; charts and graphs, to explain Bible facts; outlines, to simplify; key verses; timelines; and perforated pages, for easy removal for copying. These resources make it easier to study or teach God's Word at any level.

Author: 6
Series: Video Curriculum Resource
Title: *Champions*
Publisher: Word, 1988

Num. Sess.	Group Time	Num. Pgs.	Avg. Qst.	Price	Audience	Format	Bible Study
4	60-90	N/A	Vry	159.99	New Christian	Video	Topical

Features: Intro to Study
★★★★Personal Application   Preparation Time: None ISBN: 8-01-960079-5
★★★Relationship Building Ldr. Guide Avail.: Yes   Size: 10.25 x 13.0
Subjects: Teens: Emotions, Teens: Friends, Teens: Peer Pressure
Comments: This four-session video study helps youth deal with peer pressure, excellence, disappointment, and relationships. Professional and Olympic athletes host four thirty-minute sessions: former Cardinals' quarterback Neil Loma; Los Angeles Dodger Orel Hershiser; three-time Grand Prix motorcyle racing champion Freddie Spencer; and Olympic women's basketball gold medalist Cheryl Miller. Each segment is enhanced by Christian music. A leader discussion guide helps the leader facilitate the group.

Author: **7**
Series: Design for Discipleship
Title: *Character of the Christian, The (Book Four)*
Publisher: NavPress, 1973

Num. Sess.	Group Time	Num. Pgs.	Avg. Qst.	Price	Audience	Format	Bible Study
5	60-75	48	20	2.95	New Christian	Workbk	Topical

Features: Intro to Study, Summary, Charts
  ★★ Personal Application Preparation Time: Med ISBN: 0-89109-039-8
  ★★ Relationship Building Ldr. Guide Avail.: Yes Size: 5.50 x 8.50
Subjects: Christian Living, Discipleship, Integrity, Teens: Discipleship
Comments: This is book four in a comprehensive study on basic biblical principles and standards for following Christ. Since God's desire for believers involves inner qualities as well as outward behavior, it is imperative to learn what Scripture says about the Christian character. The five areas to be studied are: "The Call to Fruitful Living," "Genuine Love in Action," "Purity of Life," "Integrity in Living," and "Character in Action."

Author: **8**
Series:
Title: *Christ B. C.*
Publisher: Gospel Light Publications, 1990

Num. Sess.	Group Time	Num. Pgs.	Avg. Qst.	Price	Audience	Format	Bible Study
13	60-75	130	N/A	13.95	Beginner	Book	Charctr

Features: Intro to Leading a Study, Intro to Study, Objectives, Prayer Helps, Study Overview, Follow Up, Ldr's Notes, Handouts
  ★★★ Personal Application Preparation Time: Low ISBN: 0-8307-1448-0
  ★★★ Relationship Building Ldr. Guide Avail.: No Size: 8.50 x 11.0
Subjects: Jesus: Life/Teaching, Old Testament, Prophecy
Comments: This teacher's manual helps participants explore and understand Christ as revealed in the Old Testament. The study describes Old Testament events, personalities, symbols, and prophecies that teach about Jesus. Knowing what the Old Testament says about Christ provides participants with a deeper, more intimate relationship with Him. Included are Bible commentary notes, Bible background, life application, session plans, handouts, and leader's lesson guide sheets. A daily devotional is available.

Author: **9**
Series:
Title: *Christ B. C. (Youth Edition)*
Publisher: Gospel Light Publications, 1990

Num. Sess.	Group Time	Num. Pgs.	Avg. Qst.	Price	Audience	Format	Bible Study
13	45-75	79	N/A	13.95	Beginner	Book	Charctr

Features: Intro to Leading a Study, Intro to Study, Objectives, Prayer Helps, Study Overview, Follow Up, Ldr's Notes, Drawings, Handouts, Maps, Publicity Ideas
  ★★★ Personal Application Preparation Time: Low ISBN: 0-8307-1453-7
  ★★★★ Relationship Building Ldr. Guide Avail.: No Size: 8.50 x 11.0
Subjects: Teens: Jesus' Life, Teens: Old Testament, Teens: Senior High
Comments: This teacher's manual helps youth groups explore and understand Christ as revealed in the Old Testament. The study describes Old Testament events, personalities, symbols, and prophecies that teach about Jesus. Knowing what the Old Testament says about Christ provides participants with a deeper, more intimate relationship with Him. Included are helpful articles, teacher's Bible studies, lesson plans, reproducible students' worksheets, and clip art. A supplemental daily devotional is available.

Author: **10**
Series: Discover Life
Title: *Climbing Higher*
Publisher: Church Development Resources, 1989

Num. Sess.	Group Time	Num. Pgs.	Avg. Qst.	Price	Audience	Format	Bible Study
7	45-60	16	6	2.35	Beginner	Workbk	Topical

Features: Intro to Study, Follow Up, Full Scrpt Printed
  ★★★ Personal Application Preparation Time: None ISBN:
  ★★ Relationship Building Ldr. Guide Avail.: Yes Size: 8.50 x 11.0
Subjects: Christian Living, Commitments, Evangelism, Faith, Obedience, Prayer
Comments: This study challenges participants to climb higher spiritually, using the disciplines of prayer, scripture reading, commitment, faith, obedience, witnessing, and love. It explores how discipline molds a walk of faith. Homework is not required. Lessons are distributed prior to each study. Bible passages are printed, eliminating embarrassment over trying to find a passage, or bringing a Bible to a public place. Brief follow-up articles are included.

Author: **11**
Series:
Title: *Coffee Break Evangelism Manual*
Publisher: Church Development Resources, 1986

Num. Sess.	Group Time	Num. Pgs.	Avg. Qst.	Price	Audience	Format	Bible Study
7	-	66	N/A	4.95		Book	No

Features:
  Personal Application Preparation Time: ISBN:
  Relationship Building Ldr. Guide Avail.: Size: 5.50 x 8.50
Subjects: Evangelism, Small Group Resource
Comments: This book shows how to organize an evangelistic Bible study in a church that will reach neighbors and help new Christians grow and mature. Specifically it shows how to start "Coffee Break Evangelism" groups, providing the program's principles, methods of study, and material and leadership training. It also promotes a complementary children's outreach program called "Story Hour."

Author: **12**
Series: Discover Life
Title: *David: The Making of a Man of God*
Publisher: Church Development Resources, 1988

Num. Sess.	Group Time	Num. Pgs.	Avg. Qst.	Price	Audience	Format	Bible Study
7	45-60	16	6	2.35	Beginner	Workbk	Charctr

Features: Intro to Study, Follow Up, Full Scrpt Printed
  ★★★ Personal Application Preparation Time: None ISBN:
  ★★ Relationship Building Ldr. Guide Avail.: Yes Size: 8.50 x 11.0
Subjects: Bible Personalities, Faith, Psalms, Success, 1 & 2 Samuel
Comments: This study on David is from 1 and 2 Samuel and Psalms. It makes it easy to identify with David's challenges, temptations, and successes, and see how crucial faith is to life. Accompanying materials are designed for nonChristians and the nonchurched, and homework is not required. Lessons are distributed prior to each study. Bible passages are printed, thus eliminating embarrassment over students being unable to find a passage, or bringing a Bible to a public place.

Author: **13**
Series: Studies in Christian Living
Title: *Developing Your Faith (Book 5)*
Publisher: NavPress, 1964

Num. Sess.	Group Time	Num. Pgs.	Avg. Qst.	Price	Audience	Format	Bible Study
5	45-60	30	Vry	2.50	New Christian	Workbk	Topical

Features: Intro to Study
★★ Personal Application Preparation Time: Low   ISBN: 0-89109-081-9
★★ Relationship Building Ldr. Guide Avail.: No   Size: 5.50 x 8.50
Subjects: Discipleship, God, Holy Spirit, Teens: Discipleship
Comments: This five-lesson study for new believers ages fifteen and older is used by many churches for basic discipleship follow-up. Book five investigates these topics: "Who Is God?" "The Holy Spirit," "Know Your Enemy," "Our Conflict with Sin," and "The Return of Christ." This series of six studies helps new Christians establish personal Bible study and learn and practice the essentials of Christian life. This series could be used as a small group study aid for new believers.

Author: **14**
Series: Discipleship Series
Title: *Discipleship Group (Book 2)*
Publisher: Here's Life, 1983

Num. Sess.	Group Time	Num. Pgs.	Avg. Qst.	Price	Audience	Format	Bible Study
7	45-60	33	Vry	3.25	New Christian	Workbk	Topical

Features: Drawings, Charts
★★★ Personal Application Preparation Time: Low   ISBN: 0-86605-136-8
★★ Relationship Building Ldr. Guide Avail.: No   Size: 5.0 x 8.0
Subjects: Discipleship, Evangelism, Prayer
Comments: Second in a three-part discipleship series, this study helps participants achieve deeper levels of spiritual maturity and learn more effective means of winning others to Christ. Lessons cover deepening one's relationship with Christ, guiding others to live for Christ, communicating Christ's claims clearly, developing a more effective and regular prayer life, and applying God's Word to one's life.

Author: **15**
Series: Discover Your Bible
Title: *Discover Luke: Optional Lessons for Luke 5-12*
Publisher: Church Development Resources, 1983

Num. Sess.	Group Time	Num. Pgs.	Avg. Qst.	Price	Audience	Format	Bible Study
3	60-75	11	9	0.60	Beginner	Workbk	Book

Features: Intro to Study
★★★ Personal Application Preparation Time: None   ISBN:
★★ Relationship Building Ldr. Guide Avail.: No   Size: 5.50 x 8.50
Subjects: Jesus: Life/Teaching, Luke
Comments: This is an optional study on Luke 5-12 which complements the three-part series on Luke. An inductive study, it helps participants discover Bible truth themselves. Each of three lessons consists of a series of questions which, when answered, give participants a clear, personal understanding of the scripture. Application of the message in their lives and sharing with others are encouraged.

Author: **16**
Series: Discipleship Series
Title: *Discovery Group (Book 1)*
Publisher: Here's Life, 1983

Num. Sess.	Group Time	Num. Pgs.	Avg. Qst.	Price	Audience	Format	Bible Study
6	45-60	62	Vry	3.50	New Christian	Workbk	Topical

Features: Drawings
★★★ Personal Application Preparation Time: Low   ISBN: 0-86605-134-1
★★ Relationship Building Ldr. Guide Avail.: No   Size: 5.0 x 8.0
Subjects: Discipleship, Forgiveness, Holy Spirit
Comments: The first of a three-part discipleship series, this study can help participants understand the basics of establishing a relationship with God and growing in that relationship. Questions answered in the study include: How can I be sure I am a Christian? Who is Jesus Christ? How can I experience God's love and forgiveness? Who is the Holy Spirit? Can I actually live a Christlike life? If so, how?

Author: **17**
Series: Discover Life
Title: *Encounters with Christ*
Publisher: Church Development Resources, 1986

Num. Sess.	Group Time	Num. Pgs.	Avg. Qst.	Price	Audience	Format	Bible Study
7	45-60	16	6	2.35	Beginner	Workbk	Charctr

Features: Intro to Study, Follow Up, Full Scrpt Printed
★★★ Personal Application Preparation Time: None   ISBN:
★★ Relationship Building Ldr. Guide Avail.: Yes   Size: 8.50 x 11.0
Subjects: Evangelism, Grace, Jesus: Life/Teaching, Men's Issues
Comments: This study focuses on seven scenarios from Jesus' life, in which He encounters sinners, hypocrites, skeptics, and common, rich, and fearful people. It shows that God's forgiving grace is available to all through Christ. Accompanying materials are designed for nonChristians and the nonchurched, and homework is not required. Lessons are distributed prior to each study. Bible passages are printed in the study, thus eliminating embarrassment over students' inability to find a passage, or bring a Bible.

Author: **18**
Series:
Title: *Five Steps of Christian Growth*
Publisher: Campus Crusade for Christ International, 1976

Num. Sess.	Group Time	Num. Pgs.	Avg. Qst.	Price	Audience	Format	Bible Study
5	60-75	32	Vry	2.25	New Christian	Workbk	Topical

Features: Scrpt Memory Helps, Follow Up
★★ Personal Application Preparation Time: Low   ISBN: 0-918956-33-1
★★ Relationship Building Ldr. Guide Avail.: Yes   Size: 5.25 x 8.25
Subjects: Discipleship, Holy Spirit
Comments: This five-lesson study outlines the five steps of Christian growth. Lesson titles include: "How to Be Sure You Are a Christian," "How to Grow as a Christian," "How to Be Filled with the Holy Spirit," and "How to Walk in the Spirit." Participants will gain a better understanding of their own journey as Christians, and how to better counsel others. Each lesson closes with suggested personal application and further study.

Author: **19**
Series: Design for Discipleship
Title: *Foundations for Faith (Book Five)*
Publisher: NavPress, 1973

Num. Sess.	Group Time	Num. Pgs.	Avg. Qst.	Price	Audience	Format	Bible Study
5	60-75	45	21	2.95	New Christian	Workbk	Topical

Features: Intro to Study, Summary
★★ Personal Application   Preparation Time: Med   ISBN: 0-89109-040-1
★★ Relationship Building   Ldr. Guide Avail.: Yes   Size: 5.50 x 8.50
Subjects: Discipleship, Faith, God, Holy Spirit, Teens: Discipleship
Comments: This is book five in a comprehensive study series on basic biblical principles and standards for following Christ. Five foundations covered include: "Who Is God?" "The Authority of God's Word," "The Holy Spirit," "Spiritual Warfare," and "The Return of Christ." As participants better understand biblical truth, they will begin seeing more things from God's point of view.

Author: **20**
Series:
Title: *Good Things Come in Small Groups*
Publisher: InterVarsity, 1985

Num. Sess.	Group Time	Num. Pgs.	Avg. Qst.	Price	Audience	Format	Bible Study
17	-	190	N/A	8.95		Book	No

Features: Bibliography, Index
Personal Application   Preparation Time: ISBN: 0-87784-917-X
Relationship Building   Ldr. Guide Avail.:   Size: 5.50 x 8.25
Subjects: Small Group Resource
Comments: This book, on the dynamics of good group life, was actually written by a small group. It is a complete guidebook of the "ins and outs," the "ups and downs" of the life of a successful group. It discusses every facet from how to start a group to creating a churchwide strategy for growth. It explores nurture, worship, community, mission, leadership, group dynamics, and the stages of change in groups. The book includes many ideas, tips, and group activities.

Author: **21**
Series:
Title: *Group's Best Junior High Meetings (Volume 2)*
Publisher: Group Publishing, 1989

Num. Sess.	Group Time	Num. Pgs.	Avg. Qst.	Price	Audience	Format	Bible Study
35	60-90	250	Vry	15.95	New Christian	Book	Topical

Features: Intro to Leading a Study, Objectives, Prayer Helps, Ldr's Notes, Handouts, Charts
★★★★ Personal Application   Preparation Time: None   ISBN: 1-559-45009-6
★★★★ Relationship Building   Ldr. Guide Avail.: No   Size: 8.25 x 11.0
Subjects: Teens: Family, Teens: Junior High, Teens: Peer Pressure, Teens: Relationships
Comments: This, the second volume of a two-part series, provides thirty-five complete meeting plans that focus on topics important to junior high students, such as coping with peer pressure, getting along better with parents, making room for God, building self-confidence, and exploring tough issues. Easy-to-use plans and guidelines are provided, as well as activities, games, and Bible studies. These programs can be used in any junior high setting, youth group meeting, and Sunday school setting.

Author: **22**
Series:
Title: *Group's Best Junior High Meetings (Volume 1)*
Publisher: Group Publishing, 1987

Num. Sess.	Group Time	Num. Pgs.	Avg. Qst.	Price	Audience	Format	Bible Study
58	60-90	320	Vry	18.95	New Christian	Book	Topical

Features: Intro to Leading a Study, Objectives, Prayer Helps, Ldr's Notes, Drawings, Handouts
★★★★ Personal Application   Preparation Time: None   ISBN: 0-931529-58-1
★★★★ Relationship Building   Ldr. Guide Avail.: No   Size: 8.25 x 11.0
Subjects: Teens: Christian Liv, Teens: Decisions, Teens: Ethics, Teens: Family, Teens: Friends, Teens: Junior High
Comments: Volume 1 of a two-part series provides fifty-eight ready-to-use meeting schedules to help junior high students with self-image, friendship, family, faith, values, decisions, life issues, service, and seasonal and special events. Easy-to-use plans and guidelines are provided, as well as activities, games, and Bible studies. These programs can be used in any junior high setting, youth group meeting, Sunday school setting, and Bible study group.

Author: **23**
Series: Studies in Christian Living
Title: *Growing as a Christian (Book 4)*
Publisher: NavPress, 1964

Num. Sess.	Group Time	Num. Pgs.	Avg. Qst.	Price	Audience	Format	Bible Study
5	45-60	30	Vry	2.50	New Christian	Workbk	Topical

Features: Intro to Study
★★ Personal Application   Preparation Time: None   ISBN: 0-89109-080-0
★★ Relationship Building   Ldr. Guide Avail.: No   Size: 5.50 x 8.50
Subjects: Discipleship, Integrity, Obedience, Teens: Discipleship
Comments: This five-lesson study for new believers ages fifteen and older is used by many churches for basic discipleship follow-up. Book four explores Christian character in five chapters: "Maturing in Christ," "Demonstrating Christ," "Developing Integrity," "Growing in Discipleship," and "Obedience and Blessing." This series of six studies helps new Christians establish personal Bible study and learn and practice the essentials of Christian life.

Author: **24**
Series: Growing in Christ
Title: *Growing in Christ*
Publisher: NavPress, 1957

Num. Sess.	Group Time	Num. Pgs.	Avg. Qst.	Price	Audience	Format	Bible Study
13	45-60	80	Vry	4.95	New Christian	Workbk	Topical

Features: Intro to Study, Prayer Helps, Scrpt Memory Helps, Drawings
★★ Personal Application   Preparation Time: Low   ISBN: 0-89109-157-2
★★ Relationship Building   Ldr. Guide Avail.: No   Size: 5.50 x 8.50
Subjects: Christian Living, Discipleship, Forgiveness, Prayer
Comments: This unabridged combination of "Lessons on Assurance" and "Lessons on Christian Living" is a thirteen-week follow-up course for new Christians. Questions and exercises are keyed to memory verses, and a special section includes memory verse cards that correspond to each chapter. Topics covered include: "Assurance of Salvation," "Answered Prayer," "Victory over Sin," "Forgiveness," "Guidance," "Putting Christ First in Your Life," "Relying on the Lord's Strength," and "The Importance of the Bible."

Author: **25**
Series: Design for Discipleship
Title: *Growing in Discipleship (Book Six)*
Publisher: NavPress, 1973

Num. Sess.	Group Time	Num. Pgs.	Avg. Qst.	Price	Audience	Format	Bible Study
5	60-75	46	18	2.95	New Christian	Workbk	Topical

Features: Intro to Study, Summary, Charts, Maps
★★ Personal Application   Preparation Time: Med   ISBN: 0-89109-041-X
★★ Relationship Building   Ldr. Guide Avail.: Yes   Size: 5.50 x 8.50
Subjects: Discipleship, Evangelism, Stewardship, Teens: Discipleship
Comments: This is book six in a comprehensive study series on basic biblical principles and standards for following Christ. The following lessons reinforce that Christians should share the blessings they receive from the Lord: "What Is a Disciple?," "The Responsible Steward," "Helping Others Find Christ," "Follow-up," and "World Vision." The series is designed to help participants establish personal Bible study, examine Bible truths, and learn and practice essentials of discipleship. Homework is suggested.

Author: **26**
Series:
Title: *Headline News Discussion Starters*
Publisher: Group Publishing, 1990

Num. Sess.	Group Time	Num. Pgs.	Avg. Qst.	Price	Audience	Format	Bible Study
40	30-40	97	7	8.95	Beginner	Book	Topical

Features: Intro to Study, Drawings, Photos, Charts
★★★★ Personal Application   Preparation Time: None   ISBN: 1-559-45000-2
★★★★ Relationship Building   Ldr. Guide Avail.: No   Size: 7.0 x 10.0
Subjects: Teens: Decisions, Teens:Drugs/Drinking, Teens: Ethics, Teens: Sexuality
Comments: This book provides forty lessons on issues teenagers want to talk about. Each is a real-life news story with mind-stirring, scripturally based guestions to guide discussions on building Christian faith. Issues include racism, violence, hunger, abortion, failure, AIDS, drugs, cheating, sex, and drinking. These discussion starters are perfect for youth group meetings, Sunday school, lock-ins, and retreats.

Author: **27**
Series:
Title: *"Highly Recommended: Coffee Break"*
Publisher: Church Development Resources, 1991

Num. Sess.	Group Time	Num. Pgs.	Avg. Qst.	Price	Audience	Format	Bible Study
-		N/A	N/A	14.95		Video	

Features:
Personal Application   Preparation Time: ISBN:
Relationship Building   Ldr. Guide Avail.:   Size: 4.50 x 8.50
Subjects: Evangelism, Small Group Resource
Comments: This 23-minute video opens with a testimony of a young girl finding Jesus. It presents a visual picture of the activities and results of a Coffee Break Evangelistic Bible study program, which can be implemented in any church. It provides both a history of Coffee Break and statistics on its growth. The program is specifically designed to be nonthreatening, and no prior Bible knowledge is required. The curricula available takes an inductive approach. Story Hour for children is available.

Author: **28**
Series:
Title: *Husbands and Wives: God's Design for the Family*
Publisher: NavPress, 1980

Num. Sess.	Group Time	Num. Pgs.	Avg. Qst.	Price	Audience	Format	Bible Study
6	60-90	95	23	4.95	New Christian	Workbk	Topical

Features: Bibliography, Study Overview, Summary, Ldr's Notes, Charts
★★★ Personal Application   Preparation Time: Med   ISBN: 0-89109-028-2
★★★ Relationship Building   Ldr. Guide Avail.: No   Size: 5.50 x 8.50
Subjects: Family, Love, Marriage, Relationships, Sexual Issues, Singles Issues
Comments: This six-lesson study for engaged, married, or single men and women describes what the Scriptures say about values, roles, expectations, and conflicts in marriage. Specific biblical teaching, important for both marriage partners, is explored. It includes self-image; communication, love, and conflicts; the sexual relationship; and the responsibilities of husbands and wives. The study will help participants develop fresh outlooks on marriage and deeper commitments to each other.

Author: **29**
Series: Discover Life
Title: *James: Faith at Work*
Publisher: Church Development Resources, 1988

Num. Sess.	Group Time	Num. Pgs.	Avg. Qst.	Price	Audience	Format	Bible Study
7	45-60	16	6	2.35	Beginner	Workbk	Book

Features: Intro to Study, Follow Up, Full Scrpt Printed
★★★ Personal Application   Preparation Time: None   ISBN:
★★ Relationship Building   Ldr. Guide Avail.: Yes   Size: 8.50 x 11.0
Subjects: Evangelism, Faith, James, Men's Issues
Comments: This verse-by-verse study of James helps participants understand what faith means in everyday life. Areas covered include "Trials and Temptations," "Listening and Doing," "Faith and Deeds," and "Taming the Tongue." Accompanying materials are designed for nonChristians and the nonchurched, and homework is not required. Lessons are distributed prior to each study. Bible passages are printed, thus eliminating potential embarrassment over trying to find a passage, or bringing a Bible to a public place.

Author: **30**
Series: Studies in Christian Living
Title: *Knowing Jesus Christ (Book 1)*
Publisher: NavPress, 1964

Num. Sess.	Group Time	Num. Pgs.	Avg. Qst.	Price	Audience	Format	Bible Study
3	45-60	29	Vry	2.50	New Christian	Workbk	Topical

Features: Intro to Study, Full Scrpt Printed
★★ Personal Application   Preparation Time: Low   ISBN: 0-89109-077-0
★★ Relationship Building   Ldr. Guide Avail.: No   Size: 5.50 x 8.50
Subjects: Discipleship, Teens: Discipleship, Teens: Jesus' Life
Comments: This three-lesson study for new believers ages fifteen and older is used by many churches for basic discipleship follow-up. Book one includes: "Who Is Jesus Christ?" "The Work of Jesus Christ" and "Eternal Life in Christ." This series of six studies helps new Christians establish personal Bible study and learn and practice the essentials of Christian life. This series could be used as a small-group study aid for new believers.

Author: 31
Series: Growing in Christ
Title: *Lessons on Assurance*
Publisher: NavPress, 1957

Num. Sess.	Group Time	Num. Pgs.	Avg. Qst.	Price	Audience	Format	Bible Study
5	45-60	32	8	2.50	New Christian	Workbk	Topical

Features: Intro to Study, Scrpt Memory Helps, Full Scrpt Printed, Drawings
   ★★★ Personal Application Preparation Time: Low   ISBN: 0-89109-160-2
    ★★ Relationship Building Ldr. Guide Avail.: No   Size: 5.50 x 8.50
Subjects: Christian Living, Discipleship, God's Promises, Prayer
Comments: This study for new Christians presents short Bible studies on five basic promises God gives believers: assurance of salvation, answered prayer, victory over sin, forgiveness, and guidance. Each study concentrates on a Bible passage that presents one of God's promises, and participants are encouraged to memorize it. These lessons are particularly useful in groups or classes for beginners.

Author: 32
Series: Growing in Christ
Title: *Lessons on Christian Living*
Publisher: NavPress, 1957

Num. Sess.	Group Time	Num. Pgs.	Avg. Qst.	Price	Audience	Format	Bible Study
8	45-60	46	12	2.50	New Christian	Workbk	Topical

Features: Intro to Study, Prayer Helps, Scrpt Memory Helps
    ★★ Personal Application Preparation Time: Low   ISBN: 0-89109-162-9
    ★★ Relationship Building Ldr. Guide Avail.: No   Size: 5.50 x 8.50
Subjects: Christian Living, Church Life, Discipleship, Money, Stewardship
Comments: In this study participants will learn eight principles and promises God gives His children, and their corresponding responsibilities and privileges. The eight principles include: putting Christ first, relying on the Lord's strength, the importance of the Bible, love, giving, the church, good works, and witnessing. For each principle there is a memory verse.

Author: 33
Series:
Title: *Living Proof*
Publisher: NavPress, 1990

Num. Sess.	Group Time	Num. Pgs.	Avg. Qst.	Price	Audience	Format	Bible Study
12	75-90	96	Vry	199.0	New Christian	Video	Topical

Features: Intro to Study, Bibliography, Prayer Helps, Digging Deeper Quest, Follow Up, Drawings, Photos, Book Incl, Video Study Guide
  ★★★★ Personal Application Preparation Time: Low   ISBN: 9-900739-82-5
  ★★★★ Relationship Building Ldr. Guide Avail.: Yes   Size: 10.50 x 11.50
Subjects: Evangelism, Small Group Resource
Comments: This twelve-lesson video study on lifestyle evangelism includes memorable characters, humor, and scenes that may startle participants, who learn to share the gospel with their friends, neighbors, and coworkers. Participants learn how to develop relationships with unbelievers, model the Christian message in their lives, and eventually present the Bible's claims in a nonthreatening manner. The discussion guide includes warm-up questions, notes for the video segment, discussion questions and more.

Author: 34
Series:
Title: *Making Peace with the Pieces of My Life*
Publisher: Faith at Work, 1988

Num. Sess.	Group Time	Num. Pgs.	Avg. Qst.	Price	Audience	Format	Bible Study
6	45-60	28	Vry	2.50	New Christian	Book	Topical

Features: No Grp Discussion Quest
    ★★ Personal Application Preparation Time: Low   ISBN:
    ★★ Relationship Building Ldr. Guide Avail.: No   Size: 5.50 x 8.50
Subjects: Christian Living, Friendships, Reconciliation, Relationships, Wholeness
Comments: This six-lesson study, derived from a series of articles reprinted from Faith at Work magazine, covers six aspects of "making peace." It helps participants understand peace from a biblical perspective and apply it in their own lives; with family, friends, and enemies; at work; and in general, with the earth. It assumes that the peace of Christ is a lifetime process of searching, rather than achieving a perfect solution. The use of this study series is one way to guide the process.

Author: 35
Series: Discover Life
Title: *Man and His World, A*
Publisher: Church Development Resources, 1988

Num. Sess.	Group Time	Num. Pgs.	Avg. Qst.	Price	Audience	Format	Bible Study
7	45-60	16	6	2.35	Beginner	Workbk	Topical

Features: Follow Up, Full Scrpt Printed
   ★★★ Personal Application Preparation Time: None   ISBN:
    ★★ Relationship Building Ldr. Guide Avail.: Yes   Size: 8.50 x 11.0
Subjects: Christian Living, Evangelism, Friendships, Marriage, Men's Issues, Money, Relationships, Work·
Comments: This seven-week study focuses on humanity's outer world, discussing topics such as work, friends, children, money, goals, marriage, and spirituality. Accompanying materials are designed for nonChristians and the nonchurched, and homework is not required. Lessons are distributed prior to each study. Bible passages are printed, eliminating potential embarrassment over trying to find passages, or about bringing a Bible to a public place. The leader's guide provides additional questions.

Author: 36
Series:
Title: *Men's Life Training Workshop*
Publisher: Church Development Resources, 1990

Num. Sess.	Group Time	Num. Pgs.	Avg. Qst.	Price	Audience	Format	Bible Study
6	-	N/A	Vry	119.95	New Christian	Video	No

Features: Intro to Study, Study Overview, Video Study Guide
   Personal Application Preparation Time: None   ISBN:
   Relationship Building Ldr. Guide Avail.: Yes   Size: 10.25 x 12.50
Subjects: Evangelism, Small Group Resource
Comments: This training kit includes: two interactive video tapes (four and a half hours) which train men as if they were at a live workshop; "Man Alive," a twenty-minute video on men's life; complete leader's guide, notes, and helps; a student manual; "How to Organize and Conduct Men's Life," a practical outline; and complete organizational materials. The training is designed to reach and motivate men to know and follow Christ. By the end of the training, participants will be prepared to lead a group.

Author: **37**
Series: Discover Life
Title: *Nehemiah, Succeeding by Serving*
Publisher: Church Development Resources, 1988

Num. Sess.	Group Time	Num. Pgs.	Avg. Qst.	Price	Audience	Format	Bible Study
7	45-60	16	6	2.35	Beginner	Workbk	Book

Features: Follow Up, Full Scrpt Printed
★★★ Personal Application   Preparation Time: None ISBN:
★★ Relationship Building Ldr. Guide Avail.: Yes   Size: 8.50 x 11.0
Subjects: Evangelism, Ezra/Nehemiah, Joy, Obedience, Service
Comments: This verse-by-verse study of Nehemiah shows how to succeed against great odds and accomplish something important to God. Nehemiah prayed, trusted God, faced fear, and led others to discover joy. Accompanying materials are designed for nonChristians and the nonchurched, and homework is not required. Lessons are distributed prior to each study. Printed Bible passages eliminate possible embarrassment over being unable to find a passage, or over bringing a Bible to a public place.

Author: **38**
Series: Design for Discipleship
Title: *Our Hope in Christ (Book Seven)*
Publisher: NavPress, 1980

Num. Sess.	Group Time	Num. Pgs.	Avg. Qst.	Price	Audience	Format	Bible Study
7	60-75	43	Vry	2.50	New Christian	Workbk	Topical

Features: Intro to Study, Summary, Cross Ref
★★ Personal Application   Preparation Time: Med ISBN: 0-89109-042-8
★★ Relationship Building Ldr. Guide Avail.: Yes   Size: 5.50 x 8.50
Subjects: Discipleship, Hope, Teens: Discipleship, Teens: New Testament
Comments: This is book seven in a comprehensive study on basic biblical principles and standards for following Christ. Participants will learn how to study New Testament books chapter by chapter—in this case, 1 Thessalonians—a method called "comprehensive book analysis." It includes three steps: a survey of the entire book, a chapter-by-chapter analysis, and a summary. Once learned, it will enable participants to continue this kind of study as a lifetime habit.

Author: **39**
Series:
Title: *Parents & Children: God's Design for the Family*
Publisher: NavPress, 1980

Num. Sess.	Group Time	Num. Pgs.	Avg. Qst.	Price	Audience	Format	Bible Study
6	60-90	95	18	4.95	New Christian	Workbk	Topical

Features: Intro to Study, Bibliography, Study Overview, Follow Up, Ldr's Notes, Charts
★★★ Personal Application   Preparation Time: Med ISBN: 0-89109-029-0
★★★ Relationship Building Ldr. Guide Avail.: No   Size: 5.50 x 8.50
Subjects: Family, Parenting, Relationships, Singles Issues
Comments: In this study, for engaged, married, or single men and women with children or anticipating them, participants learn how to use biblical principles in rearing children. Thought-provoking lessons cover goals for parents, instruction for children, qualities for right relationships, teaching responsibility, and training and planning for the future. A chart of selected topics for training is helpful, and family projects are encouraged.

Author: **40**
Series: Discover Life
Title: *Peter: The Making of a Disciple*
Publisher: Church Development Resources, 1988

Num. Sess.	Group Time	Num. Pgs.	Avg. Qst.	Price	Audience	Format	Bible Study
7	45-60	16	6	2.35	Beginner	Workbk	Topical

Features: Intro to Study, Follow Up, Full Scrpt Printed
★★★ Personal Application   Preparation Time: None ISBN:
★★ Relationship Building Ldr. Guide Avail.: Yes   Size: 8.50 x 11.0
Subjects: Bible Personalities, Evangelism, God, Men's Issues
Comments: This study of Peter covers passages from Matthew, Luke, John, and Acts. Lessons include: "Meet the Master," "He Walked on Water," "How to Be a Rock," and more. God changed Peter from shaking reed to solid rock. Accompanying materials are designed for nonChristians and the nonchurched, and homework is not required. Lessons are distributed prior to each study. Bible passages are printed, thus eliminating possible embarrassment over trying to find a passage, or bringing a Bible to a public place.

Author: **41**
Series: Discover Life
Title: *Proverbs: Wisdom for Living*
Publisher: Church Development Resources, 1988

Num. Sess.	Group Time	Num. Pgs.	Avg. Qst.	Price	Audience	Format	Bible Study
8	45-60	20	7	2.35	Beginner	Workbk	Book

Features: Intro to Study, Follow Up, Full Scrpt Printed
★★★ Personal Application   Preparation Time: None ISBN:
★★ Relationship Building Ldr. Guide Avail.: Yes   Size: 8.50 x 11.0
Subjects: Evangelism, Proverbs, Wisdom
Comments: This study of Proverbs concerns wisdom, living, work, wealth, words, marriage, relationships, character, and religion. Accompanying materials are designed for nonChristians and the nonchurched, and homework is not required. Lessons are distributed prior to each study. Bible passages are printed, which eliminates potential embarrassment over being unable to find a passage, or over bringing a Bible to a public place. The leader's guide provides additional questions.

Author: **42**
Series:
Title: *Serendipity Bible for Groups*
Publisher: Serendipity House, 1988

Num. Sess.	Group Time	Num. Pgs.	Avg. Qst.	Price	Audience	Format	Bible Study
	60-90	N/A	Vry	19.95	Beginner	Book	Book

Features: Intro to Leading a Study, Intro to Study, Digging Deeper Quest, Full Scrpt Printed, Maps, Index
★★★ Personal Application   Preparation Time: None ISBN:
★★★ Relationship Building Ldr. Guide Avail.: No   Size: 6.50 x 9.25
Subjects: New Testament, Old Testament
Comments: This Bible for groups includes the following: the complete NIV text; thousands of "open," "dig," and "reflect" questions; 36 ready-made study courses; 96 ready-made studies on favorite Bible stories; 66 specialized book studies; 20 pages of subject indexes; and 13 full-color maps. Three levels of discussion questions include "icebreaker," "digging deeper," and "reflection." It's appropriate for beginning or advanced groups. Adding a notebook for recording responses will be helpful.

Author: **43**
Series:
Title: *Serendipity New Testament for Groups*
Publisher: Serendipity House, 1986

Num. Sess.	Group Time	Num. Pgs.	Avg. Qst.	Price	Audience	Format	Bible Study
68	60-90	690	Vry	9.95	Beginner	Book	Book

Features: Intro to Leading a Study, Intro to Study, Digging Deeper Quest, Full Scrpt Printed, Charts, Index

★★★ Personal Application   Preparation Time: None   ISBN:
★★★ Relationship Building   Ldr. Guide Avail.: No   Size: 6.50 x 9.25

Subjects: New Testament
Comments: The Serendipity New Testament for Groups includes 5,000 "flow" questions in the margin beside the biblical text; 48 ready-made studies on favorite Bible stories; 20 complete Bible study courses on popular themes; special introductions for each book in the New Testament; and a subject index of important words, people, and places. Three levels of discussion questions—"icebreaker," "digging deeper," and "reflection"—make it appropriate for beginning or advanced groups. A notebook is needed.

Author: **44**
Series: Studies in Christian Living
Title: *Serving Others (Book 6)*
Publisher: NavPress, 1964

Num. Sess.	Group Time	Num. Pgs.	Avg. Qst.	Price	Audience	Format	Bible Study
5	45-60	28	Vry	2.50	New Christian	Workbk	Topical

Features: Intro to Study, Maps

★★ Personal Application   Preparation Time: Low   ISBN: 0-89109-082-7
★★ Relationship Building   Ldr. Guide Avail.: No   Size: 5.50 x 8.50

Subjects: Discipleship, Service, Teens: Discipleship, Teens: Prayer
Comments: This five-lesson study for new believers ages fifteen and older is used by many churches for basic discipleship follow-up. Book six deals with these topics: "Helping Others Find Christ," "Follow-up," "Power in Prayer," "Scriptural Giving," and "World Vision." This series of six studies helps new Christians establish personal Bible study and learn and practice the essentials of Christian life. This series could be used as a small group aid for new believers.

Author: **45**
Series: Design for Discipleship
Title: *Spirit-filled Christian, The (Book Two)*
Publisher: NavPress, 1973

Num. Sess.	Group Time	Num. Pgs.	Avg. Qst.	Price	Audience	Format	Bible Study
5	60-75	47	17	2.50	New Christian	Workbk	Topical

Features: Intro to Study, Summary, Charts

★★ Personal Application   Preparation Time: Med   ISBN: 0-89109-037-1
★★ Relationship Building   Ldr. Guide Avail.: Yes   Size: 5.50 x 8.50

Subjects: Discipleship, Evangelism, Holy Spirit, Obedience, Prayer, Teens: Discipleship
Comments: This is book two in a comprehensive study series on basic biblical principles and standards for following Christ. Topics concern the way to live a Spirit-filled, Christ-centered life and include: "The Obedient Christian," "God's Word in Your Life," "Conversing with God," "Fellowship with Christians," and "Witnessing for Christ." This series is designed to help encourage personal Bible study, examine Bible truths, and learn and practice essentials of discipleship.

Author: **46**
Series:
Title: *Stephen Ministry at Work*
Publisher: Stephen Ministries, 1990

Num. Sess.	Group Time	Num. Pgs.	Avg. Qst.	Price	Audience	Format	Bible Study
	-	N/A	N/A	8.50			

Features: Cassette Avail

  Personal Application   Preparation Time: ISBN:
  Relationship Building   Ldr. Guide Avail.:   Size: 4.50 x 8.50

Subjects: Small Group Resource, Support
Comments: This fifteen-minute videotape takes a detailed, action-oriented look at the Stephen Series, now being used by more than fifty denominations. It uses testimonies from real people in ministry. It discusses the program's effectiveness and challenges those willing to provide lay caring ministry to become involved. The video is ideal for boards, committees, councils, and vestries. A longer, more in-depth audio tape is available.

Author: **47**
Series: Studies in Christian Living
Title: *Talking with Christ (Book 3)*
Publisher: NavPress, 1964

Num. Sess.	Group Time	Num. Pgs.	Avg. Qst.	Price	Audience	Format	Bible Study
4	45-60	30	Vry	2.50	New Christian	Workbk	Topical

Features: Intro to Study

★★ Personal Application   Preparation Time: Low   ISBN: 0-89109-079-7
★★ Relationship Building   Ldr. Guide Avail.: No   Size: 5.50 x 8.50

Subjects: Discipleship, Teens: Discipleship, Teens: Prayer
Comments: This four-lesson study for new believers ages fifteen and older is used by many churches for basic discipleship follow-up. Book three includes these topics: "The Church," "What Is the Bible?" "God's Word in Your Life," and "Principles of Prayer." This series of six studies helps new Christians establish personal Bible study and learn and practice the essentials of Christian life. This series could be used as a small group study aid for new believers.

Author: **48**
Series:
Title: *Twelve Steps, The: A Spiritual Journey*
Publisher: Recovery Publications, 1988

Num. Sess.	Group Time	Num. Pgs.	Avg. Qst.	Price	Audience	Format	Bible Study
28	105-120	230	Vry	14.95	Beginner	Workbk	Topical

Features: Intro to Study, Bibliography, Appendix, Publicity Ideas

★★★★ Personal Application   Preparation Time: Med   ISBN: 0-941405-02-8
★★★★ Relationship Building   Ldr. Guide Avail.: No   Size: 8.50 x 11.0

Subjects: Counseling, Family, Psychology, Support
Comments: This study, for individuals reared in emotionally repressive and dysfunctional families, uses the "Twelve Steps" process in a Christian context. It is written by people reared in alcoholic and dysfunctional homes. Having felt no love and security as children, they were not able to mature into healthy, functional adults. This book contains explicit, detailed writing exercises for each step on the road to recovery; it reaffirms God's dominion and can lead a person to God.

Author: **49**
Series: Design for Discipleship
Title: *Walking with Christ (Book Three)*
Publisher: NavPress, 1973

Num. Sess.	Group Time	Num. Pgs.	Avg. Qst.	Price	Audience	Format	Bible Study
5	60-75	44	19	2.50	New Christian	Workbk	Topical

Features: Intro to Study, Summary, Cartoons, Charts
★★ Personal Application Preparation Time: Med ISBN: 0-89109-038-X
★★ Relationship Building Ldr. Guide Avail.: Yes Size: 5.50 x 8.50
Subjects: Discipleship, Faith, God's Promises, Service, Teens: Discipleship
Comments: This is book three in a comprehensive study series on basic biblical principles and standards for following Christ. Participants will study five important aspects of their life with Him: "Maturing in Christ," "The Lordship of Christ," "Faith and Promises of God," "Knowing God's Will," and "Walking as a Servant." The series is designed to help participants establish personal Bible study, examine Bible truths, and learn and practice essentials of discipleship. Homework is suggested.

Author: **50**
Series: Discover Life
Title: *Woman and Her World, A*
Publisher: Church Development Resources, 1989

Num. Sess.	Group Time	Num. Pgs.	Avg. Qst.	Price	Audience	Format	Bible Study
7	45-60	16	5	2.35	Beginner	Workbk	Topical

Features: Intro to Study, Follow Up, Full Scrpt Printed
★★★ Personal Application Preparation Time: None ISBN:
★★ Relationship Building Ldr. Guide Avail.: Yes Size: 8.50 x 11.0
Subjects: Christian Living, Evangelism, Friendships, Marriage, Money, Relationships, Women's Issues, Work
Comments: Old and New Testament passages help participants explore women's unique needs and perspectives. Seven lessons review important areas of a woman's life: work, friends, children, money, goals, marriage, and spirituality. Accompanying materials are designed for nonChristians and the nonchurched, and homework is not required. Lessons are distributed prior to each study. Bible passages are printed in the study, eliminating embarrassment over trying to find a passage, or bringing a Bible to a public place.

Author: **51**
Series: Design for Discipleship
Title: *Your Life in Christ (Book One)*
Publisher: NavPress, 1973

Num. Sess.	Group Time	Num. Pgs.	Avg. Qst.	Price	Audience	Format	Bible Study
4	60-75	30	16	2.50	New Christian	Workbk	Topical

Features: Intro to Leading a Study, Summary, Charts
★★ Personal Application Preparation Time: Med ISBN: 0-89109-036-3
★★ Relationship Building Ldr. Guide Avail.: Yes Size: 5.50 x 8.50
Subjects: Discipleship, Holy Spirit, Teens: Discipleship
Comments: This is book one in a comprehensive study series on basic biblical principles and standards for following Christ. Lessons include: "God Cares for You," "The Person of Jesus Christ," "The Work of Christ," and "The Spirit Within You." The series is designed to help participants establish personal Bible study, examine Bible truths, and learn and practice essentials of discipleship. Homework is suggested.

Author: Aaseng, Rolf E. **52**
Series: Small Group Bible Studies
Title: *In the Beginning*
Publisher: Augsburg Publishing House, 1978

Num. Sess.	Group Time	Num. Pgs.	Avg. Qst.	Price	Audience	Format	Bible Study
6	60-75	24	Vry	1.15	New Christian	Book	Book

Features: Intro to Study, Prayer Helps
★★ Personal Application Preparation Time: None ISBN:
★★ Relationship Building Ldr. Guide Avail.: No Size: 8.50 x 5.50
Subjects: Genesis, God
Comments: This small pamphlet includes six sessions on the first eleven chapters of Genesis. These chapters, which differ from the chapters that follow, deal with Creation and with matters that affect all of humanity. Starting with the story of Abraham in Genesis 12, the narrative focuses on a single family and tells of God's plan of salvation for humankind. This study attempts to look more closely at what the text actually says, and to consider the contemporary meaning of the ancient words.

Author: Aaseng, Rolf E. **53**
Series: Small Group Bible Studies
Title: *Justice for a Troubled World*
Publisher: Augsburg Publishing House, 1975

Num. Sess.	Group Time	Num. Pgs.	Avg. Qst.	Price	Audience	Format	Bible Study
4	60-75	16	32	0.95	New Christian	Book	Book

Features: Intro to Study, Prayer Helps, Digging Deeper Quest
★★ Personal Application Preparation Time: None ISBN:
★★ Relationship Building Ldr. Guide Avail.: No Size: 8.50 x 5.50
Subjects: Bible Personalities, Minor Prophets
Comments: In this short, six-session study on the book of Amos the concern is not to interpret every detail and historical reference of the book. Rather, the study notes similarities to the present day and discovers what the Word of God has to say to Christians. A key passage in the book is 5:21-24, which is a cry for justice and righteousness.

Author: Aaseng, Rolf E. **54**
Series: Small Group Bible Studies
Title: *Turning the World Upside Down*
Publisher: Augsburg Publishing House, 1975

Num. Sess.	Group Time	Num. Pgs.	Avg. Qst.	Price	Audience	Format	Bible Study
8	60-75	32	34	1.25	New Christian	Book	Book

Features: Intro to Study, Prayer Helps
★★★ Personal Application Preparation Time: None ISBN:
★★★ Relationship Building Ldr. Guide Avail.: No Size: 8.50 x 5.50
Subjects: Acts, Church Life, Parables
Comments: This small pamphlet includes eight chapter-by-chapter sessions on Acts. It is a complete look at the book. The study is important because it provides information about Jesus not found in the gospels, especially certain parables and information on the post-resurrection days. It answers the question: How did the Christian Church begin? The two central figures in the book are Peter and Paul. Questions marked with a star are especially intended for group discussion.

Fresh Fruit Never Tasted So Good

Enjoy the sweetness of True Friendship. Savor the Benefits of Waiting.

And experience the Strength of Being Tender.

Introducing **Fruit of the Spirit Bible Studies**. A new series of 8 guides that give you an in-depth look at the fruit of the Holy Spirit: *Love, Joy, Peace, Patience, Kindness, Faithfulness, Gentleness, Self-Control.*

Each guide contains solid biblical principles, relevant discussion questions, and helpful leader's notes. All in a friendly, easy-to-use format.

For individual use or group study, **Fruit of the Spirit Bible Studies** contain everything you need to help the Spirit's fruit ripen in your life.

Fruit of the Spirit Bible Studies

Love: *Building Healthy Relationships*

Joy: *How to Rejoice in Any Situation*

Peace: *Overcoming Anxiety & Conflict*

Patience: *The Benefits of Waiting*

Kindness: *Reaching Out to Others*

Faithfulness: *The Foundation of True Friendship*

Gentleness: *The Strength of Being Tender*

Self-Control: *Mastering Our Passions*

Fruit of the Spirit Bible Studies.

Now available at your favorite Christian bookstore.

Zondervan

6-HOUR SERENDIPITY SEMINAR

WITH LYMAN COLEMAN
FOUNDER OF SERENDIPITY

Find out why certain churches flourish in the 90's, while others are in decline!

Here's a chance to train your small group leaders—because great small groups don't just happen.

Call for date and location nearest you.

1-800-525-9563

Serendipity House
Small Group Resources

LETTER OPENER.

In his landmark epistle to the Romans, the Apostle Paul opened the mysteries of faith and salvation for all time.

Now acclaimed teacher John MacArthur opens the spiritual riches of this letter like never before. The latest in his comprehensive commentary series on the New Testament, *Romans 1-8* examines the core themes and principles of each passage. And how they still affect life and faith in very specific ways twenty centuries after first penned.

With his engaging style and masterful, verse-by-verse exposition, MacArthur creates a reliable interpretation with practical lessons. So you can, in turn, open this classic letter for others. At your favorite bookstore, or call 800-678-6928.

Put *Joy* in Your Bible Study

Bible study shouldn't be a task, it should be a joy. You can make it a real joy just by using the *Joy of Living* Bible Study Series. It's the answer for those looking for a simple, practical, and relevant Bible study. *Joy* studies don't take long to do, yet they speak to the needs of today's Christians in a very real and helpful way. With quality explanations of biblical passages in simple terms that are easily understood, for any group or individual study. Historical background, commentary, maps and time lines are all included. They're practical studies for personal growth.

■ ***Walking in God's Way:*** Studies in Ruth and Esther. With this 7-week study, you'll see how listening to God and learning to love are at the center of the Christian walk. 5419474 $5.95

■ ***Courage to Conquer:*** Studies in Daniel. Daniel proclaimed his faith even in the face of great danger. See how God can provide us with strength, insight and courage, in this 6-week study. 5419489 $5.95

■ ***Power for Positive Living:*** Studies in Philippians and Colossians. You'll find strength to face the challenges of daily living in this enriching 8-week study. 5419493 $5.95

■ ***Living in the Light:*** Studies in 1, 2, 3 John and Jude. Christ is our brightest hope in these dark times. Focus on the fundamentals of Christianity with this 6-week study. 5419501 $5.95

■ ***Discovering God's Power:*** Studies in Genesis 1-17. God's creations are wonderful. Come to a new appreciation of His tremendous power with this 9-week study in Genesis. 5419764 $5.95

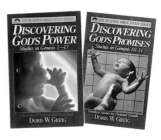

■ ***Discovering God's Promises:*** Studies in Genesis 18-31. God is faithful to those who love Him. Take a look at His providence and protection with this 9-week study. Part two of a three-part study in Genesis. 5419845 $5.95

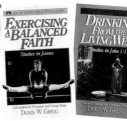

■ ***Exercising a Balanced Faith:*** Studies in James. Balance can be found through a disciplined life. You'll see how in this 8-week study in James. 5419649 $5.95

■ ***Drinking from the Living Well:*** Studies in John 1-11. Find a life of spiritual friendship with and refreshment from the living Christ, in this 12-week study of the Gospel of John. Part one of a two part study. 5419824 $5.95

Regal Books
A Division of Gospel Light

All 8 ***Joy of Living*** Bible Studies are available from your Christian Bookstore.

BIG IDEAS FOR SMALL GROUPS.

What does your small group need? Icebreakers? Discussion questions? Bible study materials? Relationship builders? There are plenty of materials to choose from, but you'll most likely have to go to separate resources to find this kind of variety.

GroupBuilder Resources are different. They're designed specifically for the needs of small groups. They're everything you need to encourage interaction, build relationships, and challenge one another to practice biblical principles.

Each book will take your small group through 8 sessions, each one thought-provoking and stimulating. Topics include hindrances to spiritual growth, developing biblical intimacy, and knowing God. There are even books designed to help launch your group or improve your group dynamics.

So if you're coming up short on materials for your small group, take a look at *GroupBuilder Resources.*

Available at your local Christian bookstore.

VICTOR BOOKS

NEW!
From Word Lifeware Video

Josh McDowell speaks to Adults and Youth Alike

How To Be a Hero To Your Kids
Video Curriculum

Josh McDowell and Dick Day share practical suggestions for positive parenting and teach moms and dads how to put these principles to work.

How To Be A Hero To Your Kids video curriculum comes with a leader's guide, reproducible discussion guide and a copy of the *How To Be a Hero To Your Kids* book. It's perfect for group study and a must for all parents.

ISBN 084-9911-540   Price $99.99

Teenage Q & A
Video Curriculum

Josh McDowell and Bill Jones collectively bring nearly 50 years of public ministry into this treasure house of practical wisdom and biblical insight. It goes to the core of issues and problems that teens face, and challenges teens not to settle for second best.

Teenage Q & A video curriculum comes equipped with a leader's guide, reproducible discussion guide and a copy of the *Teenage Q & A Book*.

ISBN 084-9911-575   Price $79.99

available at your local Christian Bookstore or by calling 1-800-299-9673.

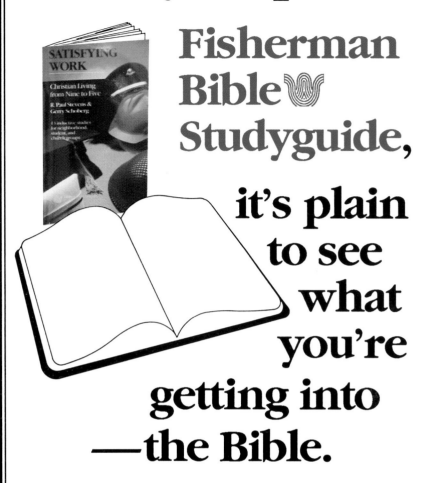

Author: Abercrombie, Katie 55
Series:
Title: *Worry, Worry, Worry: School, War and Other Scary Stuff*
(Student Book)
Publisher: Group Publishing, 1988

Num. Sess.	Group Time	Num. Pgs.	Avg. Qst.	Price	Audience	Format	Bible Study
13	45-60	82	Vry	3.95	Beginner	Workbk	Topical

Features: Objectives, Prayer Helps, Drawings, Charts
★★★★ Personal Application   Preparation Time: Low   ISBN: 0-931529-49-2
★★★★ Relationship Building   Ldr. Guide Avail.: Yes   Size: 5.50 x 8.50
Subjects: Teens: Emotions, Teens: Junior High, Teens: Senior High
Comments: This thirteen-session study helps teenagers grapple with fears, discover why they're afraid, and strengthen their faith. The lively, creative, Bible-based sessions cover topics such as: how well teens are doing in school; how they're treated by friends; losing a parent; personal appearance; violence and crime; losing a good friend; nuclear war; and more. The whys of fear and worry are exposed, and teens are led to apply faith to fear and to face problems with courage and God's peace.

Author: Ackley, Phil 56
Series: Young Fisherman Bible
Title: *Get Wise: Studies in Proverbs*
Publisher: Shaw, 1985

Num. Sess.	Group Time	Num. Pgs.	Avg. Qst.	Price	Audience	Format	Bible Study
12	50-60	92	12	2.95	Beginner	Workbk	Topical

Features: Intro to Study, Scrpt Memory Helps, Digging Deeper Quest, Full Scrpt Printed, Drawings, Charts
★★ Personal Application   Preparation Time: Low   ISBN: 0-87788-695-4
★★ Relationship Building   Ldr. Guide Avail.: Yes   Size: 6.0 x 8.0
Subjects: Teens: Christian Liv, Teens: Friends, Teens: New Testament, Teens: Relationships
Comments: This study, based on a topical arrangement of verses from Proverbs, helps teens study God's wisdom concerning friendship, foolishness, discipline, riches, poverty, the tongue, life, hope, and purity. It helps them realize the importance of being "wise" when being "ordinary" is the easy thing. The wisdom of Solomon is applicable to twentieth-century teens. Leaders are given helpful instructions for getting the most out of this study.

Author: Adams, David 57
Series: Group's Active Bible Curriculum
Title: *Gospel of John, The: Jesus' Teachings*
Publisher: Group Publishing, 1990

Num. Sess.	Group Time	Num. Pgs.	Avg. Qst.	Price	Audience	Format	Bible Study
4	35-60	47	Vry	6.95	Beginner	Workbk	Book

Features: Intro to Leading a Study, Intro to Study, Objectives, Study Overview, Ldr's Notes, Drawings, Handouts, Agenda, Publicity Ideas
★★★★ Personal Application   Preparation Time: None ISBN: 1-559-45208-0
★★★★ Relationship Building   Ldr. Guide Avail.: No   Size: 8.50 x 11.0
Subjects: Teens: Jesus' Life, Teens: New Testament, Teens: Senior High
Comments: This four-lesson study helps senior high students discover the meaning of Jesus' message. Students will learn what it means to have new life in Christ, discover ways to live out their faith, rely on Him for direction in life, uncover the excitement of following Him daily, and gain insight into Jesus' message for contemporary times. Instructions are easy to follow and provide multiple options for teachers. No student books are required.

Author: Adams, Jay E. 58
Series:
Title: *Thirst for Wholeness, A*
Publisher: Victor Books, 1988

Num. Sess.	Group Time	Num. Pgs.	Avg. Qst.	Price	Audience	Format	Bible Study
13	60-90	143	N/A	7.99	New Christian	Book	Topical

Features: Prayer Helps
★★★★ Personal Application   Preparation Time: Med   ISBN: 0-89693-455-1
★★★ Relationship Building   Ldr. Guide Avail.: Yes   Size: 5.50 x 8.0
Subjects: Christian Life, Failure, James, Obedience, Prayer, Wholeness
Comments: This book offers solutions to people whose spiritual integrity is in question. Taken from James, it concentrates on how a person can become a complete Christian from the inside out. Lessons discuss the following: resisting temptation, conquering doubt, praying effectively, having good motives, overcoming anger, being genuine, remaining faithful, and more. The closing lesson, "What All This Means to You," discusses the implications of this study on the individual. Worksheets are included.

Author: Adams, Lane 59
Series: Living Studies
Title: *How Come It's Taking Me So Long?: Steps to Spiritual Maturity*
Publisher: Tyndale House, 1975

Num. Sess.	Group Time	Num. Pgs.	Avg. Qst.	Price	Audience	Format	Bible Study
14	45-60	159	N/A	6.95	New Christian	Book	Topical

Features: No Grp Discussion Quest
★★ Personal Application   Preparation Time: Low   ISBN: 0-8423-1491-1
★ Relationship Building   Ldr. Guide Avail.: No   Size: 5.0 x 8.0
Subjects: Christian Living, Discipleship
Comments: This book uses an analogy of the invasion of an enemy-held island to help a new or growing Christian understand the process of growth. It presents a fresh biblical understanding of conversion and growth and thereby offers relief to one who wonders, "How come it's taking me so long to get better?"

Author: Adler, Ronald B. 60
Series:
Title: *Looking Out, Looking In*
Publisher: Holt, 1990

Num. Sess.	Group Time	Num. Pgs.	Avg. Qst.	Price	Audience	Format	Bible Study
9	-	370	N/A	19.90		Book	No

Features: Cartoons, Photos, Charts, Index
Personal Application   Preparation Time: ISBN: 0-03-030834-8
Relationship Building   Ldr. Guide Avail.:   Size: 8.25 x 10.25
Subjects: Small Group Resource
Comments: This book, designed to help leaders become better communicators, is presented in textbook form, with emphasis on experiential learning through exercises and other activities. Ideas are developed through a variety of readings. Chapter topics include getting started, self-concept and communication, perception, words and meanings, nonverbal communication, listening as opposed to hearing, emotions, positive relationships, and resolving conflict.

Author: Aeschliman, Gordon   **61**
Series: Global Issues
Title: *Leadership in the 21st Century*
Publisher: InterVarsity, 1990

Num. Sess.	Group Time	Num. Pgs.	Avg. Qst.	Price	Audience	Format	Bible Study
6	45-60	48	12	4.95	Beginner	Workbk	Topical

Features: Intro to Leading a Study, Intro to Study, Bibliography
★★★★ Personal Application Preparation Time: Low ISBN: 0-8308-4902-5
★★★★ Relationship Building Ldr. Guide Avail.: No Size: 5.50 x 8.25
Subjects: Caring, Ethics, Leadership, Service
Comments: This six-week study considers what it will mean to be a Christian leader in the next century, including specific requirements, and how gifts can best be used to serve Christ. It addresses vital issues such as courage, service, personal ethics, compassion for the world, ability to communicate love, and a leader's relationship with God. It helps participants understand what their roles might be as the church faces this challenge.

Author: Alexander, Myrna   **62**
Series: Woman's Workshop Series
Title: *Behold Your God: Studies on the Attributes of God*
Publisher: Zondervan, 1978

Num. Sess.	Group Time	Num. Pgs.	Avg. Qst.	Price	Audience	Format	Bible Study
13	90-120	124	18	5.95	New Christian	Workbk	Charctr

Features: Intro to Leading a Study, Intro to Study, Scrpt Memory Helps
★★ Personal Application Preparation Time: Med ISBN: 0-310-37131-7
★★ Relationship Building Ldr. Guide Avail.: No Size: 5.25 x 8.0
Subjects: God, Theology, Women's Issues
Comments: In this study of God's character and person, each lesson covers a truth about God's character: loving, supreme and sovereign, all-powerful, good, omniscient, all-wise, omnipresent, immutable, faithful, holy, just, and worthy to be praised. It prepares participants "to consistently lean on God," and "to know Him"; it also encourages practical application of this knowledge to daily living.

Author: Alexander, Myrna   **63**
Series: Woman's Workshop Series
Title: *Loving & Obeying God: Studies on 1 Samuel*
Publisher: Zondervan, 1982

Num. Sess.	Group Time	Num. Pgs.	Avg. Qst.	Price	Audience	Format	Bible Study
13	60-90	139	16	4.95	Beginner	Workbk	Book

Features: Intro to Leading a Study, Intro to Study, Study Overview, Maps
★★ Personal Application Preparation Time: Med ISBN: 0-310-37141-4
★★ Relationship Building Ldr. Guide Avail.: No Size: 5.25 x 8.0
Subjects: God, Obedience, Women's Issues, 1 & 2 Samuel
Comments: This historical narrative on Samuel describes the obedience and disobedience of key individuals who professsed love for God. It concerns men who became "living definitions of what it is to be after God's heart," in particular, Samuel and David. Participants see real people grappling with godly principles. The study includes generous background information on the history, culture, and attitudes of the Israelites and their neighbors. Key Principles from each lesson are highlighed.

Author: Alig, Ruth & Stephanie Wright   **64**
Series:
Title: *New Mothers Guide, The*
Publisher: NavPress, 1988

Num. Sess.	Group Time	Num. Pgs.	Avg. Qst.	Price	Audience	Format	Bible Study
12	60-90	190	Vry	7.95	Beginner	Workbk	Topical

Features: Intro to Study, Bibliography, Prayer Helps
★★★★ Personal Application Preparation Time: Med ISBN: 0-89109-252-8
★★ Relationship Building Ldr. Guide Avail.: No Size: 6.0 x 9.0
Subjects: Parenting, Stress, Women's Issues
Comments: This study is a twelve-month guide to help new mothers meet the challenges, joys, and frustrations of motherhood. Month by month, participants will study physical and psychological changes taking place in their minds and bodies. The Bible study will refresh the heart and spirit; journaling will record the new mother's special thoughts and emotions.

Author: Anderes, Marilyn N.   **65**
Series: Workshop Series
Title: *Workshop on Self-Giving, A*
Publisher: Zondervan, 1989

Num. Sess.	Group Time	Num. Pgs.	Avg. Qst.	Price	Audience	Format	Bible Study
12	75-90	142	26	6.95	Mature Chrstn	Workbk	Topical

Features: Intro to Leading a Study, Intro to Study, Scrpt Memory Helps, Study Overview, Drawings, Charts
★★ Personal Application Preparation Time: High ISBN: 0-310-52251-X
★★ Relationship Building Ldr. Guide Avail.: No Size: 5.25 x 8.0
Subjects: Bible Personalities, Caring, Christian Living, Service
Comments: This study draws on various Old and New Testament characters who learned the meaning of sacrificial giving. Biblical examples of "giving" include stories of help, support, undemanding love, and bonded kinship. The stories of Deborah and Barak, Jonathan and David, and Elisha and the "prominent woman" reinforce the many ways to give of one's self, and so become like Christ. Three format options for this study are shown in a chart.

Author: Anderson, Don   **66**
Series:
Title: *Abraham: Delay Is Not Denial*
Publisher: Loizeaux Brothers, 1987

Num. Sess.	Group Time	Num. Pgs.	Avg. Qst.	Price	Audience	Format	Bible Study
9	45-60	200	5	7.95	New Christian	Book	Charctr

Features: Intro to Study, Bibliography
★★ Personal Application Preparation Time: Med ISBN: 0-87213-000-2
★★ Relationship Building Ldr. Guide Avail.: No Size: 5.25 x 8.0
Subjects: Bible Personalities, Genesis, God, Obedience, Stress
Comments: This study of Genesis 11-22 deals with a basic human shortcoming—impatience. With Abraham as the role model, participants find that instant gratification is not necessary; that good things take time and God wants it that way. The study describes the pressures of "hurry" that faced Abraham and face contemporary Christians as well; and it provides biblical answers to modern dilemmas and temptations. Lessons include: "The Starting Block," "Cluttered Obedience," and more.

Author: Anderson, Don   **67**
Series:
Title: *Ecclesiastes: The Mid-Life Crisis*
Publisher: Loizeaux Brothers, 1987

Num. Sess.	Group Time	Num. Pgs.	Avg. Qst.	Price	Audience	Format	Bible Study
11	45-60	270	8	9.95	New Christian	Book	Book

Features: Intro to Study, Bibliography
  ★★ Personal Application   Preparation Time: Med   ISBN: 0-87213-001-0
  ★★ Relationship Building   Ldr. Guide Avail.: No   Size: 5.25 x 8.0
Subjects: Bible Personalities, Ecclesiastes, Men's Issues, Success
Comments: This verse-by-verse study of Ecclesiastes deals with a phenomenon faced by nearly everyone—mid-life crisis. It examines Solomon's crisis, and doesn't merely analyze the problems that bring on the trauma but provides biblical answers to questions so many face in contemporary society. It shows participants how God's Word, unaltered and intact, fully ministers to all needs. Eleven lessons follow an introduction, with titles such as: "A Man in Crisis," and "The Success Syndrome."

Author: Anderson, Don   **68**
Series:
Title: *God Wants a Relationship Not a Performance*
Publisher: Loizeaux Brothers, 1989

Num. Sess.	Group Time	Num. Pgs.	Avg. Qst.	Price	Audience	Format	Bible Study
12	45-60	290	3	9.95	New Christian	Book	Book

Features: Intro to Study, Bibliography
  ★★ Personal Application   Preparation Time: Med   ISBN: 0-87213-005-3
  ★★ Relationship Building   Ldr. Guide Avail.: No   Size: 5.25 x 8.0
Subjects: God, Relationships, Romans, Victorious Living
Comments: This study attempts to correct the misconception that Christians must perform well enough to please God; it points out that all God seeks is a relationship—and that through Christ. It leads participants verse-by-verse through Romans 5-8, a "road map for victorious living." Following an introduction that establishes God's desire for relationship with humankind, twelve lessons take students from "rethinking the reasons" God made humankind to "reaching the higher ground."

Author: Anderson, Don   **69**
Series:
Title: *James: Running Uphill into the Wind*
Publisher: Loizeaux Brothers, 1990

Num. Sess.	Group Time	Num. Pgs.	Avg. Qst.	Price	Audience	Format	Bible Study
12	45-60	300	3	9.95	New Christian	Book	Book

Features: Intro to Study, Bibliography
  ★★ Personal Application   Preparation Time: Med   ISBN: 0-87213-007-X
  ★★ Relationship Building   Ldr. Guide Avail.: No   Size: 5.25 x 8.0
Subjects: Christian Life, Failure, Faith, James, Success
Comments: Comparing the Christian life to preparation for an important race—"running uphill into the wind"—this verse-by-verse study of James provides a practical vehicle for running the race of Christian life. Becoming Christlike, as James exhorts, involves struggles, detours, successes, and failures because it is basically a battle to change people's behavior. Lesson titles include "Gut-check Christianity," "Hitting the Wall," "Working Out in the World," "The Bottom Line," and more.

Author: Anderson, Don   **70**
Series:
Title: *Joseph: Fruitful in Affliction*
Publisher: Loizeaux Brothers, 1988

Num. Sess.	Group Time	Num. Pgs.	Avg. Qst.	Price	Audience	Format	Bible Study
12	45-60	360	5	11.95	New Christian	Book	Charctr

Features: Intro to Study, Bibliography
  ★★ Personal Application   Preparation Time: Med   ISBN: 0-87213-004-5
  ★★ Relationship Building   Ldr. Guide Avail.: No   Size: 5.25 x 8.0
Subjects: Bible Personalities, Faith, Forgiveness, Genesis, Success
Comments: This study of Joseph pictures a man worth emulating in contemporary America; a man of enduring faithfulness in the midst of hardships, a wise administrator, forgiving brother, and devoted son—mainly, a man who faced real affliction with steadfast trust in God. The study is divided into three parts and twelve lessons. Part 1—"The Training"—deals with the time of great adversity in Joseph's youth. Part 2—"The Testing"—covers his growth under Pharaoh. Part 3—"The Triumph and Transition."

Author: Anderson, Don   **71**
Series:
Title: *Song of Solomon: Make Full My Joy*
Publisher: Loizeaux Brothers, 1987

Num. Sess.	Group Time	Num. Pgs.	Avg. Qst.	Price	Audience	Format	Bible Study
8	45-60	200	5	6.95	New Christian	Book	Book

Features: Intro to Study, Bibliography
  ★★ Personal Application   Preparation Time: Med   ISBN: 0-87213-002-9
  ★★ Relationship Building   Ldr. Guide Avail.: No   Size: 5.25 x 8.0
Subjects: Joy, Love, Marriage, Song of Solomon
Comments: This study examines a Bible book which, by its very inclusion in Scripture, provides God's endorsement of physical love between husband and wife. It provides participants with a beautiful model of how married love can be; it shows the joy of total giving, intimacy, and sharing within marriage. The study is broken into two parts. Part 1 lays the foundation, defining love and joy from Philippians and Ruth, in two lessons. Part 2 offers a six-lesson study of Song of Solomon.

Author: Anderson, Paul   **72**
Series: Building Books
Title: *Building Christian Character*
Publisher: Bethany House, 1980

Num. Sess.	Group Time	Num. Pgs.	Avg. Qst.	Price	Audience	Format	Bible Study
34	45-60	48	Vry	4.95	New Christian	Workbk	Topical

Features: Intro to Study, Scrpt Memory Helps
  ★★ Personal Application   Preparation Time: Low   ISBN: 0-87123-436-X
  ★★ Relationship Building   Ldr. Guide Avail.: Yes   Size: 8.50 x 11.0
Subjects: Teens: Christian Liv, Teens: Discipleship
Comments: This in-depth study for young adults uses thirty-four Bible examples to give the true meaning of Christian character traits. The examples show practical ways each trait can be applied in a Christian's life today and propose appropriate memory scriptures to reinforce the truth. Character traits include perseverance, forgiveness, self-control, gentleness, confidence, wisdom, fairness, enthusiasm, and more.

Author: Arn, Charles   **73**
Series:
Title: *Growing in Love*
Publisher: Church Growth, 1984

Num. Sess.	Group Time	Num. Pgs.	Avg. Qst.	Price	Audience	Format	Bible Study
13	60-75	112	Vry	198.0	Beginner	Video	Topical

Features: Study Overview, Ldr's Notes, Transpcy Masters, Agenda, Book Incl, Video Study Guide
  ★★★ Personal Application Preparation Time: None ISBN:
  ★★★ Relationship Building Ldr. Guide Avail.: No Size: 11.25 x 11.50
Subjects: Caring, Church Life, Love, Marriage, Relationships
Comments: This thirteen-week study helps participants learn how to express and practice Christian love. They learn that love is not just attitude, but action. And as they focus intentional Christian love toward others, they see how effectively their love encourages others to experience God's love. The kit includes complete leader's notes; instructional video; masters for overhead transparencies; and sample participant pack, including text, workbook, application guide, and personal "love quotient" inventory.

Author: Arndt, Elise   **74**
Series:
Title: *Mother's Time, A: A Realistic Approach to Time Management for Mothers*
Publisher: Victor Books, 1987

Num. Sess.	Group Time	Num. Pgs.	Avg. Qst.	Price	Audience	Format	Bible Study
13	60-90	156	N/A	7.99	Beginner	Book	Topical

Features:
  ★★★★ Personal Application Preparation Time: Med ISBN: 0-89693-338-5
  ★★★★ Relationship Building Ldr. Guide Avail.: Yes Size: 5.50 x 8.0
Subjects: Parenting, Time, Women's Issues
Comments: This study presents practical advice for modern Christian mothers, whose days are filled with diapers and teething babies, car pools, and Little League; and whose time demands exceed the supply. Participants learn that one solution to mothers' time crunch is doing God's will. Mothers can learn to deal with time pressures, accomplish the important when the urgent constantly beckons, and take time to learn each day. A leader's guide with transparency masters is available.

Author: Arndt, Elise   **75**
Series:
Title: *Mother's Touch, A*
Publisher: Victor Books, 1983

Num. Sess.	Group Time	Num. Pgs.	Avg. Qst.	Price	Audience	Format	Bible Study
13	60-75	151	N/A	7.99	Beginner	Book	Topical

Features:
  ★★★ Personal Application Preparation Time: Low ISBN: 0-88207-101-7
  ★★★ Relationship Building Ldr. Guide Avail.: Yes Size: 5.50 x 8.0
Subjects: Family, Parenting, Women's Issues
Comments: This thirteen-week study of mothers' roles in the lives of children covers such topics as: balancing a child's dependence; working outside the home; making each child feel special; integrating Christian principles into everyday life; and realizing the obligation to bring one's child to the Lord. One lesson, "New in the Nest," looks at pregnancy in an "older" woman. A leader's guide includes transparency masters.

Author: Ascroft, Winifred   **76**
Series: Basic Bible Study Series
Title: *Quickening Flame, The: A Scriptural Study of Revival*
Publisher: Aglow, 1985

Num. Sess.	Group Time	Num. Pgs.	Avg. Qst.	Price	Audience	Format	Bible Study
9	75-90	61	30	2.95	New Christian	Workbk	Topical

Features: Intro to Study, Prayer Helps, Scrpt Memory Helps, Persnl Study Quest
  ★★★ Personal Application Preparation Time: Med ISBN: 0-932305-20-2
  ★★★ Relationship Building Ldr. Guide Avail.: No Size: 5.25 x 8.25
Subjects: Charismatic Interest, Church Life, Revival
Comments: This nine-week study explores the subject of revival—the need and preparation for revival, the need for prayer, the results of revival, and more. Revival can lead to an awakening in both believers and the Church; it is to these Christians and churches that have grown cold that the call first comes. Unbelievers cannot be revived; they must be born again.

Author: Backus, William & Steven Wiese   **77**
Series:
Title: *Finding the Freedom of Self-Control*
Publisher: Bethany House, 1988

Num. Sess.	Group Time	Num. Pgs.	Avg. Qst.	Price	Audience	Format	Bible Study
13	60-75	95	Vry	3.95	New Christian	Workbk	Topical

Features: Intro to Study, Prayer Helps, Summary
  ★★★ Personal Application Preparation Time: Med ISBN: 1-556-61004-1
  ★★ Relationship Building Ldr. Guide Avail.: No Size: 5.0 x 8.0
Subjects: Accountability, Addictions, Christian Living, Self-help, Support
Comments: This study addresses the problem of self-control, whether the cause is procrastination or bondage to an addiction. Among the study's goals: to identify personal self-control problems and misbelief; to challenge participants to apply Scripture truths to life situations; to involve them in growth and initiative through specific assignments; and to break the pattern of old habits and build new habits of self-control. This study guide is designed to accompany the book by the same title.

Author: Backus, William & Marie Chapian   **78**
Series:
Title: *Telling Yourself the Truth: A Study Guide*
Publisher: Bethany House, 1981

Num. Sess.	Group Time	Num. Pgs.	Avg. Qst.	Price	Audience	Format	Bible Study
14	45-60	41	11	2.95	New Christian	Workbk	Topical

Features: Intro to Study, Cassette Avail
  ★★★ Personal Application Preparation Time: Med ISBN: 0-87123-567-6
  ★★ Relationship Building Ldr. Guide Avail.: Yes Size: 5.0 x 8.0
Subjects: Counseling, Emotions, Psychology, Self-help
Comments: This study, a companion to the book and tape by the same title, helps participants understand that most of what happens in life can be attributed to the way people think. The life-changing message, called "misbelief therapy," can help people deal with common problems in the home and in their circumstances, environment, and thinking. It is based on the Bible, not on psychological speculations. Understanding truth can help people locate and remove misbeliefs, and replace them with truth.

Author: Backus, William & Candace   **79**
Series:
Title: *Untwisting Twisted Relationships*
Publisher: Bethany House, 1989

Num. Sess.	Group Time	Num. Pgs.	Avg. Qst.	Price	Audience	Format	Bible Study
11	60-75	63	17	3.95	New Christian	Workbk	Topical

Features: Prayer Helps
★★★★ Personal Application   Preparation Time: Med   ISBN: 1-556-61089-0
★★★ Relationship Building   Ldr. Guide Avail.: Yes   Size: 5.0 x 8.0
Subjects: Christian Living, Family, Holy Spirit, Psychology, Relationships, Support
Comments: This study, to be used in conjunction with the book of the same title, helps restore close ties with family and friends. It identifies twists that prevent close personal relationships; challenges individuals to honestly apply God's truth to these situations; and encourages people to allow the Holy Spirit to get them involved in the restoration process.

Author: Bailey, James L.   **80**
Series: Men's Bible Study Series
Title: *Mark*
Publisher: Augsburg Publishing House, 1987

Num. Sess.	Group Time	Num. Pgs.	Avg. Qst.	Price	Audience	Format	Bible Study
10	30-45	48	8	3.0	New Christian	Workbk	Book

Features: Intro to Study, Prayer Helps, Summary
★★★★ Personal Application   Preparation Time: None   ISBN:
★★★★ Relationship Building   Ldr. Guide Avail.: Yes   Size: 4.50 x 9.50
Subjects: Discipleship, Mark, Men's Issues, Service
Comments: This ten-lesson study examines how the Gospel of Mark speaks to contemporary lives. It discusses important themes that help participants on the path to discipleship. Lessons focus on servanthood, trust in Jesus, the paradox of finding life by letting it go, and much more. It may be used at prayer breakfasts, men's Bible study groups, or any other men's meetings.

Author: Bajema, Edith L.   **81**
Series: Discover Your Bible
Title: *Discover Genesis: The Patriarchs*
Publisher: Church Development Resources, 1991

Num. Sess.	Group Time	Num. Pgs.	Avg. Qst.	Price	Audience	Format	Bible Study
13	45-60	47	7	2.10	Beginner	Workbk	Book

Features: Intro to Study, Glossary
★★★ Personal Application   Preparation Time: None   ISBN:
★★ Relationship Building   Ldr. Guide Avail.: Yes   Size: 5.50 x 8.50
Subjects: Bible Personalities, Faith, Genesis, God
Comments: This third study in a three-part series on Genesis continues the story of Abraham's family, tracing the history of his son Isaac, his grandson Jacob, and his great-grandson Joseph. It exposes a family involved in deceit, favoritism, violence, and jealousy, but also a magnificent faith in God. This series is intended for small group Bible study; however, it can be used profitably for personal study.

Author: Baker, Donald   **82**
Series:
Title: *God of Second Chances, The: The Remaking of Moses*
Publisher: Victor Books, 1991

Num. Sess.	Group Time	Num. Pgs.	Avg. Qst.	Price	Audience	Format	Bible Study
13	60-90	153	N/A	6.99	New Christian	Book	Charctr

Features: Intro to Study, Bibliography
★★★★ Personal Application   Preparation Time: Med   ISBN: 0-89693-000-9
★★★★ Relationship Building   Ldr. Guide Avail.: Yes   Size: 5.50 x 8.0
Subjects: Bible Personalities, Forgiveness, God
Comments: This study looks closely at the life of Moses offering new insights into his remaking by God. Believers can learn, as did Moses, that what is needed in life's baffling and bewildering experiences is not an explanation, but a firm trust in God. It paints a magnificent portrait of God's grace, forgiveness, and mercy. A leader's guide is available with reproducible student response sheets.

Author: Baker, Donald   **83**
Series: LifeGuide Bible Study
Title: *Joshua: The Power of God's Promises*
Publisher: InterVarsity, 1988

Num. Sess.	Group Time	Num. Pgs.	Avg. Qst.	Price	Audience	Format	Bible Study
12	45-60	61	12	3.95	New Christian	Workbk	Book

Features: Intro to Leading a Study, Intro to Study, Ldr's Notes
★ Personal Application   Preparation Time: Low   ISBN: 0-8308-1024-2
★ Relationship Building   Ldr. Guide Avail.: No   Size: 5.50 x 8.25
Subjects: Bible Personalities, God's Promises, Joshua, Obedience
Comments: Joshua is a book for people whose prayers seem to go unanswered, who wonder if God is really alive and active, and who desire fresh assurance of God's dependability. Practical truths describe how Christians can enjoy God's promises fulfilled in Joshua's life, as he led the Israelites through the Jordan River to conquer the Promised Land. The study reveals how Christians today can rely on God's promises when they obey His commands and how they will experience victory in everyday battles.

Author: Baker, Donald   **84**
Series: LifeGuide Bible Study
Title: *Philippians: Jesus Our Joy*
Publisher: InterVarsity, 1985

Num. Sess.	Group Time	Num. Pgs.	Avg. Qst.	Price	Audience	Format	Bible Study
9	45-60	58	11	3.95	New Christian	Workbk	Book

Features: Intro to Leading a Study, Intro to Study, Ldr's Notes
★ Personal Application   Preparation Time: Low   ISBN: 0-8308-1013-7
★ Relationship Building   Ldr. Guide Avail.: No   Size: 5.50 x 8.25
Subjects: Joy, Philippians, Prison Epistles, Suffering
Comments: Paul, writing to the Philippians from prison, said, "Rejoice in the Lord always." Paul experienced a joy not dependent on circumstances, a contentment difficulties could not suppress. This study teaches how to live joyfully in the midst of troubles by focusing attention on the One who is over every situation. The final lesson is a thematic overview which highlights the most important points for application.

Author: Baker, Pat   **85**
Series:
Title: *When a Woman Takes God at His Word*
Publisher: Tyndale House, 1986

Num. Sess.	Group Time	Num. Pgs.	Avg. Qst.	Price	Audience	Format	Bible Study
6	45-60	143	8	6.95	New Christian	Workbk	Topical

Features: Intro to Study, Prayer Helps, Scrpt Memory Helps, Prediscussion Quest
★★★ Personal Application   Preparation Time: Med   ISBN: 0-8423-7975-4
★★ Relationship Building   Ldr. Guide Avail.: No   Size: 5.0 x 8.0
Subjects: Christian Living, God, Service, Women's Issues
Comments: This study describes the fulfillment and contentment achieved when one takes God at His Word. The study's main purpose is to intensify love for God's Word, which leads to application of six special truths that enhance a Christian life. The six include the importance of Bible study, Christian concepts, waiting on God, understanding guilt, accepting one's physical body, and accepting one's life of ministry to others.

Author: Baldwin, Stanley C.   **86**
Series:
Title: *What Did Jesus Say About That?*
Publisher: Victor Books, 1975

Num. Sess.	Group Time	Num. Pgs.	Avg. Qst.	Price	Audience	Format	Bible Study
13	60-75	178	N/A	6.99	New Christian	Book	Topical

Features: Intro to Study
★★★★ Personal Application   Preparation Time: Low   ISBN: 0-88207-718-X
★★★ Relationship Building   Ldr. Guide Avail.: Yes   Size: 5.50 x 8.0
Subjects: Divorce, Eschatology, Faith, Jesus: Life/Teaching, Marriage, Money, Obedience, Prayer, Relationships
Comments: In this thirteen-week study of Christ's major teachings, participants will learn what Jesus said about the following: God, faith, the Word, Himself, prayer, following Him, sin, life after death, freedom and obedience, money, relating to others, marriage and divorce, and His return. The leader's guide offers many helps and reproducible response sheets.

Author: Balswick, Jack, et al.   **87**
Series: GroupBuilder Resources
Title: *Gift of Gender, The*
Publisher: Victor Books, 1991

Num. Sess.	Group Time	Num. Pgs.	Avg. Qst.	Price	Audience	Format	Bible Study
8	75-90	144	Vry	5.99	New Christian	Workbk	Topical

Features: Intro to Leading a Study, Objectives, Digging Deeper Quest, Follow Up, Full Scrpt Printed, Ldr's Notes, Cartoons, Persnl Study Quest
★★★★ Personal Application   Preparation Time: Low   ISBN: 0-89693-882-4
★★★ Relationship Building   Ldr. Guide Avail.: No   Size: 6.0 x 9.0
Subjects: Leadership, Marriage, Men's Issues, Parenting, Sexual Issues, Women's Issues, Work
Comments: This study helps small groups examine eight aspects of gender roles in light of scripture and embrace a biblical model for manhood and womanhood. Sessions deal with what it means to be a woman or man in today's world. Topics include traditional roles, power, control, dependence, sexuality and spirituality, fathering and mothering, friendship, gender in the workplace, and gender in leadership. Optional activities, hints for leaders, and answers to questions can be found in the leader's notes.

Author: Barker, Frank & Maureen Rank   **88**
Series:
Title: *Encounters with Jesus*
Publisher: Victor Books, 1989

Num. Sess.	Group Time	Num. Pgs.	Avg. Qst.	Price	Audience	Format	Bible Study
13	60-75	143	N/A	7.99	New Christian	Book	Topical

Features:
★★★★ Personal Application   Preparation Time: Low   ISBN: 0-89693-620-1
★★★ Relationship Building   Ldr. Guide Avail.: Yes   Size: 5.50 x 8.0
Subjects: Jesus: Life/Teaching, Work
Comments: This thirteen-week study reviews Jesus' encounters with ordinary people. Participants will realize that God meets people where they are, and He changes each life He touches. In this study Jesus encounters "The Thirsty Woman," "The Workaholic," "The Determined Doubter," "The Gambling Widow," "The Amazing Soldier," and "The Man Who Went Out on a Limb." He praised some, prodded others, and exhorted and encouraged them all to develop trust in God. A leader's guide includes reproducible response sheets.

Author: Barton, R. Ruth   **89**
Series: Fisherman Bible Studyguide
Title: *Women Like Us: Wisdom for Today's Issues*
Publisher: Shaw, 1989

Num. Sess.	Group Time	Num. Pgs.	Avg. Qst.	Price	Audience	Format	Bible Study
13	45-60	78	12	3.95	Mature Chrstn	Workbk	Topical

Features: Intro to Leading a Study, Intro to Study, Bibliography, Prayer Helps, Ldr's Notes
★★★ Personal Application   Preparation Time: None   ISBN: 0-87788-943-0
★★ Relationship Building   Ldr. Guide Avail.: No   Size: 5.0 x 8.25
Subjects: Bible Personalities, Marriage, Medical Issues, Singles Issues, Social Issues, Wisdom, Women's Issues
Comments: This study deals with contemporary female issues: singleness, sanctity of life, infertility, caring for aging parents, materialism, and the role of women in marriage and ministry. Each lesson begins with a study of a real woman whose life portrays contemporary issues: the Samaritan woman, Mary, Martha, Sarah, Abigail, Hannah, Ruth, Naomi, etc. The final chapter deals with women in the New Testament church who ministered through spiritual gifts.

Author: Baylis, Robert   **90**
Series: Fisherman Bible Studyguide
Title: *Ephesians: Living in God's Household*
Publisher: Shaw, 1976

Num. Sess.	Group Time	Num. Pgs.	Avg. Qst.	Price	Audience	Format	Bible Study
13	45-60	45	6	3.95	Mature Chrstn	Workbk	Book

Features: Intro to Leading a Study, Intro to Study, Prayer Helps
★★ Personal Application   Preparation Time: Low   ISBN: 0-87788-223-1
★★ Relationship Building   Ldr. Guide Avail.: No   Size: 5.0 x 8.25
Subjects: Church Life, Ephesians, Family, Marriage
Comments: This study is divided into two parts and is concluded with a reinforcement study. Paul wrote a letter about unity. In the study, Jew and Gentile, slave and free—all are to live as family members. The roles are defined for husband and wife, brother and sister, parent and child in regard to conduct which draws people closer together, living as members of God's household. Ephesians distills the deepest of Paul's teachings about Jesus Christ and His church.

Author: Becker, Calvin W.   **91**
Series: Teach Yourself the Bible
Title: *First and Second Timothy and Titus: Letters to Two Young Men*
Publisher: Moody Press, 1964

Num. Sess.	Group Time	Num. Pgs.	Avg. Qst.	Price	Audience	Format	Bible Study
8	60-75	64	37	3.99	New Christian	Workbk	Book

Features: Intro to Leading a Study, Exam
  ★★ Personal Application   Preparation Time: Low   ISBN: 0-8024-2646-8
  ★★ Relationship Building   Ldr. Guide Avail.: No   Size: 5.50 x 8.50
Subjects: Christian Living, Pastoral Epistles, 1 & 2 Timothy/Titus
Comments: This study of 1 and 2 Timothy and Titus—part of a twenty-five-book series—covers the Pastoral Epistles, which best reflect Paul's love. In fact, his advice to these men encourages contemporary Christians, both in their ministries and personal lives. The format includes a series of fill-in-the-blank questions, and checkups to test participants' grasp of scriptural truths. The series, although designed for self-study, also includes suggestions for group study.

Author: Beisner, E. Calvin   **92**
Series: Living Studies
Title: *God in Three Persons*
Publisher: Tyndale House, 1984

Num. Sess.	Group Time	Num. Pgs.	Avg. Qst.	Price	Audience	Format	Bible Study
6	60-90	160	N/A	7.95	Mature Chrstn	Book	Topical

Features: Intro to Study, No Grp Discussion Quest
  ★ Personal Application   Preparation Time: Med   ISBN: 0-8423-1073-8
  ★ Relationship Building   Ldr. Guide Avail.: No   Size: 5.0 x 8.0
Subjects: Apologetics, Theology
Comments: This book traces the history of the doctrine of the Trinity, revealing many little-known facts about it. The doctrine is examined from four perspectives: (1) New Testament teaching; (2) Belief prior to the time of the Nicene-Constantinopolitan Creed; (3) The Arian controversy of the fourth century; and (4) The later form commonly thought of as the "Nicene Creed." Small group study questions are not provided.

Author: Benson, Dennis C.   **93**
Series:
Title: *Dennis Benson's Creative Bible Studies: Matthew—Acts*
Publisher: Group Publishing, 1985

Num. Sess.	Group Time	Num. Pgs.	Avg. Qst.	Price	Audience	Format	Bible Study
	30-60	660	Vry	19.95	Beginner	Workbk	Book

Features: Intro to Leading a Study, Intro to Study, Prayer Helps, Ldr's Notes, Drawings, Cross Ref
  ★★★ Personal Application   Preparation Time: Low   ISBN: 0-931529-01-8
  ★★ Relationship Building   Ldr. Guide Avail.: No   Size: 6.0 x 9.0
Subjects: Teens: Bible Study, Teens: New Testament
Comments: This study, covering from Matthew through Acts, provides 401 complete, easy-to-prepare Bible studies, each including a "how-to-use" introduction, insight into scriptural meaning, and an extensive index. Each study is designed to get teenagers totally involved in experiencing the Scriptures. The studies are designed for use in a Bible class, youth meeting, or retreat setting.

Author: Benson, Dennis C.   **94**
Series:
Title: *Dennis Benson's Creative Bible Studies: Romans—Revelation*
Publisher: Group Publishing, 1988

Num. Sess.	Group Time	Num. Pgs.	Avg. Qst.	Price	Audience	Format	Bible Study
	30-60	280	Vry	12.95	Beginner	Workbk	Book

Features: Intro to Leading a Study, Intro to Study, Prayer Helps, Ldr's Notes, Drawings, Charts, Cross Ref, Topical Index
  ★★★ Personal Application   Preparation Time: Low   ISBN: 0-931529-52-2
  ★★ Relationship Building   Ldr. Guide Avail.: No   Size: 6.0 x 9.0
Subjects: Teens: Bible Study, Teens: New Testament
Comments: This study, which includes 146 studies of the biblical books from Romans to Revelation, is a companion to Benson's book on the gospels and Acts. Each easy-to-prepare study features a "how-to-use" introduction, insights into scriptural meaning, and an extensive index. The studies are designed to help teenagers understand Romans through Revelation through the use of inexpensive objects such as bread, banners, construction paper, salt, boxes, rocks, and old clothing.

Author: Berry, Jo   **95**
Series:
Title: *Beloved Unbeliever: Loving Your Husband into the Faith*
Publisher: Zondervan, 1981

Num. Sess.	Group Time	Num. Pgs.	Avg. Qst.	Price	Audience	Format	Bible Study
10	60-90	169	Vry	6.95	New Christian	Workbk	Topical

Features: Intro to Study, Charts
  ★★★★ Personal Application   Preparation Time: Med   ISBN: 0-310-42621-9
  ★★★ Relationship Building   Ldr. Guide Avail.: No   Size: 5.25 x 8.0
Subjects: Evangelism, Faith, Love, Marriage, Women's Issues
Comments: This study gives hope to unequally yoked wives. Using a scriptural framework of love, it shows how a wife can love her spouse into the Kingdom without compromising her faith. Realizing that she has been placed in the unique position of representing God to the man she loves should be an encouragement. While admitting there are no simple answers, guidance and useful suggestions are offered. Information and personal stories precede each scriptural lesson.

Author: Betea, Ann Thomas   **96**
Series: Basic Bible Study Series
Title: *God's Answer to Overeating: A Study of Scriptural Attitudes*
Publisher: Aglow, 1976

Num. Sess.	Group Time	Num. Pgs.	Avg. Qst.	Price	Audience	Format	Bible Study
12	60-75	63	18	2.95	New Christian	Workbk	Topical

Features: Intro to Study, Prayer Helps, Scrpt Memory Helps, Persnl Study Quest
  ★★★ Personal Application   Preparation Time: Med   ISBN: 0-932305-36-9
  ★★★ Relationship Building   Ldr. Guide Avail.: No   Size: 5.25 x 8.25
Subjects: Addictions, Charismatic Interest, Victorious Living, Women's Issues
Comments: This twelve-week study provides scriptural motivation for fitness and weight control. It proves through God's Word that overeating can be a spiritual problem. Physical desires are never satisfied; the more they are fed, the more they demand. Left without restraint, they become insatiable. These desires can be tamed and bad habits changed, and the power of Christ can make believers conquerors in all areas of their lives.

Author: Bickel, Kurt   **97**
Series: Group's Active Bible Curriculum
Title: *Getting Along with Parents*
Publisher: Group Publishing, 1990

Num. Sess.	Group Time	Num. Pgs.	Avg. Qst.	Price	Audience	Format	Bible Study
4	35-60	44	Vry	6.95	Beginner	Workbk	Topical

Features: Intro to Leading a Study, Intro to Study, Objectives, Study Overview, Ldr's Notes, Handouts, Agenda, Publicity Ideas
  ★★★ Personal Application   Preparation Time: None   ISBN: 1-559-45202-1
  ★★★ Relationship Building   Ldr. Guide Avail.: No   Size: 8.50 x 11.0
Subjects: Teens: Family, Teens: Senior High
Comments: This study helps Christian teenagers build quality relationships with their parents. Senior highers will learn about basic communication, parental expectations, and trust and love, and honor. It can be adapted for a Bible class or youth meeting, and activities and Bible studies are included as separate sheets that can be reproduced. The instructions are easy to follow and offer multiple options for teachers.

Author: Blankley, Ron   **98**
Series: LifeGuide Bible Study
Title: *John's Letters: Discovering Genuine Christianity*
Publisher: InterVarsity, 1990

Num. Sess.	Group Time	Num. Pgs.	Avg. Qst.	Price	Audience	Format	Bible Study
13	45-60	63	11	3.95	New Christian	Workbk	Topical

Features: Intro to Leading a Study, Intro to Study, Ldr's Notes
  ★★★ Personal Application   Preparation Time: Low   ISBN: 0-8308-1020-X
  ★★★ Relationship Building   Ldr. Guide Avail.: No   Size: 5.50 x 8.25
Subjects: Faith, 1, 2 & 3 John/Jude
Comments: This study of John's letters describes the difference between genuine Christians and those who merely profess to know Christ. John writes to expose the false claims of those whose conduct contradicts their claims. He also provides strong assurance to those whose lifestyle is consistent with their Christian faith. With power and simplicity, John helps Christians focus their attention on what really matters—both now and for eternity.

Author: Bloem, Diane Brummel   **99**
Series: Woman's Workshop Series
Title: *Growing Godly: Studies on Bible Women*
Publisher: Zondervan, 1983

Num. Sess.	Group Time	Num. Pgs.	Avg. Qst.	Price	Audience	Format	Bible Study
13	60-90	77	18	4.95	Beginner	Workbk	Charctr

Features: Intro to Study
  ★★ Personal Application   Preparation Time: Low   ISBN: 0-310-23151-5
  ★★ Relationship Building   Ldr. Guide Avail.: No   Size: 5.25 x 8.0
Subjects: Bible Personalities, Christian Living, Women's Issues
Comments: This is a study of seventeen women in the Bible, their environments, circumstances that shaped them, sins that blighted them, and their stages of growth. Participants will see how God worked in each life and recognize stages of growth as well as blights and beauties; they will become aware of and appreciate the beauty of others, and become understanding of others' circumstances. Women discussed in this study include Dinah, Miriam, Rahab, Naomi and Ruth, Lydia, and others.

Author: Bloem, Diane Brummel & Robert C.   **100**
Series: Workshop Series
Title: *Workshop on Bible Marriages, A*
Publisher: Zondervan, 1980

Num. Sess.	Group Time	Num. Pgs.	Avg. Qst.	Price	Audience	Format	Bible Study
13	60-90	95	22	4.50	New Christian	Workbk	Charctr

Features: Intro to Study, Persnl Study Quest
  ★★ Personal Application   Preparation Time: Med   ISBN: 0-310-21391-6
  ★★ Relationship Building   Ldr. Guide Avail.: No   Size: 5.25 x 8.0
Subjects: Bible Personalities, Divorce, Failure, Joy, Marriage
Comments: This study focuses on married Bible characters, such as Mr. and Mrs. Simon Peter, Abraham and Sarah, Aquila and Priscilla, Isaac and Rebekah, and Moses and Zipporah, to urge participants to more deeply study contemporary issues in marriage. Issues include how to serve God as a couple, alternatives to childlessness, multiple marriages, divorce, and in-law problems. Participants will learn that problems, joys, and personality types have changed very little over time.

Author: Bloem, Diane Brummel   **101**
Series: Workshop Series
Title: *Workshop on the Beatitudes, A*
Publisher: Zondervan, 1981

Num. Sess.	Group Time	Num. Pgs.	Avg. Qst.	Price	Audience	Format	Bible Study
13	60-90	63	18	4.50	Beginner	Workbk	Topical

Features: Intro to Study, Summary
  ★★ Personal Application   Preparation Time: None   ISBN: 0-310-42651-0
  ★★ Relationship Building   Ldr. Guide Avail.: No   Size: 5.25 x 8.0
Subjects: Christian Living, Sermon on the Mount
Comments: This study of the Beatitudes—which are part of Christ's Sermon on the Mount—explains what it means to be Christians and urges participants to examine their hearts and minds to see if they truly belong to Christ. The first lesson introduces the background, subject, and setting, and helps participants plan objectives. Lessons 2 through 10 follow a pattern of proclamation, promise, and practice. The last lesson provides for evaluation and forming an action plan.

Author: Bloem, Diane Brummel   **102**
Series: Workshop Series
Title: *Workshop on the Book of Job, A*
Publisher: Zondervan, 1986

Num. Sess.	Group Time	Num. Pgs.	Avg. Qst.	Price	Audience	Format	Bible Study
13	45-60	77	14	3.95	Beginner	Workbk	Book

Features: Intro to Study, Bibliography
  ★★ Personal Application   Preparation Time: Low   ISBN: 0-310-42781-9
  ★★ Relationship Building   Ldr. Guide Avail.: No   Size: 5.25 x 8.0
Subjects: God, Job, Obedience, Suffering
Comments: This chapter-by-chapter study of Job shows he knew what it was like to suffer and lose everything but God. His interaction with God reveals His comfort, sympathy, and place in Job's life. The lessons focus on the actions and character of each person in the book of Job, including God. They help participants learn the purpose of pain, ways to comfort sufferers and ways not to, and where God is when people are hurting.

Author: Bloem, Diane Brummel   **103**
Series: Workshop Series
Title: *Workshop on the Book of Proverbs, A*
Publisher: Zondervan, 1978

Num. Sess.	Group Time	Num. Pgs.	Avg. Qst.	Price	Audience	Format	Bible Study
15	60-75	111	20	4.95	Beginner	Workbk	Book

Features: Intro to Study, Full Scrpt Printed, Cross Ref
★★ Personal Application   Preparation Time: Med   ISBN: 0-310-21361-4
★★ Relationship Building   Ldr. Guide Avail.: No   Size: 5.25 x 8.0
Subjects: Christian Living, Joy, Proverbs, Wisdom
Comments: This study of Proverbs focuses on practical application of ancient wisdom to contemporary living. Timeless issues discussed include: wealth and poverty, justice and government, neighbors, marriage, old age/long life, work and laziness, child training, joy, reproof, and advice. Cross-referencing the Old and New Testaments allows participants to filter Solomon's wisdom and apply it to their daily lives.

Author: Bloem, Diane Brummel   **104**
Series: Workshop Series
Title: *Workshop on the Sermon on the Mount, A*
Publisher: Zondervan, 1987

Num. Sess.	Group Time	Num. Pgs.	Avg. Qst.	Price	Audience	Format	Bible Study
13	60-75	125	15	5.95	New Christian	Workbk	Book

Features: Intro to Study, Ldr's Notes
★★ Personal Application   Preparation Time: Med   ISBN: 0-310-42701-0
★★ Relationship Building   Ldr. Guide Avail.: No   Size: 5.25 x 8.0
Subjects: Emotions, Matthew, Sermon on the Mount, Ten Commandments
Comments: This study on the sermon many call the "Ten Commandments of the New Testament" introduces a new law—a law of love. It will revolutionize participants' lives, as Jesus challenges them to love their enemies, stop worrying, take no thought for tomorrow, and repay evil with good. Participants will examine their motives for doing good.

Author: Bloomfield, Arthur E.   **105**
Series:
Title: *All Things New: The Prophecies of Revelation Explained*
Publisher: Bethany House, 1960

Num. Sess.	Group Time	Num. Pgs.	Avg. Qst.	Price	Audience	Format	Bible Study
22	60-90	32	Vry	1.95	Mature Chrstn	Book	Book

Features: No Grp Discussion Quest, Charts
★ Personal Application   Preparation Time: High   ISBN: 0-87123-520-X
★ Relationship Building   Ldr. Guide Avail.: No   Size: 5.0 x 8.0
Subjects: Eschatology, Prophecy, Revelation
Comments: This study, to be used in conjunction with the book by the same title, presents the book of Revelation scene by scene. The study guide questions for each lesson are not review questions, but form outlines of the chapters. The many charts included are necessary for following the text. The study helps participants understand the nature, purpose, and method of presentation, or structure, of Revelation, a prophecy of the church and future of the saints.

Author: Blue, Ron   **106**
Series: Homebuilders Couples
Title: *Mastering Your Money in Marriage*
Publisher: Word, 1990

Num. Sess.	Group Time	Num. Pgs.	Avg. Qst.	Price	Audience	Format	Bible Study
7	60-90	139	Vry	8.99	Beginner	Workbk	Topical

Features: Charts, Appendix, Cassette Avail
★★★★ Personal Application   Preparation Time: Low   ISBN: 0-8499-8358-4
★★★ Relationship Building   Ldr. Guide Avail.: Yes   Size: 5.50 x 8.50
Subjects: Family, Marriage, Money
Comments: This study helps participants make financial matters a tool for growth instead of a bone of contention in marriage. It covers topics such as discovering the freedom and fulfillment of handling money God's way, communicating effectively about finances, working through financial differences and difficulties, developing a workable financial plan, and building relationships with other couples.

Author: Bly, Janet Chester   **107**
Series: Crisispoints for Women
Title: *When Your Marriage Disappoints You*
Publisher: NavPress, 1990

Num. Sess.	Group Time	Num. Pgs.	Avg. Qst.	Price	Audience	Format	Bible Study
4	60-75	96	16	3.95	New Christian	Workbk	Topical

Features: Intro to Study, Bibliography, Prayer Helps, Pre-discussion Quest, Follow Up
★★★★ Personal Application   Preparation Time: Med   ISBN: 0-89109-328-1
★★ Relationship Building   Ldr. Guide Avail.: No   Size: 4.25 x 7.0
Subjects: Failure, Marriage, Women's Issues
Comments: This four-lesson study—part of an eight-book series for women in crises—helps participants assess themselves, their spouses, and their marriages. Practical ideas enable them to deal with disappointments when marriage falls short of expectations. In the lessons, a magazine article format is followed by Bible study or discussion questions. Due to added sections on evaluation and extra helps, five or six sessions are recommended. The series is contemporary, nonthreatening, and easy to use.

Author: Boa, Kenneth & Larry Moody   **108**
Series:
Title: *I'm Glad You Asked*
Publisher: Victor Books, 1982

Num. Sess.	Group Time	Num. Pgs.	Avg. Qst.	Price	Audience	Format	Bible Study
13	60-75	230	N/A	9.99	Beginner	Book	Topical

Features: Intro to Study, Bibliography, Charts
★★★★ Personal Application   Preparation Time: Low   ISBN: 0-88207-354-0
★★ Relationship Building   Ldr. Guide Avail.: Yes   Size: 5.50 x 8.0
Subjects: Apologetics, Evangelism, Theology
Comments: This thirteen-lesson study helps participants become able defenders of the Christian perspective. It uncovers alternatives to the Christian worldview, then demonstrates why that worldview is valid. The text provides answers to basic questions people ask, and guides participants logically through them, using a helpful flow chart. It shows how each objection is really an opportunity to present the gospel. This study is highly illustrative and informative, and good for seekers.

Author: Bockelman, Wilfred   **109**
Series: Small Group Bible Studies
Title: *Blowing in the Wind*
Publisher: Augsburg Publishing House, 1975

Num. Sess.	Group Time	Num. Pgs.	Avg. Qst.	Price	Audience	Format	Bible Study
6	60-75	24	7	1.15	New Christian	Book	Charctr

Features: Intro to Study, Prayer Helps
★★★ Personal Application   Preparation Time: None   ISBN:
★★★ Relationship Building   Ldr. Guide Avail.: No   Size: 8.50 x 5.50
Subjects: Holy Spirit
Comments: This small pamphlet includes six sessions on the Holy Spirit. It does not promise to cover the topic completely but rather to provide insights and the opportunity to grow spiritually. The six sessions are titled: "The New Birth"; "The Promise of the Spirit"; "The Coming of the Spirit"; "Sanctification"; "Gifts of the Spirit"; and "The Spirit Speaks."

Author: Boice, James Montgomery   **110**
Series:
Title: *Ordinary Men Called by God: Abraham, Moses & David*
Publisher: Victor Books, 1982

Num. Sess.	Group Time	Num. Pgs.	Avg. Qst.	Price	Audience	Format	Bible Study
13	60-90	142	N/A	7.99	New Christian	Book	Charctr

Features: Intro to Study
★★★★ Personal Application   Preparation Time: Low   ISBN: 0-89693-047-5
★★★ Relationship Building   Ldr. Guide Avail.: Yes   Size: 5.50 x 8.0
Subjects: Bible Personalities, Church Life, Faith, Family, Service, Work
Comments: This study of Abraham, Moses, and David concerns God's call to these ordinary Old Testament men, who became extraordinary men of faith and accomplishment. Their examples of courage, faithfulness, and humility offer practical lessons in Christian living and service to God. Participants are encouraged to learn and practice the lessons and apply them in their homes, churches, businesses, and nations. The leader's guide provides goals for each lesson and reproducible transparency masters.

Author: Boomsma, Sylvia   **111**
Series: Discover Your Bible
Title: *Discover: Comfort*
Publisher: Church Development Resources, 1988

Num. Sess.	Group Time	Num. Pgs.	Avg. Qst.	Price	Audience	Format	Bible Study
11	60-75	39	7	1.80	Beginner	Workbk	Book

Features: Intro to Study, Summary, Glossary
★★★ Personal Application   Preparation Time: None   ISBN:
★★ Relationship Building   Ldr. Guide Avail.: Yes   Size: 5.50 x 8.50
Subjects: Emotions, God, Marriage, Suffering, Wisdom
Comments: This inductive study on comfort concerns scripture that speaks of the human struggle with suffering and evil. It also examines passages that speak of God's love, wisdom, and tender care for His children. This is an honest study of hard questions believers face when they experience pain or hardship. There are no pat answers, but participants will draw closer to the Father of compassion and God of all comfort.

Author: Boomsma, Sylvia   **112**
Series: Discover Your Bible
Title: *Discover Ruth*
Publisher: Church Development Resources, 1991

Num. Sess.	Group Time	Num. Pgs.	Avg. Qst.	Price	Audience	Format	Bible Study
4	45-60	20	6	0.90	Beginner	Workbk	Book

Features: Intro to Study, Glossary
★★★ Personal Application   Preparation Time: None   ISBN:
★★ Relationship Building   Ldr. Guide Avail.: Yes   Size: 5.50 x 8.50
Subjects: Bible Personalities, Faith, Obedience, Ruth
Comments: This inductive study of Ruth deals with a God of details. It shows participants that He really knows their needs and cares about how they're met. It also reveals how ordinary people in ordinary times—Ruth and Naomi—through faith and willingness to obey God caused extraordinary things to happen. Contemporary Christians see that God often does His greatest work during the hardest times in life. The study is intended for small groups, but is ideal for personal study.

Author: Borthwick, Paul   **113**
Series: Any Old Time
Title: *Any Old Time (Book 5)*
Publisher: Victor Books, 1986

Num. Sess.	Group Time	Num. Pgs.	Avg. Qst.	Price	Audience	Format	Bible Study
16	30-45	80	Vry	9.99	New Christian	Book	Topical

Features: Intro to Study, Objectives, Bibliography, Prayer Helps, Study Overview, Digging Deeper Quest, Summary, Ldr's Notes
★★★★ Personal Application   Preparation Time: None   ISBN: 0-89693-187-0
★★★★ Relationship Building   Ldr. Guide Avail.: No   Size: 8.50 x 11.0
Subjects: Teens: Evangelism, Teens: Junior High, Teens: Senior High
Comments: Book five in the "Any Old Time" series offers sixteen lessons—four on each geographical group mentioned in Acts 1:8: Jerusalem, Judea, Samaria, and the "ends of the earth." These can be used independently or consecutively. Meetings help make students aware of their responsibility to reach out to others. The sessions cover the following topics: vision for people; friendship evangelism; focusing on Christ; and outreach at your school, in your neighborhood, to the elderly, and more.

Author: Boyd, Marcella   **114**
Series: Small Group Bible Studies
Title: *Flight to Freedom*
Publisher: Augsburg Publishing House, 1976

Num. Sess.	Group Time	Num. Pgs.	Avg. Qst.	Price	Audience	Format	Bible Study
4	60-75	16	25	0.95	New Christian	Book	Book

Features: Intro to Study, Bibliography, Prayer Helps
★★★ Personal Application   Preparation Time: None   ISBN:
★★★ Relationship Building   Ldr. Guide Avail.: No   Size: 8.50 x 5.50
Subjects: Commitments, Exodus, Faith, Forgiveness, Renewal
Comments: This small pamphlet includes four sessions taken from Exodus. The goal of this study is to lead participants to a deeper understanding of their faith and a greater commitment to it. It is only God's great love that daily brings believers out of their "Egypts"—bondage to enslaving sins—into the promised land of forgiveness, renewal, redemption, love, and peace in Christ. Questions marked with a star are especially recommended for discussion.

Author: Bozeman, Hannelore   **115**
Series: Encourager Series
Title: *Energize Your Devotions: Five Ways That Work*
Publisher: Aglow, 1988

Num. Sess.	Group Time	Num. Pgs.	Avg. Qst.	Price	Audience	Format	Bible Study
5	45-60	32	21	2.25	New Christian	Workbk	Topical

Features: Intro to Study, Prayer Helps, Scrpt Memory Helps, Persnl Study Quest
★★★★ Personal Application   Preparation Time: Low   ISBN: 0-932305-50-4
★★★★ Relationship Building   Ldr. Guide Avail.: No   Size: 5.25 x 8.25
Subjects: Charismatic Interest, Devotionals, Discipleship, Prayer
Comments: This five-week study shows participants the scriptural basis for a meaningful devotional time. Lessons emphasize the importance of thanksgiving. They stress that when participants have problems with prayer, the best place to go is to the Father, and they remind participants that God's foremost purpose is to change them into the image of Christ. Lesson titles include "Come," "Praise," "Feed," "Pray," and "Respond." The study format includes specific personal application questions.

Author: Brandt, Jack   **116**
Series: The Lifechange Series
Title: *Galatians*
Publisher: NavPress, 1989

Num. Sess.	Group Time	Num. Pgs.	Avg. Qst.	Price	Audience	Format	Bible Study
12	60-90	137	17	5.95	New Christian	Workbk	Book

Features: Intro to Leading a Study, Intro to Study, Bibliography, Prayer Helps, Worship Helps, Study Overview, Digging Deeper Quest, Summary, Charts, Maps, Cross Ref, Word Study
★★★ Personal Application   Preparation Time: Med   ISBN: 0-89109-562-4
★★★ Relationship Building   Ldr. Guide Avail.: No   Size: 5.50 x 8.50
Subjects: False Teachers, Galatians
Comments: This verse-by-verse study of Galatians concerns Paul's sternest defense against false teachings. Certain people were saying, "In order to keep His favor, you have to maintain His standards by your own efforts." Paul reaffirms that Christians can only live right with God by faith in Him. Participants will gain a firm foundation of Galatians, be able to apply relevant scripture to their lives, and improve personal study skills.

Author: Breckenridge, Marilyn Saure   **117**
Series: Small Group Bible Studies
Title: *Epistle of Joy*
Publisher: Augsburg Publishing House, 1980

Num. Sess.	Group Time	Num. Pgs.	Avg. Qst.	Price	Audience	Format	Bible Study
4	60-75	16	14	0.95	New Christian	Book	Book

Features: Intro to Study, Prayer Helps
★★★ Personal Application   Preparation Time: None   ISBN:
★★★ Relationship Building   Ldr. Guide Avail.: No   Size: 8.50 x 5.50
Subjects: Faith, Joy, Philippians, Prison Epistles, Relationships, Victorious Living
Comments: This small pamphlet includes four sessions on Philippians, using a chapter-by-chapter study approach. Session 1 is "Christ: The Source"; session 2, "Christ: The Ideal"; session 3 "Christ: The Goal"; and session 4, "Christ: The Provider." Paul's letter contains no formal instruction or exposition of doctrine, but it does contain four truths: the centrality of Christ in a life of faith, the need for unity in a Christian community, salvation through faith in Jesus, and the joy of being a Christian.

Author: Breese, Dave   **118**
Series:
Title: *Know the Marks of Cults*
Publisher: Victor Books, 1975

Num. Sess.	Group Time	Num. Pgs.	Avg. Qst.	Price	Audience	Format	Bible Study
13	60-90	119	N/A	6.99	Beginner	Book	Topical

Features: Intro to Study
★★★★ Personal Application   Preparation Time: Med   ISBN: 0-89693-236-2
★★ Relationship Building   Ldr. Guide Avail.: Yes   Size: 5.50 x 8.0
Subjects: Cults
Comments: This book describes both characteristics and errors of modern cults, and tells how to avoid them. It is not a study of specific cults, but a vehicle to develop the spiritual facility for instantly recognizing marks of the cults. Recognizing cultic characteristics, coupled with early correction, can prevent future spiritual tragedy. Suggested methods for teaching and leading discussions are available in the leader's guide.

Author: Brestin, Dee   **119**
Series: Fisherman Bible Studyguide
Title: *Ecclesiastes: God's Wisdom for Evangelism*
Publisher: Shaw, 1980

Num. Sess.	Group Time	Num. Pgs.	Avg. Qst.	Price	Audience	Format	Bible Study
13	60-75	93	16	3.95	New Christian	Workbk	Book

Features: Intro to Leading a Study, Intro to Study, Bibliography, Prayer Helps
★★ Personal Application   Preparation Time: None   ISBN: 0-87788-212-6
★★ Relationship Building   Ldr. Guide Avail.: No   Size: 5.0 x 8.25
Subjects: Ecclesiastes, Wisdom
Comments: This study deals with applying God's answers to humanity's deepest questions. Three thousand years ago the writer of Ecclesiastes asked, "What is the meaning of life?" People have been struggling for the answer ever since. His conclusion is that neither wisdom, material possessions, sensual pleasure, power, nor prestige can satisfy our needs and give meaning to life. It discusses a world filled with frustration and failure, and concludes that worshipping God is the only worthwhile activity.

Author: Brestin, Dee   **120**
Series: Fisherman Bible Studyguide
Title: *Examining the Claims of Jesus*
Publisher: Shaw, 1985

Num. Sess.	Group Time	Num. Pgs.	Avg. Qst.	Price	Audience	Format	Bible Study
7	45-60	64	14	3.95	Beginner	Workbk	Topical

Features: Intro to Leading a Study, Intro to Study, Prayer Helps, Full Scrpt Printed
★★★ Personal Application   Preparation Time: Low   ISBN: 0-87788-246-0
★★ Relationship Building   Ldr. Guide Avail.: No   Size: 5.0 x 8.25
Subjects: Evangelism, Jesus: Life/Teaching
Comments: This short beginner's study guide, based on the first five chapters of John with Scripture included, examines who Christ is and what He has promised every believer. Following the first five lessons, two optional studies deal with "Who Is a Christian (Romans)?" and "The Christian's Identity and Purpose (1 Peter)." These two studies clarify the gospel, and give participants who wish to continue time to plan the next study.

Author: Brestin, Dee   **121**
Series:
Title: *Friendships of Women, The*
Publisher: Victor Books, 1988

Num. Sess.	Group Time	Num. Pgs.	Avg. Qst.	Price	Audience	Format	Bible Study
13	60-90	180	N/A	6.99	Beginner	Book	Topical

Features:
  ★★★ Personal Application Preparation Time: Med ISBN: 0-89693-432-2
  ★★★ Relationship Building Ldr. Guide Avail.: Yes Size: 5.50 x 8.0
Subjects: Bible Personalities, Friendships, Relationships, Women's Issues
Comments: This study examines the biblical friendship of Ruth and Naomi, revealing a pattern for friendship that can help women discover and focus their gifts for intimacy. Specific lessons concern why women are friendlier than men, the mentoring relationship, and reflections of Christ. A leader's guide with transparency masters is available.

Author: Brestin, Dee   **122**
Series: Fisherman Bible Studyguide
Title: *How Should a Christian Live? 1, 2 & 3 John*
Publisher: Shaw, 1985

Num. Sess.	Group Time	Num. Pgs.	Avg. Qst.	Price	Audience	Format	Bible Study
13	45-60	72	13	3.95	New Christian	Workbk	Book

Features: Intro to Leading a Study, Intro to Study, Prayer Helps, Scrpt Memory Helps
  ★★★ Personal Application Preparation Time: Low ISBN: 0-87788-351-3
  ★★ Relationship Building Ldr. Guide Avail.: No Size: 5.0 x 8.25
Subjects: Christian Living, God, Obedience, 1, 2 & 3 John/Jude
Comments: The study of John, written for new believers, encourages them to live lives of Christlike compassion and obedience. Practical questions addressed in this study include: How can I experience more of the daily presence of God? What qualities should characterize my life as a child of God? How should I handle television, magazines, and other media in my home? What is the difference between immature and mature love? How can I be sure that I am going to Heaven?

Author: Brestin, Dee   **123**
Series: Fisherman Bible Studyguide
Title: *Proverbs & Parables: God's Wisdom for Living*
Publisher: Shaw, 1975

Num. Sess.	Group Time	Num. Pgs.	Avg. Qst.	Price	Audience	Format	Bible Study
16	60-75	75	16	3.95	Beginner	Workbk	Book

Features: Intro to Leading a Study, Intro to Study, Prayer Helps
  ★★ Personal Application Preparation Time: None ISBN: 0-87788-694-6
  ★★ Relationship Building Ldr. Guide Avail.: No Size: 5.0 x 8.25
Subjects: Parables, Proverbs, Wisdom
Comments: Each chapter in this study matches the truth of an Old Testament proverb with a New Testament parable, and applies them to twentieth-century life. Both the proverbs and parables reveal the constant—wisdom of God. From Solomon, participants learn to seek God's wisdom "like silver and search for it as for hidden treasures." They will also learn that "in Christ are hidden all the treasures of wisdom and knowledge" (Colossians 2:3).

Author: Brestin, Steve & Dee   **124**
Series: Fisherman Bible Studyguide
Title: *Building Your House on the Lord: Marriage & Parenthood*
Publisher: Shaw, 1976

Num. Sess.	Group Time	Num. Pgs.	Avg. Qst.	Price	Audience	Format	Bible Study
16	60-90	78	15	3.95	New Christian	Workbk	Topical

Features: Intro to Leading a Study, Intro to Study, Prayer Helps
  ★★ Personal Application Preparation Time: None ISBN: 0-87788-099-9
  ★★ Relationship Building Ldr. Guide Avail.: No Size: 5.0 x 8.25
Subjects: Family, Marriage, Parenting
Comments: This study focuses on families and marriages built on the foundation of Jesus Christ, which stands in spite of outside pressure. It objectively presents two divergent perspectives on Christian marriage: the traditional perspective—the "hierarchical" model—and the "eqalitarian" model. Are wives to be submissive? Or should there be mutual submission under God for both man and woman? The text lends itself to both interpretations and both are explained.

Author: Brestin, Steve & Dee   **125**
Series: Fisherman Bible Studyguide
Title: *Friendship: Portraits in God's Family Album*
Publisher: Shaw, 1986

Num. Sess.	Group Time	Num. Pgs.	Avg. Qst.	Price	Audience	Format	Bible Study
12	45-60	61	12	3.95	Beginner	Workbk	Topical

Features: Intro to Leading a Study, Intro to Study, Prayer Helps
  ★★★ Personal Application Preparation Time: None ISBN: 0-87788-287-8
  ★★★ Relationship Building Ldr. Guide Avail.: No Size: 5.0 x 8.25
Subjects: Bible Personalities, Christian Living, Friendships, Relationships
Comments: The Bible abounds with stories of deep and lasting friendship, portraits of characters in God's family. This study offers insights for better, more meaningful friendships by examining historical models, including Abraham, Ruth, David and Jonathan, Mary and Elizabeth, Jesus, and Barnabas. The characteristics of commitment, unfailing kindness, and open sharing are repeated. Jesus is reflected in the faces of historical models, the One who models each of these characteristics perfectly.

Author: Brestin, Steve & Dee   **126**
Series: Fisherman Bible Studyguide
Title: *Higher Ground: Steps Toward Christian Maturity*
Publisher: Shaw, 1978

Num. Sess.	Group Time	Num. Pgs.	Avg. Qst.	Price	Audience	Format	Bible Study
14	45-60	58	14	3.95	New Christian	Workbk	Topical

Features: Intro to Leading a Study, Intro to Study, Prayer Helps, Worship Helps
  ★★★ Personal Application Preparation Time: None ISBN: 0-87788-345-9
  ★★★ Relationship Building Ldr. Guide Avail.: No Size: 5.0 x 8.25
Subjects: Discipleship, Faith, Holy Spirit, Joy, Victorious Living
Comments: Spiritual maturity can be attained, and the Scriptures show the way. This study can help every believer achieve a victorious life. Subject matter includes: the joy of salvation, the power of the Spirit-controlled life, living by faith, overcoming the valleys, effectual prayer and praise. Jesus said, "Blessed are those who hunger and thirst for righteousness, for they shall be satisfied." This study can satisfy.

Author: Brestin, Steve & Dee   **127**
Series: Fisherman Bible Studyguide
Title: *1 & 2 Peter, Jude: Called for a Purpose*
Publisher: Shaw, 1987

Num. Sess.	Group Time	Num. Pgs.	Avg. Qst.	Price	Audience	Format	Bible Study
13	45-60	77	12	3.95	New Christian	Workbk	Book

Features: Intro to Leading a Study, Intro to Study, Prayer Helps, Scrpt Memory Helps, Worship Helps

★★★ Personal Application Preparation Time: Low ISBN: 0-87788-703-9
★★ Relationship Building Ldr. Guide Avail.: No Size: 5.0 x 8.25

Subjects: Faith, False Teachers, Holiness, Hope, 1 & 2 Peter, 1, 2 & 3 John/Jude
Comments: Peter and Jude are studies of encouragement and warning. The theme "called" is followed in each lesson—"called" for a purpose, to be hopeful, to be holy, to a new identity, to submission in the world, to complete devotion to Christ, to live for God, to eternal glory, to rely on God's provision, to combat false teaching, to prepare for the Lord's return, to persevere in faith, and more. A 21-day exercise—"Practicing Your Identity"—helps participants understand God's purpose for them.

Author: Bridges, Jerry   **128**
Series:
Title: *Practice of Godliness, The*
Publisher: NavPress, 1983

Num. Sess.	Group Time	Num. Pgs.	Avg. Qst.	Price	Audience	Format	Bible Study
12	60-90	70	11	4.95	New Christian	Workbk	Topical

Features: Intro to Leading a Study

★★★ Personal Application Preparation Time: Med ISBN: 0-89109-498-9
★★ Relationship Building Ldr. Guide Avail.: No Size: 5.50 x 8.50

Subjects: Christian Living, Fruit of the Spirit, God
Comments: This study, designed to be used in conjunction with the book *The Practice of Godliness,* leads participants to growth in fear of, love for, and devotion to God—the three basic elements essential to godly living. The lessons are designed to allow the Holy Spirit to cultivate humility, contentment, thankfulness, joy, holiness, self-control, faithfulness, peace, patience and gentleness, kindness and goodness, and love.

Author: Bridges, Jerry   **129**
Series:
Title: *Pursuit of Holiness, The*
Publisher: NavPress, 1978

Num. Sess.	Group Time	Num. Pgs.	Avg. Qst.	Price	Audience	Format	Bible Study
12	45-60	55	7	3.95	New Christian	Workbk	Topical

Features: Intro to Study

★★★★ Personal Application Preparation Time: Med ISBN: 0-89109-025-8
★ Relationship Building Ldr. Guide Avail.: Yes Size: 5.50 x 8.50

Subjects: Discipleship, Holiness
Comments: This study, which accompanies the book *The Pursuit of Holiness,* guides participants toward the joy of living a life pleasing to God. The book reveals undiluted truth about sin and how to overcome it; about temptation and how to say no. The lessons bear titles like "Responsibility for Holiness," "A Holy Standing in Christ," "The Continuing Struggle with Sin," "Holiness in Body and Spirit," "Discipline," and "Holiness in an Unholy World."

Author: Bridges, Jerry   **130**
Series:
Title: *Transforming Grace*
Publisher: NavPress, 1991

Num. Sess.	Group Time	Num. Pgs.	Avg. Qst.	Price	Audience	Format	Bible Study
8	60-90	96	12	5.95	New Christian	Workbk	Topical

Features: Intro to Leading a Study, Prayer Helps, Scrpt Memory Helps, Pre-discussion Quest, Digging Deeper Quest, Follow Up, Ldr's Notes, Persnl Study Quest, Book Avail

★★★★ Personal Application Preparation Time: Low ISBN: 0-89109-644-2
★★★ Relationship Building Ldr. Guide Avail.: No Size: 5.25 x 8.25

Subjects: Christian Living, Grace
Comments: This companion guide to Bridges' book by the same name can be used without reading the book. Each session includes an excerpt from the book as well as Scripture references for discussion. Sessions help users understand what grace is and how one can live by it (as opposed to by performance or license) in practical everyday ways. Many ideas for group and personal prayer and application are included.

Author: Bridges, Jerry   **131**
Series:
Title: *Trusting God: Even When Life Hurts*
Publisher: NavPress, 1989

Num. Sess.	Group Time	Num. Pgs.	Avg. Qst.	Price	Audience	Format	Bible Study
12	60-90	112	13	5.95	New Christian	Workbk	Topical

Features: Intro to Leading a Study, Prayer Helps, Scrpt Memory Helps

★★★★ Personal Application Preparation Time: Med ISBN: 0-89109-241-2
★★★ Relationship Building Ldr. Guide Avail.: No Size: 5.50 x 8.50

Subjects: Christian Living, God
Comments: This study guide serves as a companion to the book *Trusting God,* which concerns God's sovereignty. The guide expounds on the fundamental principles of the book, the three essential truths about God: God is completely sovereign; God is infinite in wisdom; and God is perfect in love. The book is optional for completion of the study.

Author: Bright, Bill   **132**
Series: Ten Basic Steps
Title: *Christian Adventure, The (Step 1)*
Publisher: Here's Life, 1968

Num. Sess.	Group Time	Num. Pgs.	Avg. Qst.	Price	Audience	Format	Bible Study
7	60-75	39	Vry	2.25	New Christian	Workbk	Topical

Features: Intro to Leading a Study, Intro to Study, Scrpt Memory Helps

★★★ Personal Application Preparation Time: Med ISBN: 0-918956-04-8
★★ Relationship Building Ldr. Guide Avail.: Yes Size: 5.25 x 8.25

Subjects: Devotionals, Discipleship, Jesus: Life/Teaching, Teens: Discipleship
Comments: This study is step one in a ten-part series designed to lead participants toward Christian maturity. After establishing the uniqueness of Christ, it leads participants through seven lessons on topics such as: Christian certainty, Jesus' person, Christ-controlled life, five principles of growth, and Christian authority. This practical, easy-to-follow study is ideal for daily devotions; or it may be used with groups of all sizes, youth to adult.

Author: Bright, Bill   **133**
Series: Ten Basic Steps
Title: *Christian and Obedience, The (Step 6)*
Publisher: Here's Life, 1968

Num. Sess.	Group Time	Num. Pgs.	Avg. Qst.	Price	Audience	Format	Bible Study
7	60-75	31	Vry	2.25	New Christian	Workbk	Topical

Features: Intro to Leading a Study, Intro to Study, Scrpt Memory Helps
★★★ Personal Application Preparation Time: Med ISBN: 0-918956-09-9
★★ Relationship Building Ldr. Guide Avail.: Yes Size: 5.25 x 8.25
Subjects: Devotionals, Discipleship, Obedience, Teens: Discipleship
Comments: This study is step six in a ten-part series designed to lead participants toward Christian maturity. It features seven lessons on Christian obedience, including lessons on the results of God's will, obedience and purity, security, fear, the tongue, and insincerity. This practical, easy-to-follow study is ideal for daily devotions; or it may be used with groups of all sizes, youth to adult.

Author: Bright, Bill   **134**
Series: Ten Basic Steps
Title: *Christian and the Holy Spirit, The (Step 3)*
Publisher: Here's Life, 1968

Num. Sess.	Group Time	Num. Pgs.	Avg. Qst.	Price	Audience	Format	Bible Study
7	60-75	40	Vry	2.25	New Christian	Workbk	Topical

Features: Intro to Leading a Study, Intro to Study, Scrpt Memory Helps
★★★ Personal Application Preparation Time: Med ISBN: 0-918956-06-4
★★ Relationship Building Ldr. Guide Avail.: Yes Size: 5.25 x 8.25
Subjects: Devotionals, Discipleship, Holy Spirit, Jesus: Life/Teaching, Teens: Discipleship
Comments: This study is step three in a ten-part series designed to lead participants toward Christian maturity. Included within its seven lessons are ones on who the Spirit is, why He came, His relationship with Christians, and the various aspects of being Spirit-filled. This practical, easy-to-follow study is ideal for daily devotions; or it may be used with groups of all sizes, youth to adult.

Author: Bright, Bill   **135**
Series: Ten Basic Steps
Title: *Christian and the Bible, The (Step 5)*
Publisher: Here's Life, 1968

Num. Sess.	Group Time	Num. Pgs.	Avg. Qst.	Price	Audience	Format	Bible Study
8	60-75	37	Vry	2.25	New Christian	Workbk	Topical

Features: Intro to Leading a Study, Intro to Study, Scrpt Memory Helps
★★★ Personal Application Preparation Time: Med ISBN: 0-918956-08-0
★★ Relationship Building Ldr. Guide Avail.: Yes Size: 5.25 x 8.25
Subjects: Bible Study, Devotionals, Discipleship, Teens: Discipleship
Comments: This study is step five in a ten-part series designed to lead participants toward Christian maturity. It features eight lessons on Christians and the Bible, including lessons on Christ's position; the authority, power, and need for the Word; and private study methods. This practical, easy-to-follow study is ideal for daily devotions; or it may be used with groups of all sizes, youth to adult.

Author: Bright, Bill   **136**
Series: Ten Basic Steps
Title: *Christian and Witnessing, The (Step 7)*
Publisher: Here's Life, 1968

Num. Sess.	Group Time	Num. Pgs.	Avg. Qst.	Price	Audience	Format	Bible Study
7	60-75	36	Vry	2.25	New Christian	Workbk	Topical

Features: Intro to Leading a Study, Intro to Study, Scrpt Memory Helps
★★★ Personal Application Preparation Time: Med ISBN: 0-918956-10-2
★★ Relationship Building Ldr. Guide Avail.: Yes Size: 5.25 x 8.25
Subjects: Devotionals, Discipleship, Evangelism, Holy Spirit, Prayer, Teens: Discipleship
Comments: This study is step seven in a ten-part series designed to lead participants toward Christian maturity. It features seven lessons on witnessing, including one on why we should witness, another in which Jesus demonstrates how to witness, and others dealing with the qualifications and biblical authority of witnessing, prayer, and the Holy Spirit's activity in witnessing. This practical, easy-to-follow study is ideal for daily devotions; or it may be used with groups of all sizes, youth to adult.

Author: Bright, Bill   **137**
Series: Ten Basic Steps
Title: *Christian and Prayer, The (Step 4)*
Publisher: Here's Life, 1968

Num. Sess.	Group Time	Num. Pgs.	Avg. Qst.	Price	Audience	Format	Bible Study
7	60-75	31	Vry	2.25	New Christian	Workbk	Topical

Features: Intro to Leading a Study, Intro to Study, Scrpt Memory Helps
★★★ Personal Application Preparation Time: Med ISBN: 0-918956-07-2
★★ Relationship Building Ldr. Guide Avail.: Yes Size: 5.25 x 8.25
Subjects: Devotionals, Discipleship, Prayer, Teens: Discipleship, Teens: Prayer
Comments: This study is step four in a ten-part series designed to lead participants toward Christian maturity. It features seven lessons on, among other things, the purpose, privilege, procedure, power, and promise of prayer. This practical, easy-to-follow study is ideal for daily devotions; or it may be used with groups of all sizes, youth to adult.

Author: Bright, Bill   **138**
Series: Ten Basic Steps
Title: *Christian and the Abundant Life, The (Step 2)*
Publisher: Here's Life, 1968

Num. Sess.	Group Time	Num. Pgs.	Avg. Qst.	Price	Audience	Format	Bible Study
8	60-75	34	Vry	2.25	New Christian	Workbk	Topical

Features: Intro to Leading a Study, Intro to Study, Scrpt Memory Helps
★★★ Personal Application Preparation Time: Med ISBN: 0-918956-05-6
★★ Relationship Building Ldr. Guide Avail.: Yes Size: 5.25 x 8.25
Subjects: Devotionals, Discipleship, Jesus: Life/Teaching, Teens: Discipleship
Comments: This study is step two in a ten-part series designed to lead participants toward Christian maturity. Explaining Christians' abundant life, it includes eight lessons on topics such as: an appraisal of participants' spiritual lives, abundant living, the abiding life, Christian armor, and attitude. This practical, easy-to-follow study is ideal for daily devotions; or it may be used with groups of all sizes, youth to adult.

Author: Bright, Bill   **139**
Series: Ten Basic Steps
Title: *Christian and Stewardship, The (Step 8)*
Publisher: Here's Life, 1968

Num. Sess.	Group Time	Num. Pgs.	Avg. Qst.	Price	Audience	Format	Bible Study
8	60-75	40	Vry	2.25	New Christian	Workbk	Topical

Features: Intro to Leading a Study, Intro to Study, Scrpt Memory Helps
  ★★★ Personal Application   Preparation Time: Med   ISBN: 0-918956-11-0
    ★★ Relationship Building   Ldr. Guide Avail.: Yes   Size: 5.25 x 8.25
Subjects: Accountability, Devotionals, Discipleship, Stewardship, Teens: Discipleship
Comments: This study is step eight in a ten-part series designed to lead participants toward Christian maturity. It features eight lessons on stewardship, including God's ownership; stewardship of time, bodies, gifts, and possessions; and the final accounting to the Master. This practical, easy-to-follow study is ideal for daily devotions; or it may be used with groups of all sizes, youth to adult.

Author: Bright, Bill   **140**
Series: Ten Basic Steps
Title: *Handbook for Christian Maturity, A*
Publisher: Here's Life, 1982

Num. Sess.	Group Time	Num. Pgs.	Avg. Qst.	Price	Audience	Format	Bible Study
11	60-75	370	Vry	8.95	New Christian	Workbk	Topical

Features: Intro to Study, Scrpt Memory Helps
  ★★★ Personal Application   Preparation Time: Med   ISBN: 0-86605-010-8
    ★★ Relationship Building   Ldr. Guide Avail.: Yes   Size: 5.25 x 8.25
Subjects: Devotionals, Discipleship, Holy Spirit, Obedience, Prayer
Comments: This handbook is a compilation of an eleven-segment series designed to lead Christians toward maturity. It begins with the "Uniqueness of Jesus," then covers the following topics: abundant life, Holy Spirit, prayer, the Bible, obedience, witnessing, stewardship, and Old and New Testament highlights. Practical and easy to follow, it is ideal for daily devotions or Bible study for any size group, youth to adult.

Author: Bright, Bill   **141**
Series: Transferable Concept
Title: *How to Be Filled with the Spirit*
Publisher: Campus Crusade for Christ International, 1971

Num. Sess.	Group Time	Num. Pgs.	Avg. Qst.	Price	Audience	Format	Bible Study
2	45-60	58	7	2.25	New Christian	Workbk	Topical

Features: Intro to Study
  ★★★ Personal Application   Preparation Time: Med   ISBN: 0-918956-90-0
    ★ Relationship Building   Ldr. Guide Avail.: No   Size: 4.25 x 7.0
Subjects: Discipleship, Holy Spirit
Comments: This study, third in a four-part series, shows participants how to become filled with the Spirit. It cuts through all the confusion surrounding the controversial subject of the Holy Spirit and states answers clearly and simply. In two sections, which can be divided into group Bible studies, participants will learn the who, what, and why of the Spirit and how to appropriate His fullness. This series "Transferable Concept," presents practical ideas/truths to be communicated without distortion.

Author: Bright, Bill   **142**
Series: Transferable Concept
Title: *How to Be Sure You Are a Christian*
Publisher: Campus Crusade for Christ International, 1972

Num. Sess.	Group Time	Num. Pgs.	Avg. Qst.	Price	Audience	Format	Bible Study
3	45-60	63	7	2.25	New Christian	Workbk	Topical

Features: Intro to Study
  ★★★ Personal Application   Preparation Time: Med   ISBN: 0-918956-88-9
    ★ Relationship Building   Ldr. Guide Avail.: No   Size: 4.25 x 7.0
Subjects: Commitments, Discipleship, Evangelism, Faith
Comments: This study, first of a four-part series, shows participants how to be sure of salvation. Three sections, well suited for group lessons, deal with the three types of commitment—intellectual, emotional, and volitional—involved in the most important decision in a person's life. Participants will not only solidify their faith, they will learn truths to pass on to others. This study is part of a series called "Transferable Concept," practical ideas/truths to be communicated without distortion.

Author: Bright, Bill   **143**
Series: Transferable Concept
Title: *How to Experience God's Love and Forgiveness*
Publisher: Campus Crusade for Christ International, 1971

Num. Sess.	Group Time	Num. Pgs.	Avg. Qst.	Price	Audience	Format	Bible Study
3	45-60	63	7	2.25	New Christian	Workbk	Topical

Features: Intro to Study
  ★★★ Personal Application   Preparation Time: Med   ISBN: 0-918956-89-7
    ★ Relationship Building   Ldr. Guide Avail.: No   Size: 4.25 x 7.0
Subjects: Discipleship, Forgiveness, God
Comments: This study, second in a four-part series, shows participants how to experience God's love and forgiveness. Once salvation is experienced and initial joy enjoyed, Christians of all eras are faced with the challenge of living in a morally decadent world. The study outlines all the problems and challenges posed by the world, then outlines and discusses God's solution. This study is part of a series called "Transferable Concept," practical ideas/truths to be communicated without distortion.

Author: Bright, Bill   **144**
Series: Transferable Concept
Title: *How to Pray*
Publisher: Campus Crusade for Christ International, 1981

Num. Sess.	Group Time	Num. Pgs.	Avg. Qst.	Price	Audience	Format	Bible Study
7	40-50	63	6	2.25	Beginner	Workbk	Topical

Features: Intro to Leading a Study, Intro to Study, Ldr's Notes
  ★★ Personal Application   Preparation Time: Low   ISBN: 0-918956-96-X
    ★ Relationship Building   Ldr. Guide Avail.: No   Size: 4.25 x 7.0
Subjects: Prayer
Comments: This study guide explores how prayer can be a transferable concept; i.e., a truth which can be transferred (communicated) person to person, spiritual generation to generation, without distortion or dilution of its original meaning. In this case, the transferable concept is the power of prayer. In three lessons, the author answers vital questions: Who can pray? Why pray? To whom do we pray? When to pray? What to pray for? and, How can we pray with confidence? Reflective questions follow.

Author: Bright, Bill   **145**
Series: Transferable Concept
Title: *How to Walk in the Spirit*
Publisher: Campus Crusade for Christ International, 1971

Num. Sess.	Group Time	Num. Pgs.	Avg. Qst.	Price	Audience	Format	Bible Study
3	45-60	64	Vry	2.25	New Christian	Workbk	Topical

Features: Intro to Study
  ★★★ Personal Application Preparation Time: Med ISBN: 0-918956-91-9
  ★ Relationship Building Ldr. Guide Avail.: No Size: 4.25 x 7.0
Subjects: Discipleship, Faith, Holy Spirit
Comments: This study, last in a four-part series, shows participants how to walk in the Spirit. It moves Christians from simply having the power and presence of God's indwelling Spirit to a conscious recognition and application of the Spirit. Three sections take participants from recognition and preparation, to knowing the power of the Spirit, to living by faith. This study is part of a series called "Transferable Concept," practical ideas/truths to be communicated without distortion or dilution.

Author: Bright, Bill   **146**
Series: Ten Basic Steps
Title: *New Testament Highlights (Step 10)*
Publisher: Here's Life, 1968

Num. Sess.	Group Time	Num. Pgs.	Avg. Qst.	Price	Audience	Format	Bible Study
8	60-75	40	Vry	2.25	New Christian	Workbk	Topical

Features: Intro to Leading a Study, Intro to Study, Scrpt Memory Helps
  ★★★ Personal Application Preparation Time: Med ISBN: 0-918956-13-7
  ★★ Relationship Building Ldr. Guide Avail.: Yes Size: 5.25 x 8.25
Subjects: Devotionals, Discipleship, Gospels, New Testament, Teens: Discipleship
Comments: This study is step ten in a ten-part series designed to lead participants toward Christian maturity. It highlights the New Testament through eight lessons, including ones on Matthew, Mark, Luke, John, and Acts; the letters to the Romans, Corinthians, Galatians, and Thessalonians; and the Revelation of John. This practical, easy-to-follow study is ideal for daily devotions; or it may be used with groups of all sizes, youth to adult.

Author: Bright, Bill   **147**
Series: Ten Basic Steps
Title: *Old Testament Highlights (Step 9)*
Publisher: Here's Life, 1968

Num. Sess.	Group Time	Num. Pgs.	Avg. Qst.	Price	Audience	Format	Bible Study
8	60-75	41	Vry	2.25	New Christian	Workbk	Topical

Features: Intro to Leading a Study, Intro to Study, Scrpt Memory Helps, Summary
  ★★★ Personal Application Preparation Time: Med ISBN: 0-918956-12-9
  ★★ Relationship Building Ldr. Guide Avail.: Yes Size: 5.25 x 8.25
Subjects: Bible Personalities, Devotionals, Discipleship, Teens: Discipleship
Comments: This study is step nine in a ten-part series designed to lead participants toward Christian maturity. It highlights the Old Testament through eight lessons, including ones on the promised Messiah; Moses, the Passover, and Exodus; law and grace; deliverance and forgiveness; Elijah; and Jeremiah. This practical, easy-to-follow study is ideal for daily devotions; or it may be used with groups of all sizes, youth to adult.

Author: Bright, Bill   **148**
Series: Ten Basic Steps
Title: *Uniqueness of Jesus, The: Introduction*
Publisher: Here's Life, 1968

Num. Sess.	Group Time	Num. Pgs.	Avg. Qst.	Price	Audience	Format	Bible Study
7	60-75	45	Vry	2.25	New Christian	Workbk	Charctr

Features: Intro to Leading a Study, Intro to Study, Scrpt Memory Helps
  ★★★ Personal Application Preparation Time: Med ISBN: 0-918956-03-X
  ★★ Relationship Building Ldr. Guide Avail.: Yes Size: 5.25 x 8.25
Subjects: Devotionals, Discipleship, Jesus: Life/Teaching, Teens: Discipleship
Comments: This study is an introduction to a ten-part series designed to lead participants toward Christian maturity. As a preamble to the series, its seven lessons focus on Christ—who He is; His life, death, and resurrection; His followers; and His church. This practical, easy-to-follow study is ideal for daily devotions; or it may be used with groups of all sizes, youth to adult.

Author: Bright, Michael   **149**
Series: Standard Bible Studies
Title: *Second Corinthians*
Publisher: Standard Publishing, 1988

Num. Sess.	Group Time	Num. Pgs.	Avg. Qst.	Price	Audience	Format	Bible Study
13	60-80	79	Vry	3.50	New Christian	Workbk	Book

Features: Intro to Leading a Study, Objectives, Digging Deeper Quest
  ★★ Personal Application Preparation Time: Low ISBN: 0-87403-188-5
  ★★ Relationship Building Ldr. Guide Avail.: Yes Size: 8.50 x 11.0
Subjects: Forgiveness, Hope, Integrity, Joy, Service, Suffering, 2 Corinthians
Comments: This thirteen-lesson workbook, companion to Knofel Staton's study of 2 Corinthians, focuses on godly forgiveness, servant characteristics, the practices and joys of people helpers, and more. Each lesson features learning goals, lesson aims, and key ideas. Each lesson begins with introductory activities, followed by Bible study, "Digging Deeper" questions, and "What do you think?" questions. Only the leader in a small group setting needs this companion book.

Author: Briscoe, Jill   **150**
Series: Jill Briscoe Bible Study
Title: *Before You Say "Amen": Spending Time with God Through Prayer*
Publisher: Victor Books, 1989

Num. Sess.	Group Time	Num. Pgs.	Avg. Qst.	Price	Audience	Format	Bible Study
8	60-90	105	18	5.99	New Christian	Workbk	Topical

Features: Intro to Leading a Study, Intro to Study, Prayer Helps, Digging Deeper Quest, Follow Up
  ★★★★ Personal Application Preparation Time: Med ISBN: 0-89693-637-6
  ★★★★ Relationship Building Ldr. Guide Avail.: No Size: 6.0 x 9.0
Subjects: Devotionals, Prayer, Women's Issues
Comments: This study on prayer encourages participants to improve their devotional lives by practicing personal and corporate prayer. Subjects covered include: beginning to pray, praising, model prayers, conditions of prayer, and praying for others and ourselves. The final lesson provides practical ideas for more exciting prayer meetings. Each lesson provides a devotional narrative, suggestions for group discussion and prayer, and a Bible study for more advanced study.

Author: Briscoe, Jill   **151**
Series: Jill Briscoe Bible Study
Title: *Body Language: When Our Actions Speak Louder Than*
           Our Words
Publisher: Victor Books, 1987

Num. Sess.	Group Time	Num. Pgs.	Avg. Qst.	Price	Audience	Format	Bible Study
8	60-90	108	19	5.99	New Christian	Workbk	Topical

Features: Intro to Leading a Study, Bibliography, Prayer Helps,
Digging Deeper Quest, Follow Up, Agenda
   ★★★ Personal Application   Preparation Time: Med   ISBN: 0-89693-319-9
   ★★★ Relationship Building   Ldr. Guide Avail.: No   Size: 6.0 x 9.0
Subjects: Caring, Christian Living, Women's Issues
Comments: In this study on body language, when actions speak
louder than words, participants are challenged to consider how the
world is affected by what they say and do. Lessons address subjects
like: the body as a physical entity; transforming minds; changing
hearts; taming tongues; helping hands; seeing eyes; and listening
ears. Participants are reminded that there are many ways to communicate, rather than just words.

Author: Briscoe, Jill   **152**
Series: Video Curriculum Resource
Title: *By Hook or by Crook*
Publisher: Word, 1987

Num. Sess.	Group Time	Num. Pgs.	Avg. Qst.	Price	Audience	Format	Bible Study
8	75-105	N/A	Vry	199.99	New Christian	Video	Topical

Features: Prayer Helps, Follow Up, Book Incl, Video Study Guide
   ★★★★ Personal Application   Preparation Time: None ISBN: 8-01-840079-2
   ★★★ Relationship Building   Ldr. Guide Avail.: No   Size: 11.0 x 11.50
Subjects: Christian Life, Holy Spirit, Service
Comments: This video study concerns Christian lives which must
be hammered into vessels ready for surrender, for being filled with
the Holy Spirit, and ready for service. It describes, through meta-
phors, the tools Jesus used to shape Peter, a rough fisherman, into a
shepherd: boats, fish, rings, towels, roosters, fire, crutches, and pigs.
Each lesson is approximately forty-five minutes long. The study
and discussion guide is divided into three sections: "Thinking It
Through," "Talking It Over," "Taking Action."

Author: Briscoe, Jill   **153**
Series: Jill Briscoe Bible Study
Title: *Evergrowing, Evergreen: Getting to Know God in the Psalms*
Publisher: Victor Books, 1986

Num. Sess.	Group Time	Num. Pgs.	Avg. Qst.	Price	Audience	Format	Bible Study
7	60-90	96	18	5.99	New Christian	Workbk	Book

Features: Intro to Leading a Study, Bibliography, Prayer Helps,
Digging Deeper Quest, Follow Up, Full Scrpt Printed
   ★★★ Personal Application   Preparation Time: Med   ISBN: 0-89693-255-9
   ★★★ Relationship Building   Ldr. Guide Avail.: No   Size: 6.0 x 9.0
Subjects: Bible Personalities, God, Psalms, Women's Issues,
Worship
Comments: This study of seven selected psalms can help partici-
pants get to know God, themselves, and their world better. Psalms 1,
18, 23, 27, 51, 119, and 137 are included. David wrote many of the
psalms; others are attributed to Solomon, Asaph, the sons of Korah,
and Moses. Psalms are used for public as well as private worship.

Author: Briscoe, Jill   **154**
Series: Jill Briscoe Bible Study
Title: *Faith Enough to Finish*
Publisher: Victor Books, 1987

Num. Sess.	Group Time	Num. Pgs.	Avg. Qst.	Price	Audience	Format	Bible Study
8	60-90	108	20	5.99	New Christian	Workbk	Book

Features: Intro to Leading a Study, Bibliography, Prayer Helps,
Digging Deeper Quest, Follow Up, Agenda
   ★★★ Personal Application   Preparation Time: Med   ISBN: 0-89693-238-9
   ★★★ Relationship Building   Ldr. Guide Avail.: No   Size: 6.0 x 9.0
Subjects: Faith, Hebrews, Women's Issues
Comments: In this eight-lesson study of Hebrews, participants
will discover what it means to endure. First-century believers who,
because of increasing hostility, were in danger of "drifting away"
from the faith, were told to draw near and hold fast—the eternal
Son of God is supreme and sufficient. The study uses discussions
like one on Christ, "the author and finisher of our faith," to provide
that steadfastness. A notebook is recommended to record thoughts,
discoveries, and prayer requests.

Author: Briscoe, Jill   **155**
Series: Jill Briscoe Bible Study
Title: *God's Name, God's Nature*
Publisher: Victor Books, 1988

Num. Sess.	Group Time	Num. Pgs.	Avg. Qst.	Price	Audience	Format	Bible Study
9	60-90	108	17	5.99	New Christian	Workbk	Topical

Features: Intro to Leading a Study, Bibliography, Prayer Helps,
Digging Deeper Quest, Follow Up, Agenda
   ★★★ Personal Application   Preparation Time: Med   ISBN: 0-89693-584-1
   ★★★ Relationship Building   Ldr. Guide Avail.: No   Size: 6.0 x 9.0
Subjects: God, Old Testament, Women's Issues
Comments: This study is designed to teach participants more about
God through His Old Testament names, such as Elohim, Adonai,
Jehovah-Jireh, Jehovah-Rophe, Jehovah-Nissi, and Jehovah-Shalom.
God's names unlock the mystery of His nature; reveal His heart,
mind, and soul; capture the imagination; and bring believers to His
feet in wonder, love, and praise. God's names bring participants
closer to Heaven and make them more sensitive people. A notebook
is recommended to record thoughts and prayer requests.

Author: Briscoe, Jill   **156**
Series: Jill Briscoe Bible Study
Title: *Grace to Go On*
Publisher: Victor Books, 1989

Num. Sess.	Group Time	Num. Pgs.	Avg. Qst.	Price	Audience	Format	Bible Study
8	60-90	103	15	5.99	New Christian	Workbk	Topical

Features: Intro to Leading a Study, Intro to Study, Bibliography,
Prayer Helps, Digging Deeper Quest, Follow Up, Charts, Agenda
   ★★★ Personal Application   Preparation Time: Med   ISBN: 0-89693-762-3
   ★★★ Relationship Building   Ldr. Guide Avail.: No   Size: 6.0 x 9.0
Subjects: Charismatic Interest, Grace, Holy Spirit, Spiritual Gifts,
Women's Issues
Comments: This study explores symbols of the Holy Spirit which
abound in Scripture, including: the "fire" that ignites, the "wind" of
change, the "oil" of gladness, the "water" of life, the abused "dove,"
the Spirit's "gifts," the "fruit" that blossoms, and the "cloud" of
glory. Participants will experience a Holy Spirit that can enrich their
souls. A notebook is recommended to record thoughts, discoveries,
and prayer requests.

Author: Briscoe, Jill   **157**
Series: Jill Briscoe Bible Study
Title: *Heaven and Hell: A Study of the Promise and the Peril*
of Eternity
Publisher: Victor Books, 1990

Num. Sess.	Group Time	Num. Pgs.	Avg. Qst.	Price	Audience	Format	Bible Study
8	60-90	95	18	5.99	New Christian	Workbk	Topical

Features: Intro to Leading a Study, Intro to Study, Prayer Helps,
Scrpt Memory Helps, Digging Deeper Quest, Follow Up
★★★ Personal Application   Preparation Time: Med   ISBN: 0-89693-768-2
★★★ Relationship Building   Ldr. Guide Avail.: No   Size: 6.0 x 9.0
Subjects: Devotionals, Eschatology, Heaven/Hell
Comments: This study concerns the promise and peril of eternity.
Participants will find various responses to questions about afterlife, such as: What are Heaven and hell like? Where are they? Are
they physical places or states of mind? and, Where will we spend
eternity? Each lesson provides a devotional narrative, suggestions for group discussion and prayer, and a Bible study for more
advanced study. A notebook is recommended for recording thoughts,
discoveries, and prayer requests.

Author: Briscoe, Jill   **158**
Series:
Title: *"Here Am I—Send Aaron!"*
Publisher: Victor Books, 1978

Num. Sess.	Group Time	Num. Pgs.	Avg. Qst.	Price	Audience	Format	Bible Study
13	60-90	142	Vry	7.99	New Christian	Book	Book

Features: Prayer Helps
★★★ Personal Application   Preparation Time: Med   ISBN: 0-88207-767-8
★★★ Relationship Building   Ldr. Guide Avail.: Yes   Size: 5.50 x 8.0
Subjects: Bible Personalities, Exodus, God
Comments: The study of Exodus shows how God directed the children of Israel through a reluctant leader, Moses. During the "desert"
years, God miraculously transformed this insignificant saint into a
persuasive communicator, sensitive to the Lord's call. Through the
wilderness wanderings of Moses and his people, participants can
identify their own spiritual strayings and redirect and enrich their
daily lives. A leader's guide with reproducible student response
sheets is available.

Author: Briscoe, Jill   **159**
Series: Jill Briscoe Bible Study
Title: *Starlight*
Publisher: Victor Books, 1988

Num. Sess.	Group Time	Num. Pgs.	Avg. Qst.	Price	Audience	Format	Bible Study
8	60-90	108	15	5.99	New Christian	Workbk	Book

Features: Intro to Leading a Study, Intro to Study, Bibliography,
Prayer Helps, Digging Deeper Quest, Follow Up, Agenda
★★★ Personal Application   Preparation Time: Med   ISBN: 0-89693-465-9
★★★ Relationship Building   Ldr. Guide Avail.: No   Size: 6.0 x 9.0
Subjects: Bible Personalities, Esther, God, Women's Issues
Comments: This study explores how God used Esther to be a shin-
ing light in a dark world. Participants will see how God first shines
His light in their hearts, then spreads that light into the unbelieving
environment around them. A notebook is recommended to record
thoughts, discoveries, and prayer requests.

Author: Briscoe, Jill   **160**
Series: Jill Briscoe Bible Study
Title: *Women in the Life of Jesus*
Publisher: Victor Books, 1986

Num. Sess.	Group Time	Num. Pgs.	Avg. Qst.	Price	Audience	Format	Bible Study
8	60-90	96	17	5.99	New Christian	Workbk	Topical

Features: Intro to Leading a Study, Bibliography, Prayer Helps,
Digging Deeper Quest, Agenda
★★★ Personal Application   Preparation Time: Med   ISBN: 0-89693-254-0
★★★ Relationship Building   Ldr. Guide Avail.: No   Size: 6.0 x 9.0
Subjects: Bible Personalities, Jesus: Life/Teaching, Relationships,
Singles Issues, Women's Issues
Comments: This study deals with women who had an impact on
Jesus' earthly ministry, including sorrowing, sick, sexual, sinful,
single, spiritual, successful, and scheming women. By studying the
lives of Mary of Nazareth, Mary of Bethany, Rahab, Jezebel, and
many others, participants will deepen their relationship with Christ.
A notebook is recommended to record thoughts, discoveries, and
prayer requests.

Author: Briscoe, Jill   **161**
Series: Jill Briscoe Bible Study
Title: *Women Who Changed Their World: How God Uses Women to*
Make a Difference
Publisher: Victor Books, 1991

Num. Sess.	Group Time	Num. Pgs.	Avg. Qst.	Price	Audience	Format	Bible Study
8	60-90	95	18	5.99	New Christian	Workbk	Topical

Features: Intro to Leading a Study, Intro to Study, Prayer Helps,
Scrpt Memory Helps, Digging Deeper Quest, Follow Up
★★★ Personal Application   Preparation Time: Med   ISBN: 0-89693-001-7
★★★ Relationship Building   Ldr. Guide Avail.: No   Size: 6.0 x 9.0
Subjects: Bible Personalities, Faith, Forgiveness, Friendships, Relationships, Women's Issues
Comments: This study helps participants learn more about qualities that
allow women to make a difference. Women like Eve, Sarah, and Rahab
took advantage of opportunities to influence their families, friends, or
masters. Topics include: changing a woman's world through sin, a woman's
meekness, her gifts, faith, strength, love, faithfulness, and forgiveness. Each
lesson provides a devotional narrative, suggestions for group discussion and
prayer, and a Bible study for more advanced study.

Author: Briscoe, Stuart   **162**
Series:
Title: *David: A Heart for God*
Publisher: Victor Books, 1984

Num. Sess.	Group Time	Num. Pgs.	Avg. Qst.	Price	Audience	Format	Bible Study
13	60-75	170	N/A	6.99	New Christian	Book	Charctr

Features:
★★★★ Personal Application   Preparation Time: Low   ISBN: 0-89693-466-7
★★★ Relationship Building   Ldr. Guide Avail.: Yes   Size: 5.50 x 8.0
Subjects: Bible Personalities, Repentance, Senior Adults, Service,
1 & 2 Samuel
Comments: This thirteen-week study of David's triumphs, trials,
and sins offers participants hope for becoming people after God's
own heart. It leads them from a preoccupation with self to a new
heart-attitude. Discussed are the hardened, courageous, kind, and
repentant hearts. The study concludes with a discussion of retirement, and how people will or won't serve the Lord. It compares
retirees with David, who continued to serve God until the end of his
life.

Author: Briscoe, Stuart   163
Series:
Title: *What Works When Life Doesn't*
Publisher: Victor Books, 1976

Num. Sess.	Group Time	Num. Pgs.	Avg. Qst.	Price	Audience	Format	Bible Study
13	60-75	168	N/A	7.99	New Christian	Book	Topical

Features: Intro to Study
★★★★ Personal Application Preparation Time: Low ISBN: 0-88207-725-2
★★★ Relationship Building Ldr. Guide Avail.: Yes Size: 5.50 x 8.0
Subjects: Emotions, Psalms, Stress
Comments: This thirteen-week study of selected psalms shows how they not only describe the human predicament, but also prescribe principles for overcoming such life problems as discouragement, depression, fear, and stress. Lessons propose solutions to other perplexing problems and demonstrate how studying psalms can offer peace. A leader's guide includes reproducible transparency masters.

Author: Brooks, Keith L.   164
Series: Teach Yourself the Bible
Title: *Acts: Adventures of the Early Church*
Publisher: Moody Press, 1963

Num. Sess.	Group Time	Num. Pgs.	Avg. Qst.	Price	Audience	Format	Bible Study
12	60-90	96	48	3.99	New Christian	Workbk	Book

Features: Intro to Leading a Study, Intro to Study, Exam
★★ Personal Application Preparation Time: Low ISBN: 0-8024-0125-2
★★ Relationship Building Ldr. Guide Avail.: No Size: 5.50 x 8.50
Subjects: Acts
Comments: The book of Acts outlines the work of the Holy Spirit in the early Church. It is a record of His advent, activity, and power at the beginning of the Church. The format for this study—one of twenty-five in this series—includes fill-in-the-blank questions and checkups to test participants' grasp of scriptural truths. The series is designed for self-study. But suggestions for group study and a four-year plan for using the series are also included.

Author: Brooks, Keith L.   165
Series: Teach Yourself the Bible
Title: *Basic Bible Study: For New Christians*
Publisher: Moody Press, 1961

Num. Sess.	Group Time	Num. Pgs.	Avg. Qst.	Price	Audience	Format	Bible Study
8	45-60	48	22	3.99	New Christian	Workbk	Topical

Features: Intro to Leading a Study, Exam
★★ Personal Application Preparation Time: Low ISBN: 0-8024-0478-2
★★ Relationship Building Ldr. Guide Avail.: No Size: 5.50 x 8.50
Subjects: Discipleship, Prayer
Comments: This Bible study covers the basics for new Christians. Topics include: God's way of salvation, our blessings in Christ, the consecrated life, how to meet temptation, how to pray, and more. The format includes a series of fill-in-the-blank questions, and checkups test participants' grasp of scriptural truths. This twenty-five-book series is designed for self-study; however, suggestions for group study, and a four-year plan for using the series, are included.

Author: Brooks, Keith L.   166
Series: Teach Yourself the Bible
Title: *Christian Character Course*
Publisher: Moody Press, 1961

Num. Sess.	Group Time	Num. Pgs.	Avg. Qst.	Price	Audience	Format	Bible Study
8	45-60	48	31	3.99	New Christian	Workbk	Topical

Features: Intro to Leading a Study, Exam
★★ Personal Application Preparation Time: Low ISBN: 0-8024-1301-3
★★ Relationship Building Ldr. Guide Avail.: No Size: 5.50 x 8.50
Subjects: Discipleship, Ethics, Fruit of the Spirit, Service
Comments: This study examines eight characteristics of a true believer, including humility, love, purity, integrity, generosity, and steadfastness. Participants will learn about Christian ethics and practical Christian service. The format includes a series of fill-in-the-blank questions, and checkups to test participants' grasp of scriptural truths. This twenty-five-book series is designed for self-study; however, suggestions for group study are included.

Author: Brooks, Keith L.   167
Series: Teach Yourself the Bible
Title: *Colossians and Philemon: The Epistles of Truth and Love*
Publisher: Moody Press, 1964

Num. Sess.	Group Time	Num. Pgs.	Avg. Qst.	Price	Audience	Format	Bible Study
8	45-60	48	22	3.99	New Christian	Workbk	Book

Features: Intro to Leading a Study, Exam
★★ Personal Application Preparation Time: Low ISBN: 0-8024-1525-3
★★ Relationship Building Ldr. Guide Avail.: No Size: 5.50 x 8.50
Subjects: Church Life, Colossians/Philemon, False Teachers, Forgiveness, Hope, Leadership, Prison Epistles, Service, Suffering
Comments: This study—part of a twenty-five-book series—deals with letters the Apostle Paul sent to the Colossians and Philemon. The former was sent to Colosse to warn against errors of doctrine and practice; the latter was a private letter to a Colossian Christian. The format for this study includes a series of fill-in-the-blank questions, and checkups to test participants' grasp of scriptural truths. The series is designed for self-study; however, suggestions for group study are included.

Author: Brooks, Keith L.   168
Series: Teach Yourself the Bible
Title: *Ephesians: The Epistle of Christian Maturity*
Publisher: Moody Press, 1964

Num. Sess.	Group Time	Num. Pgs.	Avg. Qst.	Price	Audience	Format	Bible Study
8	60-75	64	40	3.99	New Christian	Workbk	Book

Features: Intro to Leading a Study, Exam
★★ Personal Application Preparation Time: Low ISBN: 0-8024-2333-7
★★ Relationship Building Ldr. Guide Avail.: No Size: 5.50 x 8.50
Subjects: Discipleship, Ephesians, Theology
Comments: This study of Ephesians—part of a twenty-five-book series—concerns a timeless letter for God's church. The practical and doctrinal sides of this epistle deal with a believer's place in Christ and Christ's place in a believer. The format includes a series of fill-in-the-blank questions, and checkups to test participants' grasp of scriptural truths. The series is designed for self-study; however, suggestions for group study, and a four-year plan for using the series, are included.

Author: Brooks, Keith L.   **169**
Series: Teach Yourself the Bible
Title: *First and Second Thessalonians: Jesus Is Coming Again!*
Publisher: Moody Press, 1964

Num. Sess.	Group Time	Num. Pgs.	Avg. Qst.	Price	Audience	Format	Bible Study
8	45-60	48	23	3.99	New Christian	Workbk	Book

Features: Intro to Leading a Study, Exam
  ★★ Personal Application   Preparation Time: Low   ISBN: 0-8024-2645-X
  ★★ Relationship Building   Ldr. Guide Avail.: No   Size: 5.50 x 8.50
Subjects: Eschatology, 1 & 2 Thessalonians
Comments: This study outlines the four reasons Paul wrote 1 and 2 Thessalonians: to confirm young believers, to encourage them in the face of persecution, to correct doctrinal errors, and to teach them what God has revealed about the Lord's return. The format includes a series of fill-in-the-blank questions, and checkups to test participants' grasp of scriptural truths. This twenty-five-book series is designed for self-study, but also includes group study helps.

Author: Brooks, Keith L.   **170**
Series: Teach Yourself the Bible
Title: *First Corinthians: Order in the Church*
Publisher: Moody Press, 1964

Num. Sess.	Group Time	Num. Pgs.	Avg. Qst.	Price	Audience	Format	Bible Study
12	45-60	64	24	3.99	New Christian	Workbk	Book

Features: Intro to Leading a Study, Intro to Study, Exam
  ★★ Personal Application   Preparation Time: Low   ISBN: 0-8024-2649-2
  ★★ Relationship Building   Ldr. Guide Avail.: No   Size: 5.50 x 8.50
Subjects: Church Life, 1 Corinthians
Comments: Paul wrote 1 Corinthians in response to issues concerning paganism. He appealed to predominantly Gentile church members to remember their high positions in Christ, and the reality of their union with Him. The format of this study—one of twenty-five in this series—includes a series of fill-in-the-blank questions, and checkups to test participants' grasp of scriptural truths. The series is designed for self-study; however, suggestions for group study are included.

Author: Brooks, Keith L.   **171**
Series: Teach Yourself the Bible
Title: *Galatians: The Epistle of Christian Liberty*
Publisher: Moody Press, 1963

Num. Sess.	Group Time	Num. Pgs.	Avg. Qst.	Price	Audience	Format	Bible Study
8	45-60	48	22	3.99	New Christian	Workbk	Book

Features: Intro to Leading a Study, Exam
  ★★ Personal Application   Preparation Time: Low   ISBN: 0-8024-2925-4
  ★★ Relationship Building   Ldr. Guide Avail.: No   Size: 5.50 x 8.50
Subjects: Galatians, Victorious Living
Comments: This study of Galatians—part of a twenty-five-book series—is about Paul's letter calling believers back to the pure gospel of Jesus Christ. Lessons cover the origin, maintenance, experience, superiority, effects, and practice of Christian liberty. The format includes a series of fill-in-the-blank questions; checkups test participants' grasp of scriptural truths. The series is designed for self-study; however, suggestions for group study are included.

Author: Brooks, Keith L.   **172**
Series: Teach Yourself the Bible
Title: *Great Prophetic Themes*
Publisher: Moody Press, 1962

Num. Sess.	Group Time	Num. Pgs.	Avg. Qst.	Price	Audience	Format	Bible Study
12	45-60	64	21	3.99	New Christian	Workbk	Topical

Features: Intro to Leading a Study, Exam
  ★★ Personal Application   Preparation Time: Low   ISBN: 0-8024-3320-0
  ★★ Relationship Building   Ldr. Guide Avail.: No   Size: 5.50 x 8.50
Subjects: Eschatology, Prophecy
Comments: This study of great prophetic themes—part of a twenty-five-book series—covers much of the Old and New Testaments. For example, the Lord's second coming is mentioned 318 times in the 27 books of the New Testament, and numerous times in the Old Testament. The format includes a series of fill-in-the-blank questions, and checkups to test participants' grasp of scriptural truths. The series is designed for self-study; however, suggestions for group study are included.

Author: Brooks, Keith L.   **173**
Series: Teach Yourself the Bible
Title: *Hebrews: The Beauty of Christ Unveiled*
Publisher: Moody Press, 1963

Num. Sess.	Group Time	Num. Pgs.	Avg. Qst.	Price	Audience	Format	Bible Study
13	45-60	64	22	3.99	New Christian	Workbk	Book

Features: Intro to Leading a Study, Exam
  ★★ Personal Application   Preparation Time: Low   ISBN: 0-8024-3507-6
  ★★ Relationship Building   Ldr. Guide Avail.: No   Size: 5.50 x 8.50
Subjects: Faith, Hebrews, Obedience
Comments: This study of Hebrews—part of a twenty-five-book series—concerns a book obviously inspired by God. Participants will learn of the superiority of Christ and the need for complete faith in Him and will be exhorted to obey Him in attitude and deed. The format includes a series of fill-in-the-blank questions, and checkups to test participants' grasp of scriptural truths. The series is designed for self-study; however, suggestions for group study are included.

Author: Brooks, Keith L.   **174**
Series: Teach Yourself the Bible
Title: *James: Belief in Action*
Publisher: Moody Press, 1962

Num. Sess.	Group Time	Num. Pgs.	Avg. Qst.	Price	Audience	Format	Bible Study
8	45-60	48	29	3.99	New Christian	Workbk	Topical

Features: Intro to Leading a Study, Exam
  ★★ Personal Application   Preparation Time: Low   ISBN: 0-8024-4227-7
  ★★ Relationship Building   Ldr. Guide Avail.: No   Size: 5.50 x 8.50
Subjects: Beliefs, Faith, James
Comments: This study of James emphasizes works as the fruit of faith and evidence of justification. It is based entirely on the new birth and a living salvation through Jesus Christ. The format includes a series of fill-in-the-blank questions; checkups test participants' grasp of scriptural truths. This twenty-five-book series is designed for self-study; however, suggestions for group study, and a four-year plan for using the series, are included.

Author: Brooks, Keith L.   **175**
Series: Teach Yourself the Bible
Title: *Luke: The Gospel of God's Man*
Publisher: Moody Press, 1964

Num. Sess.	Group Time	Num. Pgs.	Avg. Qst.	Price	Audience	Format	Bible Study
12	60-90	96	57	3.99	New Christian	Workbk	Book

Features: Intro to Leading a Study, Charts, Exam
★★ Personal Application Preparation Time: Low ISBN: 0-8024-5047-4
★★ Relationship Building Ldr. Guide Avail.: No Size: 5.50 x 8.50
Subjects: Jesus: Life/Teaching, Luke
Comments: This study concerns Luke's account of the man who was completely God, and God who became completely man. It covers Christ's life from birth to Ascension. A chart listing distinctive features of the gospels is beneficial. The format includes a series of fill-in-the-blank questions; checkups are included to test participants' grasp of scriptural truths. This twenty-five-book series is designed for self-study; however, suggestions for group study are included.

Author: Brooks, Keith L.   **176**
Series: Teach Yourself the Bible
Title: *Mark: The Gospel of God's Servant*
Publisher: Moody Press, 1964

Num. Sess.	Group Time	Num. Pgs.	Avg. Qst.	Price	Audience	Format	Bible Study
12	60-90	77	35	3.99	New Christian	Workbk	Book

Features: Intro to Leading a Study, Exam
★★ Personal Application Preparation Time: Low ISBN: 0-8024-5200-0
★★ Relationship Building Ldr. Guide Avail.: No Size: 5.50 x 8.50
Subjects: Jesus: Life/Teaching, Mark, Service
Comments: This study of Mark is part of a twenty-five-book series. Mark is a gospel of service, presenting Jesus Christ as Servant obedient even to death. Written primarily for Gentiles, it shows participants how to become servants of Christ. The format includes a series of fill-in-the-blank questions, and checkups to test partipants' grasp of scriptural truths. The series is designed for self-study; however, suggestions for group study, and a four-year plan for using the series, are included.

Author: Brooks, Keith L.   **177**
Series: Teach Yourself the Bible
Title: *Matthew: The Gospel of God's King*
Publisher: Moody Press, 1963

Num. Sess.	Group Time	Num. Pgs.	Avg. Qst.	Price	Audience	Format	Bible Study
12	60-90	96	48	3.99	New Christian	Workbk	Book

Features: Intro to Leading a Study, Exam
★★ Personal Application Preparation Time: Low ISBN: 0-8024-5212-4
★★ Relationship Building Ldr. Guide Avail.: No Size: 5.50 x 8.50
Subjects: Jesus: Life/Teaching, Matthew
Comments: The Gospel of Matthew serves as a bridge between Judaism and Christianity. Christ is presented as Mediator of a New Covenant, which began when His blood was shed. The format for this study includes fill-in-the-blank questions and checkups to test participants' grasp of scriptural truths. This twenty-five-book series is designed for self-study; however, suggestions for group study, and a four-year plan for using the series, are included.

Author: Brooks, Keith L.   **178**
Series: Teach Yourself the Bible
Title: *Philippians: The Epistle of Christian Joy*
Publisher: Moody Press, 1963

Num. Sess.	Group Time	Num. Pgs.	Avg. Qst.	Price	Audience	Format	Bible Study
8	45-60	48	24	3.99	New Christian	Workbk	Book

Features: Intro to Leading a Study, Exam
★★ Personal Application Preparation Time: Low ISBN: 0-8024-6506-4
★★ Relationship Building Ldr. Guide Avail.: No Size: 5.50 x 8.50
Subjects: Church Life, Joy, Philippians, Prison Epistles, Service, Suffering, Victorious Living
Comments: This study of Philippians—part of a twenty-five-book series—reflects Paul's affection for the first church he established. Participants will benefit from studying the problems Philippian believers encountered as their congregation grew. The format includes a series of fill-in-the-blank questions, and check-ups to test participants' grasp of scriptural truths. The series is designed for self-study; however, suggestions for group study are included.

Author: Brooks, Keith L.   **179**
Series: Teach Yourself the Bible
Title: *Practical Bible Doctrine*
Publisher: Moody Press, 1962

Num. Sess.	Group Time	Num. Pgs.	Avg. Qst.	Price	Audience	Format	Bible Study
12	60-75	80	33	3.99	New Christian	Workbk	Topical

Features: Intro to Leading a Study, Exam
★★ Personal Application Preparation Time: Low ISBN: 0-8024-6733-4
★★ Relationship Building Ldr. Guide Avail.: No Size: 5.50 x 8.50
Subjects: Apologetics, Eschatology, Holy Spirit, Satan
Comments: This study of practical Bible doctrine—part of a twenty-five-book series—was written for new believers. Subjects include the inspiration of Scripture, Christ's incarnation and second coming, the Holy Spirit, and Satan. The format includes a series of fill-in-the-blank questions, and checkups to test participants' grasp of scriptural truths. The series is designed for self-study; however, suggestions for group study, and a four-year plan for using the series, are included.

Author: Brooks, Keith L.   **180**
Series: Teach Yourself the Bible
Title: *Revelation: The Future Foretold*
Publisher: Moody Press, 1962

Num. Sess.	Group Time	Num. Pgs.	Avg. Qst.	Price	Audience	Format	Bible Study
12	45-60	80	23	3.99	New Christian	Workbk	Book

Features: Intro to Leading a Study, Exam
★★ Personal Application Preparation Time: Low ISBN: 0-8024-7308-3
★★ Relationship Building Ldr. Guide Avail.: No Size: 5.50 x 8.50
Subjects: Revelation
Comments: This study of Revelation—part of a twenty-five-book series—clarifies a believer's God-given future. Christ's return should encourage participants to serve Him through holy lives until that time. The format includes a series of fill-in-the-blank questions, and checkups to test participants' grasp of scriptural truths. The series is designed for self-study; however, suggestions for group study, and a four-year plan for using the series, are included.

Author: Brooks, Keith L.   **181**
Series: Teach Yourself the Bible
Title: *Romans: The Gospel for All*
Publisher: Moody Press, 1962

Num. Sess.	Group Time	Num. Pgs.	Avg. Qst.	Price	Audience	Format	Bible Study
12	60-90	80	40	3.99	New Christian	Workbk	Book

Features: Intro to Leading a Study, Intro to Study, Exam
★★ Personal Application   Preparation Time: Low   ISBN: 0-8024-7372-5
★★ Relationship Building   Ldr. Guide Avail.: No   Size: 5.50 x 8.50
Subjects: Faith, Grace, Romans, Theology
Comments: Paul prepared the way for his visit to a predominantly Gentile church in Rome with a letter. This letter, called Romans, systematically sets forth the doctrine of justification by faith. The format for this study—one of twenty-five in this series—includes fill-in-the-blank questions and checkups to test participants' grasp of scriptural truths. The series is designed for self-study; however, suggestions for group study, and a four-year plan of study, are included.

Author: Brown, David   **182**
Series: Serendipity Support Group
Title: *Newly Married: How to Have a Great First Year*
Publisher: Serendipity House, 1990

Num. Sess.	Group Time	Num. Pgs.	Avg. Qst.	Price	Audience	Format	Bible Study
14	60-90	96	12	5.45	Beginner	Workbk	Topical

Features: Intro to Leading a Study, Objectives, Bibliography, Prayer Helps, Full Scrpt Printed, Ldr's Notes, Cartoons, Agenda
★★★★ Personal Application   Preparation Time: None   ISBN:
★★★★ Relationship Building   Ldr. Guide Avail.: No   Size: 6.50 x 9.0
Subjects: Marriage, Young Marrieds
Comments: This study deals with issues common to couples in their first year of marriage. It shows how to make the year one of growth and not just painful adjustment. It deals with questions such as, "What happens when the wedding bells stop tolling, or when friends and family visit, or when you have to get down to the business of being married?" and, "How do you get to know each other?"

Author: Brown, William E.   **183**
Series:
Title: *Making Sense of Your Faith: Believing in an Age of Doubt*
Publisher: Victor Books, 1989

Num. Sess.	Group Time	Num. Pgs.	Avg. Qst.	Price	Audience	Format	Bible Study
13	60-90	177	6	6.99	New Christian	Book	Topical

Features: Intro to Study, Bibliography
★★★★ Personal Application   Preparation Time: Med   ISBN: 0-89693-624-4
★★★ Relationship Building   Ldr. Guide Avail.: Yes   Size: 5.50 x 8.0
Subjects: Apologetics, Faith, Heaven/Hell
Comments: This study will help participants make sense of their faith, and equip them to explain it to skeptical friends and loved ones. They will be challenged to understand answers to difficult questions such as: "How can we prove that God exists?" "Why should we trust the Bible?" "How can we be sure that there is a heaven?" and "Why is Jesus Christ the only way of salvation?" Participants are urged to become tough-minded Christians. A leader's guide with reproducible student response sheets is available.

Author: Bubna, Donald & Sarah Ricketts   **184**
Series: Living Studies
Title: *Building People Through a Caring, Sharing Fellowship*
Publisher: Tyndale House, 1978

Num. Sess.	Group Time	Num. Pgs.	Avg. Qst.	Price	Audience	Format	Bible Study
12	60-90	153	N/A	7.95	New Christian	Book	Topical

Features: No Grp Discussion Quest
★★ Personal Application   Preparation Time: Low   ISBN: 0-8423-0187-9
★★ Relationship Building   Ldr. Guide Avail.: No   Size: 5.0 x 8.0
Subjects: Leadership, Small Group Resource
Comments: This book responds to the question "What are we supposed to be doing, anyway?" and explores practical steps a church can take to become a caring, sharing fellowship. Chapter titles include: "Let's Eat Together!" "Talking Together," "Come Cry with Me," and "The Witnessing Church."

Author: Burnham, David & Sue   **185**
Series: Pacesetters
Title: *Convinced: New Directions for Active People from John*
Publisher: Tyndale House, 1975

Num. Sess.	Group Time	Num. Pgs.	Avg. Qst.	Price	Audience	Format	Bible Study
22	45-60	120	13	3.50	Beginner	Workbk	Book

Features: Intro to Leading a Study, Full Scrpt Printed
★★ Personal Application   Preparation Time: None   ISBN: 0-8423-0427-4
★★ Relationship Building   Ldr. Guide Avail.: No   Size: 3.50 x 8.0
Subjects: Jesus: Life/Teaching, John, Service
Comments: This study on John, "the beloved disciple" and eyewitness to Jesus' ministry, includes lesson titles like: "God Reveals Himself," "First Encounters," "Authority Unveiled," "A Religious Man Meets Jesus," "Samaritans Meet the Savior," "A Weighted Witness," and others, ending with a call to serve. Additional scripture for each lesson is listed in the back of this study. Pacesetters are small enough to carry and use in the midst of an active schedule.

Author: Burnham, David & Sue   **186**
Series: Pacesetters
Title: *Encouraged: New Directions for Active People from Psalms*
Publisher: Tyndale House, 1980

Num. Sess.	Group Time	Num. Pgs.	Avg. Qst.	Price	Audience	Format	Bible Study
10	45-60	74	13	2.95	Beginner	Workbk	Book

Features: Intro to Leading a Study, Full Scrpt Printed
★★ Personal Application   Preparation Time: None   ISBN: 0-8423-0762-1
★★ Relationship Building   Ldr. Guide Avail.: No   Size: 3.50 x 8.0
Subjects: God, Psalms
Comments: This study on Psalms includes lessons titled: "The Happy Person," "The Lord Is My Shepherd," "The Lord Is My Light," "The Rewards of Faith," "God's Plan for the Believer," "The Majesty of God," "The Lord Is My Refuge," and others. Additional scripture for each lesson is listed in the back of this study. Pacesetters are small enough to carry and use in the midst of an active schedule.

Author: Burnham, David & Sue   **187**
Series: Pacesetters
Title: *Equipped: New Directions for Active People from Ephesians*
Publisher: Tyndale House, 1978

Num. Sess.	Group Time	Num. Pgs.	Avg. Qst.	Price	Audience	Format	Bible Study
13	45-60	77	10	2.95	Beginner	Workbk	Book

Features: Intro to Leading a Study, Summary, Full Scrpt Printed
★★Personal Application   Preparation Time: None   ISBN: 0-8423-0772-9
★★Relationship Building   Ldr. Guide Avail.: No   Size: 3.50 x 8.0
Subjects: Ephesians, Prayer, Relationships
Comments: This study on Ephesians includes brief lessons on "Paul in Ephesus," "God's Master Plan," "Prayer and Power," "Death and Life," "Enemies No Longer," "Paul's Mission," "Paul's Prayer," and others. Additional scriptures for each lesson are listed in the back of this study. Pacesetter studies are small enough to carry and use in the midst of an active schedule.

Author: Burnham, David & Sue   **188**
Series: Pacesetters
Title: *Informed: New Directions for Active People from Luke*
Publisher: Tyndale House, 1978

Num. Sess.	Group Time	Num. Pgs.	Avg. Qst.	Price	Audience	Format	Bible Study
24	45-60	158	13	3.50	Beginner	Workbk	Book

Features: Intro to Leading a Study, Summary, Full Scrpt Printed
★★Personal Application   Preparation Time: None   ISBN: 0-8423-1599-3
★★Relationship Building   Ldr. Guide Avail.: No   Size: 3.50 x 8.0
Subjects: Forgiveness, Jesus: Life/Teaching, Love, Luke, Marriage
Comments: This study on Luke begins with two birth announcements, then moves through the childhood of Jesus, John the Baptist, the great temptation, a new lifestyle, true authority, compassion and forgiveness, freedom, discipleship, love in action, the Lord's Prayer, then through Jesus' life and ministry to His resurrection. Additional scriptures for each lesson are listed in the back of the study. Pacesetters are small enough to carry and use in the midst of an active schedule.

Author: Burnham, David & Sue   **189**
Series: Pacesetters
Title: *Motivated: New Directions for Active People from Acts*
Publisher: Tyndale House, 1978

Num. Sess.	Group Time	Num. Pgs.	Avg. Qst.	Price	Audience	Format	Bible Study
22	45-60	139	12	3.50	Beginner	Workbk	Book

Features: Intro to Leading a Study, Summary, Full Scrpt Printed
★★Personal Application   Preparation Time: None   ISBN: 0-8423-4557-4
★★Relationship Building   Ldr. Guide Avail.: No   Size: 3.50 x 8.0
Subjects: Acts, Church Life
Comments: This study on Acts includes lessons entitled: "Why Acts Was Written"; "The Church Prepares for Action"; "Pentecost: The Church Receives Power"; "The First Church Miracle"; "The First Persecution"; "Discipline in the Church"; and "Delegation in the Church." The study ends with a lesson on Paul's voyage to Rome. Additional scripture for each lesson is listed in the back of this study. Pacesetters are small enough to carry and use in the midst of an active schedule.

Author: Burnham, Sue   **190**
Series: Pacesetters
Title: *Energized: New Directions for Active People on Personal Growth*
Publisher: Tyndale House, 1981

Num. Sess.	Group Time	Num. Pgs.	Avg. Qst.	Price	Audience	Format	Bible Study
9	45-60	70	10	2.95	Beginner	Workbk	Topical

Features: Intro to Leading a Study, Summary, Full Scrpt Printed
★★Personal Application   Preparation Time: None   ISBN: 0-8423-0763-X
★★Relationship Building   Ldr. Guide Avail.: No   Size: 3.50 x 8.0
Subjects: Emotions, Relationships, Self-esteem, Stress, Victorious Living
Comments: This topical study, which deals with personal growth, includes lessons on self-worth, maturity in relationships, healthy anxiety, depression, anger, spiritual warfare, and power. Summary statements and additional scriptures for each chapter are listed in the back of this study. Pacesetters are small enough to carry and use in the midst of an active schedule.

Author: Bush, Barbara   **191**
Series: Woman's Workshop Series
Title: *Heart Trouble: Studies on Christian Character*
Publisher: Zondervan, 1985

Num. Sess.	Group Time	Num. Pgs.	Avg. Qst.	Price	Audience	Format	Bible Study
11	90-120	140	12	5.95	Beginner	Workbk	Topical

Features: Intro to Leading a Study, Digging Deeper Quest, Drawings
★★Personal Application   Preparation Time: Low   ISBN: 0-310-29431-2
★★Relationship Building   Ldr. Guide Avail.: No   Size: 5.25 x 8.0
Subjects: Christian Living, Emotions, Women's Issues
Comments: This study on Christian character—specifically the heart attitude—seeks biblical answers to questions about the heart. It probes and reveals: "What our habits reveal about us"; "If our actions speak of Christ in our lives"; "If our words expose heart disease such as envy or self-centeredness"; and "What the hidden intents of our hearts are." Participants will identify the kind of heart God intends for His children.

Author: Bush, Barbara   **192**
Series: Woman's Workshop Series
Title: *Mastering Motherhood*
Publisher: Zondervan, 1981

Num. Sess.	Group Time	Num. Pgs.	Avg. Qst.	Price	Audience	Format	Bible Study
14	60-90	165	9	6.95	Beginner	Workbk	Topical

Features: Intro to Leading a Study
★★Personal Application   Preparation Time: Med   ISBN: 0-310-43031-3
★★Relationship Building   Ldr. Guide Avail.: No   Size: 5.25 x 8.0
Subjects: Family, Parenting, Self-esteem, Women's Issues
Comments: This study on "mastering motherhood" investigates biblical patterns of parenting, and the roles and responsibilities of mothers in contemporary society. It will reassure mothers of their vital place in society, and renew their vision of motherhood as a strategic part of God's plan for the family. Chapter titles include: "Fighting the Current," "Preventive Discipline," and "Building Self-esteem in Children." A section titled "Before You Read On" is not recommended for group use.

Author: Bush, Laura DuVall   **193**
Series: A Bible Study for Women
Title: *Breaking Down the Walls*
Publisher: Victor Books, 1989

Num. Sess.	Group Time	Num. Pgs.	Avg. Qst.	Price	Audience	Format	Bible Study
9	60-75	95	Vry	5.99	New Christian	Workbk	Topical

Features: Intro to Leading a Study, Intro to Study, Prayer Helps, Study Overview, Follow Up, Ldr's Notes
★★★★ Personal Application   Preparation Time: Med   ISBN: 0-89693-669-4
★★★ Relationship Building   Ldr. Guide Avail.: No   Size: 6.0 x 9.0
Subjects: Ephesians, Relationships, Women's Issues
Comments: This study on relationships in Christ, from Ephesians, helps participants see how God breaks down walls of hostility, isolation, pride, immorality, and disunity that threaten healthy relationships. Participants' relationships with God enable them to develop relationships with others; and those relationships can only exist insofar as they are in Christ. Each lesson contains inductive study questions, a narrative section, and a five-day guide for follow-up study.

Author: Buswell, Sara   **194**
Series: Challenge Bible Study
Title: *Challenge of Old Testament Women 1, The*
Publisher: Baker Book House, 1986

Num. Sess.	Group Time	Num. Pgs.	Avg. Qst.	Price	Audience	Format	Bible Study
13	60-75	180	7	6.95	New Christian	Book	Charctr

Features: Intro to Study
★★ Personal Application   Preparation Time: Med   ISBN: 0-8010-0928-6
★★ Relationship Building   Ldr. Guide Avail.: No   Size: 5.25 x 7.50
Subjects: Bible Personalities, Obedience, Old Testament, Women's Issues
Comments: In this study, thirteen Old Testament women are examined for their relationships, circumstances, and personality traits—which apply today as well. The women are grouped into four categories: women of obedience (Sarah, Ruth, and Esther); women of disobedience (Eve and Lot's wife); women of subterfuge and deceit (Rebekah and Rachel); and women with a message (Deborah, Huldah, Miriam, Abigail, Naaman's maid, and Naomi). The study plan includes scripture passages and directions for using the questions.

Author: Buswell, Sara   **195**
Series: Challenge Bible Study
Title: *Challenge of Old Testament Women 2, The*
Publisher: Baker Book House, 1987

Num. Sess.	Group Time	Num. Pgs.	Avg. Qst.	Price	Audience	Format	Bible Study
13	60-75	190	7	6.95	New Christian	Book	Charctr

Features: Intro to Study
★★ Personal Application   Preparation Time: Med   ISBN: 0-8010-0932-4
★★ Relationship Building   Ldr. Guide Avail.: No   Size: 5.25 x 7.50
Subjects: Bible Personalities, Faith, Old Testament, Service, Women's Issues
Comments: In this study, fifteen Old Testament women are examined for their relationships, circumstances, and personality traits, which apply today as well. The women are grouped into four categories: women of faith (Hannah, the Shunammite woman, and Jochebed); women rejected or set aside (Hagar, Zipporah, Job's wife, and Leah); women of seduction (Delilah, Potiphar's wife, and Bathsheba); and women of hospitality (widow of Zarephath, Rahab, Deborah, Keturah, and Abishag).

Author: Buswell, Sara   **196**
Series: Challenge Bible Study
Title: *"Here Am I": Responding to God's Call*
Publisher: Baker Book House, 1989

Num. Sess.	Group Time	Num. Pgs.	Avg. Qst.	Price	Audience	Format	Bible Study
13	60-75	174	6	6.95	New Christian	Book	Charctr

Features: Intro to Study, Charts
★★ Personal Application   Preparation Time: Med   ISBN: 0-8010-0972-3
★★ Relationship Building   Ldr. Guide Avail.: No   Size: 5.25 x 7.50
Subjects: Bible Personalities, Men's Issues, Service
Comments: This study examines eleven Old and New Testament men whom God summoned to serve His Kingdom. They include Adam, Abraham, Isaac, Jacob, Joseph, Moses, Samuel, David, Isaiah, Ananias, and Jesus. After a study of these men, who humbly yet positively responded to God's call, the last chapter challenges participants to respond. In the study plan, questions precede each lesson; scripture passages, commentary, directions for using the questions, and selected hymns are included.

Author: Byram, Alice & Paula Rinehart   **197**
Series:
Title: *Healing the Broken Places*
Publisher: NavPress, 1988

Num. Sess.	Group Time	Num. Pgs.	Avg. Qst.	Price	Audience	Format	Bible Study
8	60-90	82	10	4.95	Beginner	Workbk	Topical

Features: Intro to Study, Bibliography, Follow Up
★★★ Personal Application   Preparation Time: Med   ISBN: 0-89109-147-5
★★ Relationship Building   Ldr. Guide Avail.: No   Size: 5.50 x 8.50
Subjects: Divorce, Forgiveness, Marriage, Women's Issues
Comments: This study for divorced women deals with the pain of rejection, confronting loss, coping with anger and forgiveness, and hope for tomorrow. God, who mends broken hearts, can help participants recover from divorce, and show how as well. Eight lessons and penetrating journaling exercises aid in the process of restoration.

Author: Cairns, JoAnn   **198**
Series:
Title: *Kingdom, the Power & the Glory, The*
Publisher: NavPress, 1989

Num. Sess.	Group Time	Num. Pgs.	Avg. Qst.	Price	Audience	Format	Bible Study
28	45-60	400	8	7.95	New Christian	Workbk	Topical

Features: Intro to Leading a Study, Intro to Study, Prayer Helps, Scrpt Memory Helps, Charts, Maps
★★★ Personal Application   Preparation Time: Med   ISBN: 0-89109-184-X
★★ Relationship Building   Ldr. Guide Avail.: Yes   Size: 7.0 x 9.0
Subjects: Devotionals, New Testament
Comments: This devotional journey through the New Testament includes twenty-eight lessons, each divided into five subdivisions which can be completed at one sitting. Charts help participants organize the information. The devotions follow significant people, places, and events of the New Testament; and result in a knowledge of Jesus Christ, not just as a historical figure but as Savior, Lord, and Friend. It's ideal for personal devotional study, or for group use, through a detailed leader's guide.

Author: Cairns, JoAnn   **199**
Series:
Title: *Saints, Sinners, and a Sovereign God: A New Look at the Old Testament*
Publisher: NavPress, 1988

Num. Sess.	Group Time	Num. Pgs.	Avg. Qst.	Price	Audience	Format	Bible Study
24	45-60	400	10	7.95	New Christian	Workbk	Topical

Features: Intro to Leading a Study, Prayer Helps, Scrpt Memory Helps, Charts
  ★★★ Personal Application   Preparation Time: Med   ISBN: 0-89109-186-6
   ★★ Relationship Building   Ldr. Guide Avail.: Yes   Size: 7.0 x 9.0
Subjects: Bible Personalities, Old Testament
Comments: This study of the Old Testament is for personal use during daily quiet time, or in a group Bible study. Participants spending twenty to thirty minutes a day will cover Genesis to Malachi in twenty-four weeks. In this topical overview, participants are challenged by the faith of Old Testament men and women who put their lives on the line and came to know God in an intimate way. A comprehensive leader's guide is available.

Author: Campbell, Donald K.   **200**
Series:
Title: *Joshua: Leader Under Fire*
Publisher: Victor Books, 1981

Num. Sess.	Group Time	Num. Pgs.	Avg. Qst.	Price	Audience	Format	Bible Study
13	60-75	143	N/A	7.99	New Christian	Book	Book

Features: Intro to Study
 ★★★★ Personal Application   Preparation Time: Low   ISBN: 0-89693-502-7
   ★★★ Relationship Building   Ldr. Guide Avail.: Yes   Size: 5.50 x 8.0
Subjects: Faith, Joshua, Leadership
Comments: This thirteen-week study helps participants strive to be courageous like Joshua, a man who stands out among Bible characters as vigorous, forthright, and fearless. His tasks, like those of modern believers, were not easy; he needed strong faith in God and persistence. Studying Joshua, participants learn leadership under fire, how to trust God as they face the hard tasks, and how to persevere in the midst of opposition. The leader's guide has many helps and reproducible transparency masters.

Author: Campbell, Donald K.   **201**
Series:
Title: *Judges: Leaders in Crisis Times*
Publisher: Victor Books, 1989

Num. Sess.	Group Time	Num. Pgs.	Avg. Qst.	Price	Audience	Format	Bible Study
13	60-90	178	N/A	6.99	New Christian	Book	Book

Features: Study Overview, Maps
  ★★★ Personal Application   Preparation Time: Med   ISBN: 0-89693-741-0
  ★★★ Relationship Building   Ldr. Guide Avail.: Yes   Size: 5.50 x 8.0
Subjects: Bible Personalities, Judges, Service
Comments: This is a study of Judges, a book that offers practical advice to modern culture. Written to a generation much like this one, Judges provides, as role models, men and women who faithfully served God in dark and ugly times. These men and women—such as Deborah, Gideon, Jephthah, and Samson—show participants how to live for God in an increasingly secular and pagan society.

Author: Campbell, Dr. Ross   **202**
Series:
Title: *How to Really Love Your Child*
Publisher: Victor Books, 1977

Num. Sess.	Group Time	Num. Pgs.	Avg. Qst.	Price	Audience	Format	Bible Study
13	60-75	132	N/A	6.99	New Christian	Book	Topical

Features: Intro to Study
 ★★★★ Personal Application   Preparation Time: Low   ISBN: 0-88207-751-1
 ★★★★ Relationship Building   Ldr. Guide Avail.: Yes   Size: 5.50 x 8.50
Subjects: Parenting, Wholeness
Comments: This thirteen-week study provides perspectives on parent-child relationships. Lessons detail three practical things that will help children feel loved and find emotional wholeness: the necessity of physical touch, positive eye contact, and how to give focused attention. The study is practical and immediately applicable. A leader's guide provides many helpful charts.

Author: Campbell, Pam & Stan   **203**
Series: BibleLog for Adults
Title: *Good News to Go (Book 2)*
Publisher: Victor Books, 1991

Num. Sess.	Group Time	Num. Pgs.	Avg. Qst.	Price	Audience	Format	Bible Study
13	60-75	180	Vry	6.99	New Christian	Workbk	Book

Features: Intro to Leading a Study, Prayer Helps, Scrpt Memory Helps, Pre-discussion Quest, Digging Deeper Quest, Summary, Ldr's Notes, Cartoons, Persnl Study Quest, Charts
 ★★★★ Personal Application   Preparation Time: Med   ISBN: 0-89693-868-9
   ★★★ Relationship Building   Ldr. Guide Avail.: No   Size: 6.0 x 9.0
Subjects: Bible Personalities, Church Life, New Testament, Prayer, Worship
Comments: This study—the second in a four-book series that propels adults through the New Testament in one year—covers Acts through 1 Corinthians. Leader's notes include icebreakers, study questions, suggestions for prayer, optional ideas, and assignments. Participants go on the road with Peter and Paul to study how the church began and why they're entitled to certain privileges as Christians, and to discover some guidelines for complicated areas of life.

Author: Campbell, Pam & Stan   **204**
Series: BibleLog for Adults
Title: *Home at Last (Book 4)*
Publisher: Victor Books, 1991

Num. Sess.	Group Time	Num. Pgs.	Avg. Qst.	Price	Audience	Format	Bible Study
13	60-75	180	Vry	6.99	New Christian	Workbk	Book

Features: Intro to Leading a Study, Prayer Helps, Scrpt Memory Helps, Pre-discussion Quest, Digging Deeper Quest, Summary, Ldr's Notes, Cartoons, Persnl Study Quest, Charts
 ★★★★ Personal Application   Preparation Time: Med   ISBN: 0-89693-870-0
   ★★★ Relationship Building   Ldr. Guide Avail.: No   Size: 6.0 x 9.0
Subjects: Faith, Heaven/Hell, New Testament
Comments: This study—the last in a four-book series that propels adults through the New Testament in one year—covers Hebrews through Revelation. Leader's notes include icebreakers, study questions, suggestions for prayer, optional ideas, and assignments. Participants will get a good overview of faith from a perspective of past, present, and future. Written like a travelog, the BibleLog series entertains while challenging adults to discover and apply Bible truths for themselves.

Author: Campbell, Pam & Stan   **205**
Series: BibleLog for Adults
Title: *Priority Mail (Book 3)*
Publisher: Victor Books, 1991

Num. Sess.	Group Time	Num. Pgs.	Avg. Qst.	Price	Audience	Format	Bible Study
13	60-75	180	Vry	6.99	New Christian	Workbk	Book

Features: Intro to Leading a Study, Prayer Helps, Scrpt Memory Helps, Pre-discussion Quest,Digging Deeper Quest, Summary, Ldr's Notes, Cartoons, Persnl Study Quest, Charts
★★★★ Personal Application   Preparation Time: Med   ISBN: 0-89693-869-7
★★★ Relationship Building   Ldr. Guide Avail.: No   Size: 6.0 x 9.0
Subjects: God's Promises, New Testament
Comments: The third in a four-book series that propels adults through the New Testament in one year, this study covers 2 Corinthians through Philemon. Leader's notes include icebreakers, study questions, suggestions for prayer, optional ideas, and assignments. Participants examine Paul's letters for practical advice, deep truths, and incredible promises. Written like a travelog, the BibleLog series entertains and challenges adults to discover and apply Bible truths for themselves.

Author: Campbell, Pam & Stan   **206**
Series: BibleLog for Adults
Title: *When God Left Footprints (Book 1)*
Publisher: Victor Books, 1991

Num. Sess.	Group Time	Num. Pgs.	Avg. Qst.	Price	Audience	Format	Bible Study
13	60-75	180	Vry	6.99	New Christian	Workbk	Book

Features: Intro to Leading a Study, Objectives, Prayer Helps, Scrpt Memory Helps, Pre-discussion Quest, Digging Deeper Quest, Summary, Ldr's Notes, Cartoons, Persnl Study Quest, Charts
★★★★ Personal Application   Preparation Time: Med   ISBN: 0-89693-867-0
★★★ Relationship Building   Ldr. Guide Avail.: No   Size: 6.0 x 9.0
Subjects: Gospels, Jesus: Life/Teaching, New Testament, Relationships
Comments: This study—the initial volume in a four-book series that propels adults through the New Testament in one year—covers Matthew through John. Leader's notes include icebreakers, study questions, suggestions for prayer, optional ideas, and assignments. Participants get a behind-the-scenes comparison of Matthew, Mark, Luke, and John's pictures of the unique character of Jesus. Written like a travelog, the BibleLog series entertains while challenging adults to discover and apply Bible truths.

Author: Campbell, Roger   **207**
Series:
Title: *Staying Positive in a Negative World*
Publisher: Victor Books, 1984

Num. Sess.	Group Time	Num. Pgs.	Avg. Qst.	Price	Audience	Format	Bible Study
13	60-75	129	N/A	6.99	New Christian	Book	Topical

Features: Intro to Study
★★★★ Personal Application   Preparation Time: Low   ISBN: 0-89693-377-6
★★★ Relationship Building   Ldr. Guide Avail.: Yes   Size: 5.50 x 8.0
Subjects: Emotions, Joy, Relationships
Comments: This thirteen-week study helps participants struggling with negative attitudes replace them with healthy, God-honoring positive attitudes. It addresses attitudes which, if allowed to continue, can devastate people emotionally and physically and affect their relationships with others, their churches, and other institutions. The final lessons challenge participants to a changed life full of adventure and joy. A leader's guide includes transparency masters.

Author: Campbell, Ross, M.D.   **208**
Series:
Title: *How to Really Love Your Teenager*
Publisher: Victor Books, 1981

Num. Sess.	Group Time	Num. Pgs.	Avg. Qst.	Price	Audience	Format	Bible Study
13	60-90	132	N/A	6.99	Beginner	Book	Topical

Features:
★★★ Personal Application   Preparation Time: Med   ISBN: 0-88207-274-9
★★★ Relationship Building   Ldr. Guide Avail.: Yes   Size: 5.50 x 8.0
Subjects: Parenting, Teens: Psychology, Teens: Self-esteem
Comments: This study will help parents communicate unconditional love to their teens, thus giving their teens a greater sense of worth. It addresses topics such as unconditional love, focused attention, showing affection, encouraging teens spiritually and intellectually, and causes and cures for teen depression and teenage anger. A leader's guide with transparency masters is available.

Author: Campbell, Stan   **209**
Series: Any Old Time
Title: *Any Old Time (Book 4)*
Publisher: Victor Books, 1985

Num. Sess.	Group Time	Num. Pgs.	Avg. Qst.	Price	Audience	Format	Bible Study
15	30-45	80	Vry	9.99	Beginner	Book	Topical

Features: Intro to Study, Objectives, Bibliography, Prayer Helps, Study Overview, Digging Deeper Quest, Ldr's Notes
★★★★ Personal Application   Preparation Time: None   ISBN: 0-89693-640-6
★★★★ Relationship Building   Ldr. Guide Avail.: No   Size: 8.50 x 11.0
Subjects: Teens: Junior High, Teens: Senior High
Comments: Book four of the "Any Old Time" series can help youth group leaders plan for holiday and special event programs. The sessions are ready to use and contain opening games, warm-up activities, relevant Bible application, and a wrap-up section. Included are studies for the following holidays and special events: Christmas (two sessions), Easter (two sessions), New Year's, Halloween, Independence Day, Valentine's Day, church picnic, Thanksgiving, Labor Day, Mother's Day, Father's Day, and graduation.

Author: Campbell, Stan   **210**
Series: Any Old Time
Title: *Any Old Time (Book 3)*
Publisher: Victor Books, 1985

Num. Sess.	Group Time	Num. Pgs.	Avg. Qst.	Price	Audience	Format	Bible Study
16	30-45	80	Vry	9.99	Beginner	Book	Topical

Features: Intro to Study, Objectives, Bibliography, Study Overview, Digging Deeper Quest, Ldr's Notes
★★★★ Personal Application   Preparation Time: None   ISBN: 0-88207-648-5
★★★★ Relationship Building   Ldr. Guide Avail.: No   Size: 8.50 x 11.0
Subjects: Teens: Emotions, Teens: Junior High, Teens: Relationships, Teens: Senior High
Comments: These sixteen creative lessons for youth are designed to be used independently or as four separate four-part units, each focused on a central theme. Each session contains opening games, warm-up activities, biblical application, and a wrap-up section. Topics include fear, priorities, self-effort, death, dating, evolution, abundant life, faith, preparing for the future, building stronger friendships, showing love at home, judgment and the will of God, and handling problems.

Author: Campbell, Stan   **211**
Series: BibleLog Series
Title: *Fighters & Writers (Book 3)*
Publisher: Victor Books, 1988

Num. Sess.	Group Time	Num. Pgs.	Avg. Qst.	Price	Audience	Format	Bible Study
13	60-75	142	Vry	5.99	Beginner	Workbk	Book

Features: Intro to Study, Cartoons
★★★ Personal Application   Preparation Time: Med   ISBN: 0-89693-863-8
★★★ Relationship Building   Ldr. Guide Avail.: Yes   Size: 5.50 x 8.0
Subjects: Teens: Bible/Pers., Teens: Old Testament, Teens: Sexuality
Comments: This study—part of an eight-book Old and New Testament series for youth—covers Ezra to Song of Songs. Each session includes three steps: focus—on the topic; discovering—interactive Bible study; and response—application. Through Ezra, Nehemiah, Esther, and Job, participants come face to face with pain, joy, sex, death, and hope. Written like a travelog, this series entertains while providing students with indelible Bible stories and truth.

Author: Campbell, Stan   **212**
Series: BibleLog Series
Title: *From the Desk of the Apostle Paul (Book 7)*
Publisher: Victor Books, 1989

Num. Sess.	Group Time	Num. Pgs.	Avg. Qst.	Price	Audience	Format	Bible Study
13	60-75	154	Vry	5.99	Beginner	Workbk	Book

Features: Intro to Study, Cartoons
★★★ Personal Application   Preparation Time: Med   ISBN: 0-89693-386-5
★★★ Relationship Building   Ldr. Guide Avail.: Yes   Size: 5.50 x 8.0
Subjects: Teens: Bible/Pers., Teens: New Testament
Comments: This study—part of an eight-book Old and New Testament series for youth—covers 2 Corinthians through Philemon. Each session includes three steps: focus—on the topic; discovering—interactive Bible study; and response—application. Participants see Paul's ancient letters with their modern applicability, still full of hope and incredible promise. Written like a travelog, this series entertains while giving students indelible Bible stories and truth.

Author: Campbell, Stan   **213**
Series: BibleLog Series
Title: *Growing Pains: The Church Hits the Road (Book 6)*
Publisher: Victor Books, 1989

Num. Sess.	Group Time	Num. Pgs.	Avg. Qst.	Price	Audience	Format	Bible Study
13	60-75	154	Vry	5.99	Beginner	Workbk	Book

Features: Intro to Study, Cartoons
★★★ Personal Application   Preparation Time: Med   ISBN: 0-89693-384-9
★★★ Relationship Building   Ldr. Guide Avail.: Yes   Size: 5.50 x 8.0
Subjects: Teens: Bible/Pers., Teens: New Testament
Comments: This study—part of an eight-book Old and New Testament series for youth—covers Acts through 1 Corinthians. Each session includes three steps: focus—on the topic; discovering—interactive Bible study; and response—or application. Participants go "on the road" with Peter and Paul, to see how the Church was started, and find out why they are entitled to many privileges as Christians. Written like a travelog, this series entertains while providing students with indelible Bible stories and truth.

Author: Campbell, Stan   **214**
Series: Young Teen Feedback Elective
Title: *Higher Love (Leader's Book)*
Publisher: Victor Books, 1991

Num. Sess.	Group Time	Num. Pgs.	Avg. Qst.	Price	Audience	Format	Bible Study
12	60-90	128	Vry	12.99	New Christian	Workbk	Topical

Features: Intro to Leading a Study, Objectives, Pre-discussion Quest, Digging Deeper Quest, Follow Up, Summary, Ldr's Notes, Handouts
★★★★ Personal Application   Preparation Time: Med   ISBN: 0-89693-789-5
★★★★ Relationship Building   Ldr. Guide Avail.: Yes   Size: 8.50 x 11.0
Subjects: Teens: Junior High, Teens: Relationships
Comments: This Young Teen Feedback Elective begins with the question "What is love?" It examines commonly held opinions of love and contrasts those with the biblical definition of love. This leader's book offers three four-week studies and includes reproducible student sheets.

Author: Campbell, Stan   **215**
Series: BibleLog Series
Title: *Jesus: God Undercover (Book 5)*
Publisher: Victor Books, 1989

Num. Sess.	Group Time	Num. Pgs.	Avg. Qst.	Price	Audience	Format	Bible Study
13	60-75	154	Vry	5.99	Beginner	Workbk	Book

Features: Intro to Study, Cartoons, Charts
★★★ Personal Application   Preparation Time: Med   ISBN: 0-89693-382-2
★★★ Relationship Building   Ldr. Guide Avail.: Yes   Size: 5.50 x 8.0
Subjects: Teens: Jesus' Life, Teens: New Testament
Comments: This study—part of an eight-book Old and New Testament series for youth—covers Matthew through John. Each session includes three steps: focus—on the topic; discovering—interactive Bible study; and response—application. Participants get a behind-the-scenes comparison of Matthew, Mark, Luke, and John's picture of the unique character of Jesus. Written like a travelog, this series entertains while providing students with indelible Bible stories and truth.

Author: Campbell, Stan   **216**
Series: Young Teen Feedback Elective
Title: *Nobody Like Me (Leader's Book)*
Publisher: Victor Books, 1986

Num. Sess.	Group Time	Num. Pgs.	Avg. Qst.	Price	Audience	Format	Bible Study
12	30-45	86	Vry	12.99	New Christian	Book	Topical

Features: Intro to Study, Handouts
★★★★ Personal Application   Preparation Time: None   ISBN: 0-89693-188-9
★★★★ Relationship Building   Ldr. Guide Avail.: Yes   Size: 8.50 x 11.0
Subjects: Teens: Bible/Pers., Teens: Old Testament, Teens: Relationships, Teens: Self-image
Comments: This twelve-lesson study helps young teens discover God's answers to their self-image questions. It helps them deal with day-to-day problems like failure (based on Judges), image distorters (based on Bible characters), and popularity (based on Psalms). The format offers three four-week studies with reproducible student sheets. They can be used separately as short studies, or consecutively as a twelve-week elective. A student book is available.

Author: Campbell, Stan 217
Series: BibleLog Series
Title: *Saga Begins, The (Book 1)*
Publisher: Victor Books, 1988

Num. Sess.	Group Time	Num. Pgs.	Avg. Qst.	Price	Audience	Format	Bible Study
13	60-75	154	Vry	5.99	Beginner	Workbk	Book

Features: Intro to Study, Cartoons, Charts, Maps
★★★ Personal Application   Preparation Time: Med   ISBN: 0-89693-656-2
★★★ Relationship Building   Ldr. Guide Avail.: Yes   Size: 5.50 x 8.0
Subjects: Teens: Family, Teens: Old Testament, Teens: Relationships
Comments: This study—part of an eight-book Old and New Testament series for youth—covers Genesis through Ruth. Each session includes three steps: focus—on the topic; discovering—interactive Bible study; and response—application. Participants will study betrayal, homosexuality, rape, family problems, and other evils. Positive biblical examples will challenge them to handle pressures, take risks based on God's promises, identify opportunities, and develop loving relationships.

Author: Campbell, Stan 218
Series: BibleLog Series
Title: *Saga Never Ends, The (Book 8)*
Publisher: Victor Books, 1989

Num. Sess.	Group Time	Num. Pgs.	Avg. Qst.	Price	Audience	Format	Bible Study
13	60-75	154	Vry	5.99	Beginner	Workbk	Book

Features: Intro to Study, Cartoons
★★★ Personal Application   Preparation Time: Med   ISBN: 0-89693-388-1
★★★ Relationship Building   Ldr. Guide Avail.: Yes   Size: 5.50 x 8.0
Subjects: Teens: New Testament
Comments: This study—part of an eight-book Old and New Testament series for youth—covers Hebrews through Revelation. Each session includes three steps: focus—on the topic; discovering—interactive Bible study; and response—application. Participants move through the last nine books of the Bible, collecting valuable insights into the past, good advice for the present, and great expectations for the future.

Author: Campbell, Stan 219
Series: BibleLog Series
Title: *That's the Way the Kingdom Crumbles (Book 2)*
Publisher: Victor Books, 1988

Num. Sess.	Group Time	Num. Pgs.	Avg. Qst.	Price	Audience	Format	Bible Study
13	60-75	154	Vry	5.99	Beginner	Workbk	Book

Features: Intro to Study, Cartoons
★★★ Personal Application   Preparation Time: Med   ISBN: 0-89693-658-9
★★★ Relationship Building   Ldr. Guide Avail.: Yes   Size: 5.50 x 8.0
Subjects: Teens: Christian Liv, Teens: Old Testament
Comments: This study—part of an eight-book Old and New Testament series for youth—covers 1 Samuel through 2 Chronicles. Each session includes three steps: focus—on the topic; discovering—interactive Bible study; and response—application. Positive examples of people of faith who refused to crumble challenge participants to depend on God rather than themselves, learn to overcome failures, and face the future with courage.

Author: Campbell, Stan 220
Series: BibleLog Series
Title: *What's This World Coming To? (Book 4)*
Publisher: Victor Books, 1988

Num. Sess.	Group Time	Num. Pgs.	Avg. Qst.	Price	Audience	Format	Bible Study
13	60-72	154	Vry	5.99	Beginner	Workbk	Book

Features: Intro to Study, Cartoons
★★★ Personal Application   Preparation Time: Med   ISBN: 0-89693-865-4
★★★ Relationship Building   Ldr. Guide Avail.: Yes   Size: 5.50 x 8.0
Subjects: Teens: Old Testament
Comments: This study—part of an eight-book Old and New Testament series for youth—covers Isaiah through Malachi. Each session includes three steps: focus—on the topic; discovering—interactive Bible study; and response—application. Old Testament prophets foretell doom and destruction, as well as promises of God's provision and salvation. Participants learn about the relevance of those messages in contemporary society.

Author: Campolo, Anthony, Jr. 221
Series: Critical Issues Series
Title: *Power Delusion, The: A Serious Call to Consider Jesus' Approach to Power*
Publisher: Victor Books, 1983

Num. Sess.	Group Time	Num. Pgs.	Avg. Qst.	Price	Audience	Format	Bible Study
13	60-75	165	N/A	7.99	New Christian	Book	Topical

Features:
★★★★ Personal Application   Preparation Time: Med   ISBN: 0-88207-292-7
★★★★ Relationship Building   Ldr. Guide Avail.: Yes   Size: 5.50 x 8.0
Subjects: Relationships, Success, Wholeness
Comments: This study explores Christian attitudes concerning power. As participants struggle in a world that worships power—in the family, at school, in the office, at church, on the corporate level, or on the social scene—they will see that the worship of power is inherently wrong. They will be confronted by Christ, who emptied Himself of power and chose to triumph from a position of weakness—the Cross. A leader's guide with transparency masters is available.

Author: Campolo, Anthony, Jr. 222
Series:
Title: *Success Fantasy, The*
Publisher: Victor Books, 1980

Num. Sess.	Group Time	Num. Pgs.	Avg. Qst.	Price	Audience	Format	Bible Study
13	60-75	144	N/A	7.99	New Christian	Book	Topical

Features:
★★★★ Personal Application   Preparation Time: Low   ISBN: 0-88207-796-1
★★★ Relationship Building   Ldr. Guide Avail.: Yes   Size: 5.50 x 8.0
Subjects: Cults, Ethics, Singles Issues, Success
Comments: This study concerns success and how it is measured in contemporary culture. Chapter titles range from "School Daze" to "Symptoms of Mid-Life Males (and the Mid-Life Woman)" to "Single People" and finally "Throwaway People." Questions answered in the lessons include: Is success the birthright of the good? the blessing of God? the doctrine of a cult? or the way to wealth, power, and prestige? The leader's guide includes reproducible transparency masters.

Author: Campolo, Tony   **223**
Series: Video Curriculum Resource
Title: *You Can Make a Difference*
Publisher: Word, 1984

Num. Sess.	Group Time	Num. Pgs.	Avg. Qst.	Price	Audience	Format	Bible Study
13	60-90	N/A	Vry	159.99	Begi nner	Video	Topical

Features: Intro to Leading a Study, Prayer Helps, Scrpt Memory Helps, Follow Up, Book Incl, Video Study Guide
★★★★ Personal Application Preparation Time: Med ISBN: 8-01-900079-8
★★★★ Relationship Building Ldr. Guide Avail.: Yes Size: 10.0 x 12.50
Subjects: Teens: Senior High, Teens: Youth Life, Youth Life
Comments: This thirteen-session video study compels young people to come to grips with the issues of commitment, vocation, dating, and discipleship, and to use spiritual power to change their world. The kit includes two video cassettes, each containing two sessions; two audio cassettes—excerpts from the video used as discussion resources; a leader's guide with step-by-step instructions; a student guide; and a copy of the companion paperback by the same title.

Author: Canales, Isaac   **224**
Series: Global Issues
Title: *Multi-Ethnicity*
Publisher: InterVarsity, 1990

Num. Sess.	Group Time	Num. Pgs.	Avg. Qst.	Price	Audience	Format	Bible Study
6	45-60	48	13	4.95	Beginner	Workbk	Topical

Features: Intro to Leading a Study, Intro to Study, Bibliography, Prayer Helps, Follow Up
★ Personal Application Preparation Time: Low ISBN: 0-8308-4905-X
★ Relationship Building Ldr. Guide Avail.: No Size: 5.50 x 8.25
Subjects: Social Issues
Comments: This six-week study helps participants explore ethnic diversity. The introduction defines God's "theology of welcome" and suggests that Christians continue to reject it; it proposes that God's way for servants of His Kingdom is one in which all ethnicities live together as His people. Leaders should read first, to determine its appropriateness for their group.

Author: Cannon, Ann   **225**
Series: Group's Active Bible Curriculum
Title: *Peer Pressure*
Publisher: Group Publishing, 1990

Num. Sess.	Group Time	Num. Pgs.	Avg. Qst.	Price	Audience	Format	Bible Study
4	35-60	48	Vry	6.95	Beginner	Workbk	Topical

Features: Intro to Leading a Study, Intro to Study, Objectives, Study Overview, Ldr's Notes, Handouts, Agenda, Publicity Ideas
★★★ Personal Application Preparation Time: None ISBN: 1-559-45103-3
★★★ Relationship Building Ldr. Guide Avail.: No Size: 8.50 x 11.0
Subjects: Teens: Decisions, Teens: Friends, Teens: Junior High, Teens: Peer Pressure
Comments: This study equips young people to deal positively with peer pressure and helps them discover specific ways to stand up to friends' negative influences. Including lessons like "From Bad News to Good News," and "Keeping Friends While Making Good Decisions," it can be adapted for a Bible class or youth meeting. Activities and Bible studies are included as separate sheets that can be reproduced. The instructions are easy to follow and offer multiple options for teachers.

Author: Carlson, E. Roald   **226**
Series: Small Group Bible Studies
Title: *One Week*
Publisher: Augsburg Publishing House, 1978

Num. Sess.	Group Time	Num. Pgs.	Avg. Qst.	Price	Audience	Format	Bible Study
6	60-75	24	20	1.15	New Christian	Book	Topical

Features: Intro to Study, Prayer Helps
★★★ Personal Application Preparation Time: None ISBN:
★★★ Relationship Building Ldr. Guide Avail.: No Size: 8.50 x 5.50
Subjects: Holy Week, Jesus: Life/Teaching
Comments: This short, six-session study of Holy Week is taken from Mark and will aid in understanding Jesus' life by clearly showing Mark's record of the events of Holy Week. Participants get a close-up of what Jesus said and did—and what was done to Him. The purpose is to provide a better understanding of "the gospel of Jesus Christ, the Son of God" (1:1). Session topics include: the parade with palms, confrontation, signs of the end, devotion and desertion, the Crucifixion, and the Resurrection.

Author: Carney, Glandion   **227**
Series: Global Issues
Title: *Urbanization*
Publisher: InterVarsity, 1990

Num. Sess.	Group Time	Num. Pgs.	Avg. Qst.	Price	Audience	Format	Bible Study
6	45-60	48	12	4.95	Beginner	Workbk	Topical

Features: Intro to Leading a Study, Intro to Study, Bibliography, Follow Up
★★ Personal Application Preparation Time: Low ISBN: 0-8308-4904-1
★★ Relationship Building Ldr. Guide Avail.: No Size: 5.50 x 8.25
Subjects: Social Issues
Comments: This six-week study helps participants explore the pitfalls and possibilities of life in the city and the urban church's mission. It discusses cities' complex make-up—all types of religious, ethnic, educational, and economic backgrounds—which can confuse rural newcomers and others who move there because there's no place else to go. It shows them trapped in ghettos, with lost support systems and spiritual poverty. Leaders should read the study first, to determine appropriateness for their group.

Author: Cassady, David   **228**
Series: Group's Active Bible Curriculum
Title: *Faith for Tough Times*
Publisher: Group Publishing, 1991

Num. Sess.	Group Time	Num. Pgs.	Avg. Qst.	Price	Audience	Format	Bible Study
4	35-60	48	Vry	6.95	New Christian	Workbk	Topical

Features: Intro to Leading a Study, Intro to Study, Objectives, Study Overview, Ldr's Notes, Drawings, Handouts, Agenda, Publicity Ideas
★★★★ Personal Application Preparation Time: None ISBN: 1-559-45216-1
★★★★ Relationship Building Ldr. Guide Avail.: No Size: 8.50 x 11.0
Subjects: Teens: Christian Liv, Teens: Emotions, Teens: Senior High
Comments: This study helps senior high students learn how faith can help when life throws a curve. In the four-lesson study, youth will discover how faith can help them deal with tragedies or disasters, learn how to respond to people who ridicule their faith, explore ways to overcome sadness and depression, and grow closer to God as they learn how to develop their faith. Instructions are easy to follow and provide multiple options for teachers. No student books are required.

Author: Castleman, Robbie 229
Series: Fisherman Bible Studyguide
Title: *David: Man After God's Own Heart (Volume 2)*
Publisher: Shaw, 1981

Num. Sess.	Group Time	Num. Pgs.	Avg. Qst.	Price	Audience	Format	Bible Study
12	45-60	63	11	3.95	New Christian	Workbk	Charctr

Features: Intro to Leading a Study, Intro to Study, Maps
★★ Personal Application Preparation Time: Low ISBN: 0-87788-165-0
★★ Relationship Building Ldr. Guide Avail.: No Size: 5.0 x 8.25
Subjects: Bible Personalities, Forgiveness, God, Integrity, Success, 1 & 2 Samuel
Comments: This second of a two-part study on David picks up in 2 Samuel 6 and concludes with 1 Kings 2, with an optional study on Psalm 139. It shows how David the king learned to handle the pressures of success through guidance, rebuke, patience, forgiveness, and discipline. Participants can learn with David how to maintain personal integrity while coping with conflict and depression. By observing and learning from David's character and actions, people can learn to be God's kindred spirits—after God's own heart.

Author: Castleman, Robbie 230
Series: Fisherman Bible Studyguide
Title: *David: Man After God's Own Heart (Volume 1)*
Publisher: Shaw, 1981

Num. Sess.	Group Time	Num. Pgs.	Avg. Qst.	Price	Audience	Format	Bible Study
12	45-60	70	10	3.95	New Christian	Workbk	Charctr

Features: Intro to Leading a Study, Intro to Study, Prayer Helps, Maps
★★ Personal Application Preparation Time: None ISBN: 0-87788-164-2
★★ Relationship Building Ldr. Guide Avail.: No Size: 5.0 x 8.25
Subjects: Bible Personalities, God, Loneliness, Obedience, Success, 1 & 2 Samuel
Comments: This is the first of a two-volume study of the life of David. Continuing through 2 Samuel 5, with an optional study on Psalm 40, it is for people who are lonely, depressed, afraid, joyful, sorrowful, pressured, discouraged, successful, faithless, obedient, or disobedient. This volume deals with the preparation of David to become God's own king over Israel. At least twenty years passed between David's anointing and his coronation; he learned to deal with the pressure of uncertainty.

Author: Castleman, Robbie 231
Series: Fisherman Bible Studyguide
Title: *Elijah: Obedience in a Threatening World*
Publisher: Shaw, 1986

Num. Sess.	Group Time	Num. Pgs.	Avg. Qst.	Price	Audience	Format	Bible Study
10	45-60	64	10	3.95	New Christian	Workbk	Charctr

Features: Intro to Leading a Study, Intro to Study, Prayer Helps, Maps
★★ Personal Application Preparation Time: Low ISBN: 0-87788-218-5
★★ Relationship Building Ldr. Guide Avail.: No Size: 5.0 x 8.25
Subjects: Bible Personalities, Christian Living, Emotions, Faith, Obedience, Prayer
Comments: Examining Elijah's life as he experienced God's faithfulness and provision, this study will challenge Christians to be obedient to God, even in the midst of an unsympathetic culture. Elijah was human, a "man of like passion." He gave in to fear and depression and felt outnumbered, misunderstood, and insecure. But he found power in obedience and prayer. This character study offers strong guidance for those who want to build their faith and prayer life.

Author: Ceckowski, Karen 232
Series: Group's Active Bible Curriculum
Title: *Joy of Serving, The*
Publisher: Group Publishing, 1991

Num. Sess.	Group Time	Num. Pgs.	Avg. Qst.	Price	Audience	Format	Bible Study
4	35-60	46	Vry	6.95	New Christian	Workbk	Topical

Features: Intro to Leading a Study, Intro to Study, Objectives, Study Overview, Ldr's Notes, Drawings, Handouts, Agenda, Publicity Ideas
★★★★ Personal Application Preparation Time: None ISBN: 1-559-45210-2
★★★★ Relationship Building Ldr. Guide Avail.: No Size: 8.50 x 11.0
Subjects: Teens: Christian Liv, Teens: Senior High
Comments: This four-lesson study helps senior high students discover the excitement of serving others. Students will build self-worth as they discover the satisfaction of serving others, learn to serve with enthusiasm, explore Jesus' life of servanthood, and build confidence by accepting the challenge of helping others. Instructions are easy to follow and provide multiple options for teachers. No student books are required.

Author: Chilstrom, Herbert W. 233
Series: Men's Bible Study Series
Title: *Hebrews*
Publisher: Augsburg Publishing House, 1986

Num. Sess.	Group Time	Num. Pgs.	Avg. Qst.	Price	Audience	Format	Bible Study
10	30-45	48	8	3.0	New Christian	Workbk	Book

Features: Intro to Study, Prayer Helps, Summary
★★★★ Personal Application Preparation Time: None ISBN:
★★★★ Relationship Building Ldr. Guide Avail.: Yes Size: 4.50 x 9.50
Subjects: Faith, Hebrews, Men's Issues
Comments: This ten-lesson study provide's a better understanding of Hebrews, as it discusses six characteristics of the book. They include: an unknown author; a pattern unlike any other in the New Testament; and twin themes that dominate the letter. It may be used at prayer breakfasts, men's Bible study groups, or any other men's meetings.

Author: Chisholm, Gloria 234
Series: Crisispoints for Women
Title: *When You Can't Get Along*
Publisher: NavPress, 1990

Num. Sess.	Group Time	Num. Pgs.	Avg. Qst.	Price	Audience	Format	Bible Study
5	45-60	96	13	3.95	New Christian	Workbk	Topical

Features: Intro to Study, Bibliography, Prayer Helps, Pre-discussion Quest, Digging Deeper Quest
★★★★ Personal Application Preparation Time: Med ISBN: 0-89109-331-1
★★ Relationship Building Ldr. Guide Avail.: No Size: 4.25 x 7.0
Subjects: Relationships, Women's Issues
Comments: This five-lesson study—part of an eight-book series for women in crises—helps participants face conflict by exploring: past experiences, destructive and productive conflict, the proper perspective, blocked resolution, and healing. In the lessons, a magazine article format is followed by Bible study or discussion questions. Due to added sections on evaluation, additional study, and activities, six or seven sessions are recommended. The series is contemporary, nonthreatening, and easy to use.

Author: Cho, Dr. Paul Yonggi & Harold Hostetler   **235**
Series:
Title: *Successful Home Cell Groups*
Publisher: Bridge Publishing, 1981

Num. Sess.	Group Time	Num. Pgs.	Avg. Qst.	Price	Audience	Format	Bible Study
15	-	176	N/A	6.95		Book	No

Features:
    Personal Application   Preparation Time: ISBN: 0-88270-513-X
    Relationship Building   Ldr. Guide Avail.:   Size: 5.50 x 8.0
Subjects: Small Group Resource
Comments: This book describes how Dr. Cho was led to his dynamic principle of growth, and details everything necessary to make home cell groups work. Chapter titles include: "Personal Ambition: Key to Disaster"; "Selling the Program to the Church"; "Satan's Counterattack: The Seven Obstacles"; "Home Cell Groups"; "Motivating Lay Leadership"; and "Preaching to a Growing Church."

Author: Christensen, Chuck & Winnie   **236**
Series: Fisherman Bible Studyguide
Title: *Acts 1-12: God Moves in the Early Church*
Publisher: Shaw, 1979

Num. Sess.	Group Time	Num. Pgs.	Avg. Qst.	Price	Audience	Format	Bible Study
15	45-60	68	9	3.95	New Christian	Workbk	Book

Features: Intro to Leading a Study, Intro to Study, Prayer Helps, Maps
  ★★Personal Application   Preparation Time: None   ISBN: 0-87788-007-7
  ★★Relationship Building   Ldr. Guide Avail.: No   Size: 5.0 x 8.25
Subjects: Acts, Church Life, Holy Spirit, Joy, Service
Comments: In this study of Acts, groups will discuss the successes and failures of the New Testament church and will encourage the same power in today's local church. In the chapter-by-chapter study Luke, the author of Acts, lays down the pattern for local church life: a community of joyful believers; empowered by the Spirit; serving the Lord and one another; actively enlarging their circle of fellowship; tasting both persecution and God's protection; and participating in His supernatural work.

Author: Christensen, Chuck & Winnie   **237**
Series: Fisherman Bible Studyguide
Title: *James: Faith in Action*
Publisher: Shaw, 1975

Num. Sess.	Group Time	Num. Pgs.	Avg. Qst.	Price	Audience	Format	Bible Study
10	45-60	55	7	3.95	New Christian	Workbk	Book

Features: Intro to Leading a Study, Intro to Study, Prayer Helps, Follow Up
  ★★Personal Application   Preparation Time: Low   ISBN: 0-87788-421-8
  ★★Relationship Building   Ldr. Guide Avail.: No   Size: 5.0 x 8.25
Subjects: Faith, James
Comments: This study of James centers on important goals for a mature Christian. Each chapter includes an introduction; goals—spiritual maturity and the victor's crown; and how the goals are achieved—dealing with hindrances, then calling faith into action. The "Putting It to Work" section following each segment provides an opportunity to apply the lessons in a modern world of instability, Christian infighting, materialism, and words without actions.

Author: Christensen, Chuck & Winnie   **238**
Series: Fisherman Bible Studyguide
Title: *Mark: God in Action*
Publisher: Shaw, 1972

Num. Sess.	Group Time	Num. Pgs.	Avg. Qst.	Price	Audience	Format	Bible Study
18	60-75	94	10	3.95	New Christian	Workbk	Book

Features: Intro to Leading a Study, Intro to Study, Prayer Helps, Maps
  ★★Personal Application   Preparation Time: None   ISBN: 0-87788-309-2
  ★★Relationship Building   Ldr. Guide Avail.: No   Size: 5.0 x 8.25
Subjects: Jesus: Life/Teaching, Mark
Comments: This chapter-by-chapter study, ideal for beginning groups, is fast paced and effective in describing the person of Jesus—His teaching, healing, feeding the hungry, defeating the Devil, and training disciples to carry on His life-giving activities in their personal lives, church, and community. It reveals the spiritual principles underlying the Savior's teaching. Jesus is portrayed as a total man through daily events, energy, strain, strength, compassion, and full dependency upon God the Father.

Author: Christensen, Chuck & Winnie   **239**
Series: Fisherman Bible Studyguide
Title: *Paul: Thirteenth Apostle*
Publisher: Shaw, 1986

Num. Sess.	Group Time	Num. Pgs.	Avg. Qst.	Price	Audience	Format	Bible Study
15	45-60	57	10	3.95	New Christian	Workbk	Charctr

Features: Intro to Leading a Study, Intro to Study, Prayer Helps, Maps
  ★★Personal Application   Preparation Time: None   ISBN: 0-87788-652-0
  ★★Relationship Building   Ldr. Guide Avail.: No   Size: 5.0 x 8.25
Subjects: Acts, Bible Personalities, Obedience
Comments: A chapter-by-chapter study of Acts 13-28 describes Paul as he is miraculously converted, then begins to minister, preach and write. Paul emerges as a dynamic leader used by God to spearhead Christian outreach to Gentiles. Paul faced many difficulties, from prison to shipwreck, but he learned to trust God for help and wisdom. Paul serves as a role model for God's called-for steadfastness under pressure in contemporary crises.

Author: Christensen, Winnie   **240**
Series: Fisherman Bible Studyguide
Title: *Women Who Achieved for God*
Publisher: Shaw, 1984

Num. Sess.	Group Time	Num. Pgs.	Avg. Qst.	Price	Audience	Format	Bible Study
14	45-60	83	11	3.95	Beginner	Workbk	Charctr

Features: Intro to Leading a Study, Intro to Study, Prayer Helps
  ★★Personal Application   Preparation Time: None   ISBN: 0-87788-937-6
  ★★Relationship Building   Ldr. Guide Avail.: No   Size: 5.0 x 8.25
Subjects: Bible Personalities, God, Obedience, Women's Issues
Comments: This study gives insights into lives of women of faith whose willingness to act upon God's leading make them achievers for Him. Some of the achievers are little-known women, such as Zelophehad's daughters. Others, such as Deborah and Esther, are well-known role models for Christian women today. This five-part study issues a challenge to participants to respond to God with the same obedience and courage as shown by these great women.

Author: Christensen, Winnie   **241**
Series: Fisherman Bible Studyguide
Title: *Women Who Believed God*
Publisher: Shaw, 1983

Num. Sess.	Group Time	Num. Pgs.	Avg. Qst.	Price	Audience	Format	Bible Study
13	45-60	77	12	3.95	Beginner	Workbk	Charctr

Features: Intro to Leading a Study, Intro to Study, Prayer Helps
  ★★ Personal Application Preparation Time: None ISBN: 0-87788-936-8
  ★★ Relationship Building Ldr. Guide Avail.: No Size: 5.0 x 8.25
Subjects: Bible Personalities, God, Prayer, Relationships, Women's Issues
Comments: This study is divided into six parts: an introduction, followed by lessons on women who overcame their past, women who prayed, women worshiping, women who developed positive family relationships, and women who never stopped growing. Each Bible character shares the following characteristics: a knowledge of the past, balanced perspective on the present, hope for the future, determination in spite of mistakes, and a personal relationship with God.

Author: Christenson, Evelyn   **242**
Series:
Title: *Gaining Through Losing*
Publisher: Victor Books, 1980

Num. Sess.	Group Time	Num. Pgs.	Avg. Qst.	Price	Audience	Format	Bible Study
13	90-120	180	N/A	6.99	New Christian	Workbk	Topical

Features: Intro to Study, Transpcy Masters, Cassette Avail
  ★★★★ Personal Application Preparation Time: Low ISBN: 0-88207-344-3
  ★★★★ Relationship Building Ldr. Guide Avail.: Yes Size: 5.50 x 8.0
Subjects: Christian Life, Divorce, Emotions, Failure, Faith, Grief, Money, Suffering, Women's Issues
Comments: This study shows how God can take life's disappointments and tragedies and turn them into unbelievable gains. Participants discover how such setbacks as death, separation, divorce, sickness, suffering, and financial loss can be used by God to make people spiritually richer. The study's gains-through-losing experiences are reinforced by biblical precepts. A leader's guide with transparency masters is available.

Author: Christenson, Evelyn   **243**
Series:
Title: *"Lord Change Me!"*
Publisher: Victor Books, 1977

Num. Sess.	Group Time	Num. Pgs.	Avg. Qst.	Price	Audience	Format	Bible Study
12	60-90	190	N/A	7.99	New Christian	Book	Topical

Features: Intro to Study, Prayer Helps
  ★★★★ Personal Application Preparation Time: Med ISBN: 0-88207-756-2
  ★★★ Relationship Building Ldr. Guide Avail.: Yes Size: 5.50 x 8.0
Subjects: Christian Living, God, Satan, Wisdom, Women's Issues
Comments: This study was developed out of fourteen months of life-changing personal experience with God. It outlines seven methods God uses to perfect His change, and how He provides direction and means for changing lives. It points out how either subconscious or deliberate ways of thinking can be influenced by other people, sensual selves, demons, or by God. Participants can identify their sources of instruction by wisdom produced in their lives—by how they are changed.

Author: Christenson, Evelyn   **244**
Series:
Title: *What Happens When Women Pray*
Publisher: Victor Books, 1975

Num. Sess.	Group Time	Num. Pgs.	Avg. Qst.	Price	Audience	Format	Bible Study
13	60-90	144	N/A	7.99	New Christian	Book	Topical

Features: Intro to Study
  ★★★★ Personal Application Preparation Time: Med ISBN: 0-88207-715-5
  ★★★★ Relationship Building Ldr. Guide Avail.: Yes Size: 5.50 x 8.0
Subjects: Prayer, Women's Issues
Comments: This study presents practical, yet thoroughly biblical lessons on prayer. It is based on experiences at prayer seminars that resulted in thousands of women learning to pray. Participants will learn what happens when prayer becomes a real dynamic in their lives and their churches. A leader's guide with transparency masters is available.

Author: Christenson, Larry   **245**
Series: Trinity Bible Series
Title: *Christ & His Church*
Publisher: Bethany House, 1973

Num. Sess.	Group Time	Num. Pgs.	Avg. Qst.	Price	Audience	Format	Bible Study
61	60-75	146	Vry	5.95	Beginner	Workbk	Book

Features: Intro to Leading a Study, Intro to Study, Scrpt Memory Helps, Exam
  ★★ Personal Application Preparation Time: Med ISBN:
  ★★ Relationship Building Ldr. Guide Avail.: Yes Size: 8.50 x 11.0
Subjects: Teens: New Testament
Comments: This study, at two lessons per week, leads youth through the entire New Testament in approximately one year. It's part of a three-study series that covers the entire Bible in three years. Each lesson includes reading for enjoyment; summarization of the main story line; answering fill-in-the-blank questions; noting, footnoting, and underlining important truths and teachings; and memorizing passages. The notebook structure provides an easy-to-use format. A test and an answer key are available.

Author: Christenson, Larry & Nordis   **246**
Series:
Title: *Christian Couple, The: A Study Guide*
Publisher: Bethany House, 1979

Num. Sess.	Group Time	Num. Pgs.	Avg. Qst.	Price	Audience	Format	Bible Study
8	45-60	44	2	1.50	New Christian	Workbk	Topical

Features: Intro to Study, Persnl Study Quest
  ★★★ Personal Application Preparation Time: Med ISBN: 0-87123-046-1
  ★★ Relationship Building Ldr. Guide Avail.: Yes Size: 5.0 x 8.0
Subjects: Commitments, Hope, Marriage, Sexual Issues
Comments: This study, prepared for use with the book by the same title, examines some important dynamics of husband-wife relationships. Lessons concern hope and difficulty, commitment, sexual relationship, love needing a boost, roles, unity, going on, and more. Both men and women are challenged to succeed as husbands and wives. Each lesson has a stated purpose, an introduction, personal assignment, and group discussion questions.

Author: Christenson, Larry   **247**
Series:
Title: *Christian Family, The*
Publisher: Bethany House, 1972

Num. Sess.	Group Time	Num. Pgs.	Avg. Qst.	Price	Audience	Format	Bible Study
9	60-90	63	Vry	2.95	New Christian	Workbk	Topical

Features: Intro to Study, Prayer Helps, Ldr's Notes, Appendix, Cassette Avail
★★★ Personal Application   Preparation Time: Med   ISBN: 0-87123-071-2
★★★ Relationship Building   Ldr. Guide Avail.: Yes   Size: 5.0 x 8.0
Subjects: Family, Relationships
Comments: This study, companion to the book by the same title, features two parts. The first consists of establishing "Divine Order" in the home, and has to do with the relationship of order and authority between the various members in a family. The second part is "Practicing the Presence of Jesus." The lessons lead participants through the two parts simultaneously, featuring consecutive readings from both parts. A guide for using companion cassettes is included.

Author: Christenson, Larry   **248**
Series: Trinity Bible Series
Title: *Covenant, The*
Publisher: Bethany House, 1973

Num. Sess.	Group Time	Num. Pgs.	Avg. Qst.	Price	Audience	Format	Bible Study
58	60-75	144	Vry	5.95	Beginner	Workbk	Book

Features: Intro to Leading a Study, Intro to Study, Scrpt Memory Helps, Exam
★★ Personal Application   Preparation Time: Med   ISBN:
★★ Relationship Building   Ldr. Guide Avail.: Yes   Size: 8.50 x 11.0
Subjects: Teens: Old Testament
Comments: This study, at two lessons per week, leads youth through the first half the Old Testament approximately in one year. It's part of a three-study series that covers the entire Bible in three years. Each lesson includes reading for enjoyment; summarization of the main story line; answering fill-in-the-blank questions; noting, footnoting, and underlining important truths and teachings; and memorizing passages. The notebook structure provides an easy-to-use format. A test and an answer key are available.

Author: Christenson, Larry   **249**
Series: Trinity Bible Series
Title: *Kingdom, The*
Publisher: Bethany House, 1972

Num. Sess.	Group Time	Num. Pgs.	Avg. Qst.	Price	Audience	Format	Bible Study
59	60-75	136	Vry	5.95	Beginner	Workbk	Book

Features: Intro to Leading a Study, Intro to Study, Scrpt Memory Helps, Exam
★★ Personal Application   Preparation Time: Med   ISBN:
★★ Relationship Building   Ldr. Guide Avail.: Yes   Size: 8.50 x 11.0
Subjects: Teens: Old Testament
Comments: This study, at two lessons per week, leads youth through the second half the Old Testament in approximately one year. It's part of a three-study series which covers the entire Bible in three years. Each lesson includes reading for enjoyment; summarization of the main story line; answering fill-in-the-blank questions; noting, footnoting, and underlining important truths and teachings; and memorizing passages. The notebook structure provides an easy-to-use format. A test and an answer key are available.

Author: Chromey, Rick   **250**
Series: Group's Active Bible Curriculum
Title: *Money: A Christian Perspective*
Publisher: Group Publishing, 1991

Num. Sess.	Group Time	Num. Pgs.	Avg. Qst.	Price	Audience	Format	Bible Study
4	35-60	48	Vry	6.95	New Christian	Workbk	Topical

Features: Intro to Leading a Study, Intro to Study, Objectives, Study Overview, Ldr's Notes, Drawings, Handouts, Agenda, Publicity Ideas
★★★★ Personal Application   Preparation Time: None   ISBN: 1-559-45212-9
★★★★ Relationship Building   Ldr. Guide Avail.: No   Size: 8.50 x 11.0
Subjects: Teens: Christian Liv, Teens: Senior High
Comments: This study helps senior high students learn to use money wisely. Its four lessons portray the dangers of materialism and greed, uncover students' feelings about money and wealth, explore how to become "rich" in God's eyes, and learn practical ways to manage personal spending. Instructions are easy to follow and provide multiple options for teachers. No student books are required.

Author: Church Discipleship Ministries   **251**
Series: The 2:7 Series
Title: *Growing Strong in God's Family*
Publisher: NavPress, 1974

Num. Sess.	Group Time	Num. Pgs.	Avg. Qst.	Price	Audience	Format	Bible Study
10	90-120	146	Vry	8.95	New Christian	Workbk	Topical

Features: Intro to Study, Scrpt Memory Helps, Follow Up, Summary, Ldr's Notes, Charts
★★★★ Personal Application   Preparation Time: Med   ISBN: 0-89109-165-3
★★★★ Relationship Building   Ldr. Guide Avail.: No   Size: 8.50 x 11.50
Subjects: Discipleship, Evangelism, Prayer, Relationships
Comments: This initial study of The 2:7 Series gives an introduction to the basics of Bible study, prayer, scripture memory, and devotional time. It covers memorization of verses, effective quiet time, development of an evangelistic prayer list, conversational prayer techniques, and more. Benefits include a closer relationship with God, a keener sense of priorities, renewed concern for nonChristian friends, and growing camaraderie with a study group. Leadership training for instructors is required.

Author: Church Discipleship Ministries   **252**
Series: The 2:7 Series
Title: *2:7 Series Course 2, The: The Growing Disciple*
Publisher: NavPress, 1979

Num. Sess.	Group Time	Num. Pgs.	Avg. Qst.	Price	Audience	Format	Bible Study
11	90-120	100	Vry	8.95	Mature Chrstn	Workbk	Topical

Features: Intro to Study, Scrpt Memory Helps, Summary, Charts
★★★★ Personal Application   Preparation Time: Med   ISBN: 0-89109-167-X
★★★★ Relationship Building   Ldr. Guide Avail.: Yes   Size: 8.50 x 11.50
Subjects: Discipleship, Fruit of the Spirit, Integrity
Comments: This is the second book in a five-book study that emphasizes Bible study, prayer, scripture memory, and devotional time. This course focuses on the call to fruitful living, friendship evangelism, love in action, purity of life, integrity in living, and more. Completion of courses 1 and 2 will give participants stronger foundations in Christian life, basic ministry skills, and presenting the gospel. Scripture cards and prayer sheets enhance the study. Leadership training for instructors is required. Not available in bookstores.

Author: Church Discipleship Ministries   **253**
Series: The 2:7 Series
Title: *2:7 Series Course 3, The: The Ministering Disciple*
Publisher: NavPress, 1979

Num. Sess.	Group Time	Num. Pgs.	Avg. Qst.	Price	Audience	Format	Bible Study
11	90-120	148	Vry	10.00	Mature Chrstn	Workbk	Topical

Features: Scrpt Memory Helps, Summary, Charts, Maps
★★★★ Personal Application   Preparation Time: Med   ISBN: 0-89109-168-8
★★★★ Relationship Building   Ldr. Guide Avail.: Yes   Size: 8.50 x 11.50
Subjects: Discipleship, Evangelism
Comments: This is the third book in a five-book study that emphasizes Bible study, prayer, scripture memory, and devotional time. This course focuses on fine-tuning witnessing skills, learning to effectively lead an evangelistic Bible study, building friendships with nonChristians, and world vision. It includes practical ways to stay involved with "the harvest"; scripture cards and forms are included. Leadership training for instructors is required. Not available in bookstores.

Author: Church Discipleship Ministries   **254**
Series: The 2:7 Series
Title: *2:7 Series Course 4, The: The Ministering Disciple*
Publisher: NavPress, 1979

Num. Sess.	Group Time	Num. Pgs.	Avg. Qst.	Price	Audience	Format	Bible Study
11	90-120	390	Vry	10.00	Mature Chrstn	Workbk	Book

Features: Scrpt Memory Helps, Summary, Charts
★★★★ Personal Application   Preparation Time: Med   ISBN: 0-89109-169-6
★★★★ Relationship Building   Ldr. Guide Avail.: Yes   Size: 8.50 x 11.50
Subjects: Bible Study, Discipleship
Comments: The fourth in a five-book study that emphasizes Bible study, prayer, scripture memory, and devotional time, this course focuses on how to minister in triads, how to minister one-on-one, how to do effective follow-up, and how to do inductive Bible Study. Scripture cards and forms are included. Leadership training for instructors is required. Not available in bookstores.

Author: Church Discipleship Ministries   **255**
Series: The 2:7 Series
Title: *2:7 Series Course 5, The: The Ministering Disciple*
Publisher: NavPress, 1979

Num. Sess.	Group Time	Num. Pgs.	Avg. Qst.	Price	Audience	Format	Bible Study
11	90-120	220	Vry	10.00	Mature Chrstn	Workbk	Book

Features: Scrpt Memory Helps, Summary
★★★★ Personal Application   Preparation Time: Med   ISBN: 0-89109-170-X
★★★★ Relationship Building   Ldr. Guide Avail.: Yes   Size: 8.50 x 11.50
Subjects: Discipleship, 1 & 2 Thessalonians
Comments: This final study in this series that emphasizes Bible study, prayer, scripture memory, and devotional time, surveys the book of 1 Thessalonians while teaching inductive Bible study and provides for extended prayer time. An evaluation of The 2:7 Series concludes the study. Scripture cards and forms are included. Leadership training for instructors is required. Not available in bookstores.

Author: Church Discipleship Ministries   **256**
Series: The 2:7 Series
Title: *2:7 Series Course 1, The: The Growing Disciple*
Publisher: NavPress, 1979

Num. Sess.	Group Time	Num. Pgs.	Avg. Qst.	Price	Audience	Format	Bible Study
11	90-120	116	Vry	8.95	Mature Chrstn	Workbk	Topical

Features: Intro to Study, Prayer Helps, Scrpt Memory Helps, Summary, Drawings, Cartoons
★★★★ Personal Application   Preparation Time: Med   ISBN: 0-89109-166-1
★★★★ Relationship Building   Ldr. Guide Avail.: Yes   Size: 8.50 x 11.50
Subjects: Discipleship, Prayer
Comments: This is the first of a five-book study that emphasizes Bible study, prayer, scripture memory, and devotional time. This course focuses on maturing in Christ, spiritual warfare, knowing God's will, preparing a personal testimony, prayer, and more. Completion of "Growing Strong in God's Family," the initial study in The 2:7 Series, is a prerequisite to the course, and leadership training is required for course instructors. Scripture cards and prayer sheets enhance the study. Not available in bookstores.

Author: Coddington, Dean & Donald Orvis   **257**
Series: Lay Action Ministry
Title: *Christianity in the Workplace: Your Faith on the Job*
Publisher: Lay Action Ministry Program, 1989

Num. Sess.	Group Time	Num. Pgs.	Avg. Qst.	Price	Audience	Format	Bible Study
12	60-90	128	Vry	5.95	New Christian	Workbk	Topical

Features: Ldr's Notes
★★★ Personal Application   Preparation Time: Low   ISBN: 0-89191-485-4
★★★ Relationship Building   Ldr. Guide Avail.: Yes   Size: 5.25 x 8.25
Subjects: Decision Making, Ethics, Faith, Relationships, Work
Comments: This practical study helps Christians relate their faith to tough career issues. Topics included are: biblical principles applied to job priorities and decision making; working spouses; relationships on the job; dealing with Christians in business; unemployment; ethical questions; changing careers; and more. This series helps equip and involve laypeople in ministry. Homework is recommended.

Author: Coleman, Lyman & Denny Rydberg   **258**
Series: Serendipity Youth
Title: *All the Way: On Discipleship*
Publisher: Serendipity House, 1989

Num. Sess.	Group Time	Num. Pgs.	Avg. Qst.	Price	Audience	Format	Bible Study
6	40-90	48	Vry	2.95	Beginner	Workbk	Topical

Features: Digging Deeper Quest, Full Scrpt Printed, Ldr's Notes, Photos
★★★★ Personal Application   Preparation Time: None   ISBN:
★★★★ Relationship Building   Ldr. Guide Avail.: No   Size: 6.50 x 9.25
Subjects: Teens: Discipleship, Teens: Junior High, Teens: Senior High
Comments: This study includes six lessons on discipleship, titled: "High adventure"; "Being available"; "Student athlete"; "Staying power"; "Breakfast of champions"; and "Giving it away." After a group-building introductory exercise, participants may opt for the "Basic Bible Study," which includes case studies followed by questions and selected scripture followed by questions, or the "Deeper Bible Study," a more in-depth study of applicable scripture concluding with personal application questions.

Author: Coleman, Lyman, et al.   **259**
Series: Serendipity Beginnings
Title: *Beginning a Basic Group: Six Sessions to Examine Your Faith*
Publisher: Serendipity House, 1991

Num. Sess.	Group Time	Num. Pgs.	Avg. Qst.	Price	Audience	Format	Bible Study
6	60-90	43	Vry	2.95	Beginner	Workbk	Topical

Features: Intro to Leading a Study, Objectives, Prayer Helps, Full Scrpt Printed, Drawings, Agenda
★★★★ Personal Application   Preparation Time: None   ISBN:
★★★★ Relationship Building   Ldr. Guide Avail.: No   Size: 6.50 x 8.25
Subjects: Christian Living, Faith, Small Group Resource
Comments: This is a six-session study designed to examine participants' faith. The lessons, which follow the Apostles' Creed, include "God, the Father," "Jesus Christ," "Holy Spirit," "Forgiveness of Sins," and "Resurrection of the Body and Life Everlasting." The format includes time for icebreakers, Bible study, and prayer. Timelines are provided for each lesson.

Author: Coleman, Lyman, et al.   **260**
Series: Serendipity Beginnings
Title: *Beginning a Serendipity Group: Six Sessions to Get Acquainted*
Publisher: Serendipity House, 1991

Num. Sess.	Group Time	Num. Pgs.	Avg. Qst.	Price	Audience	Format	Bible Study
6	60-90	43	Vry	2.95	Beginner	Workbk	Topical

Features: Intro to Leading a Study, Objectives, Prayer Helps, Full Scrpt Printed, Drawings, Agenda
★★★★ Personal Application   Preparation Time: None   ISBN:
★★★★ Relationship Building   Ldr. Guide Avail.: No   Size: 6.50 x 8.25
Subjects: Small Group Resource
Comments: This study teaches six ways for people to get acquainted and begin a small group. It begins with starting up and deciding on a covenant. The next four chapters deal with participants' spiritual condition—past, present, future—and needs. The closing chapter helps evaluate where the group goes as it progresses. The format includes time for icebreakers, Bible study, and prayer. Timelines are provided for each lesson.

Author: Coleman, Lyman & Denny Rydberg   **261**
Series: Serendipity Youth
Title: *Belonging: What's a Friend*
Publisher: Serendipity House, 1989

Num. Sess.	Group Time	Num. Pgs.	Avg. Qst.	Price	Audience	Format	Bible Study
6	40-90	48	Vry	2.95	Beginner	Workbk	Topical

Features: Digging Deeper Quest, Full Scrpt Printed, Ldr's Notes, Photos
★★★★ Personal Application   Preparation Time: None   ISBN:
★★★★ Relationship Building   Ldr. Guide Avail.: No   Size: 6.50 x 9.25
Subjects: Teens: Friends, Teens: Junior High, Teens: Relationships, Teens: Senior High
Comments: This study considers six areas of friendship: what a friend is, being friendly, building friends, breaking up fairly, loneliness, and the greatest friend. After a group-building introductory exercise, there are two options for study: "Basic Bible Study," which includes case studies followed by questions and selected scripture followed by questions; and "Deeper Bible Study," a more in-depth study of applicable scripture concluding with personal application questions.

Author: Coleman, Lyman & Denny Rydberg   **262**
Series: Serendipity Youth
Title: *Choices: On Morality*
Publisher: Serendipity House, 1989

Num. Sess.	Group Time	Num. Pgs.	Avg. Qst.	Price	Audience	Format	Bible Study
6	40-90	48	Vry	2.95	Beginner	Workbk	Topical

Features: Digging Deeper Quest, Full Scrpt Printed, Ldr's Notes, Photos
★★★★ Personal Application   Preparation Time: None   ISBN:
★★★★ Relationship Building   Ldr. Guide Avail.: No   Size: 6.50 x 9.25
Subjects: Teens: Christian Liv, Teens: Decisions, Teens: Ethics, Teens: Junior High, Teens: Sexuality
Comments: This study includes six lessons about choices on moral issues, titled: "Starting point"; Tempting choice"; "Your mind matters"; "Tongue control"; "Sex, sex, and sex"; and "Honest forgiveness." After a group-building introductory exercise, there are two options for study: "Basic Bible Study," which includes case studies followed by questions and selected scripture followed by questions; and "Deeper Bible Study," a more in-depth study of applicable scripture concluding with personal application questions.

Author: Coleman, Lyman & Denny Rydberg   **263**
Series: Serendipity Youth
Title: *Dear Me: On My Identity*
Publisher: Serendipity House, 1989

Num. Sess.	Group Time	Num. Pgs.	Avg. Qst.	Price	Audience	Format	Bible Study
7	40-90	48	Vry	2.95	Beginner	Workbk	Topical

Features: Digging Deeper Quest, Full Scrpt Printed, Ldr's Notes, Photos
★★★★ Personal Application   Preparation Time: None   ISBN:
★★★★ Relationship Building   Ldr. Guide Avail.: No   Size: 6.50 x 9.25
Subjects: Teens: Christian Liv, Teens: Junior High, Teens: Psychology, Teens: Self-image
Comments: This study considers seven areas teens face when evaluating their identities: their specialness, interest, abilities, problems, values, faith, and future. After a group-building introductory exercise, participants may choose a basic Bible study, which includes case studies followed by questions and selected scripture followed by questions, or a deeper Bible study, a more in-depth study of applicable scripture concluding with personal application questions.

Author: Coleman, Lyman & Richard Peace   **264**
Series: Mastering the Basics
Title: *Ephesians*
Publisher: Serendipity House, 1988

Num. Sess.	Group Time	Num. Pgs.	Avg. Qst.	Price	Audience	Format	Bible Study
7	60-75	64	Vry	5.95	Beginner	Workbk	Book

Features: Intro to Leading a Study, Intro to Study, Digging Deeper Quest, Summary, Full Scrpt Printed, Photos, Maps, Agenda
★★★ Personal Application   Preparation Time: Low   ISBN:
★★★ Relationship Building   Ldr. Guide Avail.: Yes   Size: 9.50 x 8.0
Subjects: Ephesians, Grace, Prison Epistles
Comments: This is a verse-by-verse, seven- or thirteen-week study of Ephesians, one of four letters known as the Prison Epistles. Paul, while in prison, wrote to churches in the Roman province of Asia. He discussed Christian living in terms of putting off the old man and putting on the new. "Mastering the Basics," a comprehensive, integrated program for personal or small group study, is expository teaching with a master teacher. Evangelism is demonstrated through the "empty chair" concept.

Author: Coleman, Lyman & Denny Rydberg   **265**
Series: Serendipity Youth
Title: *Go for It: On Becoming a Christian*
Publisher: Serendipity House, 1989

Num. Sess.	Group Time	Num. Pgs.	Avg. Qst.	Price	Audience	Format	Bible Study
7	40-90	48	Vry	2.95	Beginner	Workbk	Topical

Features: Digging Deeper Quest, Full Scrpt Printed, Ldr's Notes, Drawings, Photos
★★★★ Personal Application   Preparation Time: None   ISBN:
★★★★ Relationship Building   Ldr. Guide Avail.: No   Size: 6.50 x 9.25
Subjects: Teens: Christian Liv, Teens: Junior High
Comments: This study considers seven stages of commitments: beginnings, turning points, growing pains, struggles, life together, hanging in there, and next steps. After a group-building introductory exercise, participants can choose a basic Bible study, which includes case studies followed by questions and selected scripture followed by questions, or a deeper Bible study, a more in-depth study of applicable scripture concluding with personal application questions.

Author: Coleman, Lyman, et al.   **266**
Series: Serendipity Group
Title: *Gospel of Mark: Exploring the Life of Jesus*
Publisher: Serendipity House, 1989

Num. Sess.	Group Time	Num. Pgs.	Avg. Qst.	Price	Audience	Format	Bible Study
13	60-90	96	Vry	4.95	Beginner	Workbk	Book

Features: Intro to Study, Full Scrpt Printed
★★★ Personal Application   Preparation Time: None   ISBN:
★★★ Relationship Building   Ldr. Guide Avail.: No   Size: 6.50 x 9.0
Subjects: Jesus: Life/Teaching, Mark, Wholeness
Comments: This verse-by-verse, thirteen- or twenty-six-week study of Mark discusses biblical viewpoints on the identity of Jesus, radical lifestyles, values, conflict with "religious" people, wholeness, and why Jesus died. Three levels of discussion include "icebreakers," "digging deeper," and "reflection." Notes and commentary help participants with difficult words or passages. An insert—"Seven Common Small Group Ailments and How to Overcome Them"—is fun and provides direction for new groups.

Author: Coleman, Lyman & Denny Rydberg   **267**
Series: Serendipity Youth
Title: *Hassles: On Relationships*
Publisher: Serendipity House, 1989

Num. Sess.	Group Time	Num. Pgs.	Avg. Qst.	Price	Audience	Format	Bible Study
7	40-90	48	Vry	2.95	Beginner	Workbk	Topical

Features: Digging Deeper Quest, Full Scrpt Printed, Ldr's Notes, Photos
★★★★ Personal Application   Preparation Time: None   ISBN:
★★★★ Relationship Building   Ldr. Guide Avail.: No   Size: 6.50 x 9.25
Subjects: Teens: Relationships, Teens: Senior High, Teens: Youth Life
Comments: This study considers seven areas of relationships: life's headaches, family flare-ups, killer cliques, breakups, power plays, why me, Lord? and breaking free. After a group-building introductory exercise, participants are given two options for study: "Basic Bible Study," which includes case studies followed by questions and selected scripture followed by questions; and "Deeper Bible Study," a more in-depth study of applicable scripture concluding with personal application questions.

Author: Coleman, Lyman & Richard Peace   **268**
Series: Mastering the Basics
Title: *James*
Publisher: Serendipity House, 1986

Num. Sess.	Group Time	Num. Pgs.	Avg. Qst.	Price	Audience	Format	Bible Study
7	60-75	64	Vry	5.95	Beginner	Workbk	Book

Features: Intro to Leading a Study, Intro to Study, Digging Deeper Quest, Summary, Full Scrpt Printed, Photos, Maps, Agenda
★★★ Personal Application   Preparation Time: Low   ISBN:
★★★ Relationship Building   Ldr. Guide Avail.: Yes   Size: 9.50 x 8.0
Subjects: Ethics, Faith, James
Comments: This verse-by-verse, seven- or thirteen-week study on James reveals his ethical concerns regarding how Christian faith is to be lived daily. "Mastering the Basics," a comprehensive, integrated program for personal or small group study, is expository teaching with a master teacher. Evangelism is demonstrated through the "empty chair" concept.

Author: Coleman, Lyman & Richard Peace   **269**
Series: Mastering the Basics
Title: *Philippians*
Publisher: Serendipity House, 1986

Num. Sess.	Group Time	Num. Pgs.	Avg. Qst.	Price	Audience	Format	Bible Study
7	60-75	64	Vry	5.95	Beginner	Workbk	Book

Features: Intro to Leading a Study, Intro to Study, Digging Deeper Quest, Summary, Full Scrpt Printed, Photos, Maps, Agenda
★★★ Personal Application   Preparation Time: Low   ISBN:
★★★ Relationship Building   Ldr. Guide Avail.: Yes   Size: 9.50 x 8.0
Subjects: Joy, Philippians, Prison Epistles, Suffering, Victorious Living
Comments: This verse-by-verse, seven- or thirteen-week study is about Philippians, a book Paul wrote from prison to a church confronted with many problems. He helps them find joy in the midst of a hard situation, and also helps twentieth-century seekers put joy in perspective. Joy is not always equal to satisfaction. "Mastering the Basics," a comprehensive, integrated program for personal or small group study, is expository teaching with a master teacher. The "empty chair" concept demonstrates evangelism.

Author: Coleman, Lyman, et al.   **270**
Series: Serendipity Group
Title: *Philippians/Ephesians: Becoming a Caring Community*
Publisher: Serendipity House, 1989

Num. Sess.	Group Time	Num. Pgs.	Avg. Qst.	Price	Audience	Format	Bible Study
16	60-90	64	Vry	4.95	Beginner	Workbk	Book

Features: Intro to Study, Full Scrpt Printed
★★★ Personal Application   Preparation Time: None   ISBN:
★★★ Relationship Building   Ldr. Guide Avail.: No   Size: 6.50 x 9.0
Subjects: Caring, Ephesians, Joy, Philippians, Prison Epistles, Relationships, Stress
Comments: This verse-by-verse, eight- or ten-week study of Philippians and eight- or eleven-week study of Ephesians discusses biblical viewpoints on thriving in the midst of chaos, anxiety, stress management, discouragement, living with limits, honest relationships, and conflict resolution. Three levels of discussion include "icebreakers," "digging deeper," and "reflection." Notes and commentary help participants with difficult words or passages.

Author: Coleman, Lyman, et al.   **271**
Series: Serendipity Group
Title: *Revelation: Looking at the End of Time*
Publisher: Serendipity House, 1989

Num. Sess.	Group Time	Num. Pgs.	Avg. Qst.	Price	Audience	Format	Bible Study
13	60-90	96	Vry	4.95	Beginner	Workbk	Book

Features: Intro to Study, Full Scrpt Printed
★★★ Personal Application   Preparation Time: None   ISBN:
★★★ Relationship Building   Ldr. Guide Avail.: No   Size: 6.50 x 9.0
Subjects: Apocalyptic, Eschatology, Heaven/Hell, Revelation
Comments: This verse-by-verse, thirteen- or twenty-six-week study of Revelation discusses biblical viewpoints on Heaven, hell, wars and persecution, terror, tears, Final Judgment, Paradise found, and what difference they make. Three levels of discussion questions include "icebreakers," "digging deeper," and "reflection." Notes and commentary help participants with difficult words or passages. An insert—"Seven Common Small Group Ailments and How to Overcome Them"—is fun and provides direction for new groups.

Author: Coleman, Lyman & Richard Peace   **272**
Series: Mastering the Basics
Title: *Romans*
Publisher: Serendipity House, 1988

Num. Sess.	Group Time	Num. Pgs.	Avg. Qst.	Price	Audience	Format	Bible Study
13	60-75	128	Vry	5.95	Beginner	Workbk	Book

Features: Intro to Leading a Study, Intro to Study, Digging Deeper Quest, Summary, Full Scrpt Printed, Photos, Maps, Agenda
★★★ Personal Application   Preparation Time: Low   ISBN:
★★★ Relationship Building   Ldr. Guide Avail.: Yes   Size: 9.50 x 8.0
Subjects: Hope, Romans, Victorious Living
Comments: This verse-by-verse, thirteen- or twenty-eight-week study of Romans discusses how God will judge each person on the Final Day. Both justification and salvation are explored. "Mastering the Basics," a comprehensive, integrated program for personal or small group study, is expository teaching with a master teacher. Evangelism is demonstrated through the "empty chair" concept.

Author: Coleman, Lyman, et al.   **273**
Series: Serendipity Group
Title: *Romans: Discovering God's Plan for the World*
Publisher: Serendipity House, 1989

Num. Sess.	Group Time	Num. Pgs.	Avg. Qst.	Price	Audience	Format	Bible Study
15	60-90	80	Vry	4.95	Beginner	Workbk	Book

Features: Intro to Study, Full Scrpt Printed
★★★ Personal Application   Preparation Time: None   ISBN:
★★★ Relationship Building   Ldr. Guide Avail.: No   Size: 6.50 x 9.0
Subjects: Failure, Hope, Morals, Romans, Victorious Living
Comments: This verse-by-verse, fifteen- or twenty-seven-week study of Romans discusses biblical viewpoints on our responsibility to God's creation, moral failure, shame, inner conflict, hope, serenity, transformation, inner strength, and ultimate triumph. Three levels of discussion questions include "icebreakers," "digging deeper," and "reflection." Notes and commentary help participants with difficult words or passages.

Author: Coleman, Lyman & Denny Rydberg   **274**
Series: Serendipity Youth
Title: *Torn Between: On My Lifestyle*
Publisher: Serendipity House, 1989

Num. Sess.	Group Time	Num. Pgs.	Avg. Qst.	Price	Audience	Format	Bible Study
7	40-90	48	Vry	2.95	Beginner	Workbk	Topical

Features: Prayer Helps, Digging Deeper Quest, Full Scrpt Printed, Ldr's Notes, Drawings, Photos, Charts
★★★★ Personal Application   Preparation Time: None   ISBN:
★★★★ Relationship Building   Ldr. Guide Avail.: No   Size: 6.50 x 9.25
Subjects: Teens: Christian Liv, Teens: Junior High, Teens: Peer Pressure, Teens: Senior High
Comments: This study considers six areas that affect teenage lifestyle: peer pressure, priorities, possessions, prejudices, personal convictions, and power. After a group-building introductory exercise, there are two options for study: "Basic Bible Study," which includes case studies followed by questions and selected scripture followed by questions; and "Deeper Bible Study," a more in-depth study of applicable scripture concluding with personal application questions.

Author: Coleman, Lyman & Denny Rydberg   **275**
Series: Serendipity Youth
Title: *Up Front: On Tough Issues*
Publisher: Serendipity House, 1989

Num. Sess.	Group Time	Num. Pgs.	Avg. Qst.	Price	Audience	Format	Bible Study
7	40-90	48	Vry	2.95	Beginner	Workbk	Topical

Features: Prayer Helps, Digging Deeper Quest, Full Scrpt Printed, Ldr's Notes, Cartoons, Photos
★★★★ Personal Application   Preparation Time: None   ISBN:
★★★★ Relationship Building   Ldr. Guide Avail.: No   Size: 6.50 x 9.25
Subjects: Teens: Christian Liv, Teens: Cults, Teens:Drugs/Drinking, Teens: Emotions, Teens: Senior High
Comments: This study considers seven tough issues facing teens: greed, drugs/alcohol, lust, suicide, divorce, the occult, and death and dying. After a group-building introductory exercise, there are two options for study: "Basic Bible Study," which includes case studies followed by questions and selected scripture followed by questions; and "Deeper Bible Study," a more in-depth study of applicable scripture concluding with personal application questions.

Author: Coleman, Lyman   **276**
Series:
Title: *Youth Ministry Encyclopedia*
Publisher: Serendipity House, 1985

Num. Sess.	Group Time	Num. Pgs.	Avg. Qst.	Price	Audience	Format	Bible Study
48	35-60	240	Vry	19.95	Beginner	Book	No

Features: Digging Deeper Quest, Cartoons, Photos, Agenda
★★★★ Personal Application   Preparation Time: None   ISBN: 0-00-619822-8
★★★★ Relationship Building   Ldr. Guide Avail.: No   Size: 8.50 x 9.50
Subjects: Small Group Resource, Teens: Bible Study
Comments: The *Youth Ministry Encyclopedia* contains 200 group-building exercises for youth ministry leaders which have been gathered over a twenty-year period. Included are: 101 group games for starting youth meetings; 55 communication exercises for getting acquainted; 48 group Bible studies for small group discussions; schedules for staff training, retreats, week-long camps; and a six-session program for building a youth ministry team.

Author: Coleman, Lyman & Richard Peace 277
Series: Mastering the Basics
Title: *1 Corinthians*
Publisher: Serendipity House, 1988

Num. Sess.	Group Time	Num. Pgs.	Avg. Qst.	Price	Audience	Format	Bible Study
13	60-75	120	Vry	5.95	Beginner	Workbk	Book

Features: Intro to Leading a Study, Intro to Study, Digging Deeper Quest, Summary, Full Scrpt Printed, Photos, Maps, Agenda
★★★ Personal Application   Preparation Time: Low   ISBN:
★★★ Relationship Building   Ldr. Guide Avail.: Yes   Size: 9.50 x 8.0
Subjects: Christian Living, 1 Corinthians
Comments: This is a verse-by-verse, thirteen- or twenty-seven-week study of 1 Corinthians, a practical, issue-oriented letter in which Paul tells his readers what they ought and ought not do. "Mastering the Basics," a comprehensive, integrated series for personal or small group study, features expository teaching with a master teacher. Evangelism is demonstrated through the "empty chair" concept.

Author: Coleman, Lyman, et al. 278
Series: Serendipity Group
Title: *1 Corinthians: Taking On the Tough Issues*
Publisher: Serendipity House, 1989

Num. Sess.	Group Time	Num. Pgs.	Avg. Qst.	Price	Audience	Format	Bible Study
13	60-90	64	Vry	4.95	Beginner	Workbk	Book

Features: Intro to Study, Full Scrpt Printed
★★★ Personal Application   Preparation Time: None   ISBN:
★★★ Relationship Building   Ldr. Guide Avail.: No   Size: 6.50 x 9.0
Subjects: Addictions, Decision Making, Relationships, Sexual Issues, Spiritual Gifts, 1 Corinthians
Comments: This verse-by-verse, thirteen- or twenty-four-week study of 1 Corinthians discusses biblical viewpoints on sexual addiction, alcohol abuse, making choices, spiritual gifts, personal conflicts, legal battles, divided loyalty, death, and resurrection. Three levels of discussion questions include "icebreakers," "digging deeper," and "reflection." Notes and commentary help participants with difficult words or passages.

Author: Coleman, Lyman, et al. 279
Series: Serendipity Group
Title: *1 John/Galatians: Exposing Religious Counterfeits*
Publisher: Serendipity House, 1989

Num. Sess.	Group Time	Num. Pgs.	Avg. Qst.	Price	Audience	Format	Bible Study
12	60-90	64	Vry	4.95	Beginner	Workbk	Book

Features: Intro to Study, Full Scrpt Printed
★★★ Personal Application   Preparation Time: None   ISBN:
★★★ Relationship Building   Ldr. Guide Avail.: No   Size: 6.50 x 9.0
Subjects: Cults, Faith, False Teachers, Fruit of the Spirit, Galatians, Occult, 1, 2 & 3 John/Jude
Comments: This verse-by-verse, five- or eight-week study of 1 John and seven- or thirteen-week study of Galatians discusses biblical viewpoints on the New Age movement, cults, legalism, false teaching, what real community looks like, fruit of the Spirit, and perfect love. Three levels of discussion include "icebreakers," "digging deeper," and "reflection." Notes and commentary help participants with difficult words or passages.

Author: Coleman, Lyman & Richard Peace 280
Series: Mastering the Basics
Title: *1 Peter*
Publisher: Serendipity House, 1988

Num. Sess.	Group Time	Num. Pgs.	Avg. Qst.	Price	Audience	Format	Bible Study
7	60-75	64	Vry	5.95	Beginner	Workbk	Book

Features: Intro to Leading a Study, Intro to Study, Digging Deeper Quest, Summary, Full Scrpt Printed, Photos, Maps, Agenda
★★★ Personal Application   Preparation Time: Low   ISBN:
★★★ Relationship Building   Ldr. Guide Avail.: Yes   Size: 9.50 x 8.0
Subjects: Hope, Suffering, 1 & 2 Peter
Comments: Peter wrote his first letter to comfort and encourage Christians in the midst of "painful trials." Peter exhorts Christians to rejoice because of their great "hope." This verse-by-verse, seven- or ten-week study is a part of "Mastering the Basics," a comprehensive, integrated series for personal or small group study. Evangelism is demonstrated through the "empty chair" concept.

Author: Coleman, Lyman, et al. 281
Series: Serendipity Group
Title: *1 Peter/James: Living Through Difficult Times*
Publisher: Serendipity House, 1989

Num. Sess.	Group Time	Num. Pgs.	Avg. Qst.	Price	Audience	Format	Bible Study
16	60-90	62	Vry	4.95	Beginner	Workbk	Book

Features: Intro to Study, Full Scrpt Printed
★★★ Personal Application   Preparation Time: None   ISBN:
★★★ Relationship Building   Ldr. Guide Avail.: No   Size: 6.50 x 9.0
Subjects: Caring, Ethics, Failure, Hope, James, Suffering, Work, 1 & 2 Peter
Comments: This verse-by-verse, eight- or ten-week study of 1 Peter and eight- or twelve-week study of James discusses biblical viewpoints on coping when the world is against you, suffering abuse, embarrassment, failure, social ethics, faith at work, hope, caring for one another, and healing. Three levels of discussion include "icebreakers," "digging deeper," and "reflection." Notes and commentary help participants with difficult words or passages.

Author: Coleman, Lyman & Richard Peace 282
Series: Mastering the Basics
Title: *1 & 2 Timothy*
Publisher: Serendipity House, 1988

Num. Sess.	Group Time	Num. Pgs.	Avg. Qst.	Price	Audience	Format	Bible Study
7	60-75	64	Vry	5.95	Beginner	Workbk	Book

Features: Intro to Leading a Study, Intro to Study, Digging Deeper Quest, Summary, Full Scrpt Printed, Photos, Maps, Agenda
★★★ Personal Application   Preparation Time: Low   ISBN:
★★★ Relationship Building   Ldr. Guide Avail.: Yes   Size: 9.50 x 8.0
Subjects: False Teachers, Obedience, Pastoral Epistles, Service, 1 & 2 Timothy/Titus
Comments: The books of 1 and 2 Timothy, two of the Pastoral Epistles, were written by Paul. First Timothy gives instructions on how to cope with false teachers; 2 Timothy was written when Paul was in prison, lonely, and emploring Timothy to come to his side and accept the torch of his ministry. This verse-by-verse, seven- or thirteen-week study is part of "Mastering the Basics," a comprehensive, integrated program for personal or small group study. The series features expository teaching with a master teacher.

Author: Coleman, Lyman, et al.   **283**
Series: Serendipity Group
Title: *1 & 2 Timothy & Titus: Learning to Thrive in a Hostile World*
Publisher: Serendipity House, 1989

Num. Sess.	Group Time	Num. Pgs.	Avg. Qst.	Price	Audience	Format	Bible Study
16	60-90	64	Vry	4.95	Beginner	Workbk	Book

Features: Intro to Study, Full Scrpt Printed
  ★★★ Personal Application Preparation Time: None ISBN:
  ★★★ Relationship Building Ldr. Guide Avail.: No   Size: 6.50 x 9.0
Subjects: Leadership, Money, Pastoral Epistles, Sexual Issues, Stress, 1 & 2 Timothy/Titus
Comments: This verse-by-verse, six- or nine-week study of 1 Timothy, six-week study of 2 Timothy, and four-week study of Titus discusses biblical viewpoints on money, the opposite sex, pressure, leadership, excellence, spiritual disciplines, and staying on course. Three levels of discussion questions include "icebreakers," "digging deeper," and "reflection." Notes and commentary help participants with difficult words or passages.

Author: Collingridge, Ruth & JoAnne Sekowsky   **284**
Series: Workbook Series
Title: *Introduction to Praise: A New Look at the Old Discipline of Praise*
Publisher: Aglow, 1981

Num. Sess.	Group Time	Num. Pgs.	Avg. Qst.	Price	Audience	Format	Bible Study
11	60-75	79	15	5.95	Mature Chrstn	Workbk	Topical

Features: Intro to Study, Prayer Helps, Follow Up, Drawings, Persnl Study Quest, Charts, Cassette Avail
  ★★★ Personal Application Preparation Time: Med ISBN: 0-930756-60-6
  ★★★ Relationship Building Ldr. Guide Avail.: No   Size: 8.50 x 10.0
Subjects: Charismatic Interest, Obedience, Worship
Comments: This comprehensive ten-lesson study, plus one review lesson, will enrich participants' understanding of the form and function of praise and worship. Lessons reveal the importance of praise, why we should praise, and the different kinds of praise; how people's relationship with God deepens as they are obedient in praise and worship; and how praise helps set priorities straight, focus attention on God, and release His power. The emphasis is not theory, but practice.

Author: Colson, Charles   **285**
Series: Video Curriculum Resource
Title: *Against the Night: Living in the New Dark Ages*
Publisher: Word, 1989

Num. Sess.	Group Time	Num. Pgs.	Avg. Qst.	Price	Audience	Format	Bible Study
4	60-120	N/A	3	159.99	New Christian	Video	Topical

Features: Intro to Leading a Study, Video Study Guide, Book Avail
  ★★★★ Personal Application Preparation Time: None ISBN: 8-01-502079-4
  ★★ Relationship Building Ldr. Guide Avail.: No   Size: 10.25 x 12.50
Subjects: Church Life, Ethics, Family
Comments: This video study informs, challenges, and motivates Christians of all ages to be serious about reclaiming their cultures for Christ. The series, comprised of four forty-five-minute video sessions, analyzes the threat to Western civilization posed by relativism and individualism, and the role of Christians in countering this threat. A reproducible study guide includes outlines for each lecture, as well as questions for group discussion and their application.

Author: Connelly, Douglas   **286**
Series: LifeGuide Bible Study
Title: *Daniel: Spiritual Living in a Secular World*
Publisher: InterVarsity, 1986

Num. Sess.	Group Time	Num. Pgs.	Avg. Qst.	Price	Audience	Format	Bible Study
12	45-60	63	11	3.95	New Christian	Workbk	Book

Features: Intro to Leading a Study, Intro to Study, Ldr's Notes
  ★ Personal Application Preparation Time: Low ISBN: 0-8308-1031-5
  ★ Relationship Building Ldr. Guide Avail.: No   Size: 5.50 x 8.25
Subjects: Bible Personalities, Daniel, God, Major Prophets
Comments: This study is divided into two parts: Daniel 1-6 focuses on the life and character of Daniel as a "man" of God; Daniel 7-12 focuses on him as the "messenger" of God, and includes a series of visions given to Daniel for the Gentile nations and Israel. The study does not defend one particular prophetic system; rather, it uses Daniel to expand our understanding of God's program for the future of the world, and to promote trust in a Sovereign God for "our" future.

Author: Connelly, Douglas   **287**
Series: LifeGuide Bible Study
Title: *John: The Way to True Life*
Publisher: InterVarsity, 1990

Num. Sess.	Group Time	Num. Pgs.	Avg. Qst.	Price	Audience	Format	Bible Study
26	45-60	112	12	3.95	Beginner	Workbk	Topical

Features: Intro to Leading a Study, Intro to Study, Ldr's Notes
  ★★★ Personal Application Preparation Time: Low ISBN: 0-8308-1006-4
  ★★★ Relationship Building Ldr. Guide Avail.: No   Size: 5.50 x 8.25
Subjects: Gospels, Jesus: Life/Teaching, John
Comments: This chapter-by-chapter study of John is divided into two parts: Jesus, the living Word of God; and Jesus, the living Way to God. John encourages a fresh look at Jesus. Leaders are motivated to introduce their groups to John's gospel by comparing the four gospels in regard to authorship, audience, purpose, and message. In this way, emphasis can be placed on John's unique contribution to an understanding of Jesus Christ.

Author: Cooper, Darien B.   **288**
Series:
Title: *You Can Be the Wife of a Happy Husband*
Publisher: Victor Books, 1974

Num. Sess.	Group Time	Num. Pgs.	Avg. Qst.	Price	Audience	Format	Bible Study
13	60-75	156	N/A	7.99	New Christian	Book	Topical

Features: Intro to Study, Cassette Avail
  ★★★★ Personal Application Preparation Time: Low ISBN: 0-88207-711-2
  ★★★★ Relationship Building Ldr. Guide Avail.: Yes   Size: 5.50 x 8.0
Subjects: Joy, Marriage, Women's Issues
Comments: This thirteen-week study reviews biblical principles for a lasting, happy marriage, and promotes a clear understanding of a wife's responsibility. Lesson titles include: "Accepting Your Husband as He Is"; "Helping Your Husband Love Himself"; and "How to Handle Problems and Trials." The joy of marriage can last "till death do us part."

Author: Cosgrove, Francis M., Jr.   289
Series:
Title: *Essentials of Discipleship*
Publisher: Roper Press, 1989

Num. Sess.	Group Time	Num. Pgs.	Avg. Qst.	Price	Audience	Format	Bible Study
12	60-90	96	22	5.95	New Christian	Workbk	Topical

Features: Intro to Leading a Study, Prayer Helps, Scrpt Memory Helps
★★★★ Personal Application   Preparation Time: Med   ISBN: 0-86606-257-2
★★★★ Relationship Building Ldr. Guide Avail.: No   Size: 5.25 x 8.50
Subjects: Discipleship
Comments: This study of the book by the same title helps participants experience the great adventure of living for Christ and realize the honor of being called His disciples. It provides practical projects and methods for achieving the goal. It explains how to experience Christ's lordship, study the Bible, choose a church, enjoy true fellowship, memorize Scripture, and more.

Author: Couchman, Judith   290
Series: Crisispoints for Women
Title: *Getting a Grip on Guilt*
Publisher: NavPress, 1990

Num. Sess.	Group Time	Num. Pgs.	Avg. Qst.	Price	Audience	Format	Bible Study
4	45-60	96	15	3.95	New Christian	Workbk	Topical

Features: Intro to Study, Bibliography, Prayer Helps, Pre-discussion Quest, Follow Up
★★★★ Personal Application   Preparation Time: Med   ISBN: 0-89109-324-9
★★ Relationship Building Ldr. Guide Avail.: No   Size: 4.25 x 7.0
Subjects: Emotions, Forgiveness, Repentance, Women's Issues
Comments: This four-lesson study—part of an eight-book series for women in crises—helps participants tackle guilt; identify areas of guilt; determine if guilt is true or false; face results of true guilt; and confess, repent, and accept forgiveness. In the lessons, a magazine article format is followed by Bible study or discussion questions. Due to added sections on evaluation, additional study, and activities, five or six sessions are recommended. The series is contemporary, nonthreatening, and easy to use.

Author: Coyle, Neva   291
Series: Free to Be Thin
Title: *Abiding: Honesty in Relationship*
Publisher: Bethany House, 1980

Num. Sess.	Group Time	Num. Pgs.	Avg. Qst.	Price	Audience	Format	Bible Study
8	60-90	48	Vry	3.95	New Christian	Workbk	Topical

Features: Intro to Study, No Grp Discussion Quest, Cassette Avail
★★★ Personal Application   Preparation Time: Med   ISBN: 0-87123-411-4
★ Relationship Building Ldr. Guide Avail.: No   Size: 5.50 x 8.50
Subjects: Self-help, Support, Victorious Living
Comments: Study number three in this series, dealing with the scriptural concept of "abiding," helps participants come to a new understanding of the unique relationship God offers His children. The lessons cover affliction and oppression, crying unto the Lord, truth, relationships, and victory. The study sequence of basic journal sheets—a guide for your daily quiet time, Bible lesson, and tape—allows the fullest understanding.

Author: Coyle, Neva   292
Series: Free to Be Thin
Title: *Diligence: Temples Under Construction*
Publisher: Bethany House, 1982

Num. Sess.	Group Time	Num. Pgs.	Avg. Qst.	Price	Audience	Format	Bible Study
8	60-90	38	Vry	3.95	New Christian	Workbk	Topical

Features: No Grp Discussion Quest, Cassette Avail
★★★ Personal Application   Preparation Time: Med   ISBN: 0-87123-408-4
★ Relationship Building Ldr. Guide Avail.: No   Size: 5.50 x 8.50
Subjects: Self-help, Support, Victorious Living
Comments: Study number five in this series is designed to reinforce participants' effort; this is not the time to quit, it's the time to be diligent. A review of previous principles helps users evaluate current progress and chart future steps. The study sequence for this lesson is reversed, with tape first, then the study and assignments. Key scriptures are Ezra 6:3 ("Let the temple be rebuilt") and Ezra 6:12 ("Let it be carried out with diligence").

Author: Coyle, Neva   293
Series: Free to Be Thin
Title: *Freedom: Escape from the Ordinary*
Publisher: Bethany House, 1980

Num. Sess.	Group Time	Num. Pgs.	Avg. Qst.	Price	Audience	Format	Bible Study
6	60-90	47	Vry	3.95	New Christian	Workbk	Topical

Features: Intro to Study, No Grp Discussion Quest, Cassette Avail
★★★ Personal Application   Preparation Time: Med   ISBN: 0-87123-410-6
★ Relationship Building Ldr. Guide Avail.: No   Size: 5.50 x 8.50
Subjects: Self-help, Support, Victorious Living
Comments: Study number four in this series helps participants understand how to deal with temptation, and even be strengthened by it. It examines 1 Corinthians 10:13 from several perspectives. A study sequence of basic journal sheets—guides for daily quiet time, Bible lesson, and tape—allows fullest understanding. A calorie account sheet is also included.

Author: Coyle, Neva   294
Series: Free to Be Thin
Title: *Free to Be Thin (Study Guide No. 1), Getting Started*
Publisher: Bethany House, 1980

Num. Sess.	Group Time	Num. Pgs.	Avg. Qst.	Price	Audience	Format	Bible Study
7	60-90	61	Vry	3.95	New Christian	Workbk	Topical

Features: Intro to Study, Objectives, No Grp Discussion Quest, Follow Up, Cassette Avail
★★★ Personal Application   Preparation Time: Med   ISBN: 0-87123-163-8
★ Relationship Building Ldr. Guide Avail.: No   Size: 5.50 x 8.50
Subjects: Addictions, Self-help, Support, Victorious Living
Comments: This study, a weight-loss plan that links how to eat with how to live, can be used with the book *Free to Be Thin* and/or with the tape series of the same name. The lessons include basic journal sheets with a scripture for the day, a brief Bible study, and tape. Establishing discipline is a goal of this first study, which includes recommended diet guidelines and food facts.

Author: Coyle, Neva
295
Series: Free to Be Thin
Title: *Free to Be Thin (Study Guide No. 2), Discipline*
Publisher: Bethany House, 1980

Num. Sess.	Group Time	Num. Pgs.	Avg. Qst.	Price	Audience	Format	Bible Study
5	60-90	31	Vry	3.95	New Christian	Workbk	Topical

Features: No Grp Discussion Quest, Follow Up, Cassette Avail
★★★Personal Application   Preparation Time: Med   ISBN: 0-87123-169-7
★Relationship Building   Ldr. Guide Avail.: No   Size: 5.50 x 8.50
Subjects: Addictions, Self-help, Support, Victorious Living
Comments: This study, second in a series of eight, concerns leading disciplined lives and accomplishing God's work. This lesson covers spiritual exercise, God's provision for endurance, discipline, and correction, and includes ten principles to help achieve the goal. A sample calorie account sheet is also included.

Author: Coyle, Neva
296
Series: Free to Be Thin
Title: *Obedience: Developing a Listening Heart*
Publisher: Bethany House, 1980

Num. Sess.	Group Time	Num. Pgs.	Avg. Qst.	Price	Audience	Format	Bible Study
7	60-90	59	Vry	3.95	New Christian	Workbk	Topical

Features: Prayer Helps, No Grp Discussion Quest, Cassette Avail
★★★Personal Application   Preparation Time: Med   ISBN: 0-87123-409-2
★Relationship Building   Ldr. Guide Avail.: No   Size: 5.50 x 8.50
Subjects: Obedience, Self-help, Support, Victorious Living
Comments: Study six in this series helps participants develop a listening heart. It issues a call for obedience, which allows complete freedom from lists, guidelines, and fear, and requires listening intently to the Lord. Two principal lessons cover "The Covenant Relationship" and "Fasting." The study sequence is basic journal sheets, then Bible study and a tape.

Author: Coyle, Neva
297
Series: Free to Be Thin
Title: *Perseverance: For People Under Pressure*
Publisher: Bethany House, 1986

Num. Sess.	Group Time	Num. Pgs.	Avg. Qst.	Price	Audience	Format	Bible Study
6	60-90	57	Vry	3.95	New Christian	Workbk	Topical

Features: Intro to Study, No Grp Discussion Quest, Cassette Avail
★★★Personal Application   Preparation Time: Med   ISBN: 0-87123-888-8
★Relationship Building   Ldr. Guide Avail.: No   Size: 5.50 x 8.50
Subjects: Self-help, Stress, Support, Victorious Living
Comments: Study eight from this series is designed for those who are tempted to quit, who simply are tired of resisting the enemy, overcoming temptation, and disciplining their bodies and minds. Lessons reflect the author's personal trials and pressures and candidly reveal how God uses them to shape a believer's life. "Formula for Crisis," "The Fall," "This Is Only a Test," "Perseverance," "The Perfect Me," and "Wanting Nothing" are lesson titles.

Author: Coyle, Neva
298
Series: Free to Be Thin
Title: *Restoration: Discovering What Takes Place Between Return and Restore*
Publisher: Bethany House, 1985

Num. Sess.	Group Time	Num. Pgs.	Avg. Qst.	Price	Audience	Format	Bible Study
6	60-90	61	Vry	3.95	New Christian	Workbk	Topical

Features: Intro to Study, Scrpt Memory Helps, No Grp Discussion Quest, Cassette Avail
★★★Personal Application   Preparation Time: Med   ISBN: 0-87123-851-9
★Relationship Building   Ldr. Guide Avail.: No   Size: 5.50 x 8.50
Subjects: Renewal, Self-help, Support, Victorious Living
Comments: Study seven in this series is designed to help participants who may have faltered in their spiritual life or commitment get back on track. Lessons cover return, readiness, relief, rest, renewal, and restoration. A restoration goal planner is included. The study sequence is basic journal sheets, then Bible study and a tape.

Author: Crabb, Dr. Larry
299
Series:
Title: *Inside Out*
Publisher: NavPress, 1987

Num. Sess.	Group Time	Num. Pgs.	Avg. Qst.	Price	Audience	Format	Bible Study
4	60-75	N/A	N/A	159.0	Beginner	Video	Topical

Features: Video Study Guide
★★★★Personal Application   Preparation Time: Low   ISBN: 9-900735-92-7
★★Relationship Building   Ldr. Guide Avail.: No   Size: 10.50 x 12.50
Subjects: Counseling, Emotions, Psychology, Relationships
Comments: This four-part lecture video series helps participants experience real change, by exploring what it takes to live life with deeper honesty, humility, and freedom. Each video contains one approximately forty-five-minute-long session. Video titles are: "Don't Look Inside Me, I'm Not Sure I Like What's There"; and "I Don't Want to Admit It, but I Know Something's Wrong." The take-home guide is simply a tool to help participants reflect on the video series, it's not a study guide.

Author: Crabb, Dr. Larry
300
Series:
Title: *Inside Out*
Publisher: NavPress, 1988

Num. Sess.	Group Time	Num. Pgs.	Avg. Qst.	Price	Audience	Format	Bible Study
12	60-90	107	17	5.95	New Christian	Workbk	Topical

Features: Intro to Leading a Study, Digging Deeper Quest, Charts
★★★★Personal Application   Preparation Time: Med   ISBN: 0-89109-281-1
★★Relationship Building   Ldr. Guide Avail.: No   Size: 5.50 x 8.50
Subjects: Counseling, Emotions, Psychology, Relationships
Comments: This study, a companion to the book *Inside Out,* will help participants move toward a relationship with Christ and others that will bring the richest life possible. Each lesson is divided into five sections: an excerpt from the book that highlights the major point; "Looking Inside," a reflection on the excerpt; "Identifying the Problem," a deeper look at the point; "Exploring Relationships"; and "Moving Toward Change," the wrap-up. A closing case study shows spiritual growth through change.

Author: Cresse, Michelle   **301**
Series: Heart Issues
Title: *Jigsaw Families: Solving the Puzzle of Remarriage*
Publisher: Aglow, 1989

Num. Sess.	Group Time	Num. Pgs.	Avg. Qst.	Price	Audience	Format	Bible Study
12	60-75	138	5	8.95	Beginner	Book	Topical

Features: Intro to Study, Ldr's Notes
★★★★ Personal Application   Preparation Time: Low   ISBN: 0-932305-77-6
★★★★ Relationship Building   Ldr. Guide Avail.: No   Size: 5.25 x 8.25
Subjects: Family, Marriage, Remarriage, Support
Comments: This book helps people with problems unique to remarried couples and families. According to a 1981 survey of pastors, 40 percent of families in U.S. churches include at least one previously married person. Topics on this critical issue include: adjustment to a new family pattern, stepchildren, in-laws and former in-laws, ex-spouses, holidays, and setting priorities. Guidelines for leading support groups are provided, and questions at the end of each chapter can be used for support groups.

Author: Cuthbertson, Dr. Duane   **302**
Series:
Title: *Raising Your Child, Not Your Voice*
Publisher: Victor Books, 1986

Num. Sess.	Group Time	Num. Pgs.	Avg. Qst.	Price	Audience	Format	Bible Study
13	60-75	138	N/A	7.99	New Christian	Book	Topical

Features: Intro to Study
★★★★ Personal Application   Preparation Time: Low   ISBN: 0-89693-342-3
★★★★ Relationship Building   Ldr. Guide Avail.: Yes   Size: 5.50 x 8.0
Subjects: Family, Parenting
Comments: This thirteen-week study introduces participants to assertive scriptural parenting, offering ways to "train up" children without breaking their spirits or their parents' vocal cords. A temperament analysis test allows participants to discover their parenting style as well as their child's "bent." They will learn how to discipline in a way that fits both personalities. One lesson provides eight steps to a changed heart, based on the fourth chapter of James.

Author: Cutler, William & Richard Peace   **303**
Series: Serendipity Support Group
Title: *Blended Families: Yours, Mine, Ours*
Publisher: Serendipity House, 1990

Num. Sess.	Group Time	Num. Pgs.	Avg. Qst.	Price	Audience	Format	Bible Study
14	60-90	80	12	5.45	Beginner	Workbk	Topical

Features: Intro to Leading a Study, Objectives, Bibliography, Prayer Helps, Full Scrpt Printed, Ldr's Notes, Cartoons, Agenda
★★★★ Personal Application   Preparation Time: Low   ISBN:
★★★★ Relationship Building   Ldr. Guide Avail.: No   Size: 6.50 x 9.0
Subjects: Family, Marriage, Support
Comments: This study offers Old and New Testament insights on blended families. Lessons include "The Phenomenon Called Blended Families," "Stepfamilies vs. First Families," "The Children," "The 'Ex' Factor," "The Stretching, Straining Family Ties," "Nurturing the Marriage," and "Finding Inner Strength." Case studies, personal reflection, and biblical passages help participants deal with the issues stepparents face. This study is helpful for anyone parenting a blended family who is willing to be open.

Author: Cutler, William & Richard Peace   **304**
Series: Serendipity Support Group
Title: *Dealing with Grief & Loss: Hope in the Midst of Pain*
Publisher: Serendipity House, 1990

Num. Sess.	Group Time	Num. Pgs.	Avg. Qst.	Price	Audience	Format	Bible Study
14	60-90	80	9	5.45	Beginner	Workbk	Topical

Features: Intro to Leading a Study, Intro to Study, Objectives, Bibliography, Prayer Helps, Full Scrpt Printed, Ldr's Notes, Cartoons, Agenda
★★★★ Personal Application   Preparation Time: None   ISBN:
★★★★ Relationship Building   Ldr. Guide Avail.: No   Size: 6.50 x 9.0
Subjects: Divorce, Emotions, Grief, Hope, Suffering, Support, Work
Comments: This study, which deals with grief and loss, is based on shared feelings which can be the foundation of a support group. Death, divorce, unemployment, failed expectations, severe injury, and major illness are discussed as experiences that bring pain. The many sources of grief and loss vary from person to person, but the feelings experienced are similar: shock, denial, anger, depression, and bargaining. This study, taken from the book of Job, concludes with a promise of hope from Romans.

Author: Cutler, William & Richard Peace   **305**
Series: Serendipity Support Group
Title: *Parenting Adolescents: Easing the Way to Adulthood*
Publisher: Serendipity House, 1990

Num. Sess.	Group Time	Num. Pgs.	Avg. Qst.	Price	Audience	Format	Bible Study
14	60-90	80	10	5.45	Beginner	Workbk	Topical

Features: Intro to Leading a Study, Objectives, Bibliography, Prayer Helps, Full Scrpt Printed, Ldr's Notes, Cartoons, Agenda
★★★★ Personal Application   Preparation Time: None   ISBN:
★★★★ Relationship Building   Ldr. Guide Avail.: No   Size: 6.50 x 9.0
Subjects: Faith, Parenting, Self-esteem, Support
Comments: This study uses New Testament scriptures to address issues concerning teenagers, who are neither kids nor adults. Helpful lessons include communicating love, nurturing self-esteem, dealing with crises, and passing on the faith. Paul's ministry is examined as a model for parenting, as Paul was a "parent" to congregations he founded.

Author: Cutler, William   **306**
Series: Serendipity Support Group
Title: *Single Parents: Flying Solo*
Publisher: Serendipity House, 1991

Num. Sess.	Group Time	Num. Pgs.	Avg. Qst.	Price	Audience	Format	Bible Study
7	60-90	96	Vry	5.45	Beginner	Workbk	Topical

Features: Intro to Leading a Study, Objectives, Bibliography, Prayer Helps, Full Scrpt Printed, Ldr's Notes, Drawings, Cartoons, Agenda
★★★★ Personal Application   Preparation Time: None   ISBN:
★★★★ Relationship Building   Ldr. Guide Avail.: No   Size: 6.50 x 9.25
Subjects: Parenting, Singles Issues, Work
Comments: This study on single parenting is based on shared life experiences which can be the foundation of a support group. Issues include the following: suddenly being single; being a single working parent; dealing with an ex-spouse; creating a healthy home; embracing singleness; and developing inner strength. Derived from scriptures in Genesis and selected New Testament books, this study includes the examination of the Gospel of John on how a person becomes a Christian.

Author: Davis, Lindsey   **307**
Series: Bible Study for Christian
Title: *2 Corinthians (Volumes 1 & 2)*
Publisher: Cokesbury, 1989

Num. Sess.	Group Time	Num. Pgs.	Avg. Qst.	Price	Audience	Format	Bible Study
6	45-60	N/A	Vry	29.95	New Christian	Video	Book

Features: Intro to Leading a Study, Intro to Study, Video Study Guide
  ★★★ Personal Application   Preparation Time: Low   ISBN: 0-687-76142-5
  ★★★ Relationship Building   Ldr. Guide Avail.: Yes   Size: 4.75 x 8.0
Subjects: Accountability, Church Life, Hope, Integrity, Obedience, Repentance, Service, Suffering, 2 Corinthians
Comments: This two-volume video lecture series includes six twenty-minute lessons on Paul's second letter to the Corinthian Christians. The apostle, convinced he had been forthright and consistent in his dealings with them, made a final appeal for self-correction, for loyal submission to rightful authority, and for members of the divided church to work together for common good. It's valid, relevant subject matter for contemporary Christians. A leader's guide contains insights and questions for use in a group.

Author: DeHaan, M. R., M.D.   **308**
Series:
Title: *Hebrews*
Publisher: Zondervan, 1959

Num. Sess.	Group Time	Num. Pgs.	Avg. Qst.	Price	Audience	Format	Bible Study
26	60-90	210	N/A	7.95	Mature Chrstn	Book	Book

Features: No Grp Discussion Quest, Full Scrpt Printed, Appendix
  ★★ Personal Application   Preparation Time: None   ISBN: 0-310-23371-2
  ★★ Relationship Building   Ldr. Guide Avail.: No   Size: 5.25 x 8.0
Subjects: Faith, Hebrews, Victorious Living
Comments: This study presents a searching approach to the true meaning of Hebrews—and a clear guide to victorious living for committed Christians. Chapter titles include: "Saved—Or Half Saved"; "Neglecting Our Salvation"; "Lower Than the Angels"; "The Second Blessing"; "The Sin unto Death"; "The Rewards of Faith"; and more. The lack of group questions requires a seasoned leader to construct questions and facilitate a group study.

Author: DeHaan, M. R., M.D.   **309**
Series:
Title: *Portraits of Christ in Genesis*
Publisher: Zondervan, 1966

Num. Sess.	Group Time	Num. Pgs.	Avg. Qst.	Price	Audience	Format	Bible Study
23	60-90	190	N/A	7.95	Mature Chrstn	Book	Book

Features: Intro to Study, No Grp Discussion Quest, Full Scrpt Printed, Appendix
  ★★ Personal Application   Preparation Time: None   ISBN: 0-310-23431-X
  ★★ Relationship Building   Ldr. Guide Avail.: No   Size: 5.25 x 8.0
Subjects: Bible Personalities, Genesis, God
Comments: This study examines the lives of Adam, Abel, Isaac, Joseph, and many other biblical characters who foretold Christ and His ministry. An interesting study of Old Testament typology, it relates deep theological truths in language easily understood by laypeople. The lack of group questions requires a seasoned leader to construct questions and facilitate a group study.

Author: Demaray, Donald E.   **310**
Series: Spiritual Formation Series
Title: *Listen to Luther*
Publisher: Victor Books, 1989

Num. Sess.	Group Time	Num. Pgs.	Avg. Qst.	Price	Audience	Format	Bible Study
13	60-75	174	N/A	6.99	New Christian	Book	Topical

Features: Intro to Study
  ★★★ Personal Application   Preparation Time: Low   ISBN: 0-89693-690-2
  ★★★ Relationship Building   Ldr. Guide Avail.: Yes   Size: 5.50 x 8.0
Subjects: Angels, Discipleship, Holy Spirit, Prayer
Comments: This thirteen-lesson study concerns Martin Luther, the German Christian who stood against the religious establishment of his day. It is drawn from *Table Talk,* a six-volume collection of Luther's sayings written by one of his students. Topics include Christ, God's Word, the Holy Spirit, prayer, preachers and preaching, sin, angels, and more. Participants are encouraged to be cheered and enriched by this great Christian's musings. A separate leader's guide includes reproducible response sheets.

Author: Dettoni, John M.   **311**
Series: GroupBuilder Resources
Title: *Open to Closeness*
Publisher: Victor Books, 1991

Num. Sess.	Group Time	Num. Pgs.	Avg. Qst.	Price	Audience	Format	Bible Study
8	75-90	144	Vry	5.99	New Christian	Workbk	Topical

Features: Intro to Leading a Study, Objectives, Digging Deeper Quest, Follow Up, Full Scrpt Printed, Ldr's Notes, Cartoons, Persnl Study Quest
  ★★★★ Personal Application   Preparation Time: Low   ISBN: 0-89693-881-6
  ★★★★ Relationship Building   Ldr. Guide Avail.: No   Size: 6.0 x 9.0
Subjects: Holiness, Joy, Philippians, Relationships, Victorious Living
Comments: This study helps small groups learn about and practice building close, warm relationships as they study eight aspects of biblical intimacy found in the book of Philippians. Sessions deal with such topics as communicating affection, like-mindedness, Jesus' attitude of humility, mending relationships, holy thoughts and actions, and the gift of intimacy. Optional activities, hints for leaders, and answers to questions can be found in the leader's guide at the back of the book.

Author: Dibbert, Michael T. & Frank B. Wichern   **312**
Series:
Title: *Growth Groups*
Publisher: Zondervan, 1985

Num. Sess.	Group Time	Num. Pgs.	Avg. Qst.	Price	Audience	Format	Bible Study
11	-	140	N/A	9.95		Book	No

Features: Glossary
  Personal Application   Preparation Time: ISBN: 0-310-23121-3
  Relationship Building   Ldr. Guide Avail.:   Size: 5.50 x 8.0
Subjects: Small Group Resource
Comments: This book offers both veteran and newcomer a perspective on the purposes for groups in the church. It covers the ways groups can be structured, the processes of learning in a group context, and the important functions of group leadership. The study has three parts. Part 1 covers the foundations, the biblical and practical bases for groups. Part 2 covers the process, how growth in groups takes place. Part 3 covers skills and processes, the actual facilitation of growth.

Author: Dieterich, Henry   **313**
Series: Catholic Bible Study Guide
Title: *Faith: A Guide to Following God*
Publisher: Servant Publications, 1988

Num. Sess.	Group Time	Num. Pgs.	Avg. Qst.	Price	Audience	Format	Bible Study
9	60-75	76	5	4.95	Beginner	Workbk	Topical

Features: Intro to Study, Scrpt Memory Helps, Summary, Charts
★★★ Personal Application   Preparation Time: Low   ISBN: 0-89283-356-4
★ Relationship Building   Ldr. Guide Avail.: No   Size: 5.0 x 8.0
Subjects: Christian Living, Faith, God
Comments: This nine-part study discusses what the Bible says about faith: what it is, how it affects believers, and how to have more of it. This easy-to-use guide introduces a few pertinent questions, and provides a basis for beginning a life of faith or growing in faith. Its format includes scripture texts, commentary, questions, and exercises for in-depth study, and tips for Christian living.

Author: Dimock, Hedley G.   **314**
Series:
Title: *Groups: Leadership and Group Development*
Publisher: University Associates, 1986

Num. Sess.	Group Time	Num. Pgs.	Avg. Qst.	Price	Audience	Format	Bible Study
10	-	210	N/A	29.95		Book	No

Features: Bibliography, Charts
Personal Application   Preparation Time: ISBN: 0-88390-202-8
Relationship Building   Ldr. Guide Avail.:   Size: 6.25 x 9.25
Subjects: Small Group Resource
Comments: This book helps people working with groups improve their effectiveness in promoting growth, accomplishing tasks, and providing satisfaction for group members. The book is divided into four parts: understanding group behavior, how to observe your group, how to analyze and evaluate group growth, and planning group development. While academic in style, this book includes basic concepts transferable to the church setting.

Author: Dobson, Dr. James C.   **315**
Series:
Title: *Emotions: Can You Trust Them?*
Publisher: Regal Books, 1980

Num. Sess.	Group Time	Num. Pgs.	Avg. Qst.	Price	Audience	Format	Bible Study
6	45-60	143	Vry	3.95	New Christian	Book	Topical

Features: Intro to Study, Bibliography
★★★★ Personal Application   Preparation Time: Med   ISBN: 0-8307-0866-9
★★★★ Relationship Building   Ldr. Guide Avail.: Yes   Size: 4.25 x 7.0
Subjects: Emotions, Love, Marriage, Relationships
Comments: This study offers a detailed examination of four important emotions: guilt, romantic love, anger, and impressions. It provides practical help on the topics of knowing God's will, how to express anger, what to do about nagging guilt, and what to expect from a romantic relationship. It combines practical suggestions with biblical perspectives in ways that work in daily life. The study is written in a question/answer format suitable for individual or group study.

Author: Dobson, Dr. James C.   **316**
Series: Proven Word
Title: *Straight Talk to Men and Their Wives*
Publisher: Word, 1984

Num. Sess.	Group Time	Num. Pgs.	Avg. Qst.	Price	Audience	Format	Bible Study
18	45-60	420	6	8.99	Beginner	Book	Topical

Features: Intro to Leading a Study, Ldr's Notes, Drawings
★★ Personal Application   Preparation Time: Low   ISBN: 0-8499-2981-4
★★ Relationship Building   Ldr. Guide Avail.: No   Size: 5.50 x 8.0
Subjects: Marriage, Men's Issues, Women's Issues
Comments: This study accepts God's leadership in human relationships and asks questions such as: "What makes a man a man?" "What makes a woman a woman?" "What does the Bible say about roles?" "Where do the boundaries fall between male chauvinism and being an effective, forceful leader?" and other relevant topics for modern marriages. Built-in study questions help adapt the book to small group study.

Author: Dockrey, Karen   **317**
Series:
Title: *Family Survival Guide (Student Book)*
Publisher: Victor Books, 1988

Num. Sess.	Group Time	Num. Pgs.	Avg. Qst.	Price	Audience	Format	Bible Study
12	75-90	96	N/A	2.50	New Christian	Book	Topical

Features: Drawings
★★★★ Personal Application   Preparation Time: Low   ISBN: 0-89693-457-8
★★★★ Relationship Building   Ldr. Guide Avail.: Yes   Size: 3.50 x 6.0
Subjects: Teens: Family, Teens: Junior High
Comments: This study equips young teens to understand and work toward solving their family struggles. It helps them not only survive, but enjoy life with their families. Three four-week sessions cover: "Parent Pressure"; "Home Is Where the Heart Is"; and "Favoritism, Fights, and Rights." A leader's guide ($12.99) includes reproducible student sheets. Sessions are easy to organize and include creative start-up activities, lively Bible studies, and challenging application.

Author: Dockrey, Karen   **318**
Series: A Bible Study for Women
Title: *Living Until Jesus Comes*
Publisher: Victor Books, 1989

Num. Sess.	Group Time	Num. Pgs.	Avg. Qst.	Price	Audience	Format	Bible Study
10	60-90	96	11	5.99	New Christian	Workbk	Book

Features: Intro to Leading a Study, Intro to Study, Objectives, Scrpt Memory Helps, Follow Up, Ldr's Notes
★★★ Personal Application   Preparation Time: Med   ISBN: 0-89693-668-6
★★ Relationship Building   Ldr. Guide Avail.: No   Size: 6.0 x 9.0
Subjects: Eschatology, Faith, Grief, Women's Issues, 1 & 2 Thessalonians
Comments: This study of 1 and 2 Thessalonians equips participants to answer questions regarding Jesus' second coming. Much of the letter concerns Jesus' return, but Paul did not focus exclusively on the future. He also addressed the Thessalonians' immediate worries, questions, and problems, including hostilities toward their faith, grief over dead loved ones, pressure to conform to the world's values, deceptive prophecies, and lazy people—topics applicable today.

Author: Dockrey, Karen   **319**
Series: Young Teen Feedback Elective
Title: *What's Your Problem? (Leader Book)*
Publisher: Victor Books, 1987

Num. Sess.	Group Time	Num. Pgs.	Avg. Qst.	Price	Audience	Format	Bible Study
12	30-45	86	Vry	12.99	New Christian	Book	Topical

Features: Intro to Study, Handouts
★★★★ Personal Application   Preparation Time: None   ISBN: 0-89693-381-4
★★★★ Relationship Building   Ldr. Guide Avail.: Yes   Size: 8.50 x 11.0
Subjects: Teens: Christian Liv, Teens: Decisions, Teens: Emotions
Comments: This study responds to a popular complaint about Bible study: "It doesn't apply to my problem." This study does exactly that in three four-week studies, which provide a biblical approach to problemsolving. The three main sections are: "Your Friend's Problems" (peer counseling); "Your Own Problems" (those not talked about); and "Our Problems" (problems all Christians share). They can be used separately as short studies, or consecutively as a twelve-week elective.

Author: Dockrey, Karen   **320**
Series:
Title: *When Everyone's Looking at You (Student Book)*
Publisher: Victor Books, 1989

Num. Sess.	Group Time	Num. Pgs.	Avg. Qst.	Price	Audience	Format	Bible Study
12	75-90	96	Vry	2.50	New Christian	Book	Topical

Features: Drawings
★★★★ Personal Application   Preparation Time: Low   ISBN: 0-89693-664-3
★★★★ Relationship Building   Ldr. Guide Avail.: Yes   Size: 3.50 x 6.0
Subjects: Teens: Junior High, Teens: Peer Pressure, Teens: Relationships
Comments: This study helps teens understand peer pressure and choose effective alternatives. It demonstrates ways to find true acceptance, real friends, belonging, authentic fun, and lifelong love. Leaders can effectively teach this touchy subject without making teens defensive. A leader's guide ($12.99) offers three four-week studies with reproducible student sheets. Sessions are easy to organize and include creative start-up activities, lively Bible studies, and challenging applications.

Author: Doornenbal, Baukje & Tjitske Lemstra   **321**
Series:
Title: *Homemaking: A Bible Study for Women at Home*
Publisher: NavPress, 1981

Num. Sess.	Group Time	Num. Pgs.	Avg. Qst.	Price	Audience	Format	Bible Study
12	45-60	72	7	4.95	New Christian	Workbk	Topical

Features:
★★ Personal Application   Preparation Time: Low   ISBN: 0-89109-033-9
★★ Relationship Building   Ldr. Guide Avail.: No   Size: 5.50 x 8.50
Subjects: Parenting, Women's Issues
Comments: This study of homemaking is for women who want to be motivated and led by God's Word in their responsibilities at home. Topics include the clarification of expectations, defining one's divine task, identifying and using one's gifts, altering one's thinking about worldly things, and developing good habits for one's self and children. Homemaking is a calling.

Author: Draper, James T., Jr.   **322**
Series: Living Studies
Title: *Proverbs: Practical Directions for Living*
Publisher: Tyndale House, 1977

Num. Sess.	Group Time	Num. Pgs.	Avg. Qst.	Price	Audience	Format	Bible Study
19	45-60	159	N/A	5.95	New Christian	Book	Book

Features: Intro to Study, Bibliography, No Grp Discussion Quest, Full Scrpt Printed
★ Personal Application   Preparation Time: Low   ISBN: 0-8423-4922-7
★ Relationship Building   Ldr. Guide Avail.: No   Size: 5.0 x 8.0
Subjects: Christian Living, Proverbs, Wisdom
Comments: This book translates the teachings of Proverbs into modern terminology and makes their application practical for contemporary lives. Participants should read all of Proverbs in a single sitting prior to using this tool. God's purpose for Proverbs is found in chapter 1, verses 5 and 6: "I want those already wise to become the wiser and become leaders by exploring the depths of meaning in these nuggets of truth" (TLB). Questions for small group use are not provided.

Author: Drury, Keith   **323**
Series: Francis Asbury Press
Title: *Holiness for Ordinary People*
Publisher: Zondervan, 1983

Num. Sess.	Group Time	Num. Pgs.	Avg. Qst.	Price	Audience	Format	Bible Study
13	60-90	128	5	6.95	New Christian	Book	Topical

Features: Intro to Study, Study Overview
★★ Personal Application   Preparation Time: Med   ISBN: 0-310-20731-2
★★ Relationship Building   Ldr. Guide Avail.: No   Size: 5.25 x 8.0
Subjects: Christian Living, Holiness, Theology, Victorious Living
Comments: This study, which describes personal holiness in understandable, life-related terms, explains how every Christian can live in spiritual victory. It offers clear biblical insight into how Christians can deal with daily spiritual obstacles. It is written for all serious seekers of Christ, but especially has younger adults in mind. A separate notebook is required for recording answers to questions.

Author: Drury, Keith   **324**
Series: Group's Active Bible Curriculum
Title: *Your Life as a Disciple*
Publisher: Group Publishing, 1990

Num. Sess.	Group Time	Num. Pgs.	Avg. Qst.	Price	Audience	Format	Bible Study
4	35-60	45	Vry	6.95	New Christian	Workbk	Topical

Features: Intro to Leading a Study, Intro to Study, Objectives, Study Overview, Ldr's Notes, Handouts, Agenda, Publicity Ideas
★★★ Personal Application   Preparation Time: None   ISBN: 1-559-45204-8
★★★ Relationship Building   Ldr. Guide Avail.: No   Size: 8.50 x 11.0
Subjects: Teens: Discipleship, Teens: Senior High
Comments: This study helps Christian teenagers develop a desire to serve God and build confidence to withstand attacks to their faith. Four lessons discuss the first disciples, qualifications for being a disciple, the "cost" of being a disciple, and how to accept the responsibility of being a disciple. The course could be adapted for use in a Bible class or youth meeting, and activities and Bible studies are included as separate sheets that can be reproduced. Instructions are easy to follow, and have many options.

Author: Duckworth, John **325**
Series: Young Teen Feedback Elective
Title: *School Zone, The (Leader's Book)*
Publisher: Victor Books, 1986

Num. Sess.	Group Time	Num. Pgs.	Avg. Qst.	Price	Audience	Format	Bible Study
12	30-45	86	Vry	12.99	New Christian	Book	Topical

Features: Intro to Study, Handouts
★★★★ Personal Application   Preparation Time: None   ISBN: 0-89693-198-6
★★★★ Relationship Building   Ldr. Guide Avail.: Yes   Size: 8.50 x 11.0
Subjects: Teens: Emotions, Teens: Peer Pressure, Teens: Relationships
Comments: This twelve-lesson study helps young teens learn to live their faith at school and cope with concerns about problems such as peer pressure, competition, relationships, and authority in a school setting. Each session is based on interviews with youth, including their feedback on personal needs and concerns. This guide offers four-week studies with reproducible student sheets. A student book is available.

Author: Duckworth, Marion **326**
Series: A Bible Study for Women
Title: *Celebrate Who You Are: 9 Studies on the Identity & Roles of Women*
Publisher: Victor Books, 1990

Num. Sess.	Group Time	Num. Pgs.	Avg. Qst.	Price	Audience	Format	Bible Study
9	60-75	96	20	5.99	New Christian	Workbk	Topical

Features: Intro to Leading a Study, Intro to Study, Scrpt Memory Helps, Follow Up, Ldr's Notes
★★★★ Personal Application   Preparation Time: Med   ISBN: 0-89693-816-6
★★★ Relationship Building   Ldr. Guide Avail.: No   Size: 6.0 x 9.0
Subjects: Genesis, God, Women's Issues
Comments: In this study, women will discover that their identity and role are not synonymous. The study guides participants through Genesis 1-5 and related scripture, helping them discover a biblical view of themselves and celebrate who they are—gifted creatures called by God to use their abilities in constructive ways. Each lesson contains a series of inductive questions, a narrative section, and a section of personal questions and exercises.

Author: Duckworth, Marion **327**
Series: Tapestry Collection
Title: *Renewed on the Run*
Publisher: Victor Books, 1991

Num. Sess.	Group Time	Num. Pgs.	Avg. Qst.	Price	Audience	Format	Bible Study
9	60-90	96	Vry	5.99	New Christian	Workbk	Book

Features: Intro to Leading a Study, Intro to Study, Prayer Helps, Digging Deeper Quest, Follow Up, Ldr's Notes, Persnl Study Quest
★★★★ Personal Application   Preparation Time: Low   ISBN: 0-89693-878-6
★★★ Relationship Building   Ldr. Guide Avail.: No   Size: 6.0 x 9.0
Subjects: Renewal, Women's Issues, 1 & 2 Peter
Comments: This inductive Bible study for women on the move includes nine lessons on 1 Peter. This study helps busy contemporary women restore their purpose for living. The study includes a journaling exercise as well as prayer helps.

Author: Dugan, Richard **328**
Series: Building Books
Title: *Building Christian Commitment*
Publisher: Bethany House, 1982

Num. Sess.	Group Time	Num. Pgs.	Avg. Qst.	Price	Audience	Format	Bible Study
34	45-60	45	Vry	4.95	New Christian	Workbk	Topical

Features: Scrpt Memory Helps, Persnl Study Quest
★★ Personal Application   Preparation Time: Low   ISBN: 0-87123-831-4
★★ Relationship Building   Ldr. Guide Avail.: Yes   Size: 8.50 x 11.0
Subjects: Teens: Bible/Pers., Teens: Christian Liv, Teens: Emotions
Comments: This thirty-four-lesson study for young adults on Bible characters discusses what made them heroes, why they sometimes failed, and how they grew toward spiritual maturity. From "Joseph, the Lemonade Maker," to "Diotrephes, the Man Who Loved to Be First," these challenging studies help young people understand how to deal with discouragement, failure, obstacles, temptations, selfishness, and practical issues which face them every day.

Author: Duin, Julia **329**
Series: NetWork Discussion Guide
Title: *Wholly Single*
Publisher: Shaw, 1991

Num. Sess.	Group Time	Num. Pgs.	Avg. Qst.	Price	Audience	Format	Bible Study
8	30-45	48	5	3.50	Beginner	Workbk	Topical

Features: Intro to Leading a Study, Intro to Study, Bibliography, Follow Up, Ldr's Notes
★★★★ Personal Application   Preparation Time: Low   ISBN: 0-87788-945-7
★★★ Relationship Building   Ldr. Guide Avail.: No   Size: 5.25 x 8.25
Subjects: Loneliness, Relationships, Service, Sexual Issues, Singles Issues
Comments: Eight short lessons help single adults tackle issues such as loneliness, celibacy, sexual purity, and intimacy from a biblical perspective. As group members study, they'll focus on Jesus Christ, Himself a single. Challenging questions include: Are you allowing your singleness to make you more like Jesus? How do you react to the challenges of singleness? Does singleness enhance ministry or detract from it?

Author: Dull, Elaine & JoAnne Sekowsky **330**
Series: Enrichment Series
Title: *Teach Us to Pray: A Study of the Principles of Prayer*
Publisher: Aglow, 1980

Num. Sess.	Group Time	Num. Pgs.	Avg. Qst.	Price	Audience	Format	Bible Study
9	60-75	62	35	2.95	New Christian	Workbk	Topical

Features: Intro to Study, Prayer Helps, Scrpt Memory Helps, Digging Deeper Quest, Persnl Study Quest
★★★★ Personal Application   Preparation Time: Med   ISBN: 0-930756-49-5
★★★★ Relationship Building   Ldr. Guide Avail.: No   Size: 5.25 x 8.25
Subjects: Charismatic Interest, Fasting, Prayer
Comments: This nine-week study deals with what the Bible actually says about prayer—what it will and won't do and what we can and shouldn't expect. It is a study of the scriptural principles of prayer. Lesson titles include: "Does God Hear Our Prayers?"; "How to Pray"; "What Can We Pray For"; "Praying in the Spirit"; "Fasting"; and more.

Author: Dumke, James A.　　　　　　　　**331**
Series: Men's Bible Study Series
Title: *1 & 2 Corinthians*
Publisher: Augsburg Publishing House, 1988

Num. Sess.	Group Time	Num. Pgs.	Avg. Qst.	Price	Audience	Format	Bible Study
10	30-45	48	9	3.0	New Christian	Workbk	Book

Features: Intro to Study, Prayer Helps, Summary
★★★★ Personal Application　Preparation Time: None　ISBN:
★★★★ Relationship Building　Ldr. Guide Avail.: Yes　Size: 4.50 x 9.50
Subjects: Faith, Grace, Leadership, Men's Issues, Obedience, Service, Suffering, 1 Corinthians, 2 Corinthians
Comments: This ten-lesson study considers how Paul's letters to the troubled Corinthian church provide guidance for contemporary participants struggling to be faithful. Lessons like "Workers with God," "Say It With Love," and "Grace Sufficient" contribute to that guidance. The study may be used at prayer breakfasts, men's Bible study groups, or any other men's meetings.

Author: Dunnam, Maxie　　　　　　　　**332**
Series:
Title: *Exodus (Volumes 1-3)*
Publisher: Cokesbury, 1989

Num. Sess.	Group Time	Num. Pgs.	Avg. Qst.	Price	Audience	Format	Bible Study
11	45-60	N/A	Vry	29.95	New Christian	Video	Book

Features: Intro to Leading a Study, Intro to Study, Prayer Helps, Ldr's Notes, Video Study Guide
★★★ Personal Application　Preparation Time: Low　ISBN: 0-687-76134-4
★★★ Relationship Building　Ldr. Guide Avail.: Yes　Size: 4.75 x 8.0
Subjects: Exodus, God
Comments: This three-volume video focuses on Exodus, an exciting book on God's delivering Israel out of Egyptian bondage, protecting and sustaining them through wilderness wandering, and bringing them to Canaan. To contemporary participants, it is a picture of a spiritual journey from the bondage of sin, to freedom and full inheritance in Christ. Volume 1 covers the first seven chapters, through the hardening of Pharaoh's heart; volume 2 covers chapters 8 through 20; volume 3, chapters 21 through 40.

Author: Dunnam, Maxie　　　　　　　　**333**
Series: Bible Study for Christian
Title: *Gospel of Mark, The (Volumes 1-3)*
Publisher: Cokesbury, 1988

Num. Sess.	Group Time	Num. Pgs.	Avg. Qst.	Price	Audience	Format	Bible Study
9	90-120	128	Vry	29.95	New Christian	Audio	Book

Features: Intro to Leading a Study, Intro to Study, Prayer Helps, Video Study Guide
★★★★ Personal Application　Preparation Time: Low　ISBN: 0-687-76006-2
★★★ Relationship Building　Ldr. Guide Avail.: Yes　Size: 4.75 x 8.0
Subjects: Christian Living, Jesus: Life/Teaching, Mark
Comments: This three-volume video study covers the Gospel of Mark, giving participants a picture of Christ having returned. It shows them that, in Christ, the limitless power of God is incarnated and available to all. It's valid, relevant subject matter for contemporary Christians. A leader's guide contains insights and questions for use in a group, and the study is effective for personal use. Each volume has its own ISBN number.

Author: Dunnam, Maxie　　　　　　　　**334**
Series: Bible Study for Christian
Title: *More Than Conquerors (Volumes 1-3)*
Publisher: Cokesbury, 1988

Num. Sess.	Group Time	Num. Pgs.	Avg. Qst.	Price	Audience	Format	Bible Study
8	90-120	111	Vry	29.95	New Christian	Video	Topical

Features: Intro to Leading a Study, Intro to Study, Prayer Helps, Video Study Guide
★★★★ Personal Application　Preparation Time: Low　ISBN: 0-687-76014-3
★★★ Relationship Building　Ldr. Guide Avail.: Yes　Size: 4.75 x 8.0
Subjects: Christian Living, Faith, New Testament, Victorious Living
Comments: This three-volume video study shows participants the promise and glory of Christian life. It draws, from Paul's letters, major affirmations of Christian faith and is concentrated on the fact that Christ came to offer abundant life. A study book can be used with the videotapes, and correspondence course worksheets may be completed and returned for review by Cokesbury. A certificate is issued upon completion of the course.

Author: Dunnam, Maxie　　　　　　　　**335**
Series: Bible Study for Christian
Title: *Twelve Parables of Jesus (Volumes 1-3)*
Publisher: Cokesbury, 1988

Num. Sess.	Group Time	Num. Pgs.	Avg. Qst.	Price	Audience	Format	Bible Study
11	90-120	119	Vry	29.95	New Christian	Video	Topical

Features: Intro to Leading a Study, Intro to Study, Prayer Helps, Video Study Guide
★★★★ Personal Application　Preparation Time: Low　ISBN: 0-687-76031-3
★★★ Relationship Building　Ldr. Guide Avail.: Yes　Size: 4.75 x 8.0
Subjects: Christian Living, Parables
Comments: This three-volume study teaches Bible truth through storytelling, or parables. Through them, participants see the world in which Christ lived, as well as His mind and spirit. The study portrays lessons for living in the Kingdom of God. It's valid, relevant subject matter for contemporary Christians. A leader's guide contains insights and questions for use in a group.

Author: Dunn, Richard　　　　　　　　**336**
Series: Small Group Studies
Title: *Where Do You Think Sex Came From?*
Publisher: Victor Books, 1991

Num. Sess.	Group Time	Num. Pgs.	Avg. Qst.	Price	Audience	Format	Bible Study
6	45-60	45	Vry	4.99	Beginner	Workbk	Topical

Features: Prayer Helps, Follow Up
★★★★ Personal Application　Preparation Time: None　ISBN: 0-89693-195-1
★★★★ Relationship Building　Ldr. Guide Avail.: Yes　Size: 5.50 x 8.50
Subjects: Teens: Junior High, Teens: Peer Pressure, Teens: Senior High, Teens: Sexuality
Comments: This six-session study for high school students helps create an environment of acceptance and challenge, and offers a supportive community to strengthen their personal and spiritual growth. Topics covered include looking at God's view of sex and sexuality, expressing God-given sexuality, setting standards for dating relationships, controlling sexual desire, dealing with peer pressure, and encouraging one another to keep commitments.

Author: Dunn, Richard **337**
Series: Small Group Studies
Title: *Why Not Love All of Me?*
Publisher: Victor Books, 1991

Num. Sess.	Group Time	Num. Pgs.	Avg. Qst.	Price	Audience	Format	Bible Study
6	45-60	45	Vry	4.99	Beginner	Workbk	Topical

Features: Prayer Helps, Follow Up
★★★★ Personal Application Preparation Time: None ISBN: 0-89693-183-8
★★★★ Relationship Building Ldr. Guide Avail.: Yes Size: 5.50 x 8.50
Subjects: Teens: Junior High, Teens: Relationships, Teens: Senior High
Comments: This six-session study for high school students helps create an environment of acceptance and challenge and offers a supportive community to strengthen their personal and spiritual growth. Topics covered include a view of the whole person from God's perspective, loving God from inside out, friendships with members of the opposite sex, Christian dating, and developing a "high view" of marriage as God intended.

Author: Eclov, Lee **338**
Series: Fisherman Bible Studyguide
Title: *Church, The: Pictures of Christ's Body*
Publisher: Shaw, 1981

Num. Sess.	Group Time	Num. Pgs.	Avg. Qst.	Price	Audience	Format	Bible Study
12	45-60	55	10	3.95	New Christian	Workbk	Topical

Features: Intro to Leading a Study, Intro to Study, Follow Up
★★★ Personal Application Preparation Time: None ISBN: 0-87788-155-3
★★★ Relationship Building Ldr. Guide Avail.: No Size: 5.0 x 8.25
Subjects: Church Life, Relationships
Comments: What is the Church and how does it work? In the New Testament, Jesus and His apostles often used metaphors—word pictures such as body, bride, family, flock, light, and salt—to describe the Church in concrete ways. The first two segments of this twelve-part study highlight interrelationships within the Church. The next five examine the Church's relationship with her Lord. The last five look at the Church's relationship with the secular world.

Author: Eims, LeRoy **339**
Series:
Title: *Be a Motivational Leader*
Publisher: Victor Books, 1981

Num. Sess.	Group Time	Num. Pgs.	Avg. Qst.	Price	Audience	Format	Bible Study
13	60-90	132	N/A	6.99	Beginner	Book	Topical

Features:
★★★ Personal Application Preparation Time: Med ISBN: 0-89693-008-4
★★★ Relationship Building Ldr. Guide Avail.: Yes Size: 5.50 x 8.0
Subjects: Bible Personalities, Caring, Leadership
Comments: This study helps participants learn how to motivate and equip people to be and do their best for Christ. It outlines time-tested keys leaders need to unlock their greatest treasure—enthusiastic, involved people serving with them. Scriptural directories, especially the teaching of Solomon, and personal experiences are used in lessons on being a responsible, growing, exemplary, inspiring, efficient, caring, goal-oriented, decisive, and competent leader.

Author: Eims, LeRoy **340**
Series:
Title: *Be the Leader You Were Meant to Be*
Publisher: Victor Books, 1975

Num. Sess.	Group Time	Num. Pgs.	Avg. Qst.	Price	Audience	Format	Bible Study
13	60-90	132	N/A	6.99	New Christian	Book	Topical

Features:
★★ Personal Application Preparation Time: Med ISBN: 0-88207-723-6
★★ Relationship Building Ldr. Guide Avail.: Yes Size: 5.50 x 8.0
Subjects: Leadership
Comments: This study analyzes and applies biblical teaching on leadership. The current crisis in leadership makes this look at Old and New Testament truths and Christ's teachings, with their clear and understandable leadership principles, particularly relevant. The study uses illustrations of both biblical principles and personal experiences. A leader's guide with transparency masters is available.

Author: Engstrom Ted W. **341**
Series: NetWork Discussion Guide
Title: *Personal Integrity*
Publisher: Shaw, 1990

Num. Sess.	Group Time	Num. Pgs.	Avg. Qst.	Price	Audience	Format	Bible Study
8	30-45	45	5	3.50	Beginner	Workbk	Topical

Features: Intro to Leading a Study, Intro to Study, Follow Up, Ldr's Notes
★★★★ Personal Application Preparation Time: Low ISBN: 0-87788-671-7
★★★ Relationship Building Ldr. Guide Avail.: No Size: 5.25 x 8.25
Subjects: Accountability, Christian Living, Integrity, Money
Comments: This study will challenge Christians to place their lives under the scrutiny of Scripture regarding honesty and righteousness. Questions deal with participants' personal lives: Are people habitually truthful—even when alone with tax forms? When people fail, do they confess sins, or hide and cover up wrongs? Is integrity practiced at home as well as in the public eye? Participants will be challenged to be habitually truthful and honest.

Author: Engstrom Ted W. **342**
Series: NetWork Discussion Guide
Title: *Redeeming Time*
Publisher: Shaw, 1991

Num. Sess.	Group Time	Num. Pgs.	Avg. Qst.	Price	Audience	Format	Bible Study
8	30-45	48	5	3.50	Beginner	Workbk	Topical

Features: Intro to Leading a Study, Intro to Study, Bibliography, Follow Up, Ldr's Notes
★★★★ Personal Application Preparation Time: Low ISBN: 0-87788-718-7
★★★ Relationship Building Ldr. Guide Avail.: No Size: 5.25 x 8.25
Subjects: Stress, Time, Work
Comments: Eight short lessons help participants gain a biblical perspective on time. Questions discussed include: Who controls your time? Are you busier than ever, but accomplishing less? How can you make time for the important things in life as well as for the urgent? As participants understand the gift of time God gives them, they'll be better prepared to live according to purpose, rather than pressure.

Author: Erdahl, Lowell O.   **343**
Series: Small Group Bible Studies
Title: *Forgiveness*
Publisher: Augsburg Publishing House, 1982

Num. Sess.	Group Time	Num. Pgs.	Avg. Qst.	Price	Audience	Format	Bible Study
6	60-75	24	16	1.15	New Christian	Book	Topical

Features: Intro to Study, Prayer Helps
★★★ Personal Application Preparation Time: None ISBN:
★★★ Relationship Building Ldr. Guide Avail.: No   Size: 8.50 x 5.50
Subjects: Christian Living, Forgiveness, Relationships
Comments: This short, six-session study explores some of the many meanings of forgiveness in daily living. The goal is to gain a better understanding of the theological concept of forgiveness, and also to have a more vital experience of being both forgiven and forgiving.

Author: Erdahl, Lowell O.   **344**
Series: Small Group Bible Studies
Title: *Royalty Redeemed*
Publisher: Augsburg Publishing House, 1976

Num. Sess.	Group Time	Num. Pgs.	Avg. Qst.	Price	Audience	Format	Bible Study
4	60-75	16	21	0.95	New Christian	Book	Charctr

Features: Intro to Study, , Prayer Helps
★★★ Personal Application Preparation Time: None ISBN:
★★★ Relationship Building Ldr. Guide Avail.: No   Size: 8.50 x 5.50
Subjects: Bible Personalities, God
Comments: This small pamphlet includes four sessions on David. It concentrates on the accounts of David's early life, focusing specifically on four instances of his dealings with three prophets, Samuel, Nathan, and Gad. It also takes note of New Testament interpretations of David's significance in terms of promises made to him that find fulfillment in Christ. The main objective is to discover how God accomplishes His loving will for everyone, in spite of the person's sin and weakness.

Author: Erwin, Gayle D.   **345**
Series: Proven Word
Title: *Jesus Style, The*
Publisher: Word, 1983

Num. Sess.	Group Time	Num. Pgs.	Avg. Qst.	Price	Audience	Format	Bible Study
30	45-60	210	4	8.99	Mature Chrstn	Book	Charctr

Features: Intro to Leading a Study, Intro to Study, Ldr's Notes
★★ Personal Application Preparation Time: Low ISBN: 0-8499-2989-X
★★ Relationship Building Ldr. Guide Avail.: No   Size: 5.50 x 8.0
Subjects: Christian Living, Jesus: Life/Teaching, Service, Theology
Comments: The main theme of *The Jesus Style* is that Jesus is the full revelation of the Father and that the clearest definition of His nature is found in Jesus' teachings. The primary trait that flows through the study is servanthood. It is a condensed primer for becoming others-centered, calling participants to touch others with the spirit of servanthood. Written in short, unnumbered chapters, it is accompanied with study questions for a small group.

Author: Eschner, Kathleen Hamilton & Nancy G. Nelson   **346**
Series:
Title: *Drugs, God, and Me*
Publisher: Group Publishing, 1988

Num. Sess.	Group Time	Num. Pgs.	Avg. Qst.	Price	Audience	Format	Bible Study
8	45-60	166	N/A	9.95	New Christian	Book	Topical

Features: Intro to Study, Objectives, Bibliography, Follow Up, Drawings, Handouts, Charts
★★★★ Personal Application Preparation Time: Low ISBN: 0-931529-41-7
★★★★ Relationship Building Ldr. Guide Avail.: No   Size: 6.0 x 9.0
Subjects: Teens: Decisions, Teens:Drugs/Drinking, Teens: Emotions, Teens: Family, Teens: Junior High
Comments: This eight-session program equips junior high students with skills, Christian beliefs, and confidence needed for preventing drug abuse. It helps students value themselves as creations of God, cope with feelings and problems, understand drugs' effects, treat their bodies as temples of God, make healthy decisions, build stronger family relationships, and be a part of the solution to the drug crisis. A three-track study format can be used by young people, parents, or both. Family activities are included.

Author: Evenhouse, Neva   **347**
Series: Discover Your Bible
Title: *Discover: Acts (Part 2)*
Publisher: Church Development Resources, 1985

Num. Sess.	Group Time	Num. Pgs.	Avg. Qst.	Price	Audience	Format	Bible Study
15	60-75	56	9	2.40	Beginner	Workbk	Book

Features: Intro to Study, Summary, Maps
★★★ Personal Application Preparation Time: None ISBN:
★★ Relationship Building Ldr. Guide Avail.: Yes   Size: 5.50 x 8.50
Subjects: Acts, Church Life, Holy Spirit
Comments: This inductive study of Acts 13-22 deals with the Christian church's birth and early years. It documents opposition the church faced from both Jews and Romans, and problems within the church itself. It bears witness to God's Holy Spirit, who guided and empowered the gospel of salvation in Jesus. Participants will be inspired and challenged by the lives of God's people in the early church.

Author: Evenhouse, Neva   **348**
Series: Discover Your Bible
Title: *Discover: Acts (Part 1)*
Publisher: Church Development Resources, 1988

Num. Sess.	Group Time	Num. Pgs.	Avg. Qst.	Price	Audience	Format	Bible Study
13	60-75	48	8	2.10	Beginner	Workbk	Book

Features: Intro to Study, Summary, Charts, Glossary, Maps
★★★ Personal Application Preparation Time: None ISBN:
★★ Relationship Building Ldr. Guide Avail.: Yes   Size: 5.50 x 8.50
Subjects: Acts, Church Life, Holy Spirit
Comments: This inductive study of the book of Acts chapters 1-12 deals with the Christian church's birth and early years. It documents opposition the church faced from both Jews and Romans, and problems within the church itself. It bears witness to God's Holy Spirit, who guided and empowered the gospel of salvation in Jesus. Participants will be inspired and challenged by the lives of God's people in the early church.

Author: Evenhouse, Neva   **349**
Series: Discover Your Bible
Title: *Discover: Colossians*
Publisher: Church Development Resources, 1989

Num. Sess.	Group Time	Num. Pgs.	Avg. Qst.	Price	Audience	Format	Bible Study
6	60-75	23	7	1.10	Beginner	Workbk	Book

Features: Intro to Leading a Study, Summary, Glossary
★★★ Personal Application Preparation Time: None ISBN:
★★ Relationship Building Ldr. Guide Avail.: Yes Size: 5.50 x 8.50
Subjects: Church Life, Colossians/Philemon, Faith, False Teachers, Hope, Service, Suffering
Comments: Colossians, Paul's letter to the Christians at Colosse, communicates with all ages and cultures. He writes about knowing God, about who Jesus Christ is. His warning against false human philosophies and his practical advice on how to live out one's faith are as topical in modern churches as in ancient Colosse. Participants in this inductive study will find out more about who Jesus is, and discover why He stands at the very heart of the Christian faith.

Author: Evenhouse, Neva   **350**
Series: Discover Your Bible
Title: *Discover: Romans (Part 2)*
Publisher: Church Development Resources, 1984

Num. Sess.	Group Time	Num. Pgs.	Avg. Qst.	Price	Audience	Format	Bible Study
10	60-75	40	7	1.70	Beginner	Workbk	Book

Features: Intro to Study, Summary, Glossary
★★★ Personal Application Preparation Time: None ISBN:
★★ Relationship Building Ldr. Guide Avail.: Yes Size: 5.50 x 8.50
Subjects: Faith, Grace, Romans
Comments: This inductive study of Romans chapters 9-16 emphasizes that all people need to be put right with God, which can happen only by faith. It points out that salvation cannot be earned and is undeserved; it is God's gift. Those entering new relationships with God by faith live in union with Christ and are enabled by the Spirit to live Christian lives. These chapters help participants deal with how Christians are to treat one another.

Author: Evenhouse, Neva   **351**
Series: Discover Your Bible
Title: *Discover: Romans (Part 1)*
Publisher: Church Development Resources, 1984

Num. Sess.	Group Time	Num. Pgs.	Avg. Qst.	Price	Audience	Format	Bible Study
16	60-75	56	6	2.55	Beginner	Workbk	Book

Features: Intro to Study, Summary, Glossary
★★★ Personal Application Preparation Time: None ISBN:
★★ Relationship Building Ldr. Guide Avail.: Yes Size: 5.50 x 8.50
Subjects: Faith, Grace, Romans
Comments: This inductive study of Romans chapters 1-8 emphasizes that all people need to be put right with God, which can happen only by faith. It points out that salvation cannot be earned and is undeserved; it is God's gift. Those entering new relationships with God by faith live in union with Christ, and are enabled by the Spirit to live Christian lives. These chapters help participants deal with how Christians are to treat one another.

Author: Evenhouse, Neva   **352**
Series: Discover Your Bible
Title: *Discover: The Gospel of Mark (Part 2)*
Publisher: Church Development Resources, 1985

Num. Sess.	Group Time	Num. Pgs.	Avg. Qst.	Price	Audience	Format	Bible Study
13	60-75	48	7	2.10	Beginner	Workbk	Book

Features: Intro to Study, Summary, Maps
★★★ Personal Application Preparation Time: None ISBN:
★★ Relationship Building Ldr. Guide Avail.: Yes Size: 5.50 x 8.50
Subjects: Jesus: Life/Teaching, Mark
Comments: This inductive study of Mark chapters 9-16 offers a vigorous, straightforward account of Jesus' public ministry—from His baptism to His death and resurrection. Mark wrote this account from information he received from Roman Christians, and he pictured Jesus as a man of action, the powerful Son of God, who "did not come to be served, but to serve, and to give his life as a ransom for many" (Mark 10:45). A comprehensive leader's guide is available.

Author: Evenhouse, Neva   **353**
Series: Discover Your Bible
Title: *Discover: The Gospel of Mark (Part 1)*
Publisher: Church Development Resources, 1985

Num. Sess.	Group Time	Num. Pgs.	Avg. Qst.	Price	Audience	Format	Bible Study
13	60-75	45	7	2.10	Beginner	Workbk	Book

Features: Intro to Study, Summary, Glossary
★★★ Personal Application Preparation Time: None ISBN:
★★ Relationship Building Ldr. Guide Avail.: Yes Size: 5.50 x 8.50
Subjects: Jesus: Life/Teaching, Mark
Comments: This inductive study of Mark chapters 1-8 offers a vigorous, straightforward account of Jesus' public ministry—from His baptism to His death and resurrection. Mark wrote this account from information he received from Roman Christians, and he pictured Jesus as a man of action, the powerful Son of God, who "did not come to be served, but to serve, and to give his life as a ransom for many" (Mark 10:45). A comprehensive leader's guide is available.

Author: Evenhouse, Neva   **354**
Series: Discover Your Bible
Title: *Discover: 1 John*
Publisher: Church Development Resources, 1989

Num. Sess.	Group Time	Num. Pgs.	Avg. Qst.	Price	Audience	Format	Bible Study
6	60-75	21	6	1.10	Beginner	Workbk	Book

Features: Intro to Study, Summary, Glossary
★★★ Personal Application Preparation Time: None ISBN:
★★ Relationship Building Ldr. Guide Avail.: Yes Size: 5.50 x 8.50
Subjects: False Teachers, God, Marriage, 1, 2 & 3 John/Jude
Comments: This inductive study of 1 John helps participants learn what it means that God is "Light" and "Love." John's letter is full of imagery that helps students understand God. It also helps them better understand what it means to believe in God. The letter, written to counter false teachers, helps believers identify and resist false teachings. A comprehensive leader's guide is available.

Author: Evenson, Richard C.   **355**
Series: Small Group Bible Studies
Title: *Songs and Sighs*
Publisher: Augsburg Publishing House, 1976

Num. Sess.	Group Time	Num. Pgs.	Avg. Qst.	Price	Audience	Format	Bible Study
4	60-75	16	Vry	0.95	New Christian	Book	Topical

Features: Intro to Study, Prayer Helps
  ★★ Personal Application   Preparation Time: None   ISBN:
  ★★ Relationship Building   Ldr. Guide Avail.: No   Size: 8.50 x 5.50
Subjects: Psalms, Worship
Comments: This small pamphlet presents four lessons on selected psalms, including: Psalm 19—"A Song of Praise for Creation and Word"; Psalm 107—"An Order of Worship for People Who Have Known Troubles"; Psalms 5, 142, 51, 13, and 150—"Prayers that Cry Out to God"; and Psalm 23—"A Creed in Three States of Life." For each session there are four steps: interpretation and point-of-view; audible reading of the psalm; meditation; and discussion on what thoughts came to each participant.

Author: Eyre, Jacalyn   **356**
Series: Fruit of the Spirit
Title: *Faithfulness: The Foundation of True Friendship*
Publisher: Zondervan, 1991

Num. Sess.	Group Time	Num. Pgs.	Avg. Qst.	Price	Audience	Format	Bible Study
6	45-60	48	12	3.95	New Christian	Workbk	Topical

Features: Intro to Study, Ldr's Notes
  ★★★ Personal Application   Preparation Time: None   ISBN: 0-310-53671-5
  ★★ Relationship Building   Ldr. Guide Avail.: No   Size: 5.50 x 8.50
Subjects: Christian Living, Commitments, Forgiveness, Friendships, Fruit of the Spirit, Relationships
Comments: This six-week study looks at essential qualities participants must acquire to become faithful friends; qualities which help lay a foundation for lasting relationships. Lessons include: "A Commitment to Be There"; "A Willingness to Forgive"; "A Promise of Support"; "Honoring Our Commitments"; "Fulfilling Our Responsibilities"; and "The Rewards of Faithfulness."

Author: Eyre, Stephen   **357**
Series: LifeGuide Bible Study
Title: *Christian Beliefs*
Publisher: InterVarsity, 1989

Num. Sess.	Group Time	Num. Pgs.	Avg. Qst.	Price	Audience	Format	Bible Study
12	45-60	64	12	3.95	Beginner	Workbk	Topical

Features: Intro to Leading a Study, Intro to Study, Ldr's Notes
  ★ Personal Application   Preparation Time: Low   ISBN: 0-8308-1061-7
  ★ Relationship Building   Ldr. Guide Avail.: No   Size: 5.50 x 8.25
Subjects: Beliefs, Christian Living, God, Holy Spirit, Relationships, Theology
Comments: This discussion of Christian beliefs can provide the foundation for a healthy relationship with God and others. It begins with ways God reveals Himself and continues with strength and comfort in His power and building gratitude for a new life in Christ. It offers guidance for developing a relationship with the Holy Spirit, recognizing the effects of sin, renewing fellowship with God, and applying this knowledge in the church.

Author: Eyre, Stephen & Jacalyn   **358**
Series: LifeGuide Bible Study
Title: *Matthew: Being Discipled by Jesus*
Publisher: InterVarsity, 1987

Num. Sess.	Group Time	Num. Pgs.	Avg. Qst.	Price	Audience	Format	Bible Study
24	45-60	96	12	3.95	New Christian	Workbk	Book

Features: Intro to Leading a Study, Intro to Study, Ldr's Notes
  ★ Personal Application   Preparation Time: Low   ISBN: 0-8308-1003-X
  ★ Relationship Building   Ldr. Guide Avail.: No   Size: 5.50 x 8.25
Subjects: Grief, Jesus: Life/Teaching, Matthew, Suffering
Comments: This two-part study of Matthew will help produce better disciples and disciplemakers. The first part, "Discovering the King," focuses on the identity and authority of Jesus; the second part, "The Rejection and Resurrection of the King," focuses on Jesus as He encounters opposition and persecution. It culminates in a look at the Cross and the Resurrection. Matthew, a tax collector, was most concerned with practical application: how to handle anger, envy, suffering, grief, and more.

Author: Eyre, Stephen   **359**
Series: Fruit of the Spirit
Title: *Patience: The Benefits of Waiting*
Publisher: Zondervan, 1991

Num. Sess.	Group Time	Num. Pgs.	Avg. Qst.	Price	Audience	Format	Bible Study
6	45-60	48	12	3.95	New Christian	Workbk	Topical

Features: Intro to Study, Ldr's Notes
  ★★★ Personal Application   Preparation Time: None   ISBN: 0-310-53681-2
  ★★ Relationship Building   Ldr. Guide Avail.: No   Size: 5.50 x 8.50
Subjects: Christian Living, Forgiveness, Fruit of the Spirit, Obedience
Comments: This six-week study, using passages from Proverbs and the New Testament, helps participants appreciate God's kindness so that they will be motivated to be kind to others. Lessons include: "The Benefits of Patience," "The Blessings of Perseverance," "The Virtue of Slowness," "Patience and Forgiveness," "Waiting for the Lord," and "Waiting Until the End."

Author: Finley, Tom   **360**
Series:
Title: *Complete Junior High Bible Study Resource Book #10, The*
Publisher: Gospel Light Publications, 1989

Num. Sess.	Group Time	Num. Pgs.	Avg. Qst.	Price	Audience	Format	Bible Study
13	30-60	190	Vry	14.95	Beginner	Workbk	Topical

Features: Intro to Leading a Study, Intro to Study, Objectives, Prayer Helps, Scrpt Memory Helps, Follow Up, Drawings, Cartoons, Handouts, Publicity Ideas
  ★★★★ Personal Application   Preparation Time: Low   ISBN:
  ★★★★ Relationship Building   Ldr. Guide Avail.: No   Size: 11.0 x 8.50
Subjects: Teens: Bible/Pers., Teens: Junior High, Teens: Old Testament
Comments: This thirteen-week study contains everything necessary for honing junior high students' leadership abilities, and teaching a sensitivity to God as displayed by Abraham, Moses, David, and Daniel. The resource contains session plans for the leader, reproducible classroom worksheets, and take-home sheets. Also included are lecture-oriented Bible study outlines. Action games and clip art illustrations enhance the study.

Author: Finley, Tom   361
Series:
Title: *Complete Junior High Bible Study Resource Book # 3, The*
Publisher: Gospel Light Publications, 1988

Num. Sess.	Group Time	Num. Pgs.	Avg. Qst.	Price	Audience	Format	Bible Study
13	30-60	165	Vry	14.95	Beginner	Workbk	Topical

Features: Intro to Leading a Study, Intro to Study, Objectives, Prayer Helps, Scrpt Memory Helps, Follow Up, Drawings, Cartoons, Handouts, Publicity Ideas
★★★★ Personal Application   Preparation Time: Low   ISBN:
★★★★ Relationship Building   Ldr. Guide Avail.: No   Size: 11.0 x 8.50
Subjects: Teens: Christian Liv, Teens: Decisions, Teens: Junior High, Teens: New Testament, Teens: Relationships
Comments: This thirteen-week study contains everything necessary for teaching important lessons learned from Christ's parables. Lessons titles include "Making Choices," "Building One's Life on Christ," "Being Obedient," "A Believer's Attitude," "Living the Christian Life," and more. The strengthening of participants' relationships with Christ is stressed. The resource includes session plans for the leader, reproducible classroom worksheets, take-home sheets, action games, and clip art.

Author: Finley, Tom   362
Series:
Title: *Complete Junior High Bible Study Resource Book #11, The*
Publisher: Gospel Light Publications, 1989

Num. Sess.	Group Time	Num. Pgs.	Avg. Qst.	Price	Audience	Format	Bible Study
13	30-60	190	Vry	14.95	Beginner	Workbk	Topical

Features: Intro to Leading a Study, Intro to Study, Objectives, Prayer Helps, Scrpt Memory Helps, Follow Up, Drawings, Cartoons, Handouts, Publicity Ideas
★★★★ Personal Application   Preparation Time: Low   ISBN:
★★★★ Relationship Building   Ldr. Guide Avail.: No   Size: 1.0 x 8.50
Subjects: Teens: Discipleship, Teens: Junior High, Teens: New Testament
Comments: This thirteen-week study covers important truths from Ephesians. Topics include spiritual blessings, wisdom, inner strength, unity, maturity, armor, and more. The resource contains session plans for the leader, reproducible classroom worksheets, and take-home sheets. Also included are lecture-oriented Bible study outlines for each lesson. Action games and clip art illustrations enhance the study.

Author: Finley, Tom   363
Series:
Title: *Complete Junior High Bible Study Resource Book #12, The*
Publisher: Gospel Light Publications, 1990

Num. Sess.	Group Time	Num. Pgs.	Avg. Qst.	Price	Audience	Format	Bible Study
13	30-60	210	Vry	14.95	Beginner	Workbk	Charctr

Features: Intro to Leading a Study, Intro to Study, Objectives, Prayer Helps, Scrpt Memory Helps, Follow Up, Drawings, Cartoons, Handouts, Publicity Ideas
★★★★ Personal Application   Preparation Time: Low   ISBN:
★★★★ Relationship Building   Ldr. Guide Avail.: No   Size: 11.0 x 8.50
Subjects: Teens: Bible/Pers., Teens: New Testament, Teens: Old Testament
Comments: This thirteen-week study contains everything necessary for teaching junior high students about several wonderful but often overlooked Bible characters. Those discussed include Ehud, Deborah, Gideon, Hannah, the widow of Zaraphath, Naaman, Josiah, Anna, and others. The resource contains session plans for the leader, reproducible classroom worksheets, and take-home sheets. Also included are lecture-oriented Bible study outlines. Action games and clip art illustrations enhance the study.

Author: Finley, Tom   364
Series:
Title: *Complete Junior High Bible Study Resource Book # 5, The*
Publisher: Gospel Light Publications, 1988

Num. Sess.	Group Time	Num. Pgs.	Avg. Qst.	Price	Audience	Format	Bible Study
13	30-60	180	Vry	14.95	Beginner	Workbk	Topical

Features: Intro to Leading a Study, Intro to Study, Objectives, Prayer Helps, Scrpt Memory Helps, Follow Up, Drawings, Cartoons, Handouts, Publicity Ideas
★★★★ Personal Application   Preparation Time: Low   ISBN:
★★★★ Relationship Building   Ldr. Guide Avail.: No   Size: 11.0 x 8.50
Subjects: Teens: Junior High, Teens: Relationships
Comments: This thirteen-week study contains everything necessary for teaching junior high students about Christians' relationships with God, with themselves, and with others. The resource contains session plans for the leader, reproducible classroom worksheets, and take-home sheets. It also includes lecture-oriented Bible study outlines, action games, and clip art illustrations.

Author: Finley, Tom   365
Series:
Title: *Complete Junior High Bible Study Resource Book # 1, The*
Publisher: Gospel Light Publications, 1987

Num. Sess.	Group Time	Num. Pgs.	Avg. Qst.	Price	Audience	Format	Bible Study
13	30-60	190	Vry	14.95	Beginner	Workbk	Topical

Features: Intro to Leading a Study, Intro to Study, Objectives, Prayer Helps, Scrpt Memory Helps, Follow Up, Drawings, Cartoons, Handouts, Publicity Ideas
★★★★ Personal Application   Preparation Time: Low   ISBN:
★★★★ Relationship Building   Ldr. Guide Avail.: No   Size: 11.0 x 8.50
Subjects: Teens: Bible Study, Teens: Christian Liv, Teens: Discipleship, Teens: Friends, Teens: Junior High, Teens: Prayer
Comments: This thirteen-week study covers the basics of Christianity. It begins with a definition of "belief," then examines the benefits of being a Christian, the cost of discipleship, Bible study, prayer, the Church, the Christlike lifestyle, love, friendship, and the world's influences. The resource contains session plans for the leader, reproducible classroom worksheets, and take-home sheets. Also included are lecture-oriented Bible study outlines, and an optional lesson on "Bible Wars."

Author: Finley, Tom   366
Series:
Title: *Complete Junior High Bible Study Resource Book # 6, The*
Publisher: Gospel Light Publications, 1988

Num. Sess.	Group Time	Num. Pgs.	Avg. Qst.	Price	Audience	Format	Bible Study
13	30-60	164	Vry	14.95	Beginner	Workbk	Topical

Features: Intro to Leading a Study, Intro to Study, Objectives, Prayer Helps, Scrpt Memory Helps, Follow Up, Drawings, Cartoons, Handouts, Publicity Ideas
★★★★ Personal Application   Preparation Time: Low   ISBN:
★★★★ Relationship Building   Ldr. Guide Avail.: No   Size: 11.0 x 8.50
Subjects: Teens: Jesus' Life, Teens: Junior High
Comments: This thirteen-week study contains everything necessary for teaching junior high students about the symbols used to describe Jesus Christ's nature and work: Word, Light, Lamb, Living Water, Bread, Door, Great Physician, Good Shepherd, Resurrection and Life, Vine, High Priest, and Risen Lord. The resource contains session plans for the leader, reproducible classroom worksheets, and take-home sheets. Action games and clip art illustrations enhance the study.

Author: Finley, Tom   **367**
Series:
Title: *Complete Junior High Bible Study Resource Book # 7, The*
Publisher: Gospel Light Publications, 1988

Num. Sess.	Group Time	Num. Pgs.	Avg. Qst.	Price	Audience	Format	Bible Study
13	30-60	180	Vry	14.95	Beginner	Workbk	Topical

Features: Intro to Leading a Study, Intro to Study, Objectives, Prayer Helps, Scrpt Memory Helps, Follow Up, Drawings, Cartoons, Handouts, Publicity Ideas
★★★★ Personal Application   Preparation Time: Low   ISBN:
★★★★ Relationship Building   Ldr. Guide Avail.: No   Size: 11.0 x 8.50
Subjects: Teens: Christian Liv, Teens: Junior High
Comments: This thirteen-week study contains everything necessary for teaching junior high students about God's power, as demonstrated in the early days of the Church. Examples include the power to forgive, share, change, and reach out. The resource contains session plans for the leader, reproducible classroom worksheets, and take-home sheets. Also included are lecture-oriented Bible study outlines. Action games and clip art illustrations enhance the study.

Author: Finley, Tom   **368**
Series:
Title: *Complete Junior High Bible Study Resource Book # 9, The*
Publisher: Gospel Light Publications, 1989

Num. Sess.	Group Time	Num. Pgs.	Avg. Qst.	Price	Audience	Format	Bible Study
13	30-60	190	Vry	14.95	Beginner	Workbk	Topical

Features: Intro to Leading a Study, Intro to Study, Objectives, Prayer Helps, Scrpt Memory Helps, Follow Up, Drawings, Cartoons, Handouts, Publicity Ideas
★★★★ Personal Application   Preparation Time: Low   ISBN:
★★★★ Relationship Building   Ldr. Guide Avail.: No   Size: 11.0 x 8.50
Subjects: Teens: Discipleship, Teens: Junior High, Teens: Theology
Comments: This thirteen-week study contains everything necessary for teaching junior high students profound and life-changing, but easy-to-understand, theological concepts. Chapter titles include: "God," "Grace," "Peace," "Love," "Sin," "Faith," "Worship," "Stewardship," and more. The resource contains session plans for the leader, reproducible classroom worksheets, and take-home sheets. Also included are lecture-oriented Bible study outlines. Action games and clip art illustrations enhance the study.

Author: Finley, Tom   **369**
Series:
Title: *Complete Junior High Bible Study Resource Book # 2, The*
Publisher: Gospel Light Publications, 1987

Num. Sess.	Group Time	Num. Pgs.	Avg. Qst.	Price	Audience	Format	Bible Study
12	30-60	190	Vry	14.95	Beginner	Workbk	Topical

Features: Intro to Leading a Study, Intro to Study, Objectives, Prayer Helps, Scrpt Memory Helps, Follow Up, Drawings, Cartoons, Handouts, Publicity Ideas
★★★★ Personal Application   Preparation Time: Low   ISBN:
★★★★ Relationship Building   Ldr. Guide Avail.: No   Size: 11.0 x 8.50
Subjects: Teens: Jesus' Life, Teens: Junior High, Teens: New Testament
Comments: This twelve-week study, based on Mark's gospel, contains everything necessary for teaching junior high students about Christ. It reveals Christ's identity, His power, and how He handled temptation. Other lessons cover the parable of the sower, self-denial, the humble servant, Christ's predictions of our future, giving one's life to God, the Crucifixion, the Resurrection, and restoration after a believer denies Him. Many helps are provided for leaders, as well as an optional thirteenth lesson on "His Birth."

Author: Finley, Tom   **370**
Series:
Title: *Complete Junior High Bible Study Resource Book # 8, The*
Publisher: Gospel Light Publications, 1989

Num. Sess.	Group Time	Num. Pgs.	Avg. Qst.	Price	Audience	Format	Bible Study
13	30-60	190	Vry	14.95	Beginner	Workbk	Topical

Features: Intro to Leading a Study, Intro to Study, Objectives, Prayer Helps, Scrpt Memory Helps, Follow Up, Drawings, Cartoons, Handouts, Publicity Ideas
★★★★ Personal Application   Preparation Time: Low   ISBN:
★★★★ Relationship Building   Ldr. Guide Avail.: No   Size: 11.0 x 8.50
Subjects: Teens: Christian Liv, Teens: Junior High
Comments: This thirteen-week study contains everything necessary for teaching junior high students practical ways to demonstrate their faith, and about character qualities to set as their goals. Character qualities studied include faith, goodness, and more. The resource contains session plans for the leader, reproducible classroom worksheets, and take-home sheets. Action games and clip art illustrations enhance the study.

Author: Fishel, Kent M. & John W. Rayls   **371**
Series: Cornerstone Series
Title: *Believing the Bible*
Publisher: Zondervan, 1987

Num. Sess.	Group Time	Num. Pgs.	Avg. Qst.	Price	Audience	Format	Bible Study
31	60-90	112	N/A	5.95	Beginner	Workbk	Topical

Features: Intro to Study, Bibliography, Scrpt Memory Helps, Digging Deeper Quest, Drawings, Appendix
★★ Personal Application   Preparation Time: Med   ISBN: 0-310-39761-8
★ Relationship Building   Ldr. Guide Avail.: No   Size: 5.25 x 8.0
Subjects: Apologetics, Teens: Devotionals, Teens: Senior High
Comments: This thirty-one-day devotional focuses on the historical accuracy, reliability, and trustworthiness of the Bible. While intended for teenagers, adults may find it a good introduction to the Bible. For this small group study, the leader must develop appropriate review questions.

Author: Fishel, Kent M. & John W. Rayls   **372**
Series: Cornerstone Series
Title: *Resurrection Evidences: A Bible Study*
Publisher: Zondervan, 1985

Num. Sess.	Group Time	Num. Pgs.	Avg. Qst.	Price	Audience	Format	Bible Study
31	60-90	105	N/A	1.95	New Christian	Workbk	Topical

Features: Intro to Study, Bibliography, Drawings, Appendix
★ Personal Application   Preparation Time: Med   ISBN: 0-310-46102-2
★ Relationship Building   Ldr. Guide Avail.: No   Size: 5.25 x 8.0
Subjects: Apologetics, Teens: Devotionals, Teens: Senior High
Comments: This thirty-one-day devotional focuses on the Resurrection and its importance for believers today. Christ's resurrection forms the foundation of Christian faith; and the series offers proof that it is a historical event. The study is designed for one lesson per day. However, for groups, five lessons can be reviewed in one weekly meeting for six weeks. It's suitable for high school students and adults.

Author: Fisher, Mary 373
Series: Global Issues
Title: *People and Technology*
Publisher: InterVarsity, 1990

Num. Sess.	Group Time	Num. Pgs.	Avg. Qst.	Price	Audience	Format	Bible Study
6	45-60	47	13	4.95	Beginner	Workbk	Topical

Features: Intro to Leading a Study, Intro to Study, Bibliography, Follow Up
★★ Personal Application Preparation Time: Low ISBN: 0-8308-4909-2
★★ Relationship Building Ldr. Guide Avail.: No Size: 5.50 x 8.25
Subjects: Faith, Morals, Social Issues
Comments: This six-week study explores how faith and life intersect in an increasingly complex technological society. Questions addressed include: "Is technology leading us to think differently about ourselves?" and "Is it drawing us away from the mysteries of human relationships?" The introduction states that technology can't help produce an improved moral dimension of life and ministry; it sometimes has to be bypassed for the sake of moral living. Leaders should read first, to determine appropriateness.

Author: Flanagan, Dr. Bill 374
Series:
Title: *Divorce Recovery Workshop: Rebuilding the Castle That Has Come Down*
Publisher: Gospel Films, 1990

Num. Sess.	Group Time	Num. Pgs.	Avg. Qst.	Price	Audience	Format	Bible Study
6	105-120	34	Vry	149.95	Begi nner	Video	Topical

Features: Intro to Study, Bibliography, Study Overview, Agenda, Appendix, Publicity Ideas, Video Study Guide
★★★★ Personal Application Preparation Time: Low ISBN:
★★★★ Relationship Building Ldr. Guide Avail.: Yes Size: 14.0 x 9.0
Subjects: Divorce, Forgiveness, Relationships, Singles Issues
Comments: This three-tape, six-part video workshop deals with divorce recovery. The information is based on Jim Smoke's *Growing Through Divorce,* which should be read prior to taking the course. The six sessions include: "Is This Really Happening to Me," "Coping with Your Ex-spouse," "Assuming New Responsibilities," "Being a Single Parent," "Finding and Experiencing Forgiveness," and "Thinking About New Relationships." The leader's guide includes many "helps" and reproducible participant sheets.

Author: Floding, Matthew & Carolyn Nystrom 375
Series: Young Fisherman Bible
Title: *Who Am I?: A Look in the Mirror*
Publisher: Shaw, 1987

Num. Sess.	Group Time	Num. Pgs.	Avg. Qst.	Price	Audience	Format	Bible Study
8	50-60	60	13	2.95	Beginner	Workbk	Topical

Features: Intro to Study, Scrpt Memory Helps, Full Scrpt Printed
★★ Personal Application Preparation Time: Low ISBN: 0-87788-932-5
★★ Relationship Building Ldr. Guide Avail.: Yes Size: 6.0 x 8.0
Subjects: Teens: Peer Pressure, Teens: Psychology, Teens: Relationships, Teens: Self-image
Comments: This study will help teens answer questions about self-image, changes, and growth. It promotes and guides a self-analysis of their relationship with God and people, by leading them to the Bible for answers. As teens discover and shape their identities, study passages lay the groundwork for pursuing questions such as: Who am I—really? Where do I come from (origin)? Why am I here (purpose)? Leaders are encouraged to be sensitive to participants' responses.

Author: Flynn, Leslie B. 376
Series:
Title: *Other Twelve, The*
Publisher: Victor Books, 1988

Num. Sess.	Group Time	Num. Pgs.	Avg. Qst.	Price	Audience	Format	Bible Study
13	60-75	166	N/A	7.99	New Christian	Book	Charctr

Features: Intro to Study
★★★★ Personal Application Preparation Time: Low ISBN: 0-89693-423-3
★★★ Relationship Building Ldr. Guide Avail.: Yes Size: 5.50 x 8.0
Subjects: Bible Personalities, Failure, Success
Comments: This thirteen-week study explores twelve contemporaries of Paul who helped spread the gospel. They were real people who lived, grew, learned, failed, and succeeded. They were associated with the apostle, and are presented in the chronological order in which they entered Paul's life. Among them are Stephen, the martyr; Barnabas, the supporter; Mark, the restored; James, the Lord's brother; and Titus, the troubleshooter. A leader's guide includes transparency masters.

Author: Flynn, Leslie B. 377
Series:
Title: *Twelve, The*
Publisher: Victor Books, 1982

Num. Sess.	Group Time	Num. Pgs.	Avg. Qst.	Price	Audience	Format	Bible Study
13	60-75	141	N/A	7.99	New Christian	Book	Charctr

Features:
★★★ Personal Application Preparation Time: Low ISBN: 0-88207-310-9
★★★ Relationship Building Ldr. Guide Avail.: Yes Size: 5.50 x 8.0
Subjects: Bible Personalities, Jesus: Life/Teaching
Comments: In this thirteen-week study, Jesus disciples answer several questions, such as "Who were they?" "What were they like before they met Jesus?" and "How did He change them?" The disciples were ordinary men until Jesus touched their lives. The study examines their personalities and actions as recorded in Scripture. A leader's guide includes reproducible transparency masters.

Author: Flynn, Leslie B. 378
Series:
Title: *19 Gifts of the Spirit*
Publisher: Victor Books, 1974

Num. Sess.	Group Time	Num. Pgs.	Avg. Qst.	Price	Audience	Format	Bible Study
13	60-75	200	N/A	7.99	New Christian	Book	Topical

Features: Intro to Study
★★★ Personal Application Preparation Time: Low ISBN: 0-88207-701-5
★★★ Relationship Building Ldr. Guide Avail.: Yes Size: 5.50 x 8.0
Subjects: Spiritual Gifts
Comments: This thirteen-week study answers frequently asked questions on spiritual gifts, including, "What are the 19 gifts?" "Are they all for today?" "What is their purpose?" and "How can one discover and put to use his own gifts?" Answers to these questions, plus a careful examination of gifts revealed in the Bible, are included in this in-depth study. Participants will learn to discover, develop, and use their gifts to build up other believers.

Author: Ford, Leighton **379**
Series: LifeGuide Bible Study
Title: *Meeting Jesus*
Publisher: InterVarsity, 1988

Num. Sess.	Group Time	Num. Pgs.	Avg. Qst.	Price	Audience	Format	Bible Study
13	45-60	79	12	3.95	Beginner	Workbk	Topical

Features: Intro to Leading a Study, Intro to Study, Ldr's Notes
  ★★Personal Application Preparation Time: Low ISBN: 0-8308-1060-9
  ★★Relationship Building Ldr. Guide Avail.: No   Size: 5.50 x 8.25
Subjects: Evangelism, Gospels, Jesus: Life/Teaching
Comments: A study for anyone who wants a fresh look at Jesus. The gospels—Matthew, Mark, Luke, and John—although similar, have unique perspectives on the story of Jesus. This study guide selects thirteen key facets of the story of Jesus that disclose His person, teaching, actions, and claims. Each study explores who Jesus was, and what He can be in our lives today.

Author: Foster, Harry **380**
Series:
Title: *Normal Christian Life, The*
Publisher: Christian Literature Crusade, 1976

Num. Sess.	Group Time	Num. Pgs.	Avg. Qst.	Price	Audience	Format	Bible Study
14	45-60	52	10	5.95	Beginner	Book	Topical

Features: Intro to Study
  ★★★★Personal Application Preparation Time: Low ISBN: 0-87508-418-4
  ★★Relationship Building Ldr. Guide Avail.: No   Size: 4.25 x 7.0
Subjects: Christian Life, Faith
Comments: This is a companion guide to the book by the same title. Each of fourteen chapters draws attention to salient factors and suggests questions for thought and discussion. This classic study traces in practical terms the steps along the pathway of faith and presents God's eternal purpose in simple terms. Its central theme: "Christ Our Life."

Author: Friesen, Garry & J. Robin Maxon **381**
Series:
Title: *Decision Making and the Will of God*
Publisher: Multnomah Press, 1983

Num. Sess.	Group Time	Num. Pgs.	Avg. Qst.	Price	Audience	Format	Bible Study
12	90-120	41	N/A	2.95	New Christian	Book	Topical

Features: Intro to Leading a Study, Intro to Study
  ★★★Personal Application Preparation Time: Med ISBN: 0-88070-021-1
  ★★★Relationship Building Ldr. Guide Avail.: No   Size: 5.50 x 8.50
Subjects: Christian Life, Decision Making
Comments: This study guide is designed to lead Christians through the process of determining God's will for their lives. Divided into twelve lessons, it should be completed in three months; and although individuals can use it, the intended use is for small groups. Each session is divided into parts: purpose, questions to consider, case studies, exercises, projects, and discussion. Lesson titles include: "You Have Heard It Said," "In Search of the Missing Dot," and more.

Author: Fromer, Margaret & Carolyn Nystrom **382**
Series: Young Fisherman Bible
Title: *Acts: Mission Accomplished*
Publisher: Shaw, 1979

Num. Sess.	Group Time	Num. Pgs.	Avg. Qst.	Price	Audience	Format	Bible Study
16	50-60	93	14	2.95	New Christian	Workbk	Book

Features: Intro to Study, Drawings, Maps, Exam
  ★★Personal Application Preparation Time: Low ISBN: 0-87788-010-7
  ★★Relationship Building Ldr. Guide Avail.: Yes Size: 6.0 x 8.0
Subjects: Teens: Discipleship, Teens: New Testament
Comments: This chapter-by-chapter study of Acts 13-28 is a companion to Fromer and Nystrom's study on Acts 1-12. It discusses topics such as: How can I experience the Holy Spirit's power? Why choose Jesus? Do I quit too soon? What's a good Christian fight? Can God make a slave feel free? Who is my God? What can I do when I'm discouraged? Am I a fake? and, Christian: definition please?

Author: Fromer, Margaret **383**
Series: Fisherman Bible Studyguide
Title: *Genesis: Walking with God (Revised Edition)*
Publisher: Shaw, 1991

Num. Sess.	Group Time	Num. Pgs.	Avg. Qst.	Price	Audience	Format	Bible Study
25	45-60	96	12	3.95	Beginner	Workbk	Book

Features: Intro to Leading a Study, Intro to Study, Prayer Helps, Follow Up
  ★★★Personal Application Preparation Time: None ISBN: 0-87788-359-9
  ★★Relationship Building Ldr. Guide Avail.: No   Size: 5.0 x 8.25
Subjects: Bible Personalities, Genesis, God
Comments: This study, which combines two former titles into one expanded edition, explores such fascinating Bible characters as Adam, Eve, Noah, Abraham, Sarah, Isaac, Jacob, and Joseph. In meeting some of God's first friends, and studying Bible passages in Genesis, participants learn to walk more intimately with Him.

Author: Fromer, Margaret & Sharrel Keyes **384**
Series: Fisherman Bible Studyguide
Title: *Jonah, Habakkuk & Malachi: Living Responsibly*
Publisher: Shaw, 1982

Num. Sess.	Group Time	Num. Pgs.	Avg. Qst.	Price	Audience	Format	Bible Study
12	45-60	68	11	3.95	Beginner	Workbk	Book

Features: Intro to Leading a Study, Intro to Study, Prayer Helps, Ldr's Notes
  ★★★Personal Application Preparation Time: None ISBN: 0-87788-432-3
  ★★Relationship Building Ldr. Guide Avail.: No   Size: 5.0 x 8.25
Subjects: Bible Personalities, Holiness, Minor Prophets, Old Testament
Comments: This study of Jonah, Habakkuk, and Malachi shows how, then and now, God confronts individuals through His prophets, reminding them of His holiness, of His character, of the breadth of His perspective and love, and of the kind of responsible living He desires for all people. Each book demonstrates the prophet's change of heart toward God and His ways, as the prophet gains a deeper understanding of what it means to live responsibly in God's sight. Optional questions precede each lesson.

Author: Fromer, Margaret & Sharrel Keyes   **385**
Series: Fisherman Bible Studyguide
Title: *Let's Pray Together*
Publisher: Shaw, 1974

Num. Sess.	Group Time	Num. Pgs.	Avg. Qst.	Price	Audience	Format	Bible Study
8	45-60	63	6	3.95	New Christian	Workbk	Topical

Features: Intro to Leading a Study, Intro to Study, Prayer Helps, Full Scrpt Printed, Ldr's Notes
★★★★ Personal Application   Preparation Time: None   ISBN: 0-87788-801-9
★★★★ Relationship Building   Ldr. Guide Avail.: No   Size: 5.0 x 8.25
Subjects: Discipleship, Prayer
Comments: Prayer is taught as the expression of a living relationship with Jesus, who speaks, listens and answers, and shows how it can be more effective in your life. Groups will discuss the context of eight prayers taken from the Bible, and will pray together based on these biblical models. This study becomes a workshop in which prayer is immediately practiced. The study includes "quiet time" assignments.

Author: Fromer, Margaret & Sharrel Keyes   **386**
Series: Fisherman Bible Studyguide
Title: *Letters to the Thessalonians*
Publisher: Shaw, 1975

Num. Sess.	Group Time	Num. Pgs.	Avg. Qst.	Price	Audience	Format	Bible Study
8	45-60	47	10	3.95	New Christian	Workbk	Book

Features: Intro to Leading a Study, Intro to Study, Pre-discussion Quest, Ldr's Notes
★★ Personal Application   Preparation Time: Low   ISBN: 0-87788-489-7
★★ Relationship Building   Ldr. Guide Avail.: No   Size: 5.0 x 8.25
Subjects: False Teachers, Theology, 1 & 2 Thessalonians
Comments: This study is a response to the questions and problems new Christians were facing in Thessalonica. Paul's ministry there had been cut short, so his letters continued the discipleship course. Four things stand out: Paul's deep personal love for his readers; his concern that they stand for the truth about God and Jesus; his insistence that this right doctrine make a practical difference in their lives; and his instruction about Jesus' coming again from Heaven so that they will not be misled by false teachers.

Author: Fromer, Margaret & Sharrel Keyes   **387**
Series: Fisherman Bible Studyguide
Title: *Letters to Timothy: Discipleship in Action*
Publisher: Shaw, 1974

Num. Sess.	Group Time	Num. Pgs.	Avg. Qst.	Price	Audience	Format	Bible Study
13	45-60	80	12	3.95	New Christian	Workbk	Book

Features: Intro to Leading a Study, Intro to Study, Pre-discussion Quest, Ldr's Notes, Charts
★★ Personal Application   Preparation Time: Low   ISBN: 0-87788-490-0
★★ Relationship Building   Ldr. Guide Avail.: No   Size: 5.0 x 8.25
Subjects: Caring, Discipleship, Leadership, 1 & 2 Timothy/Titus
Comments: This chapter-by-chapter study of 1 & 2 Timothy is practical for those who struggle with a sense of inadequacy in the face of church problems and errant doctrine. Paul's letters to Timothy reflect Timothy's need for encouragement and confidence building. Paul's example of how to care and love, build up, and pray for others is one all can learn from. The study also covers developing leadership within the Christian community.

Author: Fromer, Paul & Margaret   **388**
Series: Workshop Series
Title: *Workshop on the Book of Philippians, A*
Publisher: Zondervan, 1982

Num. Sess.	Group Time	Num. Pgs.	Avg. Qst.	Price	Audience	Format	Bible Study
10	60-75	106	12	4.95	New Christian	Workbk	Book

Features: Intro to Leading a Study, Intro to Study, Prayer Helps, Scrpt Memory Helps, Pre-discussion Quest, Follow Up, Full Scrpt Printed, Ldr's Notes, Maps
★★★ Personal Application   Preparation Time: Med   ISBN: 0-310-44771-2
★★ Relationship Building   Ldr. Guide Avail.: No   Size: 5.25 x 8.0
Subjects: Christian Living, Emotions, Hope, Joy, Philippians, Prison Epistles, Psychology, Stress, Victorious Living
Comments: This study of Philippians helps participants who are struggling to cope put into perspective concerns such as their roles in life, boredom with routine, anxiety, depression, and dissatisfaction. It combines sound biblical study with insights from popular psychology, and addresses the issues: "What to do when the roof falls in," "How to turn feelings into actions," "How God gives contentment—no matter what," and "Why some think 'humility' is a nasty word."

Author: Fromer, Paul & Margaret   **389**
Series: Workshop Series
Title: *Workshop on the Book of Colossians, A*
Publisher: Zondervan, 1986

Num. Sess.	Group Time	Num. Pgs.	Avg. Qst.	Price	Audience	Format	Bible Study
10	60-75	128	15	5.95	New Christian	Workbk	Book

Features: Intro to Leading a Study, Intro to Study, Follow Up, Full Scrpt Printed, Ldr's Notes, Persnl Study Quest
★★★ Personal Application   Preparation Time: Low   ISBN: 0-310-44801-8
★★ Relationship Building   Ldr. Guide Avail.: No   Size: 5.25 x 8.0
Subjects: Christian Living, Colossians/Philemon, Emotions, God, Hope, Prison Epistles, Relationships
Comments: This study of Colossians shows that life can have order even in the midst of chaos. Questions help participants deal with several "how to's," including becoming friendly with God, instead of disinterested; overcoming feelings of helplessness; living in the middle of life's hurts; and finding "something more" in relationships. Participants will find hope and answers for life's hard questions. A homework section reinforces each lesson.

Author: Fryling, Alice   **390**
Series:
Title: *Disciple-Makers' Handbook*
Publisher: InterVarsity, 1989

Num. Sess.	Group Time	Num. Pgs.	Avg. Qst.	Price	Audience	Format	Bible Study
13	-	210	N/A	8.95	Mature Chrstn	Book	No

Features: Intro to Study, Bibliography, Appendix
Personal Application   Preparation Time: ISBN: 0-8308-1266-0
Relationship Building   Ldr. Guide Avail.:   Size: 5.50 x 8.25
Subjects: Caring, Discipleship, Faith, Friendships, Relationships, Small Group Resource
Comments: This book shows readers how to help others grow in their faith. It describes how to begin a healthy discipling relationship, and how to disciple. It offers practical help in the following: overcoming fears about discipling others, beginning a discipling relationship, learning to be a friend, learning how people change, modeling the Christian life, using Scripture in disciplemaking, helping a friend who hurts, and helping others share their faith. Many chapters also include time-tested resources.

Author: Fryling, Alice & Robert 391
Series:
Title: *Handbook for Engaged Couples, A*
Publisher: InterVarsity, 1977

Num. Sess.	Group Time	Num. Pgs.	Avg. Qst.	Price	Audience	Format	Bible Study
15	45-60	72	6	4.95	Beginner	Workbk	Topical

Features: Intro to Study, Bibliography
★★★★ Personal Application Preparation Time: Low ISBN: 0-87784-363-5
★★★★ Relationship Building Ldr. Guide Avail.: No Size: 5.50 x 8.25
Subjects: Commitments, Marriage, Parenting, Relationships
Comments: This fifteen-week study is primarily for engaged couples who view engagement as a serious commitment that leads to the deepest and most permanent of human relationships. It encourages open, honest communication in the light of Scripture. It helps familiarize couples with each other's long-range ambitions, vacation preferences, and philosophy on child-rearing. It also helps them resolve differences. The study covers the time of engagement, as well as the first months together.

Author: Fryling, Alice & Robert 392
Series:
Title: *Handbook for Married Couples, A*
Publisher: InterVarsity, 1984

Num. Sess.	Group Time	Num. Pgs.	Avg. Qst.	Price	Audience	Format	Bible Study
13	45-60	92	5	4.95	Beginner	Workbk	Topical

Features: Intro to Study, Bibliography
★★★ Personal Application Preparation Time: Low ISBN: 0-87784-923-4
★★★ Relationship Building Ldr. Guide Avail.: No Size: 5.50 x 8.25
Subjects: Decision Making, Failure, Joy, Marriage, Money, Sexual Issues
Comments: This fourteen-week study is designed for husbands and wives who want to stay out of marital trouble and focus on a course of growth and joy. It helps them achieve a nurtured marriage that is also fun. The format features a manageable series of readings and exercises, and homework is recommended. Topics covered include communication, conflict resolution, decision making, money, spiritual growth, sexual fulfillment, failure, and setting goals.

Author: Fuelling, Daniel W. & Audrey E. Rothmaler 393
Series: Small Group Bible Studies
Title: *End-times*
Publisher: Augsburg Publishing House, 1984

Num. Sess.	Group Time	Num. Pgs.	Avg. Qst.	Price	Audience	Format	Bible Study
4	60-75	16	11	0.95	New Christian	Book	Topical

Features: Intro to Study, Prayer Helps
★★★ Personal Application Preparation Time: None ISBN:
★★★ Relationship Building Ldr. Guide Avail.: No Size: 8.50 x 5.50
Subjects: Apocalyptic, God
Comments: This small pamphlet includes four sessions on the end times. When Christians speak of end times, they are usually referring to events that will occur at the end of history (the Greek word for this is *apocalypse*). Their purpose is to encourage those living in troubled times. This study looks at the relationship of Old and New Testament apocalyptic images, some common apocalyptic terms, and the heart of the apocalyptic message—God's sovereign rule.

Author: Gabriel, Ginger 394
Series:
Title: *Being a Woman of God*
Publisher: Here's Life, 1984

Num. Sess.	Group Time	Num. Pgs.	Avg. Qst.	Price	Audience	Format	Bible Study
12	45-60	61	Vry	4.25	New Christian	Workbk	Topical

Features: Intro to Study, Drawings, Charts
★★ Personal Application Preparation Time: Low ISBN: 0-86605-144-9
★★ Relationship Building Ldr. Guide Avail.: No Size: 5.0 x 8.0
Subjects: Emotions, Friendships, Relationships, Singles Issues, Women's Issues
Comments: This is a women's Bible study of qualities that result in God's blessings and enhanced personal effectiveness. Topics of interest to both single and married women include self-acceptance, relationship with God, development of close friends, and emotional needs. Each lesson is assigned a specific objective.

Author: Gage, Joy P. 395
Series: A Bible Study for Women
Title: *Heart for Obedience, A*
Publisher: Victor Books, 1988

Num. Sess.	Group Time	Num. Pgs.	Avg. Qst.	Price	Audience	Format	Bible Study
8	60-90	96	9	5.99	New Christian	Workbk	Book

Features: Intro to Study, Objectives, Follow Up, Ldr's Notes, Persnl Study Quest
★★★ Personal Application Preparation Time: Med ISBN: 0-89693-421-7
★★ Relationship Building Ldr. Guide Avail.: No Size: 6.0 x 9.0
Subjects: Numbers/Deuteronomy, Failure, God's Promises, Obedience, Repentance, Service, Women's Issues
Comments: This study of Deuteronomy helps participants see that even after failure they can make a new start. Eight lessons address disobedience, the path to restoration, repentance and restoration, serving God, being open to change, God's promises, focusing on His person, and being aware of God's mercies. Participants can rid themselves of failure and imperfection by growing in obedience to Him.

Author: Gage, Joy P. 396
Series: A Bible Study for Women
Title: *Wrestling with Obedience*
Publisher: Victor Books, 1991

Num. Sess.	Group Time	Num. Pgs.	Avg. Qst.	Price	Audience	Format	Bible Study
8	60-75	94	14	5.99	Beginner	Workbk	Charctr

Features: Intro to Study, Prayer Helps, Ldr's Notes
★★★★ Personal Application Preparation Time: Med ISBN: 0-89693-147-1
★★★ Relationship Building Ldr. Guide Avail.: No Size: 6.0 x 9.0
Subjects: Bible Personalities, Commitments, Exodus, God, Obedience, Women's Issues
Comments: This 8-week study provides important principles for growing in obedience to God. It examines Moses' life in looking at the struggles people go through. It starts with making a commitment, then dealing with the obstacles, saying "yes" to God, persisting, leaving the results to God, gaining a perspective on the promises, standing on the promises, and guarding against setbacks. Moses reflects obedience continuing to develop, because he continued to obey whether or not he wanted to.

Author: Gaiser, Frederick J.   **397**
Series: Men's Bible Study Series
Title: *Psalms*
Publisher: Augsburg Publishing House, 1988

Num. Sess.	Group Time	Num. Pgs.	Avg. Qst.	Price	Audience	Format	Bible Study
10	30-45	48	12	3.0	New Christian	Workbk	Book

Features: Intro to Study, Prayer Helps, Summary
★★★★ Personal Application   Preparation Time: None   ISBN:
★★★★ Relationship Building   Ldr. Guide Avail.: Yes   Size: 4.50 x 9.50
Subjects: Men's Issues, Psalms, Victorious Living
Comments: This ten-lesson study explores—in three groups of three sessions each—how Psalms responds to three important questions: "Who am I?" "Who is my neighbor?" and "Who is God?" The tenth lesson examines the confident Christian life, which acknowledges that "the Lord is my shepherd." It may be used at prayer breakfasts, men's Bible study groups, or any other men's meetings.

Author: Galvin, Dr. James C., et al.   **398**
Series: Life Application
Title: *Daniel*
Publisher: Tyndale House, 1989

Num. Sess.	Group Time	Num. Pgs.	Avg. Qst.	Price	Audience	Format	Bible Study
13	60-90	84	12	4.95	New Christian	Workbk	Book

Features: Intro to Leading a Study, Intro to Study, Study Overview, Digging Deeper Quest, Full Scrpt Printed, Drawings, Charts, Maps, Cross Ref
★★★ Personal Application   Preparation Time: Med   ISBN: 0-8423-2731-2
★★★ Relationship Building   Ldr. Guide Avail.: No   Size: 6.50 x 9.0
Subjects: Caring, Daniel, Faith, God, Major Prophets
Comments: This study, which contains the complete text of Daniel, gives a historical account of the faithful Jews who lived in captivity and shows how God is in control of Heaven and earth, directing the nations and caring for His people. The study is divided into two main sections, Daniel's life (1:1–6:28) and Daniel's visions (7:1–12:13). Questions lead to application of biblical truth and action plans.

Author: Galvin, Dr. James C., et al.   **399**
Series: Life Application
Title: *Mark*
Publisher: Tyndale House, 1989

Num. Sess.	Group Time	Num. Pgs.	Avg. Qst.	Price	Audience	Format	Bible Study
13	60-90	120	10	4.95	New Christian	Workbk	Book

Features: Intro to Leading a Study, Intro to Study, Study Overview, Digging Deeper Quest, Full Scrpt Printed, Drawings, Charts, Maps, Cross Ref, Appendix
★★★ Personal Application   Preparation Time: Med   ISBN: 0-8423-2715-0
★★★ Relationship Building   Ldr. Guide Avail.: No   Size: 6.50 x 9.0
Subjects: Jesus: Life/Teaching, Mark
Comments: This study contains the complete text of Mark, which presents the person, work, and teachings of Jesus. Mark was the first gospel written, and the other gospels quote all but thirty-one of its verses. Mark records more miracles than any other gospel. The study has three main parts: Jesus' birth and preparation; Jesus' message and ministry; and Jesus' death and resurrection. Questions lead to application of biblical truth and action plans.

Author: Galvin, Dr. James C., et al.   **400**
Series: Life Application
Title: *1, 2 Timothy & Titus*
Publisher: Tyndale House, 1989

Num. Sess.	Group Time	Num. Pgs.	Avg. Qst.	Price	Audience	Format	Bible Study
13	60-90	84	15	4.95	New Christian	Workbk	Book

Features: Intro to Leading a Study, Intro to Study, Study Overview, Digging Deeper Quest, Full Scrpt Printed, Drawings, Charts, Maps, Cross Ref
★★★ Personal Application   Preparation Time: Med   ISBN: 0-8423-2734-7
★★★ Relationship Building   Ldr. Guide Avail.: No   Size: 6.50 x 9.0
Subjects: Church Life, Faith, Leadership, Marriage, Obedience, Pastoral Epistles, Service, Theology, 1 & 2 Timothy/Titus
Comments: This study contains the complete text of 1 and 2 Timothy and Titus. First Timothy is a personal letter and a handbook of church administration and discipline. It offers instructions on right beliefs and instructions for the church and its leaders. Second Timothy reveals Paul's heart and his priorities: sound doctrine, steadfast faith, confident endurance, and enduring love. It offers foundations of Christian service. Titus is similar to 1 Timothy with its instructions to church leaders.

Author: Gangel, Kenneth O.   **401**
Series:
Title: *Unwrap Your Spiritual Gifts: A Complete Coverage of God-Given Abilities*
Publisher: Victor Books, 1983

Num. Sess.	Group Time	Num. Pgs.	Avg. Qst.	Price	Audience	Format	Bible Study
13	60-90	117	N/A	6.99	New Christian	Book	Topical

Features:
★★★ Personal Application   Preparation Time: Med   ISBN: 0-88207-102-5
★★ Relationship Building   Ldr. Guide Avail.: Yes   Size: 5.50 x 8.0
Subjects: Christian Living, Church Life, New Testament, Spiritual Gifts
Comments: This study reviews abilities which help participants identify and use God-given spiritual gifts. By studying the New Testament, participants learn the difference between spiritual gifts and natural talents. Believers are encouraged to go beyond identifying their gifts to developing and using them for growing a local church and for building up all believers. A leader's guide with transparency masters is available.

Author: Gates, Rebecca   **402**
Series: A Bible Study for Women
Title: *Beauty of a Disciplined Life, The*
Publisher: Victor Books, 1987

Num. Sess.	Group Time	Num. Pgs.	Avg. Qst.	Price	Audience	Format	Bible Study
10	60-90	96	9	5.99	New Christian	Workbk	Book

Features: Intro to Leading a Study, Intro to Study, Objectives, Follow Up, Summary, Ldr's Notes
★★★ Personal Application   Preparation Time: Med   ISBN: 0-89693-248-6
★★ Relationship Building   Ldr. Guide Avail.: No   Size: 6.0 x 9.0
Subjects: Friendships, Marriage, Money, Proverbs, Relationships, Self-esteem, Stress, Wisdom, Women's Issues
Comments: These ten lessons from Proverbs help participants acquire and practice self-discipline that can help contemporary women resolve problems such as hectic schedules, financial burdens, marital stress, relational problems, and low self-esteem. Lessons cover the disciplines of wisdom, marital faithfulness, energy, quietness, speech, humility, planning, financial management, friendship, and trust.

Author: Getz, Gene A.   **403**
Series:
Title: *Measure of a Man, The*
Publisher: Regal Books, 1974

Num. Sess.	Group Time	Num. Pgs.	Avg. Qst.	Price	Audience	Format	Bible Study
21	45-60	220	Vry	6.95	New Christian	Book	Topical

Features: Intro to Study
★★★ Personal Application Preparation Time: Low ISBN: 0-8307-1031-0
★★ Relationship Building Ldr. Guide Avail.: No Size: 5.25 x 8.0
Subjects: Church Life, Discipleship, Leadership, Men's Issues, Pastoral Epistles, Service, 1 & 2 Timothy/Titus
Comments: This study gives the Apostle Paul's profile for Christian maturity. Through his letters to Timothy and Titus, he spells out in detail the qualifications for men who serve as leaders in the church. However, most of the twenty characteristics and qualities are applied to all Christians in other letters; and Paul speaks to women as well. Following an introduction are twenty-one lessons with titles like: "Above Reproach," "Husband of One Wife," "Not Addicted to Wine," "Not Quick-Tempered," and more.

Author: Getz, Gene A.   **404**
Series: Biblical Renewal Series
Title: *Building Up One Another*
Publisher: Victor Books, 1976

Num. Sess.	Group Time	Num. Pgs.	Avg. Qst.	Price	Audience	Format	Bible Study
13	60-75	120	N/A	6.99	New Christian	Book	Topical

Features: Intro to Study
★★★★ Personal Application Preparation Time: Low ISBN: 0-88207-744-9
★★★ Relationship Building Ldr. Guide Avail.: Yes Size: 5.50 x 8.0
Subjects: Caring, Church Life, Relationships, Service
Comments: This study discusses twelve significant actions Christians must take toward one another to build up the Body of Christ. Each lesson includes a practical section, a series of steps for employing these actions. The twelve actions include, among others, honoring, accepting, greeting, serving, submitting, and encouraging one another.

Author: Getz, Gene A.   **405**
Series: Biblical Renewal Series
Title: *Encouraging One Another*
Publisher: Victor Books, 1981

Num. Sess.	Group Time	Num. Pgs.	Avg. Qst.	Price	Audience	Format	Bible Study
13	60-75	143	N/A	7.99	New Christian	Book	Topical

Features: Intro to Study, Maps
★★★★ Personal Application Preparation Time: Low ISBN: 0-88207-256-0
★★★ Relationship Building Ldr. Guide Avail.: Yes Size: 5.50 x 8.0
Subjects: Acts, Bible Personalities, Caring, Church Life, Relationships
Comments: This study stresses the need for Christians to encourage one another. A major portion follows the chronological and sequential development of Christianity in the book of Acts. Barnabas, whose name means "son of encouragement," is an outstanding model. His "encouraging" lifestyle illustrates the process of mutual ministry for every member of the Body of Christ. Each chapter closes with a challenge, prayer, or "life response" segment.

Author: Getz, Gene A.   **406**
Series:
Title: *Joseph: Finding God's Strength in Times of Trial*
Publisher: Regal Books, 1983

Num. Sess.	Group Time	Num. Pgs.	Avg. Qst.	Price	Audience	Format	Bible Study
13	60-75	168	Vry	6.95	New Christian	Book	Topical

Features:
★★★★ Personal Application Preparation Time: Med ISBN: 0-8307-1347-6
★★★★ Relationship Building Ldr. Guide Avail.: Yes Size: 5.0 x 8.0
Subjects: Bible Personalities, Parenting, Suffering
Comments: This study shows, through a look at Joseph's life, that God sometimes allows His children to suffer in order to accomplish His special purposes for their lives. Participants will find strength in God's arms when suffering, as did Joseph. This study looks at the effects of family background, what happens when parents show favoritism, and more. A separate leader's guide offers an eight- to thirteen-week study format. A reproducible lesson handout section is included.

Author: Getz, Gene A.   **407**
Series: Biblical Renewal Series
Title: *Loving One Another*
Publisher: Victor Books, 1979

Num. Sess.	Group Time	Num. Pgs.	Avg. Qst.	Price	Audience	Format	Bible Study
13	60-75	143	N/A	7.99	New Christian	Book	Topical

Features: Charts
★★★★ Personal Application Preparation Time: Low ISBN: 0-88207-786-4
★★★ Relationship Building Ldr. Guide Avail.: Yes Size: 5.50 x 8.0
Subjects: Caring, Church Life, Evangelism
Comments: This study offers a total New Testament perspective on evangelism. God's plan is that His body of believers become a community in which personal witnessing and evangelistic preaching are intensely productive. This study shows participants how to achieve greater unity and fruitfulness, in their lives as well as their churches. Each chapter closes with a "Personal Response" section designed to challenge to action.

Author: Getz, Gene A.   **408**
Series:
Title: *Measure of a Woman, The*
Publisher: Regal Books, 1977

Num. Sess.	Group Time	Num. Pgs.	Avg. Qst.	Price	Audience	Format	Bible Study
14	45-60	140	Vry	7.95	Beginner	Book	Topical

Features: Intro to Leading a Study, Intro to Study
★★★ Personal Application Preparation Time: Low ISBN: 0-8307-1386-7
★★ Relationship Building Ldr. Guide Avail.: No Size: 5.0 x 8.0
Subjects: Family, Women's Issues, Work, 1 & 2 Peter, 1 & 2 Timothy/Titus
Comments: This biblical study of womanhood and femininity offers tested and proven guidelines from 1 Timothy, Titus, and 1 Peter. God's Word differentiates between the world's view of female beauty and the higher, more meaningful standards that make a woman pleasing in His sight. Among the topics discussed are God's perspective on beauty, what makes a woman worthy of respect, how to feel good about oneself, what makes a wife a good lover, and how career and family mix.

Author: Getz, Gene A.   **409**
Series: Biblical Renewal Series
Title: *Praying for One Another*
Publisher: Victor Books, 1982

Num. Sess.	Group Time	Num. Pgs.	Avg. Qst.	Price	Audience	Format	Bible Study
13	60-75	132	N/A	6.99	New Christian	Book	Topical

Features: Intro to Study, Charts
★★★★ Personal Application Preparation Time: Low ISBN: 0-88207-351-6
★★★ Relationship Building Ldr. Guide Avail.: Yes Size: 5.50 x 8.0
Subjects: Caring, Christian Life, Prayer
Comments: This study focuses on corporate, or "body," prayer, rather than personal, or individual, prayer. Both kinds of prayer are important. Yet in Acts, nearly all references to prayer concern prayer in groups. This study traces the activities and growth of the early Church, demonstrating how "body" praying can be a key to releasing God's power. Topics covered include prayer as a privilege, the meaning of "continuous" prayer, the importance of praise in prayers, and more. Transparency masters are included.

Author: Getz, Gene A.   **410**
Series: Biblical Renewal Series
Title: *Serving One Another*
Publisher: Victor Books, 1984

Num. Sess.	Group Time	Num. Pgs.	Avg. Qst.	Price	Audience	Format	Bible Study
13	60-75	153	N/A	7.99	New Christian	Book	Topical

Features:
★★★★ Personal Application Preparation Time: Low ISBN: 0-88207-612-4
★★★ Relationship Building Ldr. Guide Avail.: Yes Size: 5.50 x 8.0
Subjects: Caring, Church Life, Relationships, Service
Comments: This study explores biblical standards of servanthood, based on selected passages from Paul's letters. Participants will be challenged to complete multiple-choice statements such as: "When I'm asked to take part in some form of Christian ministry I always agree, make excuses, or run for cover"; or "Being a good servant means I will always help, help when I feel like it, do what I'm told, or lose control." No matter what the response, there's always room for improvement.

Author: Gibson, Eva & Steve Price   **411**
Series: Building Books
Title: *Building Christian Values*
Publisher: Bethany House, 1989

Num. Sess.	Group Time	Num. Pgs.	Avg. Qst.	Price	Audience	Format	Bible Study
34	45-60	68	Vry	4.95	New Christian	Workbk	Topical

Features: Intro to Study
★★ Personal Application Preparation Time: Low ISBN: 1-556-61024-6
★★ Relationship Building Ldr. Guide Avail.: Yes Size: 8.50 x 11.0
Subjects: Teens: Christian Liv, Teens: Decisions, Teens: Discipleship, Teens: Ethics
Comments: This thirty-four-lesson in-depth study is designed to help young adults develop value systems that harmonize with the holiness of God, and equip them with God's Word to help them make wise decisions. Five major sections track values that can be built by looking at who God is, by participating in the wisdom of Jesus Christ, through practical application of God's Word, by seeing how Joseph grew spiritually, and by living what we believe.

Author: Gibson, Eva & Steve Price   **412**
Series: Building Books
Title: *Building Christian Confidence*
Publisher: Bethany House, 1987

Num. Sess.	Group Time	Num. Pgs.	Avg. Qst.	Price	Audience	Format	Bible Study
34	45-60	79	Vry	4.95	New Christian	Workbk	Topical

Features: Intro to Study, Scrpt Memory Helps
★★ Personal Application Preparation Time: Low ISBN: 0-87123-934-5
★★ Relationship Building Ldr. Guide Avail.: Yes Size: 8.50 x 11.0
Subjects: Teens: Discipleship
Comments: This thirty-four-lesson study offers young people a deepened understanding of God and how He has created them. It helps them examine the truth of their own unique position in God's creative design, through consideration of four major issues: "Seeing My Partnership," "Seeing My Person," "Seeing My Potential," and "Seeing My Possibilities."

Author: Gillespie, Mike   **413**
Series: Young Teen Feedback Elective
Title: *Character Witnesses (Leader's Book)*
Publisher: Victor Books, 1991

Num. Sess.	Group Time	Num. Pgs.	Avg. Qst.	Price	Audience	Format	Bible Study
12	30-45	81	Vry	12.99	New Christian	Book	Topical

Features: Intro to Study, Handouts
★★★★ Personal Application Preparation Time: None ISBN: 0-89693-837-9
★★★★ Relationship Building Ldr. Guide Avail.: Yes Size: 8.50 x 11.0
Subjects: Teens: Christian Liv, Teens: Discipleship
Comments: This study of twelve Bible characters presents the development of integrity in a way that helps young teens examine their own characters—and develop important traits like honesty, patience, reverence, and love. Each study is based on interviews with youth, including their feedback on personal needs and concerns. The format offers three four-week studies with reproducible student sheets. A student book is available.

Author: Gillespie, Mike   **414**
Series:
Title: *Fun Old Testament Bible Studies*
Publisher: Group Publishing, 1989

Num. Sess.	Group Time	Num. Pgs.	Avg. Qst.	Price	Audience	Format	Bible Study
32	30-60	172	N/A	12.95	New Christian	Book	Book

Features: Intro to Study, Objectives, Prayer Helps, Follow Up, Drawings, Handouts, Maps, Index
★★★★ Personal Application Preparation Time: Low ISBN: 0-931529-64-6
★★★★ Relationship Building Ldr. Guide Avail.: No Size: 8.50 x 11.0
Subjects: Teens: Friends, Teens: Old Testament, Teens: Peer Pressure
Comments: This book provides thirty-two Old Testament studies on themes important to teenagers, including forgiveness, peer pressure, temptation, friendship, making mistakes, and more. Each session is designed to help teenagers experience Bible drama and then apply what they've learned to their own problems and concerns. The studies include attention-getting openers, activities, reproducible handouts, and step-by-step session preparation notes.

Author: Gillespie, Mike   **415**
Series: Group's Active Bible Curriculum
Title: *Making Good Decisions*
Publisher: Group Publishing, 1991

Num. Sess.	Group Time	Num. Pgs.	Avg. Qst.	Price	Audience	Format	Bible Study
4	35-60	48	Vry	6.95	Beginner	Workbk	Topical

Features: Intro to Leading a Study, Intro to Study, Objectives, Study Overview, Ldr's Notes, Drawings, Handouts, Agenda, Publicity Ideas
★★★★ Personal Application   Preparation Time: None   ISBN: 1-559-45209-9
★★★★ Relationship Building   Ldr. Guide Avail.: No   Size: 8.50 x 11.0
Subjects: Teens: Christian Liv, Teens: Decisions, Teens: Senior High
Comments: This study helps senior high students make wise, faith-based choices. Its four lessons provide practical skills to help them build confidence in decision making; understand how the Bible helps them exercise good judgment; experience Christian growth as they discover the importance of faith in decision making; and experience hope as they learn how God helps them rebound from past mistakes. Instructions are easy to follow and provide multiple options for teachers. Student books not required.

Author: Gillespie, Mike   **416**
Series:
Title: *Youth & Parents Together: Facing Life's Struggles (Participants Book)*
Publisher: Group Publishing, 1988

Num. Sess.	Group Time	Num. Pgs.	Avg. Qst.	Price	Audience	Format	Bible Study
13	45-75	93	5	3.95	New Christian	Workbk	Topical

Features: Intro to Study, Objectives, Drawings, Charts, Publicity Ideas
★★★★ Personal Application   Preparation Time: Low   ISBN: 0-931529-29-8
★★★★ Relationship Building   Ldr. Guide Avail.: Yes   Size: 5.50 x 8.50
Subjects: Parenting, Teens: Emotions, Teens: Junior High
Comments: This thirteen-session family curriculum strengthens bonds, builds communication channels, and enhances spiritual growth between junior high age youngsters and their parents. Subjects addressed include loneliness, impatience, anger, facing persecution, temptation, forgiveness, compassion, building trust, and communication. The accompanying leader's guide ($10.95) provides step-by-step preparation tips, Bible references, session outlines, and timing guides.

Author: Glaphré   **417**
Series: Woman's Workshop Series
Title: *Talking with God: Studies on Prayer*
Publisher: Zondervan, 1985

Num. Sess.	Group Time	Num. Pgs.	Avg. Qst.	Price	Audience	Format	Bible Study
12	90-120	153	Vry	6.95	New Christian	Workbk	Topical

Features: Intro to Study, Prayer Helps, Scrpt Memory Helps, Worship Helps, Ldr's Notes, Persnl Study Quest
★★★ Personal Application   Preparation Time: Low   ISBN: 0-310-45301-1
★★★ Relationship Building   Ldr. Guide Avail.: No   Size: 5.25 x 8.0
Subjects: Prayer, Women's Issues
Comments: This study on prayer helps participants increase the desire and discipline necessary to mature in prayer. However, before beginning this study they should ask, "Do I want to improve my prayer life?" and, "Will I pray?" A serious study, it is suited for those who have never prayed, who struggle to pray consistently and fervently, and who already find prayer meaningful but want to improve their prayer life.

Author: Glasser, Arthur F.   **418**
Series: Global Issues
Title: *Spiritual Conflict*
Publisher: InterVarsity, 1990

Num. Sess.	Group Time	Num. Pgs.	Avg. Qst.	Price	Audience	Format	Bible Study
6	45-60	48	12	4.95	Beginner	Workbk	Topical

Features: Intro to Leading a Study, Intro to Study, Bibliography, Prayer Helps, Follow Up
★ Personal Application   Preparation Time: Low   ISBN: 0-8308-4901-7
★ Relationship Building   Ldr. Guide Avail.: No   Size: 5.50 x 8.25
Subjects: Satan
Comments: This six-week study helps participants understand spiritual conflict and prepare for battle with principalities and powers. Satan and the battle with supernatural powers are mentioned in all of Paul's epistles. He says these powers have generated a spirit of open revolt against God, and have penetrated all cultures and social structures, blinding people to the gospel. The subject is dealt with through inductive questions, which call for personal understanding.

Author: Going, Nancy   **419**
Series: Group's Active Bible Curriculum
Title: *Boosting Self-Esteem*
Publisher: Group Publishing, 1990

Num. Sess.	Group Time	Num. Pgs.	Avg. Qst.	Price	Audience	Format	Bible Study
4	35-60	44	Vry	6.95	Beginner	Workbk	Topical

Features: Intro to Leading a Study, Intro to Study, Objectives, Study Overview, Ldr's Notes, Handouts, Agenda, Publicity Ideas
★★★ Personal Application   Preparation Time: None   ISBN: 1-559-45100-9
★★★ Relationship Building   Ldr. Guide Avail.: No   Size: 8.50 x 11.0
Subjects: Teens: Junior High, Teens: Psychology, Teens: Relationships, Teens: Self-esteem
Comments: This study helps kids learn to feel good about themselves and develop confidence in their abilities. It includes lessons on evaluation of teen appearances, the difference between pleasing others and caring about others, identification and affirmation of unique abilities, and building self-confidence. It can be adapted for a Bible class or youth meeting, and activities and Bible studies are included as separate sheets that can be reproduced. Instructions are easy to follow.

Author: Goodboy, Eadie & Agnes Lawless   **420**
Series: Basic Bible Study Series
Title: *God's Character: A Study of His Attributes*
Publisher: Aglow, 1986

Num. Sess.	Group Time	Num. Pgs.	Avg. Qst.	Price	Audience	Format	Bible Study
9	75-90	63	25	2.95	New Christian	Workbk	Charctr

Features: Intro to Study, Prayer Helps, Scrpt Memory Helps, Persnl Study Quest
★★★ Personal Application   Preparation Time: Med   ISBN: 0-932305-32-6
★★★ Relationship Building   Ldr. Guide Avail.: No   Size: 5.25 x 8.25
Subjects: Charismatic Interest, God, Grace, Holiness, Theology, Wisdom
Comments: This nine-week study covers eight characteristics of God: mercy, faithfulness, goodness, wisdom, omnipotence, holiness, grace, and love. As the attributes or character of God is studied, participants will learn to know Him better and become more like Him.

Author: Goodboy, Eadie　　　　　　　　　**421**
Series: Basic Bible Study Series
Title: *God's Daughter: Practical Aspects of a Christian Woman's Life*
Publisher: Aglow, 1980

Num. Sess.	Group Time	Num. Pgs.	Avg. Qst.	Price	Audience	Format	Bible Study
11	60-75	60	Vry	2.95	New Christian	Workbk	Topical

Features: Intro to Study, Scrpt Memory Helps, Persnl Study Quest
　★★★ Personal Application　Preparation Time: Low　ISBN: 0-932305-45-8
　★★★ Relationship Building　Ldr. Guide Avail.: No　Size: 5.25 x 8.25
Subjects: Charismatic Interest, Relationships, Service, Women's Issues
Comments: This study examines practical aspects of the Christian walk and helps participants attain maturity in their daily lives. Two primary relationships discussed are relationships with God and with one another. Methods of ministry to others that are discussed include: maintaining peace in confusion, laying down lives in submission to one another, using gifts and abilities to serve others, and using the tongue to build up instead of tear down.

Author: Gorman, Julie A.　　　　　　　　**422**
Series: GroupBuilder Resources
Title: *Let's Get Together*
Publisher: Victor Books, 1991

Num. Sess.	Group Time	Num. Pgs.	Avg. Qst.	Price	Audience	Format	Bible Study
8	75-90	156	Vry	5.99	New Christian	Workbk	Topical

Features: Intro to Leading a Study, Objectives, Worship Helps, Digging Deeper Quest, Follow Up, Full Scrpt Printed, Ldr's Notes, Cartoons, Persnl Study Quest
　★★★★ Personal Application　Preparation Time: Low　ISBN: 0-89693-299-0
　★★★★ Relationship Building　Ldr. Guide Avail.: No　Size: 6.0 x 9.0
Subjects: Caring, Commitments, Relationships, Service, Small Group Resource
Comments: In this study participants learn about and experience eight aspects of small group life. Sessions deal with sensitive issues, such as choices, commitments, relationships, caring, changes, truth, service, and celebration. Optional activities, hints for leaders, worship ideas, and answers to questions can be found in the leader's guide at the back of the book.

Author: Gorman, Julie A.　　　　　　　　**423**
Series: GroupBuilder Resources
Title: *No Strangers to God*
Publisher: Victor Books, 1991

Num. Sess.	Group Time	Num. Pgs.	Avg. Qst.	Price	Audience	Format	Bible Study
8	75-90	144	Vry	5.99	New Christian	Workbk	Topical

Features: Intro to Leading a Study, Objectives, Digging Deeper Quest, Follow Up, Full Scrpt Printed, Ldr's Notes, Cartoons, Persnl Study Quest
　★★★★ Personal Application　Preparation Time: Low　ISBN: 0-89693-018-1
　★★★★ Relationship Building　Ldr. Guide Avail.: No　Size: 6.0 x 9.0
Subjects: Discipleship, God
Comments: This study helps small groups build meaningful relationships with God as together they study how to know Him and become His own. Sessions deal with such topics as spiritual roots, finding God in bad times, fitting in with God's plans, celebrating baptism and the Last Supper, and spiritual growth. Optional activities, hints for leaders, and answers to questions can be found in the leader's guide at the back of the book.

Author: Gorman, Julie A.　　　　　　　　**424**
Series: GroupBuilder Resources
Title: *Training Manual for Small Group Leaders, A*
Publisher: Victor Books, 1991

Num. Sess.	Group Time	Num. Pgs.	Avg. Qst.	Price	Audience	Format	Bible Study
8	60-90	132	Vry	7.99	New Christian	Book	Topical

Features: Intro to Study, Objectives, Ldr's Notes
　Personal Application　Preparation Time:　ISBN: 0-89693-266-4
　Relationship Building　Ldr. Guide Avail.:　Size: 6.0 x 9.0
Subjects: Small Group Resource
Comments: This book is a hands-on manual for training leaders of small groups. In its eight sessions leaders will learn to make good first impressions, involve members in making commitments, develop sharing questions, lead effective discussions, and develop other small group leadership skills.

Author: Gossai, Hemchand　　　　　　　　**425**
Series: Men's Bible Study Series
Title: *Amos & Hosea*
Publisher: Augsburg Publishing House, 1989

Num. Sess.	Group Time	Num. Pgs.	Avg. Qst.	Price	Audience	Format	Bible Study
10	30-45	48	11	3.0	New Christian	Workbk	Book

Features: Intro to Study, Prayer Helps, Summary
　★★★★ Personal Application　Preparation Time: None ISBN:
　★★★★ Relationship Building　Ldr. Guide Avail.: Yes　Size: 4.50 x 9.50
Subjects: Bible Personalities, Ethics, Men's Issues, Minor Prophets
Comments: This ten-lesson study of two minor Old Testament prophets focuses on how their messages concerning covenant, justice, and idolatry still have relevance for contemorary Christians. The messages of Amos and Hosea reveal volatile and even harsh realities, which participants are forced to face. The study may be used at prayer breakfasts, men's Bible study groups, or any other men's meetings.

Author: Gravrock, Mark　　　　　　　　**426**
Series: Friendship Bible Study
Title: *High Priestly Prayer, The*
Publisher: Augsburg Publishing House, 1988

Num. Sess.	Group Time	Num. Pgs.	Avg. Qst.	Price	Audience	Format	Bible Study
8	60-75	48	10	3.0	New Christian	Workbk	Topical

Features: Intro to Study, Prayer Helps, Study Overview
　★★★★ Personal Application　Preparation Time: Low　ISBN:
　★★★★ Relationship Building　Ldr. Guide Avail.: Yes　Size: 5.50 x 8.50
Subjects: God, Prayer, Relationships
Comments: This eight-lesson study looks at the "High Priestly Prayer" found in John 17. Jesus prays to His Father not only for Himself but also for His disciples, and for all believers throughout the ages. The study is an insightful look at what this prayer teaches regarding relationships with God and each other. The lesson format includes an overview, an opening, a responsive reading, Bible background, questions for reflection, a key verse, a prayer response, and an "our faith" response.

Author: Green, Roberta   **427**
Series: Young Fisherman Bible
Title: *Joshua: Promises to Keep*
Publisher: Shaw, 1982

Num. Sess.	Group Time	Num. Pgs.	Avg. Qst.	Price	Audience	Format	Bible Study
13	50-60	70	13	2.95	New Christian	Workbk	Book

Features: Intro to Study, Drawings, Maps, Exam
  ★★ Personal Application   Preparation Time: Low   ISBN: 0-87788-433-1
  ★★ Relationship Building   Ldr. Guide Avail.: Yes   Size: 6.0 x 8.0
Subjects: Friendships, Relationships, Teens: Old Testament
Comments: This chapter-by-chapter study of Joshua helps young people increase their trust in God. In the Joshua story, the Israelites enter the Promised Land, as God kept His promises. Every human being—parent, friend, preacher, or teacher—is capable of letting people down. As teens explore God's Word in this study, they'll get to know the One who can be trusted to keep His promises. How important is a promise?

Author: Greig, Doris W.   **428**
Series: Joy of Living
Title: *Courage to Conquer: Studies in Daniel*
Publisher: Regal Books, 1988

Num. Sess.	Group Time	Num. Pgs.	Avg. Qst.	Price	Audience	Format	Bible Study
6	60-90	118	36	5.95	New Christian	Workbk	Book

Features: Intro to Study, Drawings, Maps
  ★★★ Personal Application   Preparation Time: High   ISBN: 0-8307-1285-2
  ★★ Relationship Building   Ldr. Guide Avail.: No   Size: 6.0 x 9.0
Subjects: Daniel, Ethics, Faith, Major Prophets
Comments: This is a six-week study of Daniel, who proclaimed everlasting faith in the face of great danger. It reminds participants that God provides strength, insight, and courage to conquer doubts and fears, and helps people uphold Christian values in every area of life. Each lesson features prestudy activities followed by six sets of in-depth questions designed for daily study, and is wrapped up by study notes. Historical background, commentary, maps, and timelines are included.

Author: Greig, Doris W.   **429**
Series: Joy of Living
Title: *Living in the Light: Studies in 1, 2 and 3 John, and Jude*
Publisher: Regal Books, 1988

Num. Sess.	Group Time	Num. Pgs.	Avg. Qst.	Price	Audience	Format	Bible Study
6	60-90	124	35	5.95	New Christian	Workbk	Book

Features: Intro to Study, Drawings, Maps
  ★★★ Personal Application   Preparation Time: High   ISBN: 0-8307-1287-9
  ★★ Relationship Building   Ldr. Guide Avail.: No   Size: 6.0 x 9.0
Subjects: Christian Living, False Teachers, Joy, 1, 2 & 3 John/Jude
Comments: This six-week study of 1, 2 and 3 John and Jude points out that Christ is the brightest hope in dark times. It focuses on the fundamentals of Christianity: the sovereignty of Christ; how contemporary Christians should live; and how to avoid heretical teaching. Each lesson features prestudy activities followed by six sets of in-depth questions designed for daily study, and is wrapped up by study notes. Historical background, commentary, maps, and timelines are included.

Author: Greig, Doris W.   **430**
Series: Joy of Living
Title: *Power For Positive Living: Studies in Philippians and Colossians*
Publisher: Regal Books, 1988

Num. Sess.	Group Time	Num. Pgs.	Avg. Qst.	Price	Audience	Format	Bible Study
8	60-90	152	48	5.95	New Christian	Workbk	Book

Features: Intro to Study, Maps
  ★★★ Personal Application   Preparation Time: High   ISBN: 0-8307-1286-0
  ★★ Relationship Building   Ldr. Guide Avail.: No   Size: 6.0 x 9.0
Subjects: Colossians/Philemon, Hope, Joy, Philippians, Prison Epistles, Victorious Living, Wisdom
Comments: This eight-week study of Philippians and Colossians establishes one of Christ's most precious promises—that His power is always available to guide and sustain. Philippians offers joy, hope, and love; Colossians offers wisdom, knowledge, and Christ's lordship and all sufficiency. Each lesson features prestudy activities, followed by six sets of in-depth questions designed for daily study, and is wrapped up by study notes. Historical background, commentary, maps, and timelines are included.

Author: Greig, Doris W.   **431**
Series: Joy of Living
Title: *Walking in God's Way: Studies in Ruth and Esther*
Publisher: Regal Books, 1988

Num. Sess.	Group Time	Num. Pgs.	Avg. Qst.	Price	Audience	Format	Bible Study
7	60-90	131	42	5.95	New Christian	Workbk	Book

Features: Intro to Study, Drawings, Maps
  ★★★ Personal Application   Preparation Time: High   ISBN: 0-8307-1284-4
  ★★ Relationship Building   Ldr. Guide Avail.: No   Size: 6.0 x 9.0
Subjects: Bible Personalities, Esther, Faith, God, Ruth
Comments: This seven-week study of Ruth and Esther demonstrates to contemporary Christians that listening to God and learning to love is the center of a Christian walk. And, like Ruth, Boaz, Esther, and Mordecai, participants will find that life's difficult times can lead them closer to God. Each lesson begins with prestudy activities, followed by six sets of in-depth questions designed for daily study, and is wrapped up by study notes. Historical background, commentary, maps, and timelines are included.

Author: Griffin, Em   **432**
Series:
Title: *Getting Together*
Publisher: InterVarsity, 1982

Num. Sess.	Group Time	Num. Pgs.	Avg. Qst.	Price	Audience	Format	Bible Study
11	-	230	N/A	9.95		Book	No

Features: Intro to Study, Cartoons
  Personal Application   Preparation Time: ISBN: 0-87784-390-2
  Relationship Building   Ldr. Guide Avail.: No   Size: 5.50 x 8.25
Subjects: Leadership, Small Group Resource
Comments: This book focuses on what makes a good group, and discusses three types: "task groups," which have a job to do; "relationship groups," which fill a need for community; and "influence groups," which help people change. Topics covered include persuasion, expectations, leadership, and how to lead a good discussion. The "Westwood Food Co-op" is used as an analogy to the development of a small group in the introduction.

Author: Groom, Nancy   **433**
Series: Crisispoints for Women
Title: *Nobody's Perfect, So Why Do I Try to Be?*
Publisher: NavPress, 1990

Num. Sess.	Group Time	Num. Pgs.	Avg. Qst.	Price	Audience	Format	Bible Study
5	45-60	91	11	3.95	New Christian	Workbk	Topical

Features: Intro to Study, Bibliography, Prayer Helps, Pre-discussion Quest, Digging Deeper Quest
★★★★ Personal Application   Preparation Time: Med   ISBN: 0-89109-336-2
  ★★ Relationship Building   Ldr. Guide Avail.: No   Size: 4.25 x 7.0
Subjects: Emotions, Grace, Women's Issues
Comments: This five-lesson study—part of an eight-book series for women in crises—helps participants shed the compulsion for perfection and the guilt for imperfection. They will see the futility of self-sufficiency, accept God's grace, and focus on others' needs, not their own. In the lessons, a magazine article format is followed by Bible study or discussion questions. Due to added sections, six or seven sessions are recommended. The series is contemporary, nonthreatening, and easy to use.

Author: Hadaway, C. Kirk, et al.   **434**
Series:
Title: *Home Cell Groups and House Churches*
Publisher: Broadman, 1987

Num. Sess.	Group Time	Num. Pgs.	Avg. Qst.	Price	Audience	Format	Bible Study
10	-	260	N/A	10.95		Book	No

Features:
    Personal Application   Preparation Time: ISBN: 0-8054-6944-3
    Relationship Building   Ldr. Guide Avail.:   Size: 5.75 x 8.25
Subjects: Small Group Resource
Comments: This book submits that the urban church can be effective. It responds to questions like the following: "How can the urban church effectively take the gospel to the thousands of people who live near it?" and "Can the urban church hope to reach those who see no relevance in Christianity?" It gives an overview of house groups and addresses issues like the nature and growth of groups, leadership and authority, and the problems and disadvantages of house churches. Implementation guidelines are provided.

Author: Halverson, Dean C.   **435**
Series:
Title: *Crystal Clear: Understanding and Reaching New Agers*
Publisher: NavPress, 1990

Num. Sess.	Group Time	Num. Pgs.	Avg. Qst.	Price	Audience	Format	Bible Study
9	60-75	118	9	4.95	Beginner	Workbk	Topical

Features: Bibliography, Prayer Helps, Follow Up, Ldr's Notes, Glossary, Appendix
★★★★ Personal Application   Preparation Time: Low   ISBN: 0-89109-310-9
★★★★ Relationship Building   Ldr. Guide Avail.: No   Size: 5.50 x 8.50
Subjects: Cults, Faith
Comments: This study highlights the basic and profound differences between the New Age movement and the Christian faith, explaining in particular the impetus behind such phenomena as channeling, reincarnation, and crystals. The format includes a warm-up section, discussion questions, a glossary of New Age terms, an appendix on relating to New Agers, and an extensive leader notes section.

Author: Hamborg, Daphne D.   **436**
Series: Friendship Bible Study
Title: *Parables*
Publisher: Augsburg Publishing House, 1987

Num. Sess.	Group Time	Num. Pgs.	Avg. Qst.	Price	Audience	Format	Bible Study
8	60-75	48	9	3.0	New Christian	Workbk	Topical

Features: Intro to Study, Prayer Helps, Study Overview
★★★★ Personal Application   Preparation Time: Low   ISBN:
★★★★ Relationship Building   Ldr. Guide Avail.: Yes   Size: 5.50 x 8.50
Subjects: Parables
Comments: This eight-lesson study looks at eight of Jesus' parables, considering what it means to live in the Kingdom of God. Included are the parables of the sower, the pearl of great price, the vineyard laborers, the ten bridesmaids, the mustard seed, the wicked tenants, the lost coin, and the prodigal son. The lesson format includes an overview, an opening, a responsive reading, Bible background, questions for reflection, a key verse, a prayer response, and an "our faith" response.

Author: Hamlin, Dr. Judy   **437**
Series:
Title: *Small Group Leaders Training Course, The*
Publisher: NavPress, 1990

Num. Sess.	Group Time	Num. Pgs.	Avg. Qst.	Price	Audience	Format	Bible Study
6	-	210	N/A	19.95		Book	No

Features: Intro to Study, Drawings, Agenda, Publicity Ideas
    Personal Application   Preparation Time: ISBN: 0-89109-308-7
    Relationship Building   Ldr. Guide Avail.:   Size: 8.25 x 10.0
Subjects: Evangelism, Leadership, Relationships, Small Group Resource
Comments: This training manual contains all the components for conducting initial leadership training for a small group ministry. The training is "process," the how-to's. Interactive, practical, hands-on experience with fun leadership, communications/questions, witnessing, relationships, promotion and review are taught and reinforced. A participant manual is available and required. The last chapter covers the development of a leadership handbook specifically for your church.

Author: Haney, Curtis B.   **438**
Series: Small Group Bible Studies
Title: *Galatians*
Publisher: Augsburg Publishing House, 1988

Num. Sess.	Group Time	Num. Pgs.	Avg. Qst.	Price	Audience	Format	Bible Study
4	60-75	15	12	0.95	New Christian	Book	Book

Features: Intro to Study, Bibliography, Prayer Helps
★★★ Personal Application   Preparation Time: None   ISBN:
★★★ Relationship Building   Ldr. Guide Avail.: No   Size: 8.50 x 5.50
Subjects: Galatians, Repentance
Comments: This small pamphlet includes four sessions on Galatians. Paul wrote his letter to the Galatians to defend the gospel, which provided freedom from sin and guilt—a freedom religious requirements could never give. He is sending a message to those who would weaken the gospel by implementing rigid religious requirements. The four sessions include: "The Gospel Truth"; "Spiritual Life, Not Laws"; "Children and Family By Promise"; and "Spirit for Living Freely."

Author: Hansel, Tim   **439**
Series: Video Curriculum Resource
Title: *Holy Sweat*
Publisher: Word, 1986

Num. Sess.	Group Time	Num. Pgs.	Avg. Qst.	Price	Audience	Format	Bible Study
3	75-105	N/A	Vry	79.99	New Christian	Video	Topical

Features: Intro to Study, Book Incl, Video Study Guide
★★★★ Personal Application Preparation Time: Low ISBN: 8-01-501079-9
★★★ Relationship Building Ldr. Guide Avail.: No Size: 10.0 x 12.0
Subjects: Christian Life, Failure, Joy, Success
Comments: This three-part video study—for all ages—makes a powerful statement against mediocrity, conformity, and dullness. Participants, encouraged to stretch character, dreams, and abilities, are given ten keys for peak performance: start, vision, goals, courage, teamwork, excellence, acceptance of failure, perseverance, joy, and giving it all away. The video kit includes three forty-minute video segments, a study guide with questions on the video material, and a copy of the book by the same title.

Author: Hansen, Cindy S.   **440**
Series: Group's Active Bible Curriculum
Title: *Knowing God's Will*
Publisher: Group Publishing, 1990

Num. Sess.	Group Time	Num. Pgs.	Avg. Qst.	Price	Audience	Format	Bible Study
4	35-60	43	Vry	6.95	Beginner	Workbk	Topical

Features: Intro to Leading a Study, Intro to Study, Objectives, Study Overview, Ldr's Notes, Handouts, Agenda, Publicity Ideas
★★★ Personal Application Preparation Time: None ISBN: 1-559-45205-6
★★★ Relationship Building Ldr. Guide Avail.: No Size: 8.50 x 11.0
Subjects: Teens: Christian Liv, Teens: Senior High
Comments: This course challenges teenagers to explore God's direction for their lives. The subject matter covered includes knowing and doing God's will, accepting God's help, and accepting God's forgiveness. It can be adapted for use in a Bible class or youth meeting. Activities and Bible studies are included as separate sheets that can be reproduced. The instructions are easy to follow and offer multiple options for teachers.

Author: Hanusa, George   **441**
Series: Small Group Bible Studies
Title: *Faith of the Church, The*
Publisher: Augsburg Publishing House, 1978

Num. Sess.	Group Time	Num. Pgs.	Avg. Qst.	Price	Audience	Format	Bible Study
6	60-75	24	5	1.15	New Christian	Book	Topical

Features: Intro to Study, Prayer Helps
★★★ Personal Application Preparation Time: None ISBN:
★★★ Relationship Building Ldr. Guide Avail.: No Size: 8.50 x 5.50
Subjects: Church Life, Faith, God, Theology
Comments: This small pamphlet includes six sessions on the faith of the Church. The six areas covered include God, mankind, salvation, Church, Scripture, and Christian vocation. The study intends to examine the scriptural dimensions of participants' faith. It is designed to lead them to think through what they believe, as well as to be informed by the Scriptures. The goal is to learn more fully how the faith of the Church applies to their lives.

Author: Hardel, Dick   **442**
Series: Group's Active Bible Curriculum
Title: *Jesus' Death and Resurrection*
Publisher: Group Publishing, 1991

Num. Sess.	Group Time	Num. Pgs.	Avg. Qst.	Price	Audience	Format	Bible Study
4	35-60	48	Vry	6.95	New Christian	Workbk	Charctr

Features: Intro to Leading a Study, Intro to Study, Objectives, Study Overview, Ldr's Notes, Drawings, Handouts, Agenda, Publicity Ideas
★★★★ Personal Application Preparation Time: None ISBN: 1-559-45211-0
★★★★ Relationship Building Ldr. Guide Avail.: No Size: 8.50 x 11.0
Subjects: Teens: Jesus' Life, Teens: Senior High
Comments: This four-lesson study helps senior high students understand the relevance of Christ's death and resurrection for their lives. Participants will examine the significance of Jesus' Last Supper with His disciples, learn how He struggled with God's will that He die, gain insights into the strength of His relationship with God, and explore how Jesus' death on the cross provides the way to forgiveness. Instructions are easy to follow and provide multiple options for teachers.

Author: Harper, Steven   **443**
Series: Spiritual Formation Series
Title: *Embrace the Spirit*
Publisher: Victor Books, 1987

Num. Sess.	Group Time	Num. Pgs.	Avg. Qst.	Price	Audience	Format	Bible Study
13	60-90	168	N/A	7.99	New Christian	Book	Topical

Features: Intro to Study, Bibliography, Prayer Helps
★★★★ Personal Application Preparation Time: Med ISBN: 0-89693-311-3
★★★ Relationship Building Ldr. Guide Avail.: Yes Size: 5.50 x 8.0
Subjects: Discipleship, Holy Spirit
Comments: This study helps participants hear God's call to a holy partnership of spiritual development and friendship with Him. It helps them better serve Him in each day's challenges. The leader's guide helps leaders encourage activity and practical interaction and allows them to help group members put the aspects of spirituality covered in the text into practice. Transparency masters are included.

Author: Harris, Madalene   **444**
Series: Crisispoints for Women
Title: *You're Better Than You Think!*
Publisher: NavPress, 1990

Num. Sess.	Group Time	Num. Pgs.	Avg. Qst.	Price	Audience	Format	Bible Study
5	45-60	80	12	3.95	New Christian	Workbk	Topical

Features: Intro to Study, Bibliography, Prayer Helps, Scrpt Memory Helps, Pre-discussion Quest
★★★★ Personal Application Preparation Time: Med ISBN: 0-89109-327-3
★★ Relationship Building Ldr. Guide Avail.: No Size: 4.25 x 7.0
Subjects: Relationships, Self-esteem, Women's Issues, Work
Comments: This five-lesson study—part of an eight-book series for women in crises—helps participants explore roots of low self-esteem, which affects their relationships, jobs, and future. They will gain a biblical view of themselves, and will be encouraged as they recover one day at a time. In the lessons, a magazine article format is followed by Bible study or discussion questions. Due to several introductory sections, six sessions are recommended. The series is contemporary, nonthreatening, and easy to use.

Author: Harrison, Dan **445**
Series: Global Issues
Title: *Healing for Broken People*
Publisher: InterVarsity, 1990

Num. Sess.	Group Time	Num. Pgs.	Avg. Qst.	Price	Audience	Format	Bible Study
6	45-60	48	13	4.95	Beginner	Workbk	Topical

Features: Intro to Leading a Study, Intro to Study, Bibliography, Follow Up, Appendix
★★★★ Personal Application Preparation Time: Low ISBN: 0-8308-4908-4
★★★★ Relationship Building Ldr. Guide Avail.: No Size: 5.50 x 8.25
Subjects: Addictions, Emotions, Family, Psychology, Relationships, Social Issues, Work
Comments: This six-week study reveals the fact that most families have problems, sometimes significant ones. It describes the dysfunctional family, as well as negative patterns that affect relationships at work, with friends, and with spouse. Bitterness, anger, and being overcritical are characteristics ascribed to a codependent person. The study helps participants learn how to trust again, improve relationships, and become effective in ministry. It uses the "Twelve Steps" and related scripture.

Author: Haugen, Doug & Doris **446**
Series: LifeGuide Bible Study
Title: *Jonah, Joel & Amos: Seek the Lord and Live*
Publisher: InterVarsity, 1988

Num. Sess.	Group Time	Num. Pgs.	Avg. Qst.	Price	Audience	Format	Bible Study
13	45-60	64	12	3.95	New Christian	Workbk	Book

Features: Intro to Leading a Study, Intro to Study, Ldr's Notes
★ Personal Application Preparation Time: Low ISBN: 0-8308-1032-3
★ Relationship Building Ldr. Guide Avail.: No Size: 5.50 x 8.25
Subjects: Bible Personalities, God, Minor Prophets, Obedience, Old Testament, Repentance
Comments: In Jonah, Joel, and Amos, God gets people's attention because He desires their fellowship. The study is a constant reminder for twentieth-century believers to turn to God and live according to His teachings. Joel stressed that not only do we turn to God, but we return to Him, seeking God through repentance and obedience. Amos exhorts seeking "good, not evil, that you may live" (Amos 5:14). Each of the prophets challenges us to forsake hindrances that block our relationship with the Lord.

Author: Haugk, Kenneth C. **447**
Series:
Title: *Christian Caregiving: A Way of Life*
Publisher: Augsburg Publishing House, 1984

Num. Sess.	Group Time	Num. Pgs.	Avg. Qst.	Price	Audience	Format	Bible Study
20	120-150	157	Vry	9.95	New Christian	Book	Topical

Features: Prayer Helps, Agenda, Appendix, Publicity Ideas
★★★★ Personal Application Preparation Time: Low ISBN: 0-8066-2123-0
★★★★ Relationship Building Ldr. Guide Avail.: Yes Size: 5.25 x 7.75
Subjects: Caring, Christian Life, Support
Comments: This book's purpose is twofold: to describe what makes Christian caregiving distinctive, and to explain how distinctive caregiving can become a way of life for Christians. It is a resource for Christians who wonder what difference their Christianity makes in caring and relating. This practical, "how-to" manual deals with real-life issues in caring and relating, and the leader's guide is thorough and easy to use.

Author: Haystead, Wesley **448**
Series: Lay Action Ministry
Title: *Touching Tomorrow by Teaching Children*
Publisher: Lay Action Ministry Program, 1989

Num. Sess.	Group Time	Num. Pgs.	Avg. Qst.	Price	Audience	Format	Bible Study
12	60-90	144	Vry	5.95	New Christian	Workbk	Topical

Features:
★★★ Personal Application Preparation Time: Low ISBN:
★★★ Relationship Building Ldr. Guide Avail.: Yes Size: 5.25 x 8.25
Subjects: Leadership
Comments: This study emphasizes the importance of teaching children; the Bible's relevance to contemporary children; interactive training methods; the importance of being prepared to teach; effective use of time; using music in teaching; using a variety of activities, games, and puzzles; discipline of children; and sensitivity to each child. The study is divided into three in-depth units covering ministry to children, the teaching session, and teaching methods.

Author: Heald, Cynthia **449**
Series:
Title: *Becoming a Woman of Excellence*
Publisher: NavPress, 1986

Num. Sess.	Group Time	Num. Pgs.	Avg. Qst.	Price	Audience	Format	Bible Study
11	60-90	114	10	5.95	New Christian	Workbk	Topical

Features: Intro to Leading a Study, Scrpt Memory Helps, Charts
★★★ Personal Application Preparation Time: Med ISBN: 0-89109-066-5
★★ Relationship Building Ldr. Guide Avail.: No Size: 5.50 x 8.50
Subjects: Family, Obedience, Singles Issues, Wisdom, Women's Issues, Work
Comments: This study involves a goal worth pursuing—excellence. Society requires both married and single women to succeed, to achieve excellence in appearance, earning power, and family life. God also urges women to achieve excellence, but what does He ask? Eleven lessons study what excellence means in areas such as surrender, obedience, discipline, discretion, wisdom, purity, and a gentle and quiet spirit. The study includes the author's personal reflection and quotes from Christian thinkers.

Author: Heald, Cynthia **450**
Series:
Title: *Creator, My Confidant, The*
Publisher: NavPress, 1987

Num. Sess.	Group Time	Num. Pgs.	Avg. Qst.	Price	Audience	Format	Bible Study
12	45-60	93	4	4.95	Beginner	Workbk	Topical

Features: Intro to Study, Charts
★★★ Personal Application Preparation Time: Low ISBN: 0-89109-140-8
★★ Relationship Building Ldr. Guide Avail.: No Size: 5.50 x 8.50
Subjects: God, Psalms
Comments: This study of the Psalms allows men and women to follow the writers into a deeper experience of God, and to become more honest and vulnerable before God. The lessons track the psalmists' struggles and triumphs on their way to intimacy with God. Participants make fresh, personal observations using quotes from Christian authors and spend more time reflecting and less time looking for "right answers."

Author: Heald, Cynthia   **451**
Series:
Title: *Eve Out of Eden: Intimate Marriage in a Fallen World*
Publisher: NavPress, 1989

Num. Sess.	Group Time	Num. Pgs.	Avg. Qst.	Price	Audience	Format	Bible Study
12	45-60	112	6	5.95	New Christian	Workbk	Topical

Features: Intro to Leading a Study
★★★ Personal Application   Preparation Time: Low   ISBN: 0-89109-544-6
★★ Relationship Building   Ldr. Guide Avail.: No   Size: 5.50 x 8.50
Subjects: Joy, Marriage, Women's Issues
Comments: This study explores choices in a marriage, such as: How can you be a godly woman outside Eden? What are your role, purpose, and influence as a Christian wife? and, How is God's Word relevant to the challenges and temptations of today's society? Key scriptures help participants apply biblical truths to the joys and struggles of marriage.

Author: Heald, Jack & Cynthia   **452**
Series:
Title: *Adam Out of Eden: How to Strengthen Your Marriage in an Imperfect World*
Publisher: NavPress, 1989

Num. Sess.	Group Time	Num. Pgs.	Avg. Qst.	Price	Audience	Format	Bible Study
12	45-60	110	6	5.95	New Christian	Workbk	Topical

Features: Intro to Leading a Study, Scrpt Memory Helps
★★★ Personal Application   Preparation Time: Low   ISBN: 0-89109-575-6
★★ Relationship Building   Ldr. Guide Avail.: No   Size: 5.50 x 8.50
Subjects: Forgiveness, Love, Marriage, Men's Issues, Relationships
Comments: This study explores twelve proven, biblical ways to strengthen and improve marriage, including developing love that's bold, courageous, and true; cultivating a compassionate, self-sacrificial, forgiving spirit toward one's wife; discerning and meeting a wife's needs; overcoming an angry, cynical, or critical spirit; and adopting a leadership style that will build intimacy, confidence, and genuine respect into marriage.

Author: Heaner, Linda   **453**
Series: Group's Active Bible Curriculum
Title: *Making Parents Proud*
Publisher: Group Publishing, 1990

Num. Sess.	Group Time	Num. Pgs.	Avg. Qst.	Price	Audience	Format	Bible Study
4	35-60	46	Vry	6.95	Beginner	Workbk	Topical

Features: Intro to Leading a Study, Intro to Study, Objectives, Study Overview, Ldr's Notes, Drawings, Handouts, Agenda, Publicity Ideas
★★★★ Personal Application   Preparation Time: None   ISBN: 1-559-45107-6
★★★★ Relationship Building   Ldr. Guide Avail.: No   Size: 8.50 x 11.0
Subjects: Teens: Family, Teens: Junior High
Comments: This study encourages junior high youth to develop positive relationships with their parents. Four lessons help them learn to build good communications with parents, develop specific steps to gain parents' trust, explore ways to earn new freedoms, discover creative ways to show love to parents, and examine Jesus' teaching on loving others. Instructions are easy to follow and provide multiple options for teachers. No student books are required.

Author: Heck, Timothy A.   **454**
Series: Standard Bible Studies
Title: *Revelation*
Publisher: Standard Publishing, 1986

Num. Sess.	Group Time	Num. Pgs.	Avg. Qst.	Price	Audience	Format	Bible Study
13	60-80	58	Vry	3.50	New Christian	Workbk	Book

Features: Intro to Leading a Study, Objectives, Digging Deeper Quest
★★ Personal Application   Preparation Time: Low   ISBN: 0-87403-193-1
★★ Relationship Building   Ldr. Guide Avail.: Yes   Size: 8.50 x 11.0
Subjects: Obedience, Revelation, Worship
Comments: This thirteen-lesson workbook, companion to Alger M. Fitch's study of Revelation, focuses on preaching, opposition, endurance, and worship. Each lesson features learning goals, lesson aims, and key ideas. Each lesson begins with introductory activities, followed by Bible study, and "Digging Deeper" questions and "What do you think?" questions. Only the leader in a small group setting needs this companion book.

Author: Heidebrecht, Paul & Ted Scheuermann   **455**
Series: Fisherman Bible Studyguide
Title: *Men Like Us: Ordinary Men, Extraordinary God*
Publisher: Shaw, 1990

Num. Sess.	Group Time	Num. Pgs.	Avg. Qst.	Price	Audience	Format	Bible Study
13	45-60	79	12	3.95	Beginner	Workbk	Topical

Features: Intro to Leading a Study, Intro to Study, Prayer Helps, Ldr's Notes
★★★ Personal Application   Preparation Time: None   ISBN: 0-87788-544-3
★★★ Relationship Building   Ldr. Guide Avail.: No   Size: 5.0 x 8.25
Subjects: Failure, Grace, Marriage, Men's Issues, Time
Comments: This inductive study deals with issues contemporary men face—materialism, time pressure, godly fathering, keeping marriages strong, and establishing priorities—which were also faced by men in biblical times such as Barnabas, Caleb, Cornelius, Peter, and others. These Bible characters are much like men today. Their failures and weaknesses are not covered up; rather, God's grace transforms them as men today can be transformed. A small group environment can encourage, support, and produce mature Christian men.

Author: Hendricks, Howard G.   **456**
Series:
Title: *Heaven Help the Home!*
Publisher: Victor Books, 1973

Num. Sess.	Group Time	Num. Pgs.	Avg. Qst.	Price	Audience	Format	Bible Study
13	45-60	156	N/A	7.99	Beginner	Book	Topical

Features: Intro to Study
★★★ Personal Application   Preparation Time: Low   ISBN: 0-89693-674-0
★★★ Relationship Building   Ldr. Guide Avail.: Yes   Size: 5.50 x 8.0
Subjects: Family, Money, Parenting, Relationships
Comments: This study offers practical advice about family life. It identifies and explores topics from family life conferences, such as the Christian home, convictions, discipline, finances, roles and relationships, attitudes, television, and sexuality. It also provides tools for dealing with these areas inside the home to create effective families. A leader's guide provides reproducible response sheets for participants and assignments.

Author: Hendricks, Howard G.   **457**
Series:
Title: *Say It with Love*
Publisher: Victor Books, 1972

Num. Sess.	Group Time	Num. Pgs.	Avg. Qst.	Price	Audience	Format	Bible Study
13	60-75	140	N/A	7.99	New Christian	Book	Topical

Features: Intro to Study
★★★ Personal Application   Preparation Time: Low   ISBN: 0-89693-676-7
★★★ Relationship Building   Ldr. Guide Avail.: Yes   Size: 5.50 x 8.0
Subjects: Caring, Evangelism
Comments: This thirteen-lesson study instructs how to witness in everyday situations and shows how, through communication principles, participants can learn to effectively share the good news of salvation. The study is divided into four parts: "Our Message"; "Sharing the Message"; "Living the Message"; and "A Message to Share (a sample gospel presentation)." To reach a world uninterested in hearing the gospel, an emphasis must be placed on communicating through our actions, rather than words.

Author: Hendricks, Jeanne   **458**
Series:
Title: *Mother's Legacy, A*
Publisher: NavPress, 1988

Num. Sess.	Group Time	Num. Pgs.	Avg. Qst.	Price	Audience	Format	Bible Study
11	45-60	110	9	5.95	New Christian	Workbk	Topical

Features: Intro to Study
★★ Personal Application   Preparation Time: Low   ISBN: 0-89109-253-6
★★ Relationship Building   Ldr. Guide Avail.: No   Size: 5.50 x 8.50
Subjects: Bible Personalities, Parenting, Women's Issues
Comments: This study of ten Bible mothers focuses on struggles that are real to modern women. Examples which bring godly insights include Mary—faithfully obeying the seemingly impossible; Deborah—a working mom faced with apathy; Samson's mother—praying for her rebellious son; and Eve—living with the results of a wrong choice. Participants will become encouraged in their role of motherhood, and aware of its enormous influence.

Author: Henrichsen, Walter A.   **459**
Series:
Title: *Disciples Are Made Not Born*
Publisher: Victor Books, 1974

Num. Sess.	Group Time	Num. Pgs.	Avg. Qst.	Price	Audience	Format	Bible Study
13	60-90	153	N/A	7.99	Mature Chrstn	Book	Topical

Features:
★★★★ Personal Application   Preparation Time: Med   ISBN: 0-89693-442-X
★★★ Relationship Building   Ldr. Guide Avail.: Yes   Size: 5.50 x 8.0
Subjects: Discipleship, Evangelism
Comments: This study describes a modern-day disciple and shows participants how to make disciples of others. They review a process that begins with sharing the good news of the gospel and doesn't end until they've shared so completely that another person becomes fully committed to similar spiritual service. The study is practical and provocative, and is written from effective practical experience. A leader's guide with transparency masters is available.

Author: Hershey, Terry   **460**
Series:
Title: *Clear-Headed Choices in a Sexually Confused World*
Publisher: Group Publishing, 1988

Num. Sess.	Group Time	Num. Pgs.	Avg. Qst.	Price	Audience	Format	Bible Study
12	45-60	210	5	11.95	Beginner	Book	Topical

Features: Intro to Leading a Study, Intro to Study, Bibliography
★★★ Personal Application   Preparation Time: None   ISBN: 0-931529-30-1
★★★ Relationship Building   Ldr. Guide Avail.: No   Size: 6.0 x 9.0
Subjects: Teens: Decisions, Teens: Sexuality, Youth Life
Comments: This twelve-lesson study offers honest advice on making Christian decisions about sexuality. It guides young adults through the journey of sexual options, from destructive sexual choices to positive, healthy decisions. In addition to personal reflection and growth questions, case studies will stimulate further discussion and reflection. Real-life situations offer opportunities for discussions about decision-making filters, and the way people approach moral choices.

Author: Hesh, Joseph McLean   **461**
Series: The Crossroads Series
Title: *Is My Family Crazy or Is It Me?*
Publisher: NavPress, 1990

Num. Sess.	Group Time	Num. Pgs.	Avg. Qst.	Price	Audience	Format	Bible Study
6	45-60	52	8	3.95	Beginner	Workbk	Topical

Features: Intro to Study
★★★ Personal Application   Preparation Time: None   ISBN: 0-89109-343-5
★★★ Relationship Building   Ldr. Guide Avail.: Yes   Size: 5.50 x 8.50
Subjects: Teens: Family, Teens: Junior High, Teens: Relationships
Comments: This study helps junior high teens explore difficult issues related to family life, such as rules, authority, responsibility, choices, communication, brothers, and sisters. It leads them to appreciate where they fit into the process and helps them figure out where parents are coming from and how to deal with them. The material is "hands-on," and one leader's guide covers the four-book series.

Author: Hesh, Joseph McLean   **462**
Series: The Crossroads Series
Title: *Swimming for Shore in a Sea of Sharks*
Publisher: NavPress, 1990

Num. Sess.	Group Time	Num. Pgs.	Avg. Qst.	Price	Audience	Format	Bible Study
6	45-60	54	10	3.95	New Christian	Workbk	Topical

Features: Intro to Study
★★★ Personal Application   Preparation Time: None   ISBN: 0-89109-342-7
★★★ Relationship Building   Ldr. Guide Avail.: Yes   Size: 5.50 x 8.50
Subjects: Teens: Decisions, Teens: Junior High
Comments: This study for teens exposes the world's way—hedonism, materialism, narcissism, agnosticism, nihilism, and relativism—as opposed to God's way. It describes the importance of taking the "path less traveled," and provides purpose for teens confused with life. The material is "hands-on," and one leader's guide covers the four books in this series.

Author: Hesh, Joseph McLean   **463**
Series: The Crossroads Series
Title: *Under the Influence*
Publisher: NavPress, 1990

Num. Sess.	Group Time	Num. Pgs.	Avg. Qst.	Price	Audience	Format	Bible Study
6	45-60	49	7	3.95	Beginner	Workbk	Topical

Features: Intro to Study
  ★★★ Personal Application   Preparation Time: None   ISBN: 0-89109-344-3
  ★★★ Relationship Building   Ldr. Guide Avail.: Yes   Size: 5.50 x 8.50
Subjects: Teens: Junior High, Teens: Music, Teens: Peer Pressure
Comments: This study helps junior high teens differentiate between good and bad influences. They are influenced by friends, trends, culture, counterculture, movies, TV, and music, without even realizing they're being influenced. Participants will learn to recognize good influences, and eliminate bad ones before they do damage. The material is "hands-on," and one leader's guide covers the four-book series.

Author: Hesh, Joseph McLean   **464**
Series: The Crossroads Series
Title: *What's the Big Idea?*
Publisher: NavPress, 1990

Num. Sess.	Group Time	Num. Pgs.	Avg. Qst.	Price	Audience	Format	Bible Study
6	45-60	54	11	3.95	New Christian	Workbk	Topical

Features: Intro to Study
  ★★★ Personal Application   Preparation Time: None   ISBN: 0-89109-341-9
  ★★★ Relationship Building   Ldr. Guide Avail.: Yes   Size: 5.50 x 8.50
Subjects: Teens: Junior High, Teens: Peer Pressure, Teens: Relationships
Comments: This study shows life's big picture. It deals with serious questions about God—"Is He really there?" "Can I develop a relationship with Him?"; about self—"Who am I?" "Can I accept myself the way God made me?"; and about others—"How can I deal with all the pressure from others?" "How can I include God in all my relationships?" The material is "hands-on," and one leader's guide covers the four-book series.

Author: Hess, Margaret   **465**
Series: A Bible Study for Women
Title: *Triumph of Love, The*
Publisher: Victor Books, 1987

Num. Sess.	Group Time	Num. Pgs.	Avg. Qst.	Price	Audience	Format	Bible Study
10	60-90	96	10	5.99	New Christian	Workbk	Book

Features: Intro to Study, Objectives, Scrpt Memory Helps, Follow Up, Ldr's Notes
  ★★★ Personal Application   Preparation Time: Med   ISBN: 0-89693-247-8
  ★★ Relationship Building   Ldr. Guide Avail.: No   Size: 6.0 x 9.0
Subjects: Christian Living, Love, Marriage, Relationships, Ruth, Women's Issues
Comments: This study of Ruth can help women become what God wants them to be. Ruth serves as a beautiful role model, a woman of God in the midst of life's struggles. She must learn to adjust to change, handle the pain of broken relationships, try things for the first time, and wait. Love is the theme of the ten lessons.

Author: Hestenes, Roberta   **466**
Series:
Title: *Using the Bible in Groups*
Publisher: The Westminster Press, 1983

Num. Sess.	Group Time	Num. Pgs.	Avg. Qst.	Price	Audience	Format	Bible Study
7	-	118	N/A	7.95		Book	No

Features: Bibliography, Index
  Personal Application   Preparation Time: ISBN: 0-664-24561-7
  Relationship Building   Ldr. Guide Avail.:   Size: 6.0 x 9.0
Subjects: Leadership, Small Group Resource
Comments: This is a practical, basic, resource for anyone who wants to start a Bible study group. It offers successful, field-tested methods and detailed information about the importance of groups: how to begin, who can lead, how to prepare, and how to build relationships within them. The twenty Bible study methods included can be adapted according to the experience, abilities, and interests of group members. This resource should be available to all potential small group leaders.

Author: Hian, Chua Wee   **467**
Series:
Title: *Making of a Leader, The*
Publisher: InterVarsity, 1987

Num. Sess.	Group Time	Num. Pgs.	Avg. Qst.	Price	Audience	Format	Bible Study
16	-	190	N/A	7.95		Book	No

Features: Intro to Study, Bibliography
  Personal Application   Preparation Time: ISBN: 0-87784-827-0
  Relationship Building   Ldr. Guide Avail.:   Size: 5.50 x 8.25
Subjects: Leadership, Small Group Resource
Comments: This book both complements and corrects secular models of leadership, and presents portraits of biblical leaders as servants, stewards, and shepherds, all modeled on Jesus. Christ in service, obedience, prayer, relationships, and suffering should be a primary example of good leadership. Chapters also cover handling crises, dealing with problem leaders, and affirming leaders. It is appropriate for pastors, teachers, students, and laypeople who follow Christ and want to lead His way.

Author: Hillis, Don W.   **468**
Series: Teach Yourself the Bible
Title: *John: The Gospel of Light and Life*
Publisher: Moody Press, 1962

Num. Sess.	Group Time	Num. Pgs.	Avg. Qst.	Price	Audience	Format	Bible Study
12	45-60	64	22	3.99	New Christian	Workbk	Book

Features: Intro to Leading a Study, Exam
  ★★ Personal Application   Preparation Time: Low   ISBN: 0-8024-4375-3
  ★★ Relationship Building   Ldr. Guide Avail.: No   Size: 5.50 x 8.50
Subjects: God, Grace, Jesus: Life/Teaching, John, Wisdom
Comments: This study of John—part of a twenty-five-book series—concerns Christ as described by John as the "Light" and "Life." Participants will study the glory, righteousness, wisdom, and grace of God. The format includes a series of fill-in-the-blank questions, and checkups to test participants' grasp of scriptural truths. The series is designed for self-study; however, suggestions for group study, and a four-year plan for using the series, are included.

Author: Hinckley, Karen   **469**
Series: The Lifechange Series
Title: *Acts*
Publisher: NavPress, 1987

Num. Sess.	Group Time	Num. Pgs.	Avg. Qst.	Price	Audience	Format	Bible Study
20	60-90	220	15	5.95	New Christian	Workbk	Book

Features: Intro to Leading a Study, Intro to Study, Bibliography, Prayer Helps, Worship Helps, Study Overview, Digging Deeper Quest, Summary, Maps, Cross Ref, Word Study
  ★★★ Personal Application   Preparation Time: Med   ISBN: 0-89109-112-2
  ★★★ Relationship Building   Ldr. Guide Avail.: No   Size: 5.50 x 8.50
Subjects: Acts, Holy Spirit
Comments: This verse-by-verse study of Acts explores the church, born among Jesus' disciples, which grew into a worldwide force in just a few years. Jesus had left His followers with a mission, and God's Holy Spirit moved through them to fulfill it. Luke's account of how the gospel was carried from Jerusalem to Rome, despite every conceivable obstacle, challenges participants to know and live out their mission in the world.

Author: Hinckley, Karen   **470**
Series: The Lifechange Series
Title: *Deuteronomy*
Publisher: NavPress, 1986

Num. Sess.	Group Time	Num. Pgs.	Avg. Qst.	Price	Audience	Format	Bible Study
20	45-60	220	16	5.95	New Christian	Workbk	Book

Features: Intro to Leading a Study, Intro to Study, Bibliography, Prayer Helps, Worship Helps, Study Overview, Digging Deeper Quest, Summary, Charts, Maps, Cross Ref, Word Study
  ★★★ Personal Application   Preparation Time: Med   ISBN: 0-89109-065-7
  ★★★ Relationship Building   Ldr. Guide Avail.: No   Size: 5.50 x 8.50
Subjects: God, Holiness, Numbers/Deuteronomy, Wisdom
Comments: This verse-by-verse study of Deuteronomy covers Moses' last words to the Israelites as they stood on the east bank of the Jordan River and looked across at the Promised Land. Before his death, he instructs them, and modern participants as well, in God's requirements for holiness, and reaffirms the covenant between the Israelites and their Lord. This declaration of the Old Covenant, often quoted by Jesus, teaches modern Christians much about God, and offers surprisingly relevant wisdom.

Author: Hinckley, Karen   **471**
Series: The Lifechange Series
Title: *Ephesians*
Publisher: NavPress, 1985

Num. Sess.	Group Time	Num. Pgs.	Avg. Qst.	Price	Audience	Format	Bible Study
14	60-90	127	13	5.95	New Christian	Workbk	Book

Features: Intro to Leading a Study, Intro to Study, Bibliography, Prayer Helps, Worship Helps, Study Overview, Digging Deeper Quest, Summary, Charts, Maps, Cross Ref, Word Study
  ★★★ Personal Application   Preparation Time: Med   ISBN: 0-89109-054-1
  ★★★ Relationship Building   Ldr. Guide Avail.: No   Size: 5.50 x 8.50
Subjects: Ephesians, Holiness
Comments: This is a verse-by-verse study of Ephesians, Paul's letter to a young church that needed a fuller knowledge of Christ. It offers participants priceless truths about a believer's new identity in Christ, and the special calling included therein. Paul's theme is: know who you are before God through Christ, and live according to that identity. Paul praises God, prays, teaches, and explains God's blessings; he urges unity, holiness, submission, and steadfastness based on Christians' common foundation.

Author: Hinckley, Karen   **472**
Series: The Lifechange Series
Title: *Genesis*
Publisher: NavPress, 1987

Num. Sess.	Group Time	Num. Pgs.	Avg. Qst.	Price	Audience	Format	Bible Study
19	60-90	220	14	5.95	New Christian	Workbk	Book

Features: Intro to Leading a Study, Intro to Study, Bibliography, Prayer Helps, Worship Helps, Study Overview, Digging Deeper Quest, Summary, Charts, Maps, Cross Ref, Word Study
  ★★★ Personal Application   Preparation Time: Med   ISBN: 0-89109-069-X
  ★★★ Relationship Building   Ldr. Guide Avail.: No   Size: 5.50 x 8.50
Subjects: Genesis, God
Comments: This verse-by-verse study of Genesis, the first book of the Old Testament, records God's revelation to humankind from the beginning, through rebellion, then through God's task of mending His relationship with humankind. The events that unfold give form to the entire Bible, and offer participants two perspectives: one, a look at God; the other, a look at humanity.

Author: Hinckley, Karen   **473**
Series: The Lifechange Series
Title: *Isaiah*
Publisher: NavPress, 1987

Num. Sess.	Group Time	Num. Pgs.	Avg. Qst.	Price	Audience	Format	Bible Study
18	60-90	220	13	5.95	New Christian	Workbk	Book

Features: Intro to Leading a Study, Intro to Study, Bibliography, Prayer Helps, Worship Helps, Study Overview, Digging Deeper Quest, Follow Up, Charts, Maps, Cross Ref, Word Study
  ★★★ Personal Application   Preparation Time: Med   ISBN: 0-89109-111-4
  ★★★ Relationship Building   Ldr. Guide Avail.: No   Size: 5.50 x 8.50
Subjects: Christian Living, Isaiah/Jeremiah, Major Prophets, Prophecy
Comments: This is a verse-by-verse study about Isaiah, whose name means "the Lord is salvation," and who, for over forty years, made that his message. Through Isaiah, the Lord judged the proud who sought to save themselves, and comforted the humble. Isaiah's book offers participants a window into God's mind, from seven hundred years before Christ. They will gain a firm foundation of Isaiah, be able to apply relevant Scriptures to their lives, and improve personal study skills.

Author: Hinckley, Karen   **474**
Series: The Lifechange Series
Title: *James*
Publisher: NavPress, 1988

Num. Sess.	Group Time	Num. Pgs.	Avg. Qst.	Price	Audience	Format	Bible Study
12	60-90	125	15	5.95	New Christian	Workbk	Book

Features: Intro to Leading a Study, Intro to Study, Bibliography, Prayer Helps, Worship Helps, Study Overview, Digging Deeper Quest, Summary, Cross Ref, Word Study
  ★★★ Personal Application   Preparation Time: Med   ISBN: 0-89109-120-3
  ★★★ Relationship Building   Ldr. Guide Avail.: No   Size: 5.50 x 8.50
Subjects: Faith, James
Comments: This verse-by-verse study of James offers a challenge to Christians of every age to keep on growing. Participants learn that by faith humankind is reborn into the family of God; but that more than justified infants, He wants mature daughters and sons. The result should be faith that is foundational, genuine, proven, and evident to the world.

Author: Hinckley, Karen 475
Series: The Lifechange Series
Title: *John*
Publisher: NavPress, 1988

Num. Sess.	Group Time	Num. Pgs.	Avg. Qst.	Price	Audience	Format	Bible Study
22	60-90	220	15	5.95	New Christian	Workbk	Book

Features: Intro to Leading a Study, Intro to Study, Bibliography, Prayer Helps, Worship Helps, Study Overview, Digging Deeper Quest, Summary, Maps, Cross Ref, Word Study
★★★ Personal Application   Preparation Time: Med   ISBN: 0-89109-237-4
★★★ Relationship Building   Ldr. Guide Avail.: No   Size: 5.50 x 8.50
Subjects: Jesus: Life/Teaching, John
Comments: This study of John provides a beautiful biography of Christ. During His lifetime, no one truly understood His mission, but using a few carefully chosen incidents, John unfolds the truth. This study uses twenty-two lessons in a verse-by-verse chronological order to depict John's portrait of the Son of Man. Study aids follow.

Author: Hinckley, Karen 476
Series: The Lifechange Series
Title: *Joshua*
Publisher: NavPress, 1988

Num. Sess.	Group Time	Num. Pgs.	Avg. Qst.	Price	Audience	Format	Bible Study
16	60-90	173	13	5.95	New Christian	Workbk	Book

Features: Intro to Leading a Study, Intro to Study, Bibliography, Prayer Helps, Worship Helps, Study Overview, Digging Deeper Quest, Summary, Maps, Cross Ref, Word Study
★★★ Personal Application   Preparation Time: Med   ISBN: 0-89109-121-1
★★★ Relationship Building   Ldr. Guide Avail.: No   Size: 5.50 x 8.50
Subjects: God, Joshua
Comments: The verse-by-verse study of Joshua describes how God dealt with a particular people at a unique moment of history to achieve certain ends. For centuries God had promised to give the land of Canaan to the family of Abraham. He fulfilled that promise with Joshua as His general. Today as well, the Lord leads His army to take possession of its inheritance. Participants will learn unforgettable lessons about God, and what it means to be a citizen of His Kingdom.

Author: Hinckley, Karen 477
Series: The Lifechange Series
Title: *Luke (Volume 1)*
Publisher: NavPress, 1987

Num. Sess.	Group Time	Num. Pgs.	Avg. Qst.	Price	Audience	Format	Bible Study
12	60-90	155	14	5.95	New Christian	Workbk	Book

Features: Intro to Leading a Study, Intro to Study, Bibliography, Prayer Helps, Worship Helps, Study Overview, Digging Deeper Quest, Summary, Charts, Maps, Cross Ref, Word Study
★★★ Personal Application   Preparation Time: Med   ISBN: 0-89109-068-1
★★★ Relationship Building   Ldr. Guide Avail.: No   Size: 5.50 x 8.50
Subjects: Jesus: Life/Teaching, Luke, Reconciliation
Comments: In this verse-by-verse study of Luke, Paul's physician friend reveals Jesus as the man who came to save all—including women, the poor, outcast, sick, and ordinary of every nation. This Gentile's vivid, fast-moving report offers a gospel of reconciliation and celebration. Volume 1 traces Jesus' life from the announcement of His birth through His ministry in Galilee.

Author: Hinckley, Karen 478
Series: The Lifechange Series
Title: *Philippians*
Publisher: NavPress, 1987

Num. Sess.	Group Time	Num. Pgs.	Avg. Qst.	Price	Audience	Format	Bible Study
11	60-90	113	11	5.95	New Christian	Workbk	Book

Features: Intro to Leading a Study, Intro to Study, Bibliography, Prayer Helps, Worship Helps, Study Overview, Digging Deeper Quest, Summary, Maps, Cross Ref, Word Study
★★★ Personal Application   Preparation Time: Med   ISBN: 0-89109-072-X
★★★ Relationship Building   Ldr. Guide Avail.: No   Size: 5.50 x 8.50
Subjects: Joy, Philippians, Prison Epistles, Suffering, Victorious Living
Comments: In this verse-by-verse study of Philippians, participants will discover Paul's secret joy and experience his triumphant confidence in Christ. In prison for proclaiming Christ, Paul encourages and challenges his "partners in the gospel." He aims to inspire his ancient readers and modern Christians to persevere in the work of Christ, and tells them how to find peace and contentment in a perilous world.

Author: Hinckley, Karen 479
Series: The Lifechange Series
Title: *Revelation*
Publisher: NavPress, 1989

Num. Sess.	Group Time	Num. Pgs.	Avg. Qst.	Price	Audience	Format	Bible Study
15	60-90	168	16	5.95	New Christian	Workbk	Book

Features: Intro to Leading a Study, Intro to Study, Bibliography, Prayer Helps, Worship Helps, Study Overview, Digging Deeper Quest, Summary, Maps, Cross Ref, Word Study
★★★ Personal Application   Preparation Time: Med   ISBN: 0-89109-273-0
★★★ Relationship Building   Ldr. Guide Avail.: No   Size: 5.50 x 8.50
Subjects: Faith, Revelation, Satan, Suffering
Comments: This verse-by-verse study of Revelation fortifies believers pressured to deny their faith. God gave the Apostle John a series of visions as a call to stand firm. Revelation unveils events between God and Satan in the end and describes the glory that awaits believers who faithfully endure suffering. This glimpse of God's defeat of evil is a timely source of courage for contemporary Christians engaged in the same battle with Satan.

Author: Hinckley, Karen 480
Series: The Lifechange Series
Title: *Romans*
Publisher: NavPress, 1987

Num. Sess.	Group Time	Num. Pgs.	Avg. Qst.	Price	Audience	Format	Bible Study
20	60-90	210	14	5.95	New Christian	Workbk	Book

Features: Intro to Leading a Study, Intro to Study, Bibliography, Prayer Helps, Worship Helps, Study Overview, Digging Deeper Quest, Summary, Maps, Cross Ref, Word Study
★★★ Personal Application   Preparation Time: Med   ISBN: 0-89109-073-8
★★★ Relationship Building   Ldr. Guide Avail.: No   Size: 5.50 x 8.50
Subjects: Grace, Reconciliation, Romans
Comments: This verse-by-verse study on Romans exposes God's path to righteousness and shows how people can be reconciled to God and transformed into the believers He means them to be. Sin, salvation, grace, death, and resurrection are life-changing truths addressed in the study. Participants will gain a firm foundation of Romans, be able to apply relevant scripture to their lives, and build personal study skills.

Author: Hinckley, Karen   **481**
Series: The Lifechange Series
Title: *Ruth & Esther*
Publisher: NavPress, 1987

Num. Sess.	Group Time	Num. Pgs.	Avg. Qst.	Price	Audience	Format	Bible Study
10	60-90	121	11	5.95	New Christian	Workbk	Book

Features: Intro to Leading a Study, Intro to Study, Bibliography, Prayer Helps, Worship Helps, Study Overview, Digging Deeper Quest, Summary, Charts, Maps, Cross Ref, Word Study
  ★★★ Personal Application   Preparation Time: Med   ISBN: 0-89109-074-6
  ★★★ Relationship Building Ldr. Guide Avail.: No   Size: 5.50 x 8.50
Subjects: Bible Personalities, Esther, God, Obedience, Ruth
Comments: These verse-by-verse studies of Ruth and Esther reveal responses to two questions: "Is God really sovereign?" and "Can individual people make a difference in His world?" A young girl named Ruth and a middle-aged man named Boaz answer yes and go on to play crucial roles in God's plan. Over 600 years later, Mordecai and his cousin Esther save their nation by also saying yes. These stories inspire believers today to impact the world by trusting God.

Author: Hinckley, Karen   **482**
Series: The Lifechange Series
Title: *1 Corinthians*
Publisher: NavPress, 1990

Num. Sess.	Group Time	Num. Pgs.	Avg. Qst.	Price	Audience	Format	Bible Study
17	60-90	168	16	5.95	New Christian	Workbk	Book

Features: Intro to Leading a Study, Intro to Study, Bibliography, Prayer Helps, Worship Helps, Study Overview, Digging Deeper Quest, Summary, Maps, Cross Ref, Word Study
  ★★★ Personal Application   Preparation Time: Med   ISBN: 0-89109-559-4
  ★★★ Relationship Building Ldr. Guide Avail.: No   Size: 5.50 x 8.50
Subjects: Church Life, Sexual Issues, Spiritual Gifts, Worship, 1 Corinthians
Comments: This is a verse-by-verse study of 1 Corinthians, Paul's letter to a proud and prosperous church, a stern reminder to take their eyes off the external and practice purity, humility, and love. His practical instructions concerning factions, sexuality, spiritual gifts, and worship remain profoundly relevant for contemporary participants. This is not a doctrinal treatise, but a pastor's response to problems; yet it provides modern Christians with helpful information about Christian faith and practice.

Author: Hinckley, Karen   **483**
Series: The Lifechange Series
Title: *1 Peter*
Publisher: NavPress, 1986

Num. Sess.	Group Time	Num. Pgs.	Avg. Qst.	Price	Audience	Format	Bible Study
13	60-90	137	12	5.95	New Christian	Workbk	Book

Features: Intro to Leading a Study, Intro to Study, Bibliography, Prayer Helps, Worship Helps, Study Overview, Digging Deeper Quest, Summary, Charts, Maps, Cross Ref, Word Study
  ★★★ Personal Application   Preparation Time: Med   ISBN: 0-89109-052-5
  ★★★ Relationship Building Ldr. Guide Avail.: No   Size: 5.50 x 8.50
Subjects: Suffering, 1 & 2 Peter
Comments: This verse-by-verse study of 1 Peter reminds modern Christians of their rich identities in Christ. Written for young Christians facing ridicule in a pagan world, it encourages them to focus on their "living hope," and face sufferings with Christlike character. Peter's heartfelt challenge to contemporary Christianity will inspire participants to meet trials with confidence in "the God of all grace."

Author: Hinckley, Karen   **484**
Series: The Lifechange Series
Title: *1, 2 & 3 John*
Publisher: NavPress, 1988

Num. Sess.	Group Time	Num. Pgs.	Avg. Qst.	Price	Audience	Format	Bible Study
14	60-90	147	14	5.95	New Christian	Workbk	Book

Features: Intro to Leading a Study, Intro to Study, Bibliography, Prayer Helps, Worship Helps, Study Overview, Digging Deeper Quest, Summary, Maps, Cross Ref, Word Study
  ★★★ Personal Application   Preparation Time: Med   ISBN: 0-89109-114-9
  ★★★ Relationship Building Ldr. Guide Avail.: No   Size: 5.50 x 8.50
Subjects: False Teachers, 1, 2 & 3 John/Jude
Comments: This verse-by-verse study concerns 1, 2, and 3 John, John's response to false teachers at the end of the first century. The letters were circulated among troubled churches to calm members. False teachers were undermining the faith of Christians, and John responded with hard-hitting words about righteousness, love, and truth. His message continues to expose falsehood today and offers contemporary Christians confidence in their relationship with God.

Author: Hinckley, Karen   **485**
Series: The Lifechange Series
Title: *2 Timothy*
Publisher: NavPress, 1986

Num. Sess.	Group Time	Num. Pgs.	Avg. Qst.	Price	Audience	Format	Bible Study
8	60-90	85	11	5.95	New Christian	Workbk	Book

Features: Intro to Leading a Study, Intro to Study, Bibliography, Prayer Helps, Worship Helps, Study Overview, Digging Deeper Quest, Summary, Maps, Cross Ref, Word Study
  ★★★ Personal Application   Preparation Time: Med   ISBN: 0-89109-071-1
  ★★★ Relationship Building Ldr. Guide Avail.: No   Size: 5.50 x 8.50
Subjects: Church Life, Pastoral Epistles, 1 & 2 Timothy/Titus
Comments: This verse-by-verse study of 2 Timothy reveals the last preserved words of Paul, one of the church's greatest men. It becomes God's Word, revealing who He is, who we are in Him, and what He wants from us. As if writing to contemporary Christians, Paul encouraged Timothy, then guiding Paul's church at Ephesus and facing persecution from pagans and strife among believers. Paul's last words of counsel continue to instruct and inspire Christians of all times.

Author: Holbert, John   **486**
Series:
Title: *Gospel of John, The: Volume 1 & 2*
Publisher: Cokesbury, 1990

Num. Sess.	Group Time	Num. Pgs.	Avg. Qst.	Price	Audience	Format	Bible Study
7	45-60	N/A	Vry	29.95	New Christian	Video	Book

Features: Intro to Leading a Study, Intro to Study, Ldr's Notes, Video Study Guide
  ★★★ Personal Application   Preparation Time: Low   ISBN: 0-687-76176-X
  ★★★ Relationship Building Ldr. Guide Avail.: Yes   Size: 4.75 x 8.0
Subjects: Jesus: Life/Teaching, John
Comments: Even though its sources and origin are yet veiled in mystery, no document has influenced so powerfully the hearts and minds as has the Gospel of John. Nor has any New Testament book received so many diverse interpretations of its meaning. This two-volume video Bible study of John's gospel covers some of John's different ideas about how Jesus relates to the world, and what He means to the world. The two volumes include eight twenty-minute lessons, and a leader's guide.

Author: Honeycutt, Roy L.   **487**
Series: Video Curriculum Resource
Title: *Studies in the Gospel of John*
Publisher: Word, 1988

Num. Sess.	Group Time	Num. Pgs.	Avg. Qst.	Price	Audience	Format	Bible Study
4	60-90	N/A	Vry	99.99	New Christian	Video	Book

Features: Intro to Study
  ★★★ Personal Application Preparation Time: Low ISBN: 8-01-507079-1
    ★ Relationship Building Ldr. Guide Avail.: No Size: 10.0 x 12.50
Subjects: Jesus: Life/Teaching, John
Comments: This four-lesson video study focuses participants' thoughts on how the Gospel of John relates to the other three gospels, and how it parallels Old Testament scriptures that point to Jesus as the Word. Ten Bible scholars from Southern Baptist Theological Seminary in Louisville, Kentucky, were assembled for this video panel. Moderator and panel members present the subject in an academic manner, and the study guide helps clarify and reinforce the message.

Author: Hook, Martha   **488**
Series: Woman's Workshop Series
Title: *Faith: Studies on Living the Christian Life*
Publisher: Zondervan, 1977

Num. Sess.	Group Time	Num. Pgs.	Avg. Qst.	Price	Audience	Format	Bible Study
12	60-90	74	6	4.95	Beginner	Workbk	Topical

Features: Intro to Study, Charts
  ★★★ Personal Application Preparation Time: Low ISBN: 0-310-26241-0
  ★★★ Relationship Building Ldr. Guide Avail.: No Size: 5.25 x 8.0
Subjects: Christian Living, Failure, Faith, Friendships, God, Relationships, Women's Issues
Comments: This study focuses on various aspects of a woman's life: her relationship with God; husband, children, and friends; use of time and money; response to failure; and life of faith. It will help participants become all God intends; it offers guidelines for surveying women's dramatically expanding boundaries of responsibility; and it shows how they can become inwardly beautiful, whole, free, and rational.

Author: Hook, Martha   **489**
Series: Workshop Series
Title: *Workshop on the Book of Ephesians, A*
Publisher: Zondervan, 1986

Num. Sess.	Group Time	Num. Pgs.	Avg. Qst.	Price	Audience	Format	Bible Study
12	60-90	79	8	5.95	Beginner	Workbk	Book

Features: Intro to Leading a Study, Intro to Study
  ★★ Personal Application Preparation Time: Low ISBN: 0-310-26191-0
  ★★ Relationship Building Ldr. Guide Avail.: Yes Size: 5.25 x 8.0
Subjects: Christian Living, Ephesians, Faith, God, Prison Epistles, Relationships
Comments: This study of Ephesians is a "how-to" manual for building unity with God and other Christians. It includes introductory summaries of scripture passages, practical illustrations of difficult biblical interpretations, and "truths to remember" at the end of each chapter. Questions addressed include: "How does one find harmony with God?" "Is building unity with God our responsibility or His?" "Can this bridge to Heaven become a bridge to others?" and "Can we reach a unity in the faith?"

Author: Hook, Sue Vander & Rachel Kiepe   **490**
Series: Serendipity Support Group
Title: *Infertility: Coping With the Pain of Childlessness*
Publisher: Serendipity House, 1991

Num. Sess.	Group Time	Num. Pgs.	Avg. Qst.	Price	Audience	Format	Bible Study
7	60-90	96	Vry	5.45	Beginner	Workbk	Topical

Features: Intro to Leading a Study, Objectives, Bibliography, Prayer Helps, Full Scrpt Printed, Ldr's Notes, Drawings, Cartoons, Agenda
  ★★★★ Personal Application Preparation Time: None ISBN:
  ★★★★ Relationship Building Ldr. Guide Avail.: No Size: 6.50 x 9.25
Subjects: Grief, Marriage, Medical Issues, Parenting
Comments: This study of infertility explores ways to cope with the pain of childlessness. It considers the following: why being childless can be so difficult; new ways to respond to pressures and comments about childlessness; understanding childlessness as a form of grief and loss; examining medical procedures available to couples; exploring ways to restore intimacy and spontaneity to marriage; exploring adoption options; and exploring the future.

Author: Hoover, James   **491**
Series: LifeGuide Bible Study
Title: *Mark: Follow Me*
Publisher: InterVarsity, 1985

Num. Sess.	Group Time	Num. Pgs.	Avg. Qst.	Price	Audience	Format	Bible Study
22	45-75	96	14	3.95	New Christian	Workbk	Book

Features: Intro to Leading a Study, Intro to Study, Ldr's Notes
  ★ Personal Application Preparation Time: Low ISBN: 0-8308-1004-8
  ★ Relationship Building Ldr. Guide Avail.: No Size: 5.50 x 8.25
Subjects: Jesus: Life/Teaching, Mark, Service, Suffering
Comments: Mark theologically and pastorally tells the story of Jesus, showing that the Kingdom in its glory comes at the end of a path of suffering and service. Mark portrays Jesus as the Servant-King whom we should follow from suffering to glory (Mark 1:17). This twenty-two-segment study is divided into a ten-part study on "Who Is Jesus?" and a twelve-part study on "Why Did Jesus Come?" The last study in each segment serves as a review to tie together major themes.

Author: Howard, Walden   **492**
Series:
Title: *Great Biblical Themes*
Publisher: Faith at Work, 1982

Num. Sess.	Group Time	Num. Pgs.	Avg. Qst.	Price	Audience	Format	Bible Study
12	60-75	38	Vry	2.50	New Christian	Book	Topical

Features: Intro to Study
  ★★ Personal Application Preparation Time: Med ISBN:
  ★ Relationship Building Ldr. Guide Avail.: No Size: 5.50 x 8.50
Subjects: Beliefs, New Testament, Old Testament
Comments: One of a series of nine booklets, this study deals with great biblical themes. Twelve lessons lead participants through subjects from a "changing/unchanging God" to the Apostle Paul "living through loss." Lesson titles include: "Cocreators with God," "The Kingdom of God," "Dealing with Sin," "Stories of Jesus," "Death and Resurrection," "Life and Death," and more. Each unit deals with its own scripture and commentary and offers additional suggested reading.

Author: Howard, Walden   **493**
Series:
Title: *Group Encounters with the Bible*
Publisher: Faith at Work, 1977

Num. Sess.	Group Time	Num. Pgs.	Avg. Qst.	Price	Audience	Format	Bible Study
52	30-45	31	Vry	2.0	Beginner	Book	Topical

Features: Intro to Study, No Grp Discussion Quest
  ★★ Personal Application   Preparation Time: Low   ISBN:
  ★★ Relationship Building   Ldr. Guide Avail.: No   Size: 5.50 x 8.50
Subjects: Bible Study, New Testament, Old Testament
Comments: This year-long Old and New Testament study, broken into fifty-two lessons, is designed to foster personal growth among Christians meeting in small groups. The lessons serve as catalysts for meetings which participants will listen to what God says through the Bible, talk about personal concerns, and pray for group members' growth. Some lessons are entitled: "Where to find Christ"; "Christian Paradoxes"; "Jesus: God and Man"; "A Model for Prayer"; "The Claims of Christ"; and more.

Author: Howard, Walden   **494**
Series:
Title: *Journeying in the Spirit*
Publisher: Faith at Work, 1982

Num. Sess.	Group Time	Num. Pgs.	Avg. Qst.	Price	Audience	Format	Bible Study
12	60-75	33	Vry	2.0	New Christian	Book	Topical

Features:
  ★★ Personal Application   Preparation Time: Med   ISBN:
  ★ Relationship Building   Ldr. Guide Avail.: No   Size: 5.50 x 8.50
Subjects: Holy Spirit, Wisdom
Comments: One of a series of nine booklets, this study deals with various aspects of the Holy Spirit. Twelve lessons lead participants from Abraham's journey to people's wisdom in old age. Lesson titles include: "The Narrow Way," "Power for the Journey," "Nurturing Spiritual Growth," "Dreams as Guidance," "Growing in Love," "The Call to Leadership," "The Seasons of Life," and more. Each unit deals with its own scripture and commentary and offers additional suggested reading.

Author: Howard, Walden   **495**
Series:
Title: *Lessons in the Life of Faith*
Publisher: Faith at Work, 1985

Num. Sess.	Group Time	Num. Pgs.	Avg. Qst.	Price	Audience	Format	Bible Study
52	30-45	37	N/A	2.50	New Christian	Book	Topical

Features: Intro to Study, No Grp Discussion Quest
  ★★ Personal Application   Preparation Time: Low   ISBN:
  ★★ Relationship Building   Ldr. Guide Avail.: No   Size: 5.50 x 8.50
Subjects: Faith, New Testament
Comments: This year-long New Testament study, a compilation of 52 lessons, has two unique features. One, it offers four- and eight-part consecutive studies from particular Bible books, which allows participants to gain a sense of wholeness of each book studied. Two, it offers a comprehensive study of biblical themes, helping participants thoroughly understand the basic tenets of Christian faith and experience. Books covered include Peter, Luke, Colossians, and Acts, also Hebrew from the Old Testament.

Author: Huggins, Kevin   **496**
Series:
Title: *Parenting Adolescents*
Publisher: NavPress, 1990

Num. Sess.	Group Time	Num. Pgs.	Avg. Qst.	Price	Audience	Format	Bible Study
8	60-120	N/A	Vry	139.0	Beginner	Video	Topical

Features: Ldr's Notes, Book Incl, Video Study Guide
  ★★★★ Personal Application   Preparation Time: None   ISBN: 9-900735-84-6
  ★★★★ Relationship Building   Ldr. Guide Avail.: No   Size: 10.0 x 12.75
Subjects: Grace, Parenting, Psychology, Teens: Family
Comments: This eight-week video study features dramatic vignettes, interviews with parents and adolescents, and key insights and principles that provide a launching point into stimulating discussion questions. The series avoids pat answers or formulas and encourages teenagers and their families to adopt biblical principles. It helps participants view teens with grace and love and guide them; it helps them focus their energy and develop their own styles of parenting. The pace of the eight sessions can be varied.

Author: Hulme, Lucy & William   **497**
Series: Friendship Bible Study
Title: *Friendship*
Publisher: Augsburg Publishing House, 1987

Num. Sess.	Group Time	Num. Pgs.	Avg. Qst.	Price	Audience	Format	Bible Study
8	60-75	48	10	3.0	New Christian	Workbk	Topical

Features: Intro to Study, Prayer Helps, Study Overview
  ★★★★ Personal Application   Preparation Time: Low   ISBN:
  ★★★★ Relationship Building   Ldr. Guide Avail.: Yes   Size: 5.50 x 8.50
Subjects: Family, Friendships
Comments: This eight-lesson study, which invites participants to look at what it means to be a friend, draws upon biblical examples of friendship. Lessons include: "Loyalty in Friendships," "Friends in the Family," "Friendship Between the Sexes," and "Creative Conflict in Friendship." Participants are made aware that love, or friendship, can be the bridge between the secular and the spiritual. The lesson format includes an overview, an opening, a responsive reading, Bible background, and more.

Author: Hummel, Charles & Anne   **498**
Series: LifeGuide Bible Study
Title: *Genesis: God's Creative Call*
Publisher: InterVarsity, 1985

Num. Sess.	Group Time	Num. Pgs.	Avg. Qst.	Price	Audience	Format	Bible Study
26	45-75	112	12	3.95	New Christian	Workbk	Book

Features: Intro to Leading a Study, Intro to Study, Ldr's Notes
  ★ Personal Application   Preparation Time: Low   ISBN: 0-8308-1022-6
  ★ Relationship Building   Ldr. Guide Avail.: No   Size: 5.50 x 8.25
Subjects: Bible Personalities, Genesis, God
Comments: This study guides us through Genesis, focusing on the lives of Abraham, Isaac, Jacob, and Joseph. It's divided into three main parts: Genesis 1-11 which includes seven lessons on the Creation and primeval history; and Genesis 12-36 which includes twelve lessons on Abraham, Isaac, and Jacob and seven lessons on Joseph. The study is designed to stress what is said and not said in the text. Its purpose is to help participants discover the meaning of Genesis.

Author: Hummel, Charles & Anne   **499**
Series: LifeGuide Bible Study
Title: *Spiritual Gifts*
Publisher: InterVarsity, 1989

Num. Sess.	Group Time	Num. Pgs.	Avg. Qst.	Price	Audience	Format	Bible Study
12	45-60	64	12	3.95	Mature Chrstn	Workbk	Topical

Features: Intro to Leading a Study, Intro to Study, Ldr's Notes, Appendix
   ★Personal Application Preparation Time: Low   ISBN: 0-8308-1062-5
   ★Relationship Building Ldr. Guide Avail.: No   Size: 5.50 x 8.25
Subjects: Church Life, New Testament, Spiritual Gifts
Comments: This study explores the nature of spiritual gifts, describes their role in the church, and discusses how to identify one's own gift(s). The authors examine key passages and specific examples of how the gifts were manifested in the early Church. Evangelism, teaching and preaching, healing, prophecy, and tongues are dealt with in specific lessons. Appendices provide a listing of New Testament gifts and discuss the charismatic dimension.

Author: Hummel, Charles & Anne   **500**
Series: Fisherman Bible Studyguide
Title: *1 Corinthians: Problems & Solutions in a Growing Church*
Publisher: Shaw, 1981

Num. Sess.	Group Time	Num. Pgs.	Avg. Qst.	Price	Audience	Format	Bible Study
16	60-90	93	14	3.95	Mature Chrstn	Workbk	Book

Features: Intro to Leading a Study, Intro to Study
   ★★Personal Application Preparation Time: Low   ISBN: 0-87788-137-5
   ★★Relationship Building Ldr. Guide Avail.: No   Size: 5.0 x 8.25
Subjects: Accountability, Apologetics, Christian Living, Church Life, Ethics, Obedience, Relationships, Social Issues, 1 Corinthians
Comments: This study of 1 Corinthians discusses Paul's response by letter about disturbing developments in the church at Corinth. Paul spent 18 months discipling the young church; after he left, the church continued to grow, which caused new problems. Concerned about divided loyalties, immorality, and pagan lifestyles, Paul wrote a letter which highlights the principles for balanced church growth and life that still apply today. The study offers insights into ways our own culture can adversely influence the Church.

Author: Hunter, Bob & Carol   **501**
Series:
Title: *Loving Justice*
Publisher: InterVarsity, 1990

Num. Sess.	Group Time	Num. Pgs.	Avg. Qst.	Price	Audience	Format	Bible Study
12	45-60	59	11	3.95	Mature Chrstn	Workbk	Topical

Features: Intro to Leading a Study, Intro to Study, Ldr's Notes
   ★★Personal Application Preparation Time: Low   ISBN: 0-8308-1066-8
   ★★Relationship Building Ldr. Guide Avail.: No   Size: 5.50 x 8.25
Subjects: Social Issues
Comments: This study concerns the church's social conscience. Scripture includes many themes of liberation and challenges Christians to deal justly with all people. God chose the nation of Israel as His chosen people, and illustrated justice through their culture and His instruction. An honest study of the Bible reveals just how far people have strayed. This study is unusual due to topics it addresses, and because of its attempt to interpret subtleties in Scripture.

Author: Hunt, Gladys   **502**
Series: Fisherman Bible Studyguide
Title: *God Who Understands Me, The: Sermon on the Mount*
Publisher: Shaw, 1971

Num. Sess.	Group Time	Num. Pgs.	Avg. Qst.	Price	Audience	Format	Bible Study
15	60-90	87	11	3.95	Mature Chrstn	Workbk	Book

Features: Intro to Leading a Study, Intro to Study, Prayer Helps, Digging Deeper Quest
   ★★★Personal Application Preparation Time: None   ISBN: 0-87788-316-5
   ★★Relationship Building Ldr. Guide Avail.: No   Size: 5.0 x 8.25
Subjects: Christian Living, Matthew, Sermon on the Mount
Comments: This is a verse-by-verse study of Matthew, chapters 5 through 7. Comparison scriptures from other books of the Bible are used and printed in the text. The study outlines practical principles that enable people to live Christian lives. It differs from other inductive studies in that it features extensive use of material from the apostle's writings to amplify and reinforce Jesus' leading. The Sermon on the Mount provides "ground rules" for entering the Kingdom of Heaven.

Author: Hunt, Gladys   **503**
Series: Fisherman Bible Studyguide
Title: *Hebrews: From Shadows to Reality*
Publisher: Shaw, 1979

Num. Sess.	Group Time	Num. Pgs.	Avg. Qst.	Price	Audience	Format	Bible Study
13	45-60	79	11	3.95	Mature Chrstn	Workbk	Book

Features: Intro to Leading a Study, Intro to Study, Prayer Helps, Summary
   ★★Personal Application Preparation Time: Low   ISBN: 0-87788-338-6
   ★★Relationship Building Ldr. Guide Avail.: No   Size: 5.0 x 8.25
Subjects: Faith, Grace, Hebrews, Jesus: Life/Teaching
Comments: This chapter-by-chapter study of Hebrews contrasts Old Testament sacrifices with the abundant, life-changing grace available in Jesus Christ. To profit most, participants need some background in the gospels, Acts, and the Old Testament. It is a good study for those who want to understand more fully the connection between the Old Testament sacrifices and the death of Jesus Christ. Study questions help participants appreciate the reality of God-directed faith in daily life.

Author: Hunt, Gladys   **504**
Series: Fisherman Bible Studyguide
Title: *John: Eyewitness*
Publisher: Shaw, 1971

Num. Sess.	Group Time	Num. Pgs.	Avg. Qst.	Price	Audience	Format	Bible Study
24	45-60	87	10	3.95	Beginner	Workbk	Book

Features: Intro to Leading a Study, Intro to Study, Prayer Helps, Maps
   ★★Personal Application Preparation Time: Low   ISBN: 0-87788-245-2
   ★★Relationship Building Ldr. Guide Avail.: No   Size: 5.0 x 8.25
Subjects: Evangelism, Jesus: Life/Teaching, John
Comments: In this study John, an eyewitness and close follower of Christ, provides a comprehensive foundation for Christian faith, answering such questions as who Jesus Christ is and what He has done. John records both the deeds and the direct statements of Jesus. John's Gospel is background for understanding the whole of the New Testament. This study is no mere exercise; it demands a personal decision about Jesus Christ. Each lesson deals with a complete or partial chapter of John.

Author: Hunt, Gladys **505**
Series: Fisherman Bible Studyguide
Title: *Relationships*
Publisher: Shaw, 1983

Num. Sess.	Group Time	Num. Pgs.	Avg. Qst.	Price	Audience	Format	Bible Study
15	45-60	63	8	3.95	Beginner	Workbk	Topical

Features: Intro to Leading a Study, Intro to Study, Prayer Helps
  ★★★ Personal Application Preparation Time: None ISBN: 0-87788-721-7
  ★★★ Relationship Building Ldr. Guide Avail.: No Size: 5.0 x 8.25
Subjects: Christian Living, God, Relationships
Comments: The primary focus of this study is on human relationships and ways to improve relationships with God by following His example, listening to His truth, and understanding the principles He has established. This study guides the reader to discover biblical foundations for the way people's lives touch, bond, and grow, using examples of Bible relationships—some to emulate and others to avoid.

Author: Hunt, Gladys **506**
Series: Fisherman Bible Studyguide
Title: *Revelation: The Lamb Who Is the Lion*
Publisher: Shaw, 1973

Num. Sess.	Group Time	Num. Pgs.	Avg. Qst.	Price	Audience	Format	Bible Study
13	45-60	73	9	3.95	Mature Chrstn	Workbk	Book

Features: Intro to Leading a Study, Intro to Study, Summary, Maps
  ★★ Personal Application Preparation Time: Low ISBN: 0-87788-486-2
  ★★ Relationship Building Ldr. Guide Avail.: No Size: 5.0 x 8.25
Subjects: Revelation, Satan
Comments: This advanced chapter-by-chapter inductive study of Revelation, the Bible's final book which reveals the age-old conflict between good and evil, shows how believers can be conquerors with the "Victorious Lion." The Revelation demands humility in any attempt at interpretation. Its imagery and symbolism sometimes lead to a contemporary feeling of "this is it." However, after reading the signs of the times and studying Scripture diligently, opinions may be formed, then laid before His sovereignty.

Author: Hunt, Gladys **507**
Series: Fisherman Bible Studyguide
Title: *Romans: Made Righteous by Faith*
Publisher: Shaw, 1980

Num. Sess.	Group Time	Num. Pgs.	Avg. Qst.	Price	Audience	Format	Bible Study
14	45-60	74	10	3.95	New Christian	Workbk	Book

Features: Intro to Leading a Study, Intro to Study, Bibliography, Prayer Helps
  ★★ Personal Application Preparation Time: Low ISBN: 0-87788-733-0
  ★★ Relationship Building Ldr. Guide Avail.: No Size: 5.0 x 8.25
Subjects: Faith, God, Grace, Reconciliation, Romans
Comments: This is a chapter-by-chapter study of concepts of reconciliation with God, faith, grace, and righteousness as presented in Paul's letter to the Roman church. Chapters 1-5 explain God's way to righteousness by faith. In chapters 6-8, Paul adds to this good news the liberating secret to living a holy life. Chapters 9-11 are a parenthetical discussion about Jewish unbelief and the purpose of God. In chapters 12-15 Paul describes the practical work of redemption.

Author: Hunt, Gladys **508**
Series: Fisherman Bible Studyguide
Title: *Stories Jesus Told*
Publisher: Shaw, 1986

Num. Sess.	Group Time	Num. Pgs.	Avg. Qst.	Price	Audience	Format	Bible Study
12	45-60	60	12	3.95	Beginner	Workbk	Topical

Features: Intro to Leading a Study, Intro to Study, Follow Up
  ★★ Personal Application Preparation Time: None ISBN: 0-87788-791-8
  ★★ Relationship Building Ldr. Guide Avail.: No Size: 5.0 x 8.25
Subjects: Jesus: Life/Teaching, Parables
Comments: The parables are the foundation of twelve studies revolving around Jesus, the master teacher and superb storyteller. His speeches weren't dull doctrine or abstract theology, but were lively discourses full of illustrations, metaphors, and stories that caught and held the popular interest. They were also easily applicable. Twelve major parables include familiar things like seed and soil, sheep, coins, and weddings, through which Jesus introduced us to God's Kingdom, its principles, and His people.

Author: Hunt, Gladys **509**
Series: LifeGuide Bible Study
Title: *Women of the Old Testament*
Publisher: InterVarsity, 1990

Num. Sess.	Group Time	Num. Pgs.	Avg. Qst.	Price	Audience	Format	Bible Study
12	45-60	63	12	3.95	Beginner	Workbk	Charctr

Features: Intro to Leading a Study, Intro to Study, Ldr's Notes
  ★★★★ Personal Application Preparation Time: Low ISBN: 0-8308-1064-1
  ★★★ Relationship Building Ldr. Guide Avail.: No Size: 5.50 x 8.25
Subjects: Bible Personalities, Faith, Obedience, Old Testament, Women's Issues
Comments: This study concerns twelve ordinary women whose choices and actions produced extraordinary results. Through faith and strong character, they rescued their families, led people out of bondage, gave birth to kings, and saved an entire nation. Their lives demonstrate the far-reaching consequences of living every day for God. Among the remarkable women studied are Miriam, Rahab, Ruth, Naomi, Hannah, and Esther.

Author: Hybels, Bill & Jay Caress **510**
Series: SonPower Elective Series
Title: *Caution: Christians Under Construction*
Publisher: Victor Books, 1978

Num. Sess.	Group Time	Num. Pgs.	Avg. Qst.	Price	Audience	Format	Bible Study
12	60-75	143	Vry	5.99	Beginner	Book	Topical

Features:
  ★★ Personal Application Preparation Time: None ISBN: 0-88207-759-7
  ★★ Relationship Building Ldr. Guide Avail.: Yes Size: 4.25 x 7.0
Subjects: Teens: Christian Liv, Teens: Psychology, Teens: Relationships, Teens: Self-image, Teens: Senior High
Comments: This personal, simple, yet challenging study will be helpful in building relationships. It provides a blueprint for growing as a Christian and covers topics such as: exposing misconceptions about Christianity, nailing down your self-image, repairing and maintaining friendships, and building a strong spiritual foundation. A leader's guide with transparency masters is availabe. Detachable student sheets are also available.

Author: Hybels, Bill 511
Series:
Title: *Christians in the Marketplace*
Publisher: Victor Books, 1982

Num. Sess.	Group Time	Num. Pgs.	Avg. Qst.	Price	Audience	Format	Bible Study
13	60-75	144	N/A	7.99	New Christian	Book	Topical

Features: Cassette Avail
★★★★ Personal Application Preparation Time: Low ISBN: 0-88207-314-1
★★★ Relationship Building Ldr. Guide Avail.: Yes Size: 5.50 x 8.0
Subjects: Evangelism, Faith, Satan, Work
Comments: This study provides practical, biblical guidelines on how to take faith into the secular workplace. Participants are warned about the dangers of being Christian consumers in a materialistic society. When exposed to tactics Satan uses to disarm them, Christians must concentrate on shining Christ's "light" into a darkened world. Many topical questions are answered in this text. A leader's guide with transparency masters is available.

Author: Jacks, Bob & Betty 512
Series:
Title: *Your Home, A Lighthouse*
Publisher: NavPress, 1986

Num. Sess.	Group Time	Num. Pgs.	Avg. Qst.	Price	Audience	Format	Bible Study
13	-	156	N/A	6.95		Book	No

Features: Bibliography, Appendix
Personal Application Preparation Time: ISBN: 0-89109-127-0
Relationship Building Ldr. Guide Avail.: Size: 5.25 x 8.0
Subjects: Evangelism, Small Group Resource
Comments: This book describes the simple concept of using the warmth of a home as a relaxed setting in which people can consider God, His Word, and the implications for their lives. Subject matter includes how to start a group, who to invite, what to study, how to ask and answer good questions, and when to encourage a decision for Christ. The appendix section includes many "helps," such as how to explain the gospel.

Author: Jacks, Bob & Betty 513
Series:
Title: *Your Home, A Lighthouse*
Publisher: NavPress, 1990

Num. Sess.	Group Time	Num. Pgs.	Avg. Qst.	Price	Audience	Format	Bible Study
3	60-90	N/A	8	79.0	New Christian	Video	Topical

Features: Book Incl
★★★★ Personal Application Preparation Time: None ISBN: 8-900730-28-2
★★★ Relationship Building Ldr. Guide Avail.: No Size: 10.50 x 12.50
Subjects: Evangelism, Small Group Resource
Comments: This three-part video offers insights, principles, and suggestions to equip and motivate participants to use their homes to reach others for Christ. The forty-minute tapes combine lecture with situational vignettes. The guide helps participants apply principles illustrated in the video. Each session opens with a warm-up question, followed by a question on which to focus while viewing the video. Group discussion questions follow a review of the video's points.

Author: Jackson, Neta 514
Series: Building Books
Title: *Building Christian Relationships*
Publisher: Bethany House, 1984

Num. Sess.	Group Time	Num. Pgs.	Avg. Qst.	Price	Audience	Format	Bible Study
34	45-60	63	Vry	4.95	New Christian	Workbk	Topical

Features: Intro to Leading a Study
★★ Personal Application Preparation Time: Low ISBN: 0-87123-407-6
★★ Relationship Building Ldr. Guide Avail.: Yes Size: 8.50 x 11.0
Subjects: Teens: Christian Liv, Teens: Family, Teens: Relationships
Comments: This thirty-four-lesson study for young people deals with getting along with others, with God, with oneself, with family, and with friends. It is divided into four sections: (1) Attitudes which build barriers, such as pride, fear, gossip, materialism; (2) Strengthening the foundation on which to build good friendships; (3) The building blocks of Christian relationships; and (4) Application to specific relationships, such as parent and peers.

Author: Jacobson, Donald O. 515
Series: Small Group Bible Studies
Title: *People Who Care*
Publisher: Augsburg Publishing House, 1980

Num. Sess.	Group Time	Num. Pgs.	Avg. Qst.	Price	Audience	Format	Bible Study
5	60-75	16	9	1.10	New Christian	Book	Topical

Features: Intro to Study, Prayer Helps
Personal Application Preparation Time: None ISBN:
Relationship Building Ldr. Guide Avail.: No Size: 8.50 x 5.50
Subjects: Caring, Emotions, Joy, Relationships
Comments: This small pamphlet includes five sessions on human relationships. It examines the human emotions of joy, fear, grief, anger, and guilt. It differs from traditional Bible studies because it begins with human needs and looks to the Bible for affirmation rather than taking the more common approach of starting with a biblical passage. Each session begins with someone reading aloud a true account about people experiencing intense human emotions. One objective of this study is to develop a caring community.

Author: James, Edgar C. 516
Series: Teach Yourself the Bible
Title: *Epistles of Peter, The*
Publisher: Moody Press, 1964

Num. Sess.	Group Time	Num. Pgs.	Avg. Qst.	Price	Audience	Format	Bible Study
8	60-75	48	28	3.99	New Christian	Workbk	Book

Features: Intro to Leading a Study, Intro to Study, Exam
★★ Personal Application Preparation Time: Low ISBN: 0-8024-2355-8
★★ Relationship Building Ldr. Guide Avail.: No Size: 5.50 x 8.50
Subjects: False Teachers, 1 & 2 Peter
Comments: This study of 1 and 2 Peter—part of a twenty-five-book series—provides practical advice for the "last days." Peter responds to churches and believers under persecution and assault of false teachers with words of comfort and counsel. The format includes a series of fill-in-the-blank questions, and checkups to test participants' grasp of scriptural truths. The series, although designed for self-study, also includes suggestions for group study. A four-year plan for using the series is also included.

Author: James, Edgar C.   **517**
Series: Teach Yourself the Bible
Title: *2 Corinthians: Keys to Triumphant Living*
Publisher: Moody Press, 1964

Num. Sess.	Group Time	Num. Pgs.	Avg. Qst.	Price	Audience	Format	Bible Study
12	60-75	64	29	3.99	New Christian	Workbk	Book

Features: Intro to Leading a Study, Intro to Study, Exam
  ★★ Personal Application   Preparation Time: Low   ISBN: 0-8024-7680-5
  ★★ Relationship Building   Ldr. Guide Avail.: No   Size: 5.50 x 8.50
Subjects: Church Life, Hope, Integrity, Leadership, Repentance, Service, Suffering, Victorious Living, 2 Corinthians
Comments: The book of 2 Corinthians demonstrates Paul's deep concern for his converts. In this study, Paul's confidence in God is shown through topics such as: confidence through difficulty, testimony, ministry, conduct, repentance, and death. The format includes a series of fill-in-the-blank questions; and checkups test participants' grasp of scriptural truths. This twenty-five-book series is designed for self-study; however, suggestions for group study are included.

Author: Jayaprakash, Eva & Joshi   **518**
Series: Global Issues
Title: *Fundamentalistic Religion*
Publisher: InterVarsity, 1990

Num. Sess.	Group Time	Num. Pgs.	Avg. Qst.	Price	Audience	Format	Bible Study
6	45-60	48	11	4.95	New Christian	Workbk	Topical

Features: Intro to Leading a Study, Intro to Study, Prayer Helps, Digging Deeper Quest
  ★★ Personal Application   Preparation Time: Low   ISBN: 0-8308-4910-6
  ★ Relationship Building   Ldr. Guide Avail.: No   Size: 5.50 x 8.25
Subjects: Cults
Comments: This six-week study explores characteristics of fundamentalistic religions, including the Shi'ite, Marxist, Hindu and Christian fundamentalistic movements. The lessons lead participants to consider what the real "fundamentals" of faith should be and how they can be implemented through believers to action in witnessing to the world. Participants use scripture to distinguish the difference between commitment and fanaticism.

Author: Jensen, Irving L.   **519**
Series: Do-It-Yourself Bible Study
Title: *Acts*
Publisher: Here's Life, 1984

Num. Sess.	Group Time	Num. Pgs.	Avg. Qst.	Price	Audience	Format	Bible Study
48	60-90	120	Vry	7.95	New Christian	Workbk	Book

Features: Intro to Leading a Study, Intro to Study, Bibliography, Scrpt Memory Helps, Study Overview, Summary, Full Scrpt Printed, Maps
  ★★ Personal Application   Preparation Time: Med   ISBN: 0-89840-066-X
  ★★ Relationship Building   Ldr. Guide Avail.: No   Size: 7.50 x 10.0
Subjects: Acts, Church Life, Holy Spirit
Comments: This is a sentence-by-sentence, paragraph-by-paragraph, chapter-by-chapter study of the book of Acts. It presents the exciting mission of Christianity as "The Church Established," "The Church Scattered," and "The Church Extended." Each lesson is conveniently displayed on two facing pages, and a free "how to use" booklet is available from the publisher.

Author: Jensen, Irving L.   **520**
Series: Bible Self-study Guides
Title: *Acts*
Publisher: Moody Press, 1969

Num. Sess.	Group Time	Num. Pgs.	Avg. Qst.	Price	Audience	Format	Bible Study
21	60-75	104	Vry	4.99	Mature Chrstn	Workbk	Book

Features: Intro to Leading a Study, Intro to Study, Bibliography, Study Overview, Digging Deeper Quest, Follow Up, Summary, Charts, Maps, Topical Index, Word Study
  ★★★★ Personal Application   Preparation Time: Med   ISBN: 0-8024-4473-3
  ★★ Relationship Building   Ldr. Guide Avail.: No   Size: 5.50 x 8.50
Subjects: Acts, Church Life, Holy Spirit
Comments: This academic study of Acts—part of a thirty-nine-book series—concerns Luke's account of the Holy Spirit working through the apostles. The twenty-eight chapters of Acts fall into three main divisions: the church established, the church scattered, and the church extended. This series of Bible self-studies is ideal for individual, small group, or class use. Outlines, diagrams, and explanations keep participants challenged.

Author: Jensen, Irving L.   **521**
Series: Bible Self-study Guides
Title: *Colossians and Philemon*
Publisher: Moody Press, 1973

Num. Sess.	Group Time	Num. Pgs.	Avg. Qst.	Price	Audience	Format	Bible Study
8	60-75	64	Vry	4.99	Mature Chrstn	Workbk	Book

Features: Intro to Leading a Study, Intro to Study, Bibliography, Digging Deeper Quest, Follow Up, Summary, Charts, Maps, Word Study
  ★★★★ Personal Application   Preparation Time: Med   ISBN: 0-8024-4480-6
  ★★ Relationship Building   Ldr. Guide Avail.: No   Size: 5.50 x 8.50
Subjects: Colossians/Philemon, False Teachers, Forgiveness, Prison Epistles
Comments: This academic study of Colossians and Philemon—part of a 39-book series—covers two of Paul's Prison Epistles. Colossians was written to Colosse concerning heresy in the church. Paul forthrightly, positively, and boldly took the offensive against false views and evil practices. The letter to Philemon, shortest of his writings, is a masterpiece of graceful, tactful, and delicate pleading for a forgiving spirit between slave and master. Outlines, diagrams, and explanations keep participants challenged.

Author: Jensen, Irving L.   **522**
Series: Do-It-Yourself Bible Study
Title: *David: A Man After God's Own Heart*
Publisher: Here's Life, 1988

Num. Sess.	Group Time	Num. Pgs.	Avg. Qst.	Price	Audience	Format	Bible Study
13	45-60	63	Vry	4.95	New Christian	Workbk	Charctr

Features: Intro to Study, Summary, Charts, Maps
  ★★ Personal Application   Preparation Time: Low   ISBN: 0-89840-215-8
  ★★ Relationship Building   Ldr. Guide Avail.: No   Size: 5.0 x 8.0
Subjects: Bible Personalities, Failure, God, 1 & 2 Samuel
Comments: This study, which follows David's life from shepherd boy to king of Israel, provides insights into how he slew the spiritual, emotional, and physical giants in his life. It responds to three questions: Can one rise above past failure and live a fruitful life for Christ? Is it really possible to develop an intimate relationship with the God of the universe? How can I become a person after God's own heart? Each lesson is conveniently displayed on two facing pages.

Author: Jensen, Irving L.   523
Series: Bible Self-study Guides
Title: *Ecclesiastes and the Song of Solomon*
Publisher: Moody Press, 1974

Num. Sess.	Group Time	Num. Pgs.	Avg. Qst.	Price	Audience	Format	Bible Study
12	60-75	96	Vry	4.99	Mature Chrstn	Workbk	Book

Features: Intro to Leading a Study, Intro to Study, Bibliography, Digging Deeper Quest, Follow Up, Summary, Charts, Maps, Word Study

★★★★ Personal Application   Preparation Time: Med   ISBN: 0-8024-4463-6
  ★★ Relationship Building   Ldr. Guide Avail.: No   Size: 5.50 x 8.50

Subjects: Ecclesiastes, Song of Solomon

Comments: Ecclesiastes and Song of Solomon deal with life and love. Ecclesiastes evaluates life and outlines worthwhile living (the way to God); Song of Solomon is the classic book on love (the way of God). This thirty-nine-book series of Bible self-studies is ideal for individual, small group, or class use. Outlines, diagrams, and explanations keep participants challenged.

Author: Jensen, Irving L.   524
Series: Bible Self-study Guides
Title: *Ephesians*
Publisher: Moody Press, 1973

Num. Sess.	Group Time	Num. Pgs.	Avg. Qst.	Price	Audience	Format	Bible Study
10	60-75	96	Vry	4.99	Mature Chrstn	Workbk	Book

Features: Intro to Leading a Study, Intro to Study, Bibliography, Digging Deeper Quest, Follow Up, Summary, Charts, Maps, Word Study

★★★★ Personal Application   Preparation Time: Med   ISBN: 0-8024-4478-4
  ★★ Relationship Building   Ldr. Guide Avail.: No   Size: 5.50 x 8.50

Subjects: Discipleship, Ephesians

Comments: This academic study of Ephesians—part of a thirty-nine-book series—covers Paul's letter to the church at Ephesus in great detail. Ten lessons move participants from the letter's background and setting to Paul's encouraging final words on Christians' armor. This series of Bible self-studies is ideal for individual, small group, or class use. Outlines, diagrams, and explanations keep participants challenged. When completed, the series will have provided a personal study of the entire Bible.

Author: Jensen, Irving L.   525
Series: Bible Self-study Guides
Title: *Epistles of John & Jude*
Publisher: Moody Press, 1971

Num. Sess.	Group Time	Num. Pgs.	Avg. Qst.	Price	Audience	Format	Bible Study
13	60-75	112	Vry	4.99	Mature Chrstn	Workbk	Book

Features: Intro to Leading a Study, Intro to Study, Bibliography, Digging Deeper Quest, Follow Up, Summary, Charts, Maps, Word Study

★★★★ Personal Application   Preparation Time: Med   ISBN: 0-8024-4486-5
  ★★ Relationship Building   Ldr. Guide Avail.: No   Size: 5.50 x 8.50

Subjects: Church Life, Satan, 1, 2 & 3 John/Jude

Comments: In this academic study of 1, 2, and 3 John and Jude—part of a thirty-nine-book series—John and Jude address Christians who fell prey to the same deceptive devices of Satan common today. The studies deal with real problems in local churches, sound solutions, and the surety of tragic judgment. Participants will be challenged to persevere because God wants His children to remember that there is no darkness so black that His light cannot pierce it.

Author: Jensen, Irving L.   526
Series: Bible Self-study Guides
Title: *Exodus*
Publisher: Moody Press, 1967

Num. Sess.	Group Time	Num. Pgs.	Avg. Qst.	Price	Audience	Format	Bible Study
12	60-75	112	Vry	4.99	Mature Chrstn	Workbk	Book

Features: Intro to Leading a Study, Intro to Study, Bibliography, Digging Deeper Quest, Follow Up, Summary, Charts, Maps, Word Study

★★★★ Personal Application   Preparation Time: Med   ISBN: 0-8024-4451-2
  ★★ Relationship Building   Ldr. Guide Avail.: No   Size: 5.50 x 8.50

Subjects: Bible Personalities, Exodus, God, Leadership

Comments: This academic study of Exodus—part of a thirty-nine-book series—covers Moses' account of a nation's problem and closes with its redemption by God. This redemption unfolds in the following way: God appoints a leader for Israel (Moses); He makes Israel's enemy impotent through plagues; He delivers Israel from Egypt; He confirms the covenant relationship; and He institutes a program of worship through the law. Outlines, diagrams, and explanations keep participants challenged.

Author: Jensen, Irving L.   527
Series: Bible Self-study Guides
Title: *Ezekiel/Daniel*
Publisher: Moody Press, 1968

Num. Sess.	Group Time	Num. Pgs.	Avg. Qst.	Price	Audience	Format	Bible Study
12	60-75	96	Vry	4.99	Mature Chrstn	Workbk	Book

Features: Intro to Leading a Study, Intro to Study, Bibliography, Digging Deeper Quest, Follow Up, Summary, Charts, Maps, Word Study

★★★★ Personal Application   Preparation Time: Med   ISBN: 0-8024-4465-2
  ★★ Relationship Building   Ldr. Guide Avail.: No   Size: 5.50 x 8.50

Subjects: Daniel, Eschatology, Ezekiel, Major Prophets

Comments: The books of Ezekiel and Daniel, the accounts of two prophets living in exile, give attention to end-time events of world history scheduled on God's timetable. This thirty-nine-book series of Bible self-studies is ideal for individual, small group, or class use. Outlines, diagrams, and explanations keep participants challenged.

Author: Jensen, Irving L.   528
Series: Bible Self-study Guides
Title: *Ezra, Nehemiah and Esther*
Publisher: Moody Press, 1970

Num. Sess.	Group Time	Num. Pgs.	Avg. Qst.	Price	Audience	Format	Bible Study
14	60-75	96	Vry	4.99	Mature Chrstn	Workbk	Book

Features: Intro to Leading a Study, Intro to Study, Bibliography, Digging Deeper Quest, Follow Up, Summary, Charts, Maps, Word Study

★★★★ Personal Application   Preparation Time: Med   ISBN: 0-8024-4459-8
  ★★ Relationship Building   Ldr. Guide Avail.: No   Size: 5.50 x 8.50

Subjects: Esther, Ezra/Nehemiah, Faith

Comments: The books of Ezra, Nehemiah, and Esther deal with the last events recorded in the Old Testament. Ezra shows how the Lord fulfilled His promises and restored Israel to their own land; Nehemiah shows the restoration of the failing faith of the Jews; and Esther shows how the Jews were saved from extermination. This thirty-nine-book series of academic Bible self-studies is ideal for individual, small group, or class use. Outlines, diagrams, and explanations keep participants challenged.

Author: Jensen, Irving L.　　　　**529**
Series: Bible Self-study Guides
Title: *Galatians*
Publisher: Moody Press, 1973

Num. Sess.	Group Time	Num. Pgs.	Avg. Qst.	Price	Audience	Format	Bible Study
10	60-75	96	Vry	4.99	Mature Chrstn	Workbk	Book

Features: Intro to Leading a Study, Intro to Study, Bibliography, Digging Deeper Quest, Follow Up, Summary, Charts, Maps, Appendix, Word Study

★★★★ Personal Application　Preparation Time: Med　ISBN: 0-8024-4477-6
　★★ Relationship Building　Ldr. Guide Avail.: No　Size: 5.50 x 8.50
Subjects: Galatians, Holy Spirit
Comments: This academic study of Galatians—part of a thirty-nine-book series—covers Paul's first inspired letter, written to combat heresy and to confirm gospel truth. More than a doctrinal study, it will encourage and inspire participants to move forward spiritually in the power and direction of the Holy Spirit, enjoying the freedom of new life in Christ. Outlines, diagrams, and explanations keep participants challenged.

Author: Jensen, Irving L.　　　　**530**
Series: Do-It-Yourself Bible Study
Title: *General Epistles: James, Peter, John, Jude*
Publisher: Here's Life, 1985

Num. Sess.	Group Time	Num. Pgs.	Avg. Qst.	Price	Audience	Format	Bible Study
47	60-90	134	Vry	7.95	New Christian	Workbk	Book

Features: Intro to Leading a Study, Intro to Study, Bibliography, Scrpt Memory Helps, Study Overview, Summary, Full Scrpt Printed, Maps

　★★ Personal Application　Preparation Time: Med　ISBN: 0-89840-060-0
　★★ Relationship Building　Ldr. Guide Avail.: No　Size: 7.50 x 10.0
Subjects: Faith, James, 1 & 2 Peter, 1, 2 & 3 John/Jude
Comments: This is a sentence-by-sentence, paragraph-by-paragraph, chapter-by-chapter study of the General Epistles—James; 1 and 2 Peter; 1, 2, and 3 John; and Jude. Study themes include: "Faith for Living," "God's Chosen People," "Fellowship with God and His Children," "Truth and the Christian," "Fellow-Workers for the Truth," and "Keeping Yourself in the Love of God." Each lesson is conveniently displayed on two facing pages, and a free "how to use" booklet is available from the publisher.

Author: Jensen, Irving L.　　　　**531**
Series: Bible Self-study Guides
Title: *Genesis*
Publisher: Moody Press, 1967

Num. Sess.	Group Time	Num. Pgs.	Avg. Qst.	Price	Audience	Format	Bible Study
12	60-75	96	Vry	4.99	Mature Chrstn	Workbk	Book

Features: Intro to Leading a Study, Intro to Study, Bibliography, Digging Deeper Quest, Follow Up, Summary, Charts, Maps, Word Study

★★★★ Personal Application　Preparation Time: Med　ISBN: 0-8024-4450-4
　★★ Relationship Building　Ldr. Guide Avail.: No　Size: 5.50 x 8.50
Subjects: Bible Personalities, Genesis, God
Comments: This academic study of Genesis—part of a thirty-nine-book series—covers Moses' account of "the beginnings." It moves from Creation to the Fall, the Flood, Abraham's life, Isaac's life, and Jacob's life, and concludes with Joseph's life. This series of Bible self-studies is ideal for individual, small group, or class use. Outlines, diagrams, and explanations keep participants challenged.

Author: Jensen, Irving L.　　　　**532**
Series: Bible Self-study Guides
Title: *Haggai, Zechariah, Malachi*
Publisher: Moody Press, 1976

Num. Sess.	Group Time	Num. Pgs.	Avg. Qst.	Price	Audience	Format	Bible Study
11	60-75	96	Vry	4.99	Mature Chrstn	Workbk	Book

Features: Intro to Leading a Study, Intro to Study, Bibliography, Digging Deeper Quest, Follow Up, Summary, Charts, Maps

★★★★ Personal Application　Preparation Time: Med　ISBN: 0-8024-4468-7
　★★ Relationship Building　Ldr. Guide Avail.: No　Size: 5.50 x 8.50
Subjects: Bible Personalities, Christian Living, Minor Prophets, Prophecy, Reconciliation
Comments: This academic study of Haggai, Zechariah, and Malachi—part of a thirty-nine-book series—covers the last of the Old Testament prophets. Haggai's major theme is, "put first things first in your life" to renew a relationship with the Lord. Both Haggai and Zechariah's main task is to exhort the Jews to finish rebuilding the Temple. Malachi, in addition to messianic prophecies of Kingdom and judgment, offers timeless commands about everyday living.

Author: Jensen, Irving L.　　　　**533**
Series: Bible Self-study Guides
Title: *Hebrews*
Publisher: Moody Press, 1970

Num. Sess.	Group Time	Num. Pgs.	Avg. Qst.	Price	Audience	Format	Bible Study
13	60-75	104	Vry	4.99	Mature Chrstn	Workbk	Book

Features: Intro to Leading a Study, Intro to Study, Bibliography, Digging Deeper Quest, Follow Up, Summary, Charts, Maps, Word Study

★★★★ Personal Application　Preparation Time: Med　ISBN: 0-8024-4483-0
　★★ Relationship Building　Ldr. Guide Avail.: No　Size: 5.50 x 8.50
Subjects: Faith, Hebrews
Comments: This academic study of Hebrews—part of a thirty-nine-book series—covers the threat of apostasy. Thirteen lessons move participants from a background of Hebrews to confidence of faith, examples of faith, endurance of faith, and workings of faith. This series of Bible self-studies is ideal for individual, small group, or class use. Outlines, diagrams, and explanations keep participants challenged.

Author: Jensen, Irving L.　　　　**534**
Series: Do-It-Yourself Bible Study
Title: *Hebrews: And the Pastoral Epistles*
Publisher: Here's Life, 1985

Num. Sess.	Group Time	Num. Pgs.	Avg. Qst.	Price	Audience	Format	Bible Study
51	60-90	139	Vry	7.95	New Christian	Workbk	Book

Features: Intro to Leading a Study, Intro to Study, Bibliography, Scrpt Memory Helps, Study Overview, Summary, Full Scrpt Printed, Maps

　★★ Personal Application　Preparation Time: Med　ISBN: 0-89840-077-5
　★★ Relationship Building　Ldr. Guide Avail.: No　Size: 7.50 x 10.0
Subjects: Church Life, Faith, Forgiveness, Hebrews, Hope, Pastoral Epistles, Suffering, 1 & 2 Timothy/Titus
Comments: This is a sentence-by-sentence, paragraph-by-paragraph, chapter-by-chapter study of Hebrews and the Pastoral Epistles (1 and 2 Timothy, Titus, and Philemon). The study of Hebrews will help participants become more intimately acquainted with Jesus as Savior and Intercessor; the Pastoral Epistles will increase their understanding of serving effectively in a local church. Each lesson is conveniently displayed on two facing pages, and a free "how to use" booklet is available from the publisher.

Author: Jensen, Irving L.   **535**
Series: Bible Self-study Guides
Title: *Isaiah/Jeremiah*
Publisher: Moody Press, 1968

Num. Sess.	Group Time	Num. Pgs.	Avg. Qst.	Price	Audience	Format	Bible Study
12	60-75	112	Vry	4.99	Mature Chrstn	Workbk	Book

Features: Intro to Leading a Study, Intro to Study, Bibliography, Digging Deeper Quest, Follow Up, Summary, Charts, Maps, Word Study
★★★★ Personal Application   Preparation Time: Med   ISBN: 0-8024-4464-4
  ★★ Relationship Building   Ldr. Guide Avail.: No   Size: 5.50 x 8.50
Subjects: Isaiah/Jeremiah, Major Prophets, Prophecy
Comments: This twelve-lesson academic study of Isaiah and Jeremiah—part of a thirty-nine-book series—begins with a thorough overview of prophets in general. It then proceeds to Isaiah, whose message was twofold: a warning of judgment for sin, and comfort of salvation for righteousness. It concludes with Jeremiah, whose message is also twofold: "to destroy" (destruction) and "to build" (construction). The prophets will challenge all serious Bible students.

Author: Jensen, Irving L.   **536**
Series: Bible Self-study Guides
Title: *James*
Publisher: Moody Press, 1971

Num. Sess.	Group Time	Num. Pgs.	Avg. Qst.	Price	Audience	Format	Bible Study
10	60-75	112	Vry	4.99	Mature Chrstn	Workbk	Book

Features: Intro to Leading a Study, Intro to Study, Bibliography, Digging Deeper Quest, Follow Up, Summary, Charts, Maps, Word Study
★★★★ Personal Application   Preparation Time: Med   ISBN: 0-8024-4484-9
  ★★ Relationship Building   Ldr. Guide Avail.: No   Size: 5.50 x 8.50
Subjects: Christian Living, Faith, James, Prayer, Wisdom
Comments: This academic study covers James' letter to Christians who have been reconciled to God through Christ. It specifically instructs them in how to walk with God in this present life. Subjects include: patience, prayer, love, liberty, equality, humility, peace, steadfastness, self-control, and wisdom. Outlines, diagrams, and explanations keep participants challenged. This thirty-nine-book series of Bible self-studies is ideal for individual, small group, or class use.

Author: Jensen, Irving L.   **537**
Series: Bible Self-study Guides
Title: *Job*
Publisher: Moody Press, 1975

Num. Sess.	Group Time	Num. Pgs.	Avg. Qst.	Price	Audience	Format	Bible Study
13	60-75	104	Vry	3.99	Mature Chrstn	Workbk	Book

Features: Intro to Leading a Study, Intro to Study, Bibliography, Digging Deeper Quest, Follow Up, Summary, Charts, Maps, Word Study
★★★★ Personal Application   Preparation Time: Med   ISBN: 0-8024-4460-1
  ★★ Relationship Building   Ldr. Guide Avail.: No   Size: 5.50 x 8.50
Subjects: Faith, God, Job, Satan
Comments: Part of a thirty-nine-book series, this academic study covers the person of Job and his physical and spiritual experience, in which his faith was supremely tested. Its purposes are to reveal who God is, to show the kind of trust He wants for His children, and to reveal His favor toward His children, and His absolute control over Satan. It also answers how a righteous person may suffer while an evil person enjoys health and prosperity.

Author: Jensen, Irving L.   **538**
Series: Do-It-Yourself Bible Study
Title: *John*
Publisher: Here's Life, 1983

Num. Sess.	Group Time	Num. Pgs.	Avg. Qst.	Price	Audience	Format	Bible Study
68	60-90	160	Vry	7.95	New Christian	Workbk	Book

Features: Intro to Leading a Study, Intro to Study, Bibliography, Scrpt Memory Helps, Study Overview, Summary, Full Scrpt Printed, Maps
  ★★ Personal Application   Preparation Time: Med   ISBN: 0-89840-051-1
  ★★ Relationship Building   Ldr. Guide Avail.: No   Size: 7.50 x 10.0
Subjects: Jesus: Life/Teaching, John
Comments: This is a sentence-by-sentence, paragraph-by-paragraph, chapter-by-chapter study of John. It includes five major divisions: "The Prologue and Era of Incarnation," "The Years of Conflict," "The Day of Preparation," "The Hour of Sacrifice and Dawn of Victory," and "The Epilogue." Each lesson is conveniently displayed on two facing pages, and a free "how to use" booklet is available from the publisher.

Author: Jensen, Irving L.   **539**
Series: Bible Self-study Guides
Title: *John*
Publisher: Moody Press, 1970

Num. Sess.	Group Time	Num. Pgs.	Avg. Qst.	Price	Audience	Format	Bible Study
19	60-75	112	Vry	4.99	Mature Chrstn	Workbk	Book

Features: Intro to Leading a Study, Intro to Study, Bibliography, Digging Deeper Quest, Follow Up, Summary, Charts, Maps, Word Study
★★★★ Personal Application   Preparation Time: Med   ISBN: 0-8024-4472-5
  ★★ Relationship Building   Ldr. Guide Avail.: No   Size: 5.50 x 8.50
Subjects: Evangelism, Jesus: Life/Teaching, John
Comments: This academic study of John—part of a thirty-nine-book series—covers John's writings on the evangelistic founding of the church. It was primarily written to win unbelievers to a saving faith. This series of Bible self-studies is ideal for individual, small group, or class use. Outlines, diagrams, and explanations keep participants challenged.

Author: Jensen, Irving L.   **540**
Series: Bible Self-study Guides
Title: *Joshua*
Publisher: Moody Press, 1968

Num. Sess.	Group Time	Num. Pgs.	Avg. Qst.	Price	Audience	Format	Bible Study
11	60-75	80	Vry	3.99	Mature Chrstn	Workbk	Book

Features: Intro to Leading a Study, Intro to Study, Bibliography, Digging Deeper Quest, Follow Up, Summary, Charts, Maps, Word Study
★★★★ Personal Application   Preparation Time: Med   ISBN: 0-8024-4454-7
  ★★ Relationship Building   Ldr. Guide Avail.: No   Size: 5.50 x 8.50
Subjects: Joshua
Comments: This academic study of Joshua—part of a 39-book series—is the account of the conquest of Canaan. It is a history of the military campaign, and is divided into five study segments: introduction, preparation, conquest, inheritances, and consecration. This study is full of encouragement for the spiritual soldier. This series of Bible self-studies is ideal for individual, small group, or class use. Outlines, diagrams, and explanations keep participants challenged.

Author: Jensen, Irving L.　　　　　　　　**541**
Series: Bible Self-study Guides
Title: *Judges and Ruth*
Publisher: Moody Press, 1968

Num. Sess.	Group Time	Num. Pgs.	Avg. Qst.	Price	Audience	Format	Bible Study
11	60-75	96	Vry	4.99	Mature Chrstn	Workbk	Book

Features: Intro to Leading a Study, Intro to Study, Bibliography, Digging Deeper Quest, Follow Up, Summary, Charts, Maps, Word Study
★★★★ Personal Application　Preparation Time: Med　ISBN: 0-8024-4455-5
　★★ Relationship Building　Ldr. Guide Avail.: No　Size: 5.50 x 8.50
Subjects: Bible Personalities, Failure, Judges, Ruth, Women's Issues
Comments: Judges covers a period of failure, and Ruth completes the biblical history of the period of Judges. In Judges, participants learn the woes of walking outside fellowship with Christ and how fellowship can be restored. Ruth, the only book of the Bible devoted to the domestic history of a woman, presents the genealogy through which comes the Savior-King. This series of thirty-nine academic Bible self-studies is ideal for individual, small group, or class use.

Author: Jensen, Irving L.　　　　　　　　**542**
Series: Bible Self-study Guides
Title: *Leviticus*
Publisher: Moody Press, 1967

Num. Sess.	Group Time	Num. Pgs.	Avg. Qst.	Price	Audience	Format	Bible Study
10	60-75	80	Vry	3.99	Mature Chrstn	Workbk	Book

Features: Intro to Leading a Study, Intro to Study, Bibliography, Digging Deeper Quest, Follow Up, Summary, Charts, Maps, Word Study
★★★★ Personal Application　Preparation Time: Med　ISBN: 0-8024-4452-0
　★★ Relationship Building　Ldr. Guide Avail.: No　Size: 5.50 x 8.50
Subjects: Leviticus, Worship
Comments: Leviticus, Moses' third installment to the Pentateuch, records God's instructions to Israel on how they might have access to Him in worship, and walk with Him in fellowship. This academic study, part of a thirty-nine-book series of Bible self-studies, is ideal for individual, small group, or class use. Outlines, diagrams, and explanations keep participants challenged.

Author: Jensen, Irving L.　　　　　　　　**543**
Series: Bible Self-study Guides
Title: *Life of Christ*
Publisher: Moody Press, 1969

Num. Sess.	Group Time	Num. Pgs.	Avg. Qst.	Price	Audience	Format	Bible Study
15	60-75	112	Vry	4.99	Mature Chrstn	Workbk	Book

Features: Intro to Leading a Study, Intro to Study, Bibliography, Digging Deeper Quest, Follow Up, Summary, Charts, Maps, Word Study
★★★★ Personal Application　Preparation Time: Med　ISBN: 0-8024-4488-1
　★★ Relationship Building　Ldr. Guide Avail.: No　Size: 5.50 x 8.50
Subjects: Gospels, Jesus: Life/Teaching
Comments: This academic study of Christ's life covers the thirty-three years of His earthly biography. It begins before Bethlehem and ends with His resurrection. A comparative analysis of all four Gospels is presented. This thirty-nine-book series of Bible self-studies is ideal for individual, small group, or class use. Outlines, diagrams, and explanations keep participants challenged.

Author: Jensen, Irving L.　　　　　　　　**544**
Series: Do-It-Yourself Bible Study
Title: *Luke*
Publisher: Here's Life, 1985

Num. Sess.	Group Time	Num. Pgs.	Avg. Qst.	Price	Audience	Format	Bible Study
53	60-90	128	Vry	7.95	New Christian	Workbk	Book

Features: Intro to Leading a Study, Intro to Study, Bibliography, Scrpt Memory Helps, Study Overview, Summary, Full Scrpt Printed, Maps
　★★ Personal Application　Preparation Time: Med　ISBN: 0-89840-096-1
　★★ Relationship Building　Ldr. Guide Avail.: No　Size: 7.50 x 10.0
Subjects: Jesus: Life/Teaching, Luke
Comments: In this sentence-by-sentence, paragraph-by-paragraph, chapter-by-chapter study of Luke, participants will become intimately acquainted with the moving story of Jesus as the Son of Man—walking among men, the perfect God-man who offers salvation to all. Luke's special way of revealing the tender heart of Jesus and His love for others will touch readers deeply. Each lesson is conveniently displayed on two facing pages, and a free "how to use" booklet is available from the publisher.

Author: Jensen, Irving L.　　　　　　　　**545**
Series: Bible Self-study Guides
Title: *Luke*
Publisher: Moody Press, 1970

Num. Sess.	Group Time	Num. Pgs.	Avg. Qst.	Price	Audience	Format	Bible Study
13	60-75	104	Vry	4.99	Mature Chrstn	Workbk	Book

Features: Intro to Leading a Study, Intro to Study, Bibliography, Digging Deeper Quest, Follow Up, Summary, Charts, Maps, Word Study
★★★★ Personal Application　Preparation Time: Med　ISBN: 0-8024-4471-7
　★★ Relationship Building　Ldr. Guide Avail.: No　Size: 5.50 x 8.50
Subjects: Jesus: Life/Teaching, Luke
Comments: This academic study—part of a thirty-nine-book series—covers Luke's account of the full truth of Jesus' ministry. Jesus is revealed as the "Son of Man," and the book's prominent theme is "grace." A key verse is 19:10: "For the Son of man is come to seek and to save that which was lost." The key phrase, "Son of Man," is found twenty-five times in the gospel. Outlines, diagrams, and explanations keep participants challenged.

Author: Jensen, Irving L.　　　　　　　　**546**
Series: Do-It-Yourself Bible Study
Title: *Mark*
Publisher: Here's Life, 1983

Num. Sess.	Group Time	Num. Pgs.	Avg. Qst.	Price	Audience	Format	Bible Study
50	60-90	118	Vry	7.95	New Christian	Workbk	Book

Features: Intro to Leading a Study, Intro to Study, Bibliography, Scrpt Memory Helps, Study Overview, Summary, Full Scrpt Printed, Maps
　★★ Personal Application　Preparation Time: Med　ISBN: 0-89840-035-X
　★★ Relationship Building　Ldr. Guide Avail.: No　Size: 7.50 x 10.0
Subjects: Faith, Jesus: Life/Teaching, Mark
Comments: This is a sentence-by-sentence, paragraph-by-paragraph, and chapter-by-chapter study of Mark. It presents the gospel's historic facts and themes inductively, just as they are recorded. It will strengthen participants' faith in Jesus as true God, true man, and God's perfect servant. Each lesson is conveniently displayed on two facing pages, and a free "how to use" booklet is available from the publisher.

Author: Jensen, Irving L. **547**
Series: Bible Self-study Guides
Title: *Mark*
Publisher: Moody Press, 1972

Num. Sess.	Group Time	Num. Pgs.	Avg. Qst.	Price	Audience	Format	Bible Study
14	60-75	112	Vry	4.99	Mature Chrstn	Workbk	Book

Features: Intro to Leading a Study, Intro to Study, Bibliography, Digging Deeper Quest, Follow Up, Summary, Charts, Maps, Word Study
★★★★ Personal Application Preparation Time: Med ISBN: 0-8024-4470-9
★★ Relationship Building Ldr. Guide Avail.: No Size: 5.50 x 8.50
Subjects: Jesus: Life/Teaching, Mark
Comments: This academic study—part of a thirty-nine-book series—covers Mark's account of the gospel, which was directed to a Roman mind more impressed by action and power than discourse and dialogue. Mark therefore stressed "the actions, not so much the words of Jesus," to reach such an audience. Outlines, diagrams, and explanations keep participants challenged.

Author: Jensen, Irving L. **548**
Series: Do-It-Yourself Bible Study
Title: *Matthew*
Publisher: Here's Life, 1986

Num. Sess.	Group Time	Num. Pgs.	Avg. Qst.	Price	Audience	Format	Bible Study
54	60-90	126	Vry	7.95	New Christian	Workbk	Book

Features: Intro to Leading a Study, Intro to Study, Bibliography, Scrpt Memory Helps, Study Overview, Summary, Full Scrpt Printed, Maps
★★ Personal Application Preparation Time: Med ISBN: 0-89840-037-6
★★ Relationship Building Ldr. Guide Avail.: No Size: 7.50 x 10.0
Subjects: Jesus: Life/Teaching, Matthew
Comments: This sentence-by-sentence, paragraph-by-paragraph, chapter-by-chapter study of Matthew presents a first-person account of Jesus' life as seen by the publican whom Jesus called to be His disciple. Matthew's Gospel, which serves as the connecting link between the Old and New Testaments, quotes the Old Testament often, showing Jesus as the fulfillment of its prophecies. Each lesson is conveniently displayed on two facing pages, and a free "how to use" booklet is available from the publisher.

Author: Jensen, Irving L. **549**
Series: Bible Self-study Guides
Title: *Matthew*
Publisher: Moody Press, 1974

Num. Sess.	Group Time	Num. Pgs.	Avg. Qst.	Price	Audience	Format	Bible Study
15	60-75	112	Vry	4.99	Mature Chrstn	Workbk	Book

Features: Intro to Leading a Study, Intro to Study, Bibliography, Digging Deeper Quest, Follow Up, Summary, Charts, Maps, Appendix, Word Study
★★★★ Personal Application Preparation Time: Med ISBN: 0-8024-4469-5
★★ Relationship Building Ldr. Guide Avail.: No Size: 5.50 x 8.50
Subjects: Jesus: Life/Teaching, Matthew
Comments: This academic study of Matthew discusses the historical connecting link between the Old and New Testaments. The gospel narrative begins with the story of Jesus' birth and concludes with His Great Commission. This thirty-nine-book series of Bible self-studies is ideal for individual, small group, or class use. Outlines, diagrams, and explanations keep participants challenged.

Author: Jensen, Irving L. **550**
Series: Bible Self-study Guides
Title: *Minor Prophets of Israel*
Publisher: Moody Press, 1975

Num. Sess.	Group Time	Num. Pgs.	Avg. Qst.	Price	Audience	Format	Bible Study
13	60-75	112	Vry	3.99	Mature Chrstn	Workbk	Book

Features: Intro to Leading a Study, Intro to Study, Bibliography, Digging Deeper Quest, Follow Up, Summary, Charts, Maps, Word Study
★★★★ Personal Application Preparation Time: Med ISBN: 0-8024-1028-6
★★ Relationship Building Ldr. Guide Avail.: No Size: 5.50 x 8.50
Subjects: Minor Prophets, Prophecy
Comments: This academic study of Israel's minor prophets Jonah, Amos, and Hosea—part of a thirty-nine-book series—covers prophecy delivered in response to urgent situations, times when God called upon them to deliver the "Thus saith the Lord" messages. The three prophets have been compared this way: Jonah, prophet of a broken ministry; Amos, prophet of the broken law; and Hosea, prophet of a broken heart. Outline, diagrams, and explanations keep participants challenged.

Author: Jensen, Irving L. **551**
Series: Bible Self-study Guides
Title: *Minor Prophets of Judah*
Publisher: Moody Press, 1975

Num. Sess.	Group Time	Num. Pgs.	Avg. Qst.	Price	Audience	Format	Bible Study
13	60-75	104	Vry	4.99	Mature Chrstn	Workbk	Book

Features: Intro to Leading a Study, Intro to Study, Bibliography, Digging Deeper Quest, Follow Up, Summary, Charts, Maps, Word Study
★★★★ Personal Application Preparation Time: Med ISBN: 0-8024-4467-9
★★ Relationship Building Ldr. Guide Avail.: No Size: 5.50 x 8.50
Subjects: Ethics, Minor Prophets, Prophecy
Comments: Part of a thirty-nine-book series, this academic study of Judah's minor prophets—Obadiah, Joel, Micah, Nahum, Zephaniah, and Habakkuk—reveals that each spoke to people's definite needs, as disclosed by God through revelation. The subjects—materialism, rising crime, adultery, general disregard for God, and more—are timeless and speak to contemporary Christians as well. Outlines, diagrams, and explanations keep participants challenged.

Author: Jensen, Irving L. **552**
Series: Bible Self-study Guides
Title: *Numbers and Deuteronomy*
Publisher: Moody Press, 1967

Num. Sess.	Group Time	Num. Pgs.	Avg. Qst.	Price	Audience	Format	Bible Study
14	60-75	112	Vry	3.99	Mature Chrstn	Workbk	Book

Features: Intro to Leading a Study, Intro to Study, Bibliography, Digging Deeper Quest, Follow Up, Summary, Charts, Maps
★★★★ Personal Application Preparation Time: Med ISBN: 0-8024-4453-9
★★ Relationship Building Ldr. Guide Avail.: No Size: 5.50 x 8.50
Subjects: Christian Living, God, Numbers/Deuteronomy
Comments: This academic study of Numbers and Deuteronomy covers Moses' account of truths about God, about God's people, and about the blessed everyday living God wants His children to enjoy. Prominent teachings of Numbers include probation and pilgrimage; and Deuteronomy features instruction and prospects. Outlines, diagrams, and explanations keep participants challenged. This thirty-nine-book series of Bible self-studies is ideal for individual, small group, or class use.

Author: Jensen, Irving L. 553
Series: Bible Self-study Guides
Title: *Philippians*
Publisher: Moody Press, 1973

Num. Sess.	Group Time	Num. Pgs.	Avg. Qst.	Price	Audience	Format	Bible Study
8	60-75	64	Vry	3.99	Mature Chrstn	Workbk	Book

Features: Intro to Leading a Study, Intro to Study, Bibliography, Digging Deeper Quest, Follow Up, Summary, Charts, Maps, Word Study
★★★★ Personal Application   Preparation Time: Med   ISBN: 0-8024-4479-2
  ★★ Relationship Building Ldr. Guide Avail.: No   Size: 5.50 x 8.50
Subjects: Joy, Philippians, Prison Epistles, Suffering
Comments: This academic study—part of a thirty-nine-book series—covers Paul's letter to the saints at Philippi. Paul's purpose in writing was more practical than doctrinal; therefore a detailed outline is not apparent in the letter's structure. Paul does teach about the doctrines of the person and work of Christ, however, in this, the last of the Prison Epistles. Outlines, diagrams, and explanations keep participants challenged.

Author: Jensen, Irving L. 554
Series: Do-It-Yourself Bible Study
Title: *Prison Epistles: 1 and 2 Thessalonians*
Publisher: Here's Life, 1987

Num. Sess.	Group Time	Num. Pgs.	Avg. Qst.	Price	Audience	Format	Bible Study
40	60-90	114	Vry	7.95	New Christian	Workbk	Book

Features: Intro to Leading a Study, Intro to Study, Bibliography, Scrpt Memory Helps, Study Overview, Summary, Full Scrpt Printed, Maps
  ★★ Personal Application   Preparation Time: Med   ISBN: 0-89840-180-1
  ★★ Relationship Building Ldr. Guide Avail.: No   Size: 7.50 x 10.0
Subjects: Church Life, Colossians/Philemon, Ephesians, Eschatology, Forgiveness, Philippians, Prison Epistles, Suffering, 1 & 2 Thessalonians
Comments: In a sentence-by-sentence, paragraph-by-paragraph, and chapter-by-chapter study of the epistles Paul wrote from prison—Ephesians, Philippians, and Colossians—participants will meditate on the truths of the person and work of Christ. Then, a study of 1 and 2 Thessalonians focuses on the most climactic event of all history—the second coming of Christ—and provides a fresh understanding of its meaning and purpose. Each lesson is conveniently displayed on two facing pages.

Author: Jensen, Irving L. 555
Series: Bible Self-study Guides
Title: *Proverbs*
Publisher: Moody Press, 1976

Num. Sess.	Group Time	Num. Pgs.	Avg. Qst.	Price	Audience	Format	Bible Study
13	60-75	88	Vry	4.99	Mature Chrstn	Workbk	Book

Features: Intro to Leading a Study, Intro to Study, Bibliography, Digging Deeper Quest, Follow Up, Summary, Charts, Maps, Appendix, Word Study
★★★★ Personal Application   Preparation Time: Med   ISBN: 0-8024-4462-8
  ★★ Relationship Building Ldr. Guide Avail.: No   Size: 5.50 x 8.50
Subjects: Christian Living, Ethics, Proverbs, Wisdom
Comments: The book of Proverbs reveals God's detailed instructions and exhortations to His people concerning their thought-and-deed life. Proverbs mainly addresses personal ethics, including believers' walks with God on this earth. The proverbs are profitable for all people, saved and unsaved. This thirty-nine-book series of academic Bible self-studies is ideal for individual, small group, or class use. Outlines, diagrams, and explanations keep participants challenged.

Author: Jensen, Irving L. 556
Series: Do-It-Yourself Bible Study
Title: *Psalms*
Publisher: Here's Life, 1989

Num. Sess.	Group Time	Num. Pgs.	Avg. Qst.	Price	Audience	Format	Bible Study
44	60-90	112	Vry	7.95	New Christian	Workbk	Book

Features: Intro to Leading a Study, Intro to Study, Bibliography, Scrpt Memory Helps, Study Overview, Summary, Full Scrpt Printed, Maps
  ★★ Personal Application   Preparation Time: Med   ISBN: 0-89840-202-6
  ★★ Relationship Building Ldr. Guide Avail.: No   Size: 7.50 x 10.0
Subjects: God, Psalms, Worship
Comments: In this sentence-by-sentence, paragraph-by-paragraph, and chapter-by-chapter study of the longest book of the Bible, Psalms, participants will gain rich insights as they worship and praise the names and nature of God. The study reveals the character of David, both humble shepherd boy and king of Israel. Each lesson is conveniently displayed on two facing pages, and a free "how to use" booklet is available from the publisher.

Author: Jensen, Irving L. 557
Series: Bible Self-study Guides
Title: *Psalms*
Publisher: Moody Press, 1968

Num. Sess.	Group Time	Num. Pgs.	Avg. Qst.	Price	Audience	Format	Bible Study
11	60-75	128	Vry	4.99	Mature Chrstn	Workbk	Book

Features: Intro to Leading a Study, Intro to Study, Bibliography, Digging Deeper Quest, Follow Up, Summary, Charts, Maps, Word Study
★★★★ Personal Application   Preparation Time: Med   ISBN: 0-8024-4461-X
  ★★ Relationship Building Ldr. Guide Avail.: No   Size: 5.50 x 8.50
Subjects: Psalms
Comments: This psalm-by-psalm review is divided into eleven lessons. Psalms, seventy-three of which are ascribed to David, is a practical book that provides two benefits: it furnishes models of devotion, and it teaches truth in terms of human experience. This series of thirty-nine Bible self-studies is ideal for individual, small group, or class use. Outlines, diagrams, and explanations keep participants challenged.

Author: Jensen, Irving L. 558
Series: Do-It-Yourself Bible Study
Title: *Revelation*
Publisher: Here's Life, 1985

Num. Sess.	Group Time	Num. Pgs.	Avg. Qst.	Price	Audience	Format	Bible Study
42	60-90	110	Vry	7.95	New Christian	Workbk	Book

Features: Intro to Leading a Study, Intro to Study, Bibliography, Scrpt Memory Helps, Study Overview, Summary, Full Scrpt Printed, Maps
  ★★ Personal Application   Preparation Time: Med   ISBN: 0-89840-081-3
  ★★ Relationship Building Ldr. Guide Avail.: No   Size: 7.50 x 10.0
Subjects: Apocalyptic, Revelation
Comments: This is a sentence-by-sentence, paragraph-by-paragraph, and chapter-by-chapter study on Revelation. It can help participants understand the end times of this world. Unbelievers may be led to Christ the Savior, and believers will be alerted to live God-pleasing lives in light of Christ's return. Each lesson is conveniently displayed on two facing pages, and a free "how to use" booklet is available from the publisher.

Author: Jensen, Irving L.   **559**
Series: Bible Self-study Guides
Title: *Revelation*
Publisher: Moody Press, 1971

Num. Sess.	Group Time	Num. Pgs.	Avg. Qst.	Price	Audience	Format	Bible Study
14	60-75	142	Vry	4.99	Mature Chrstn	Workbk	Book

Features: Intro to Leading a Study, Intro to Study, Bibliography, Digging Deeper Quest, Follow Up, Summary, Charts, Maps, Word Study
★★★★ Personal Application   Preparation Time: Med   ISBN: 0-8024-4487-3
  ★★ Relationship Building   Ldr. Guide Avail.: No   Size: 5.50 x 8.50
Subjects: Revelation, Stress
Comments: Revelation is a record of John's dramatic God-inspired visions. Addressed to believers during a time of troubles and darkness, Revelation also encourages contemporary Christians to persevere under the stress of persecution. The hope is for justice which ultimately triumphs at the enthronement of Christ. Outlines, diagrams, and explanations keep participants challenged. This thirty-nine-book series is ideal for individual, small group, or class use.

Author: Jensen, Irving L.   **560**
Series: Do-It-Yourself Bible Study
Title: *Romans*
Publisher: Here's Life, 1983

Num. Sess.	Group Time	Num. Pgs.	Avg. Qst.	Price	Audience	Format	Bible Study
43	60-90	114	Vry	7.95	New Christian	Workbk	Book

Features: Intro to Leading a Study, Intro to Study, Bibliography, Scrpt Memory Helps, Study Overview, Summary, Full Scrpt Printed
  ★★ Personal Application   Preparation Time: Med   ISBN: 0-89840-036-8
  ★★ Relationship Building   Ldr. Guide Avail.: No   Size: 7.50 x 10.0
Subjects: Grace, Romans
Comments: This is a sentence-by-sentence, paragraph-by-paragraph, chapter-by-chapter study of Romans. It presents all the book's historical facts and themes inductively, just as they are recorded. The themes include the need, way, life, scope, and service of salvation. Each lesson is conveniently displayed on two facing pages, and a free "how to use" booklet is available from the publisher.

Author: Jensen, Irving L.   **561**
Series: Bible Self-study Guides
Title: *Romans*
Publisher: Moody Press, 1969

Num. Sess.	Group Time	Num. Pgs.	Avg. Qst.	Price	Audience	Format	Bible Study
14	60-75	112	Vry	4.99	Mature Chrstn	Workbk	Book

Features: Intro to Leading a Study, Intro to Study, Bibliography, Digging Deeper Quest, Follow Up, Summary, Charts, Maps, Word Study
★★★★ Personal Application   Preparation Time: Med   ISBN: 0-8024-4474-1
  ★★ Relationship Building   Ldr. Guide Avail.: No   Size: 5.50 x 8.50
Subjects: Grace, Romans
Comments: In Romans, Paul writes to tell Roman Christians of his plan to visit them, and to enlist their support for his proposed trip to Spain. The underlying purpose of this academic study is to give a comprehensive interpretation of the gospel. This thirty-nine-book series of Bible self-studies is ideal for individual, small group, or class use. Outlines, diagrams, and explanations keep participants challenged.

Author: Jensen, Irving L.   **562**
Series: Do-It-Yourself Bible Study
Title: *Ruth & Mary: Women of Courage*
Publisher: Here's Life, 1990

Num. Sess.	Group Time	Num. Pgs.	Avg. Qst.	Price	Audience	Format	Bible Study
13	45-60	72	Vry	4.95	New Christian	Workbk	Charctr

Features: Intro to Leading a Study, Intro to Study, Bibliography, Summary, Charts, Maps
  ★★ Personal Application   Preparation Time: Low   ISBN: 0-89840-269-7
  ★★ Relationship Building   Ldr. Guide Avail.: No   Size: 5.0 x 8.0
Subjects: Bible Personalities, Obedience, Women's Issues
Comments: In this study, Ruth and Mary share their success in finding courage when it seemed that everything and everyone was against them. They learned to praise God and be thankful during trying situations, and trusted God despite an unsure future. The study helps women gain insights into their walk with God and discover obedience to Him in the midst of oppressing circumstances. Each lesson is conveniently displayed on two facing pages.

Author: Jensen, Irving L.   **563**
Series: Do-It-Yourself Bible Study
Title: *1 Corinthians*
Publisher: Here's Life, 1983

Num. Sess.	Group Time	Num. Pgs.	Avg. Qst.	Price	Audience	Format	Bible Study
40	60-90	100	Vry	7.95	New Christian	Workbk	Book

Features: Intro to Leading a Study, Intro to Study, Bibliography, Scrpt Memory Helps, Study Overview, Summary, Full Scrpt Printed, Maps
  ★★ Personal Application   Preparation Time: Med   ISBN: 0-89840-116-X
  ★★ Relationship Building   Ldr. Guide Avail.: No   Size: 7.50 x 10.0
Subjects: Relationships, 1 Corinthians
Comments: This is a sentence-by-sentence, paragraph-by-paragraph, and chapter-by-chapter study of 1 Corinthians. It explores solutions to problems faced by Christians in the early church, especially those involving interpersonal relationships. The solutions follow the Apostle Paul's diagnoses of the problems. Each lesson is conveniently displayed on two facing pages, and a free "how to use" booklet is available from the publisher.

Author: Jensen, Irving L.   **564**
Series: Bible Self-study Guides
Title: *1 Corinthians*
Publisher: Moody Press, 1972

Num. Sess.	Group Time	Num. Pgs.	Avg. Qst.	Price	Audience	Format	Bible Study
14	60-75	112	Vry	4.99	Mature Chrstn	Workbk	Book

Features: Intro to Leading a Study, Intro to Study, Bibliography, Digging Deeper Quest, Follow Up, Summary, Charts, Maps, Word Study
★★★★ Personal Application   Preparation Time: Med   ISBN: 0-8024-4475-X
  ★★ Relationship Building   Ldr. Guide Avail.: No   Size: 5.50 x 8.50
Subjects: Christian Living, 1 Corinthians
Comments: Part of a thirty-nine-book series, this academic study covers Paul's first letter to a Corinthian church plagued with problems. Two main benefits of studying 1 Corinthians are seeing God's diagnosis of modern Christians' spiritual maladies, and learning His prescriptions for cure. This series of Bible self-studies is ideal for individual, small group, or class use. Outlines, diagrams, and explanations keep participants challenged.

Author: Jensen, Irving L.　　　　　　　　**565**
Series: Bible Self-study Guides
Title: *1 Kings with Chronicles*
Publisher: Moody Press, 1968

Num. Sess.	Group Time	Num. Pgs.	Avg. Qst.	Price	Audience	Format	Bible Study
10	60-75	112	Vry	4.99	Mature Chrstn	Workbk	Book

Features: Intro to Leading a Study, Intro to Study, Bibliography, Digging Deeper Quest, Follow Up, Summary, Charts, Maps, Word Study
★★★★ Personal Application　Preparation Time: Med　ISBN: 0-8024-4457-1
　★★ Relationship Building　Ldr. Guide Avail.: No　Size: 5.50 x 8.50
Subjects: Kings/Chronicles
Comments: This academic study of 1 Kings and Chronicles—part of a thirty-nine-book series—traces the course of Israel's history from the division of the nation after the death of King Solomon. The study is organized around 1 Kings, and since parts of Chronicles cover the same time period, parallel accounts will be followed. This series of Bible self-studies is ideal for individual, small group, or class use.

Author: Jensen, Irving L.　　　　　　　　**566**
Series: Bible Self-study Guides
Title: *1 & 2 Peter*
Publisher: Moody Press, 1971

Num. Sess.	Group Time	Num. Pgs.	Avg. Qst.	Price	Audience	Format	Bible Study
12	60-75	96	Vry	3.99	Mature Chrstn	Workbk	Book

Features: Intro to Leading a Study, Intro to Study, Bibliography, Digging Deeper Quest, Follow Up, Summary, Charts, Maps, Word Study
★★★★ Personal Application　Preparation Time: Med　ISBN: 0-8024-4485-7
　★★ Relationship Building　Ldr. Guide Avail.: No　Size: 5.50 x 8.50
Subjects: Faith, False Teachers, Suffering, 1 & 2 Peter
Comments: This academic study of 1 and 2 Peter—part of a thirty-nine-book series—covers Peter's letter to exiles, mostly Jewish believers persecuted by dispersion for their Christian faith. The themes of 1 and 2 Peter are hope in the midst of severe trial. While it also addresses external opposition to Christians, it addresses dangers originating inside—namely, apostasy and false teaching. Outlines, diagrams, and explanations keep participants challenged.

Author: Jensen, Irving L.　　　　　　　　**567**
Series: Bible Self-study Guides
Title: *1 & 2 Samuel*
Publisher: Moody Press, 1968

Num. Sess.	Group Time	Num. Pgs.	Avg. Qst.	Price	Audience	Format	Bible Study
16	60-75	112	Vry	3.99	Mature Chrstn	Workbk	Book

Features: Intro to Leading a Study, Intro to Study, Bibliography, Digging Deeper Quest, Follow Up, Summary, Charts, Maps, Word Study
★★★★ Personal Application　Preparation Time: Med　ISBN: 0-8024-4456-3
　★★ Relationship Building　Ldr. Guide Avail.: No　Size: 5.50 x 8.50
Subjects: Bible Personalities, 1 & 2 Samuel
Comments: The two books of Samuel record the history of the kingdom era of Israel, including the kingdom of David, a foreteller of Christ's kingdom. The sixteen lessons of this academic study move participants from the background and survey of 1 Samuel to 2 Samuel and a review of David's reign, sin, and troubles. The study concludes with restoration from the hand of God. This thirty-nine-book series of Bible self-studies is ideal for individual, small group, or class use.

Author: Jensen, Irving L.　　　　　　　　**568**
Series: Bible Self-study Guides
Title: *1 & 2 Thessalonians*
Publisher: Moody Press, 1974

Num. Sess.	Group Time	Num. Pgs.	Avg. Qst.	Price	Audience	Format	Bible Study
12	60-75	96	Vry	3.99	Mature Chrstn	Workbk	Book

Features: Intro to Leading a Study, Intro to Study, Bibliography, Digging Deeper Quest, Follow Up, Summary, Charts, Maps, Appendix, Word Study
★★★★ Personal Application　Preparation Time: Med　ISBN: 0-8024-4481-4
　★★ Relationship Building　Ldr. Guide Avail.: No　Size: 5.50 x 8.50
Subjects: Faith, Theology, 1 & 2 Thessalonians
Comments: This academic study of—part of a thirty-nine-book series—covers Paul's two letters to the Thessalonians, which focus on Christ's return. The first letter commends Christians for their faith, exposes sin, exhorts young converts, and responds to false charges against Paul. The second letter goes one step further, instructing, exhorting, commending, and addressing doctrinal and practical correction. Outlines, diagrams, and explanations keep participants challenged.

Author: Jensen, Irving L.　　　　　　　　**569**
Series: Bible Self-study Guides
Title: *1 & 2 Timothy and Titus*
Publisher: Moody Press, 1973

Num. Sess.	Group Time	Num. Pgs.	Avg. Qst.	Price	Audience	Format	Bible Study
16	60-75	96	Vry	3.99	Mature Chrstn	Workbk	Book

Features: Intro to Leading a Study, Intro to Study, Bibliography, Digging Deeper Quest, Follow Up, Summary, Charts, Maps, Appendix, Word Study
★★★★ Personal Application　Preparation Time: Med　ISBN: 0-8024-4482-2
　★★ Relationship Building　Ldr. Guide Avail.: No　Size: 5.50 x 8.50
Subjects: Pastoral Epistles, 1 & 2 Timothy/Titus
Comments: This academic study begins with 1 Timothy, moves to Titus, and closes with 2 Timothy, Paul's last recorded words of urgency, triumph, and tender care. This thirty-nine-book series of Bible self-studies is ideal for individual, small group, or class use. Outlines, diagrams, and explanations keep participants challenged.

Author: Jensen, Irving L.　　　　　　　　**570**
Series: Do-It-Yourself Bible Study
Title: *2 Corinthians/Galatians*
Publisher: Here's Life, 1987

Num. Sess.	Group Time	Num. Pgs.	Avg. Qst.	Price	Audience	Format	Bible Study
37	60-90	107	Vry	7.95	New Christian	Workbk	Book

Features: Intro to Leading a Study, Intro to Study, Bibliography, Scrpt Memory Helps, Study Overview, Summary, Full Scrpt Printed, Maps
　★★ Personal Application　Preparation Time: Med　ISBN: 0-89840-164-X
　★★ Relationship Building　Ldr. Guide Avail.: No　Size: 7.50 x 10.0
Subjects: Church Life, Commitments, False Teachers, Galatians, Hope, Integrity, Leadership, Service, 2 Corinthians
Comments: This sentence-by-sentence, paragraph-by-paragraph, and chapter-by-chapter study of 2 Corinthians and Galatians will inspire participants to total commitment as ambassadors for Christ. It will expand one's view of the ministry of the gospel, and show how to steer clear of the false doctrine of legalism. Each lesson is conveniently displayed on two facing pages, and a free "how to use" booklet is available from the publisher.

Author: Jensen, Irving L.   **571**
Series: Bible Self-study Guides
Title: *2 Corinthians*
Publisher: Moody Press, 1972

Num. Sess.	Group Time	Num. Pgs.	Avg. Qst.	Price	Audience	Format	Bible Study
13	60-75	112	Vry	4.99	Mature Chrstn	Workbk	Book

Features: Intro to Leading a Study, Intro to Study, Bibliography, Digging Deeper Quest, Follow Up, Summary, Charts, Maps, Word Study
★★★★ Personal Application   Preparation Time: Med   ISBN: 0-8024-4476-8
  ★★ Relationship Building   Ldr. Guide Avail.: No   Size: 5.50 x 8.50
Subjects: Church Life, Hope, Integrity, Leadership, Repentance, Service, Suffering, 2 Corinthians
Comments: This academic study of 2 Corinthians—part of a thirty-nine-book series—covers Paul's letter to Corinthians who encountered obstacles in proclaiming the gospel. Emphasizing solutions to problems, Paul discusses his dilemma of convincing Corinthian brethren that he was a true apostle of Christ, preaching the true gospel of God. Participants will gain a deeper appreciation of Paul, and a more firm conviction of the truth and power of the gospel he preached.

Author: Jensen, Irving L.   **572**
Series: Bible Self-study Guides
Title: *2 Kings with Chronicles*
Publisher: Moody Press, 1968

Num. Sess.	Group Time	Num. Pgs.	Avg. Qst.	Price	Audience	Format	Bible Study
11	60-75	112	Vry	3.99	Mature Chrstn	Workbk	Book

Features: Intro to Leading a Study, Intro to Study, Bibliography, Digging Deeper Quest, Follow Up, Summary, Charts, Maps, Word Study
★★★★ Personal Application   Preparation Time: Med   ISBN: 0-8024-4458-X
  ★★ Relationship Building   Ldr. Guide Avail.: No   Size: 5.50 x 8.50
Subjects: Kings/Chronicles, Victorious Living
Comments: This academic study of 2 Kings and 1 and 2 Chronicles helps participants sort out items of lesser importance in order to concentrate on the important. At the conclusion of the study—part of a thirty-nine-book series—participants see that only Christ, the King of kings, can provide permanent peace. This series of Bible self-studies is ideal for individual, small group, or class use. Outlines, diagrams, and explanations keep participants challenged.

Author: Johnson, David W. & Frank P.   **573**
Series:
Title: *Joining Together: Group Theory and Group Skills*
Publisher: Prentice-Hall, 1991

Num. Sess.	Group Time	Num. Pgs.	Avg. Qst.	Price	Audience	Format	Bible Study
13	-	490	N/A	42.0		Book	No

Features: Bibliography, Summary, Drawings, Cartoons, Photos, Charts, Index, Appendix
     Personal Application   Preparation Time: ISBN: 0-13-511858-1
     Relationship Building   Ldr. Guide Avail.:   Size: 7.0 x 9.25
Subjects: Small Group Resource
Comments: This book on skills-oriented group dynamics integrates research, theory, skill-building exercises, and applications into specific group situations. It provides the theory and experience needed to develop high skill levels of group interaction, by offering an interdisciplinary perspective, appealing pedagogical aids, diagnostic materials to evaluate knowledge and skills, and much more. The index makes it useful for quick reference.

Author: Johnson, Jan   **574**
Series: A Bible Study for Women
Title: *When It Hurts to Grow*
Publisher: Victor Books, 1991

Num. Sess.	Group Time	Num. Pgs.	Avg. Qst.	Price	Audience	Format	Bible Study
8	60-75	96	15	5.99	New Christian	Workbk	Book

Features: Intro to Study, Prayer Helps, Ldr's Notes
★★★★ Personal Application   Preparation Time: Med   ISBN: 0-89693-197-8
  ★★★ Relationship Building   Ldr. Guide Avail.: No   Size: 6.0 x 9.0
Subjects: Faith, Hebrews, Suffering, Women's Issues
Comments: This in-depth eight-week study of Hebrews 12:1-17 deals with "discipline of the Lord." It shows that God's discipline includes both specific acts He initiates, and typical daily hardships through which believers grow. Like a parent, God teaches, loves, and disciplines so that a person's relationship with Him will grow deeper. Participants are encouraged as they learn to endure suffering and conquer trials with God's help.

Author: Johnson, Lin   **575**
Series: Fisherman Bible Studyguide
Title: *Encouraging Others: Biblical Models for Caring*
Publisher: Shaw, 1991

Num. Sess.	Group Time	Num. Pgs.	Avg. Qst.	Price	Audience	Format	Bible Study
12	45-60	64	12	3.95	New Christian	Workbk	Topical

Features: Intro to Leading a Study, Intro to Study, Prayer Helps, Follow Up
★★★ Personal Application   Preparation Time: None   ISBN: 0-87788-221-5
★★★ Relationship Building   Ldr. Guide Avail.: No   Size: 5.0 x 8.25
Subjects: Bible Personalities, Caring, Christian Living, Faith
Comments: These studies provide models from scripture for encouraging people and building them up in their faith. It shows the needs God's people have for advice and encouragement, as they live their faith in this world; it helps them persevere in their goals to become more like Christ. Participants will learn to become and practice being "spiritual cheerleaders" to other believers.

Author: Johnson, Lin   **576**
Series: Young Teen Feedback Elective
Title: *Friends: Who Needs Them? (Leader's Book)*
Publisher: Victor Books, 1988

Num. Sess.	Group Time	Num. Pgs.	Avg. Qst.	Price	Audience	Format	Bible Study
12	30-45	77	Vry	12.99	New Christian	Book	Topical

Features: Intro to Study, Handouts
★★★★ Personal Application   Preparation Time: None   ISBN: 0-89693-610-4
★★★★ Relationship Building   Ldr. Guide Avail.: Yes   Size: 8.50 x 11.0
Subjects: Teens: Friends, Teens: Peer Pressure
Comments: This twelve-lesson study helps young teens develop the biblical qualities of a friend, develop friendship skills, and overcome problems in friendships. Each session is based on interviews with youth and includes feedback on personal needs and concerns. The format offers three four-week studies with reproducible student sheets. They can be used separately as short studies, or consecutively as a twelve-week elective. A student book is available.

Author: Johnson, Lin   **577**
Series: A Bible Study for Women
Title: *Growing Season, The*
Publisher: Victor Books, 1987

Num. Sess.	Group Time	Num. Pgs.	Avg. Qst.	Price	Audience	Format	Bible Study
9	60-90	95	15	5.99	New Christian	Workbk	Topical

Features: Intro to Leading a Study, Intro to Study, Objectives, Scrpt Memory Helps, Summary, Ldr's Notes, Charts
★★★ Personal Application   Preparation Time: Med   ISBN: 0-89693-009-2
  ★★ Relationship Building   Ldr. Guide Avail.: No   Size: 6.0 x 9.0
Subjects: Christian Living, Fruit of the Spirit, Women's Issues
Comments: This study explores nine "fruits of the Spirit." Love, joy, peace, patience, kindness, goodness, faithfulness, gentleness, and self-control are qualities of character that believers must seek. Such character is grown through cooperation of the Holy Spirit, who prepares, plants, prunes, and produces His fruit in believers. God expects Christians to be involved in the cultivation process, to work at developing fruit.

Author: Johnson, Reginald   **578**
Series: Spiritual Formation Series
Title: *Celebrate, My Soul!*
Publisher: Victor Books, 1988

Num. Sess.	Group Time	Num. Pgs.	Avg. Qst.	Price	Audience	Format	Bible Study
13	60-90	180	N/A	7.99	New Christian	Book	Topical

Features: Bibliography, Charts
★★★★ Personal Application   Preparation Time: Med   ISBN: 0-89693-580-9
  ★★★ Relationship Building   Ldr. Guide Avail.: Yes   Size: 5.50 x 8.0
Subjects: Discipleship, Leadership
Comments: This study introduces the use of personality types for spiritual awareness and growth. It allows participants to try various personality types, including energizers, stabilizers, crusaders, renewers, organizers, analyzers, encouragers, and enhancers. A temperament concept exercise is included. The leader's guide suggests teaching ideas and provides reproducible transparency masters and assignments for participants.

Author: Jones, Kenneth E.   **579**
Series:
Title: *Divorce & Remarriage: In The Bible*
Publisher: Warner Press, 1989

Num. Sess.	Group Time	Num. Pgs.	Avg. Qst.	Price	Audience	Format	Bible Study
13	60-75	112	6	3.95	New Christian	Book	Topical

Features: Intro to Study, Bibliography
★★★ Personal Application   Preparation Time: Low   ISBN: 0-87162-503-2
★★★ Relationship Building   Ldr. Guide Avail.: Yes   Size: 4.25 x 7.0
Subjects: Divorce, Marriage
Comments: This study maps out a path that leads participants to a clear understanding of God's full intent for family living. Everything is supported by Scripture. Areas covered include the following: modern problems with marriage, marriage in the Bible, divorce in the Old Testament, divorce in the gospels, divorced and remarried pastors, and more. A leader's guide includes Bible passages, teaching goals, an introduction, questions for discussion, and a plan for the session.

Author: Joy, Donald   **580**
Series: Spiritual Formation Series
Title: *Walk On! Let God Make You Whole and Holy in Your Daily Life*
Publisher: Victor Books, 1988

Num. Sess.	Group Time	Num. Pgs.	Avg. Qst.	Price	Audience	Format	Bible Study
13	60-90	178	N/A	7.99	New Christian	Book	Topical

Features: Bibliography
★★★★ Personal Application   Preparation Time: Med   ISBN: 0-89693-578-7
  ★★★ Relationship Building   Ldr. Guide Avail.: Yes   Size: 5.50 x 8.0
Subjects: Discipleship, God, Holiness, Wholeness
Comments: This study is one in a series called "Spiritual Formation," which taken together, becomes "an invitation to friendship with God." In this book, participants will examine common life experiences in chapters with titles like: "Wrestling with Identity," "Searching for Intimacy," "Avoiding the Pleasure Trap," "Dealing with Doubt," and "Confronting and Releasing." This series leads to the affirmation that Jesus is Lord. This book has 10 chapters; a topical list of selective readings is included.

Author: Kaplan, David B.   **581**
Series: Small Group Bible Studies
Title: *Psalm 23*
Publisher: Augsburg Publishing House, 1986

Num. Sess.	Group Time	Num. Pgs.	Avg. Qst.	Price	Audience	Format	Bible Study
4	60-75	16	12	0.95	New Christian	Book	Topical

Features: Intro to Study, Prayer Helps, Full Scrpt Printed
★★★★ Personal Application   Preparation Time: None   ISBN:
★★★★ Relationship Building   Ldr. Guide Avail.: No   Size: 8.50 x 5.50
Subjects: God, Psalms, Worship
Comments: This short, four-session study analyzes the phrases in Psalm 23. The session titles include "The Lord Is My Shepherd," "In Green Pastures," "Through the Dark Valley," and "All the Days of My Life." God's preserving, providing, and protecting activities are brought to light, and participants are encouraged to share throughout the study about how God has provided in their lives. The study also discusses the use of Psalm 23 in corporate worship.

Author: Kaplan, David B.   **582**
Series: Small Group Bible Studies
Title: *Suffering*
Publisher: Augsburg Publishing House, 1982

Num. Sess.	Group Time	Num. Pgs.	Avg. Qst.	Price	Audience	Format	Bible Study
6	60-75	24	20	1.15	New Christian	Book	Topical

Features: Intro to Study, Prayer Helps
    Personal Application   Preparation Time: None   ISBN:
    Relationship Building   Ldr. Guide Avail.: No   Size: 8.50 x 5.50
Subjects: Romans, Suffering
Comments: This small pamphlet contains six lessons on suffering and the Suffering Servant. It explores the scriptural dimensions of human suffering, both its sources and present significance. The scriptural text is Romans 8:22, part of a longer passage in which Paul suggests that our present suffering is not a death rattle at all, but rather the birth pangs of a new creation.

Author: Karssen, Gien **583**
Series:
Title: *Her Name Is Woman (Book 1)*
Publisher: NavPress, 1975

Num. Sess.	Group Time	Num. Pgs.	Avg. Qst.	Price	Audience	Format	Bible Study
24	60-75	200	6	8.95	New Christian	Book	Charctr

Features: Intro to Leading a Study, Intro to Study, Full Scrpt Printed, Cross Ref
★★★ Personal Application   Preparation Time: Med   ISBN: 0-89109-420-2
★★ Relationship Building   Ldr. Guide Avail.: No   Size: 5.25 x 8.0
Subjects: Bible Personalities, Singles' Issues, Women's Issues
Comments: This study of twenty-four Old and New Testament women illustrates the importance of a woman's spiritual side, and challenges modern women to live their lives wholeheartedly for God. Some of the women studied include Lydia (businesswoman), Priscilla (spiritual leader), Sarah (honored wife and mother), and Anna (aging widow). Married or single, happy or brokenhearted, secure or shaken, participants will identify with one of these women. For group study, a notebook is needed for responses.

Author: Karssen, Gien **584**
Series:
Title: *Her Name Is Woman (Book 2)*
Publisher: NavPress, 1977

Num. Sess.	Group Time	Num. Pgs.	Avg. Qst.	Price	Audience	Format	Bible Study
24	60-75	240	6	8.95	New Christian	Book	Charctr

Features: Intro to Leading a Study, Intro to Study, Full Scrpt Printed, Cross Ref
★★★ Personal Application   Preparation Time: Med   ISBN: 0-89109-424-5
★★ Relationship Building   Ldr. Guide Avail.: No   Size: 5.25 x 8.0
Subjects: Bible Personalities, Failure, Success, Women's Issues
Comments: This continuing study offers participants twenty-five more Bible women to explore. Deborah, Delilah, Ruth, Bathsheba, Jezebel, Mary Magdalene, and others become alive and relevant to contemporary women. Participants will discover why some women succeed while others fail. For group study, a notebook is needed for responses and prayer requests.

Author: Kerr, John S. **585**
Series: Friendship Bible Study
Title: *Discipleship*
Publisher: Augsburg Publishing House, 1988

Num. Sess.	Group Time	Num. Pgs.	Avg. Qst.	Price	Audience	Format	Bible Study
8	60-75	48	18	3.0	New Christian	Workbk	Topical

Features: Intro to Study, Prayer Helps, Study Overview
★★★★ Personal Application   Preparation Time: Low   ISBN:
★★★★ Relationship Building   Ldr. Guide Avail.: Yes   Size: 5.50 x 8.50
Subjects: Discipleship, Faith
Comments: This eight-lesson study is a biblical guide for contemporary disciples who seek to follow Christ and live out their commitment of faith. It asks, in various ways, one basic question: "What does that mean for me?" The lesson format includes an overview, an opening, a responsive reading, Bible background, questions for reflection, a key verse, a prayer response, and an "our faith" response.

Author: Keyes, Sharrel **586**
Series: Fisherman Bible Studyguide
Title: *Luke: Following Jesus*
Publisher: Shaw, 1983

Num. Sess.	Group Time	Num. Pgs.	Avg. Qst.	Price	Audience	Format	Bible Study
20	45-60	93	12	3.95	New Christian	Workbk	Book

Features: Intro to Leading a Study, Intro to Study, Prayer Helps, Persnl Study Quest, Maps
★★★ Personal Application   Preparation Time: Low   ISBN: 0-87788-511-7
★★ Relationship Building   Ldr. Guide Avail.: No   Size: 5.0 x 8.25
Subjects: Caring, Faith, Jesus: Life/Teaching, Luke, Obedience
Comments: This study follows Luke's account of Jesus caring and healing people, righting injustice and teaching people spiritual and moral truth. Jesus teaches faithfulness to Him; putting aside personal priorities; learning to love people who are unkind; freeing oneself from hypocrisy, greed, and ambition. The study is a topical approach to Luke, guiding participants to an understanding of what it means to "follow Jesus."

Author: Kimbrough, Marjorie **587**
Series:
Title: *Matthew: Volume 1 & 2*
Publisher: Cokesbury, 1990

Num. Sess.	Group Time	Num. Pgs.	Avg. Qst.	Price	Audience	Format	Bible Study
8	45-60	N/A	Vry	29.95	New Christian	Video	Book

Features: Intro to Leading a Study, Intro to Study, Ldr's Notes, Video Study Guide
★★★ Personal Application   Preparation Time: Low   ISBN: 0-687-76182-4
★★★ Relationship Building   Ldr. Guide Avail.: Yes   Size: 4.75 x 8.0
Subjects: Jesus: Life/Teaching, Matthew
Comments: This two-volume video lecture series discusses Matthew, which scholars believe was the favorite and most used gospel by the early Church, and perhaps the first recorded gospel. It concerns not only Christ's story, but why, to whom, and by whom it was written. In each volume, four twenty-minute lessons give participants a verse-by-verse exposition. A comprehensive leader's guide is included for use in group study.

Author: Kimmel, Tim **588**
Series:
Title: *Surviving Life in the Fast Lane*
Publisher: NavPress, 1990

Num. Sess.	Group Time	Num. Pgs.	Avg. Qst.	Price	Audience	Format	Bible Study
9	45-60	96	9	5.95	New Christian	Book	Topical

Features: Intro to Study, Prayer Helps, Scrpt Memory Helps, Prediscussion Quest, Follow Up, Full Scrpt Printed, Ldr's Notes
★★★★ Personal Application   Preparation Time: None   ISBN: 0-89109-293-5
★★★★ Relationship Building   Ldr. Guide Avail.: No   Size: 5.50 x 8.50
Subjects: Christian Living, Family, Forgiveness, Friendships, Relationships, Stress, Suffering, Work
Comments: This study helps participants explore and apply six keys to genuine rest for the family in life, marriage, friendships, work, and in their relationship with God. The six include forgiveness, living within the boundaries of God's Word, having an eternal perspective, resting in the midst of suffering, learning contentment, and managing our resources and strengths. The leader's notes section is helpful, especially for new leaders.

Author: King, Pat & George O. Wood   **589**
Series: Enrichment Series
Title: *Beatitudes, The: Expressing the Character of Jesus*
Publisher: Aglow, 1984

Num. Sess.	Group Time	Num. Pgs.	Avg. Qst.	Price	Audience	Format	Bible Study
10	60-75	62	17	2.95	New Christian	Workbk	Charctr

Features: Intro to Study, Prayer Helps, Scrpt Memory Helps, Digging Deeper Quest, Persnl Study Quest
★★★★ Personal Application   Preparation Time: Med   ISBN: 0-930756-92-4
★★★★ Relationship Building   Ldr. Guide Avail.: No   Size: 5.25 x 8.25
Subjects: Charismatic Interest, Christian Living, Jesus: Life/Teaching, Sermon on the Mount
Comments: This ten-week study shows participants that God wants Christ's character to be worked out in their lives. They will come to a new understanding of godly sorrow, learn how to handle people who persecute them because of the gospel, and learn how to bring peace to a confused world. The study covers the Beatitudes, the scriptural pattern of Christ's life, and reveals eight traits of a committed Christian.

Author: King, Pat   **590**
Series: Encourager Series
Title: *Growing Up Strong: Principles of Christian Development*
Publisher: Aglow, 1988

Num. Sess.	Group Time	Num. Pgs.	Avg. Qst.	Price	Audience	Format	Bible Study
4	45-60	30	Vry	2.25	New Christian	Workbk	Topical

Features: Intro to Study, Prayer Helps, Scrpt Memory Helps, Persnl Study Quest
★★★★ Personal Application   Preparation Time: Low   ISBN: 0-932305-59-8
★★★★ Relationship Building   Ldr. Guide Avail.: No   Size: 5.25 x 8.25
Subjects: Charismatic Interest, Discipleship, Forgiveness, Fruit of the Spirit
Comments: In this four-week study, Bible stories are used to richly illustrate gardening and farming and to demonstrate Christian development. The intended meaning of these stories is lost on many who live in modern urban areas. Lessons respond to questions like "What does the Bible mean when it speaks of 'shallow and rocky soils' or 'roots of bitterness'?" "How does pruning a tree relate to a Christian's life?" "What is spiritual fruit?" and "How do we cultivate it?" A journal assignment is included.

Author: Kjos, Berit   **591**
Series: A Bible Study for Women
Title: *Wardrobe from the King, A*
Publisher: Victor Books, 1988

Num. Sess.	Group Time	Num. Pgs.	Avg. Qst.	Price	Audience	Format	Bible Study
8	60-90	96	16	5.99	New Christian	Workbk	Topical

Features: Intro to Study, Objectives, Prayer Helps, Ldr's Notes, Charts
★★★ Personal Application   Preparation Time: Med   ISBN: 0-89693-419-5
★★ Relationship Building   Ldr. Guide Avail.: No   Size: 6.0 x 9.0
Subjects: Christian Living, Emotions, Failure, Grief, Loneliness, Women's Issues
Comments: These eight studies examine how God offers a wardrobe that will protect believers through every storm of life. They will help participants battle guilt, discouragement, boredom, fear, loneliness, rejection, hopelessness, and failure by presenting the protection of God's armor. Living in God's safety begins with understanding, affirming, and trusting in every piece of protective clothing He offers.

Author: Klos, Frank W.   **592**
Series: Friendship Bible Study
Title: *1 & 2 Timothy*
Publisher: Augsburg Publishing House, 1988

Num. Sess.	Group Time	Num. Pgs.	Avg. Qst.	Price	Audience	Format	Bible Study
8	60-75	48	10	3.0	New Christian	Workbk	Book

Features: Intro to Study, Prayer Helps, Study Overview
★★★★ Personal Application   Preparation Time: Low   ISBN:
★★★★ Relationship Building   Ldr. Guide Avail.: Yes   Size: 5.50 x 8.50
Subjects: Christian Living, Church Life, Pastoral Epistles, 1 & 2 Timothy/Titus
Comments: This eight-lesson study encourages participants to examine the issues of Christian living within the church and in the modern world. Paul's letters challenge congregational members and leaders to preserve and proclaim the gospel in all its purity and power. The lesson format includes an overview, an opening, a responsive reading, Bible background, questions for reflection, a key verse, a prayer response, and an "our faith" response.

Author: Klug, Ron   **593**
Series: Fisherman Bible Studyguide
Title: *Job: God's Answer to Suffering*
Publisher: Shaw, 1982

Num. Sess.	Group Time	Num. Pgs.	Avg. Qst.	Price	Audience	Format	Bible Study
13	45-60	61	9	3.95	Mature Chrstn	Workbk	Book

Features: Intro to Leading a Study, Intro to Study, Prayer Helps, Follow Up
★★ Personal Application   Preparation Time: None   ISBN: 0-87788-430-7
★★ Relationship Building   Ldr. Guide Avail.: No   Size: 5.0 x 8.25
Subjects: Faith, Job, Suffering
Comments: In this study, participants will identify with Job as he wrestles with deep personal questions on illness, loss, disappointment, suffering, and death. Job maintains faith in the God of strength and love who cares for him in the midst of suffering. Some of the questions posed by the study include: Why, God? Why has this happened to me? Why do good people suffer? Why doesn't God do something about pain? How can I make sense out of my life?

Author: Klug, Ron   **594**
Series: Young Fisherman Bible
Title: *Philippians: Be Glad!*
Publisher: Shaw, 1983

Num. Sess.	Group Time	Num. Pgs.	Avg. Qst.	Price	Audience	Format	Bible Study
12	50-60	70	12	2.95	New Christian	Workbk	Book

Features: Intro to Study, Scrpt Memory Helps, Worship Helps, Drawings, Exam
★★ Personal Application   Preparation Time: Low   ISBN: 0-87788-681-4
★★★ Relationship Building   Ldr. Guide Avail.: Yes   Size: 6.0 x 8.0
Subjects: Teens: Christian Liv, Teens: New Testament
Comments: In this chapter-by-chapter study of Philippians, teens discover how they can begin to view experiences as Paul did, and how because of Christ they can be full of joy every day for the rest of their lives. In his letter, Paul said, "I rejoice, you should rejoice, too." That's an amazing statement from a man who faced worldly troubles, including sickness, imprisonment, doubt, rejection, and despair.

Author: Klug, Ron   **595**
Series: Fisherman Bible Studyguide
Title: *Philippians: God's Guide to Joy*
Publisher: Shaw, 1979

Num. Sess.	Group Time	Num. Pgs.	Avg. Qst.	Price	Audience	Format	Bible Study
8	45-60	40	13	3.95	Beginner	Workbk	Book

Features: Intro to Leading a Study, Intro to Study, Prayer Helps
★★ Personal Application Preparation Time: Low ISBN: 0-87788-680-6
★★ Relationship Building Ldr. Guide Avail.: No Size: 5.0 x 8.25
Subjects: Joy, Philippians, Prison Epistles, Suffering
Comments: This study presents the meaning of joy from Paul, who faced head-on all the troubles of the world—supernatural evil as well as human misunderstanding, sickness, abandonment, persecution, imprisonment, doubt, and despair—and still could say, "Rejoice in the Lord always!" The apostle's letter to the church at Philippi is filled with joy, gladness, and rejoicing. At the end of each study is a section titled "Focus on Joy."

Author: Klug, Ron   **596**
Series: Fisherman Bible Studyguide
Title: *Psalms: A Guide to Prayer & Praise*
Publisher: Shaw, 1979

Num. Sess.	Group Time	Num. Pgs.	Avg. Qst.	Price	Audience	Format	Bible Study
15	45-60	69	12	3.95	Beginner	Workbk	Book

Features: Intro to Study, Prayer Helps, Worship Helps, Digging Deeper Quest, Follow Up
★★ Personal Application Preparation Time: None ISBN: 0-87788-699-7
★★ Relationship Building Ldr. Guide Avail.: No Size: 5.0 x 8.25
Subjects: God, Psalms
Comments: This study of sixteen representative psalms and their literary types leads participants on an exploration of the most beloved book of the Bible. It offers insights into who God is and how to experience deepening growth in a relationship with Him.

Author: Klug, Ron   **597**
Series: Young Fisherman Bible
Title: *Real Questions, The: Searching the Psalms for Answers*
Publisher: Shaw, 1984

Num. Sess.	Group Time	Num. Pgs.	Avg. Qst.	Price	Audience	Format	Bible Study
12	50-60	75	14	2.95	Beginner	Workbk	Topical

Features: Intro to Study, Prayer Helps, Scrpt Memory Helps, Worship Helps, Drawings, Exam
★★ Personal Application Preparation Time: Low ISBN: 0-87788-701-2
★★ Relationship Building Ldr. Guide Avail.: Yes Size: 6.0 x 8.0
Subjects: Teens: Old Testament, Teens: Prayer, Teens: Relationships, Teens: Theology, Teens: Youth Life
Comments: This study, from twelve psalms, can help teens respond emotionally and intellectually to the questions of God's existence, evil, depression, death, and other concerns. Teens can learn to recognize God's care, understand themselves, face their fears, and anticipate the future confidently. Because the psalms are meant to be sung, each study includes a song or hymn based on the psalm being studied. Thorough leader notes are provided.

Author: Knudsen, Stephen   **598**
Series: Small Group Bible Studies
Title: *Ten Gifts*
Publisher: Augsburg Publishing House, 1976

Num. Sess.	Group Time	Num. Pgs.	Avg. Qst.	Price	Audience	Format	Bible Study
6	60-75	24	29	1.15	New Christian	Book	Topical

Features: Intro to Study, Bibliography
★★★ Personal Application Preparation Time: None ISBN:
★★★ Relationship Building Ldr. Guide Avail.: No Size: 8.50 x 5.50
Subjects: Ten Commandments
Comments: This short, six-session study on the Ten Commandments provides an opportunity to study and discuss their relevance today. It portrays them as gifts from a loving and gracious God, as guides steering one away from any actions not in keeping with the covenant relationship but providing great freedom for positive response, and as friends of the gospel. The words *covenant* and *law* are both discussed.

Author: Koester, Nancy   **599**
Series: Small Group Bible Studies
Title: *By Grace Through Faith*
Publisher: Augsburg Publishing House, 1982

Num. Sess.	Group Time	Num. Pgs.	Avg. Qst.	Price	Audience	Format	Bible Study
6	60-75	24	14	1.15	New Christian	Book	Book

Features: Intro to Study, Prayer Helps
★★★ Personal Application Preparation Time: None ISBN:
★★★ Relationship Building Ldr. Guide Avail.: No Size: 8.50 x 5.50
Subjects: Christian Living, Church Life, Ephesians, Faith, Grace
Comments: This small pamphlet includes six sessions on Ephesians. The themes of Ephesians are varied, from lofty heights of praise to practical instruction for living. Major concerns include unity among believers, the purpose of the Church, and the proper Christian path; however, the heartbeat of the letter is found in Ephesians 2:8-9: "grace through faith." Ephesians divides into two parts: chapters 1-3 describe God's plan and our place in it; chapters 4-6 instruct Christians in daily living.

Author: Koester, Nancy   **600**
Series: Small Group Bible Studies
Title: *Simon Peter*
Publisher: Augsburg Publishing House, 1984

Num. Sess.	Group Time	Num. Pgs.	Avg. Qst.	Price	Audience	Format	Bible Study
4	60-75	24	16	0.95	New Christian	Book	Charctr

Features: Intro to Study, Prayer Helps
Personal Application Preparation Time: None ISBN:
Relationship Building Ldr. Guide Avail.: No Size: 8.50 x 5.50
Subjects: Bible Personalities, Failure, Service
Comments: This short four-session study is on Peter, best known of the original twelve disciples. He had a remarkable life, and Scripture shows him to be a man with many human failings that have endeared him to generations. He could act and speak boldly; he could also be confused and afraid. Although he had human failings, he let himself be used by God in a powerful way. This study looks at a few important events from Peter's life and discusses how his experiences speak to believers' lives today.

Author: Koester, Nancy   **601**
Series: Friendship Bible Study
Title: *1, 2, 3 John*
Publisher: Augsburg Publishing House, 1986

Num. Sess.	Group Time	Num. Pgs.	Avg. Qst.	Price	Audience	Format	Bible Study
8	60-75	48	10	3.0	New Christian	Workbk	Book

Features: Intro to Study, Prayer Helps, Study Overview
★★★★ Personal Application   Preparation Time: Low   ISBN:
★★★★ Relationship Building   Ldr. Guide Avail.: Yes   Size: 5.50 x 8.50
Subjects: Faith, Love, Marriage, 1, 2 & 3 John/Jude
Comments: This eight-lesson study emphasizes Christian love and considers how that love can be realized in daily life. Questions explored in this study include: "What is the Christian message?" "What does it mean to be a child of God?" and "How can we put our faith into practice?" The lesson format includes an overview, an opening, a responsive reading, Bible background, questions for reflection, a key verse, a prayer response, and an "our faith" response.

Author: Kohlhafer, Mina   **602**
Series:
Title: *Rees Howells Workbook*
Publisher: Christian Literature Crusade, 1989

Num. Sess.	Group Time	Num. Pgs.	Avg. Qst.	Price	Audience	Format	Bible Study
16	105-120	105	Vry	3.95	Mature Chrstn	Workbk	Topical

Features: Intro to Study, Ldr's Notes
★★ Personal Application   Preparation Time: Med   ISBN: 0-87508-299-8
★★ Relationship Building   Ldr. Guide Avail.: No   Size: 5.50 x 8.50
Subjects: Faith, Prayer
Comments: This study guide, based on the biography of Rees Howells, shows participants how to deal with total surrender, learn to love the unlovely, and find the key to prevailing prayer. They see Howells become the channel of a mighty revival in Africa, teach the principles of divine healing, and progress in faith until world events seemed affected by his prayers. The study guide applies spiritual principles in a practical manner.

Author: Korth, Russ, et al.   **603**
Series: God in You
Title: *Alive! God in Intimate Relationship with You*
Publisher: NavPress, 1986

Num. Sess.	Group Time	Num. Pgs.	Avg. Qst.	Price	Audience	Format	Bible Study
12	45-60	65	6	4.95	Beginner	Workbk	Topical

Features: Intro to Study, Cartoons, Charts
★★★ Personal Application   Preparation Time: Low   ISBN: 0-89109-093-2
★★ Relationship Building   Ldr. Guide Avail.: Yes   Size: 7.0 x 9.0
Subjects: Christian Living, Discipleship, Evangelism, God, Prayer, Relationships
Comments: This study shows participants the benefits of a deepening relationship with God. Old and New Testament passages provide the basis for lessons on giving new life, lighting the way, residing in God, providing fullness, granting access, giving guidance, being a companion, assuring triumph, reviving by His Word, and responding to prayers. Participants will learn how to keep relationships fresh, meaningful, and full of life. Journaling—keeping a weekly record of what you learn—is recommended.

Author: Korth, Russ, et al.   **604**
Series: God in You
Title: *Changed! Reflecting Your Love for God*
Publisher: NavPress, 1986

Num. Sess.	Group Time	Num. Pgs.	Avg. Qst.	Price	Audience	Format	Bible Study
12	45-60	65	6	4.95	Beginner	Workbk	Topical

Features: Intro to Study, Cartoons, Charts
★★★ Personal Application   Preparation Time: Low   ISBN: 0-89109-096-7
★★ Relationship Building   Ldr. Guide Avail.: Yes   Size: 7.0 x 9.0
Subjects: Christian Living, Discipleship, Evangelism, Family, God
Comments: This study concerns changes in people which allow them to reflect their love for God. Changes God makes on the inside, which are revealed on the outside, don't come automatically. Many are slow in coming. Lessons cover renewing; loving; being humble, generous, submissive, and uncompromising; purity; sensitivity; being a good family member; and being worshipful. Each lesson begins with a cartoon and concludes with a summary statement, hymn verse, scripture reference, or a quote.

Author: Korth, Russ, et al.   **605**
Series: God in You
Title: *Fulfilled! Enjoying God's Purpose for You*
Publisher: NavPress, 1986

Num. Sess.	Group Time	Num. Pgs.	Avg. Qst.	Price	Audience	Format	Bible Study
12	45-60	65	5	4.95	Beginner	Workbk	Topical

Features: Intro to Study, Cartoons, Charts, Maps
★★★ Personal Application   Preparation Time: Low   ISBN: 0-89109-097-5
★★ Relationship Building   Ldr. Guide Avail.: Yes   Size: 7.0 x 9.0
Subjects: Christian Living, Discipleship, Evangelism, Faith, God, Service, Work
Comments: This study is designed to help Christians lead a more fulfilled life. Many look for fulfillment in material goods; others by losing themselves in careers. In this study, the Scriptures lead participants to God's purpose for their lives, and fulfillment. Lesson titles include: "Offering Yourself," "Working Together," "Helping Others Grow," "Balancing Your Faith," "Caring Enough to Act," and "Praying as a Body." Lessons begin with a cartoon and end with a summary statement, hymn verse, scripture reference, or quote.

Author: Korth, Russ, et al.   **606**
Series: God in You
Title: *Jesus! God in You Made Possible*
Publisher: NavPress, 1986

Num. Sess.	Group Time	Num. Pgs.	Avg. Qst.	Price	Audience	Format	Bible Study
12	45-60	71	7	4.95	Beginner	Workbk	Charctr

Features: Intro to Study, Cartoons, Charts
★★★ Personal Application   Preparation Time: Low   ISBN: 0-89109-092-4
★★ Relationship Building   Ldr. Guide Avail.: Yes   Size: 7.0 x 9.0
Subjects: Discipleship, Evangelism, God, Gospels
Comments: This study examines Jesus through eyewitness accounts of His life. Each lesson deals with one specific portion of Scripture, from Matthew, Mark, Luke, John, or Acts. Participants will see Jesus called Immanuel, the Word, Savior, Friend of Sinners, Master, Christ, Servant, Bread of Life, Great High Priest, Man of Sorrows, Lord God Omnipotent, and King of Kings. Each lesson begins with a cartoon and concludes with a summary statement, hymn verse, scripture reference, or quote.

Author: Korth, Russ, et al.   **607**
Series: God in You
Title: *Powerful! God Enabling You*
Publisher: NavPress, 1986

Num. Sess.	Group Time	Num. Pgs.	Avg. Qst.	Price	Audience	Format	Bible Study
12	45-60	63	7	4.95	Beginner	Workbk	Topical

Features: Intro to Study, Objectives, Summary, Cartoons, Charts
  ★★★ Personal Application   Preparation Time: Low   ISBN: 0-89109-095-9
  ★★ Relationship Building   Ldr. Guide Avail.: Yes   Size: 7.0 x 9.0
Subjects: Christian Living, Discipleship, Evangelism, Faith, God, Prayer, Suffering
Comments: This study explores twelve scriptural passages in short lessons and introduces participants to God's power and His armor: the Scriptures, prayer, and faith. Through His Holy Spirit, and through cooperation with others, participants can find strength to testify and persevere. This study proves that God's power can enable one to overcome adversity and accomplish great things. Participants can discover how to realize God's power for facing trials, and learn how to prepare for difficulties to come.

Author: Korth, Russ, et al.   **608**
Series: God in You
Title: *Rich! God Meeting Your Deepest Needs*
Publisher: NavPress, 1986

Num. Sess.	Group Time	Num. Pgs.	Avg. Qst.	Price	Audience	Format	Bible Study
12	45-60	63	7	4.95	Beginner	Workbk	Topical

Features: Intro to Study, Cartoons, Charts
  ★★★ Personal Application   Preparation Time: Low   ISBN: 0-89109-094-0
  ★★ Relationship Building   Ldr. Guide Avail.: Yes   Size: 7.0 x 9.0
Subjects: Christian Living, Discipleship, Evangelism, God, Grace, Hope, Wisdom
Comments: This study shows how God touches people's lives by meeting their deepest needs, including love, grace, peace, acceptance, clear conscience, wisdom, comfort, freedom, provision, family, courage, and hope. Each lesson begins with a cartoon and concludes with a summary statement, hymn verse, additional scripture reference, or a quote from a famous theologian. An appendix for developing study skills is helpful.

Author: Kuhatschek, Jack   **609**
Series: LifeGuide Bible Study
Title: *David: A Heart for God*
Publisher: InterVarsity, 1990

Num. Sess.	Group Time	Num. Pgs.	Avg. Qst.	Price	Audience	Format	Bible Study
12	45-60	62	11	3.95	Beginner	Workbk	Charctr

Features: Intro to Leading a Study, Intro to Study, Ldr's Notes
  ★★★ Personal Application   Preparation Time: Low   ISBN: 0-8308-1063-3
  ★★★ Relationship Building   Ldr. Guide Avail.: No   Size: 5.50 x 8.25
Subjects: Bible Personalities, God, 1 & 2 Samuel
Comments: This twelve-week study of David's life helps participants discover what it means to have a passionate heart for God. It observes David from childhood to the end of his life, selecting key events which reveal his multifaceted character. Contemporary role models are desperately needed—not comic-book superheroes impossible to imitate, but flesh-and-blood people. David is such a role model.

Author: Kuhatschek, Jack   **610**
Series: LifeGuide Bible Study
Title: *Galatians: Why God Accepts Us*
Publisher: InterVarsity, 1990

Num. Sess.	Group Time	Num. Pgs.	Avg. Qst.	Price	Audience	Format	Bible Study
12	45-60	64	11	3.95	Beginner	Workbk	Topical

Features: Intro to Leading a Study, Intro to Study, Ldr's Notes
  ★★★ Personal Application   Preparation Time: Low   ISBN: 0-8308-1011-0
  ★★ Relationship Building   Ldr. Guide Avail.: No   Size: 5.50 x 8.25
Subjects: Christian Living, Galatians, God, Repentance
Comments: This study is a testimony to the futility of people trying to earn God's acceptance when they are already accepted in Christ. Since the world often accepts only the attractive, smart, wealthy, or powerful, many people think they must work harder, live better, pray longer, and witness more to impress God. Paul's message frees Christians from living with guilt, offers fresh assurance of God's love, and provides renewed power to serve Him.

Author: Kuhatschek, Jack   **611**
Series: Fruit of the Spirit
Title: *Peace: Overcoming Anxiety and Conflict*
Publisher: Zondervan, 1991

Num. Sess.	Group Time	Num. Pgs.	Avg. Qst.	Price	Audience	Format	Bible Study
6	45-60	48	12	3.95	New Christian	Workbk	Topical

Features: Intro to Study, Ldr's Notes
  ★★★ Personal Application   Preparation Time: None   ISBN: 0-310-53741-X
  ★★ Relationship Building   Ldr. Guide Avail.: No   Size: 5.50 x 8.50
Subjects: Christian Living, Emotions, Fruit of the Spirit, God, Relationships, Stress
Comments: This six-week study, using selected Psalms and New Testament passages, explores God's prescription for peace. It helps participants discover how to cope with anxiety, feel safe in God's care, and live at peace with others. It helps answer these questions: How can one experience the "peace which transcends all understanding"? and, How can we guard our hearts and minds from the stress of everyday life?

Author: Kuhatschek, Jack   **612**
Series: LifeGuide Bible Study
Title: *Romans: Becoming New in Christ*
Publisher: InterVarsity, 1986

Num. Sess.	Group Time	Num. Pgs.	Avg. Qst.	Price	Audience	Format	Bible Study
21	45-60	94	10	3.95	New Christian	Workbk	Book

Features: Intro to Leading a Study, Intro to Study, Ldr's Notes
  ★ Personal Application   Preparation Time: Low   ISBN: 0-8308-1008-0
  ★ Relationship Building   Ldr. Guide Avail.: No   Size: 5.50 x 8.25
Subjects: Jesus: Life/Teaching, Romans
Comments: Romans is the clearest and fullest explanation of the gospel in the Bible. Today, many preach a gospel which lacks clarity and substance. People make decisions to "follow Christ" without clear understanding of the meaning of His death and resurrection. Paul, in his letter to the Romans, expresses what he would have liked to have said in person. This guide is divided into two parts, one containing twelve studies and the other with nine.

Author: Kuhatschek, Jack   **613**
Series: Fruit of the Spirit
Title: *Self-Control: Mastering Our Passions*
Publisher: Zondervan, 1991

Num. Sess.	Group Time	Num. Pgs.	Avg. Qst.	Price	Audience	Format	Bible Study
6	45-60	48	12	3.95	New Christian	Workbk	Topical

Features: Intro to Study, Ldr's Notes
  ★★★ Personal Application   Preparation Time: None   ISBN: 0-310-53731-2
  ★★ Relationship Building   Ldr. Guide Avail.: No   Size: 5.50 x 8.50
Subjects: Accountability, Christian Living, Fruit of the Spirit, Money
Comments: This six-week study, using passages from Proverbs and the New Testament, helps participants master self-control over their passions. It explores five crucial areas of control: the tongue, the body, desires, appetites, and finances. The final study considers what it means to clothe oneself with Jesus Christ.

Author: Kuhatschek, Jack   **614**
Series: LifeGuide Bible Study
Title: *Self-Esteem: Seeing Ourselves As God Sees Us*
Publisher: InterVarsity, 1990

Num. Sess.	Group Time	Num. Pgs.	Avg. Qst.	Price	Audience	Format	Bible Study
9	45-60	62	11	3.95	New Christian	Workbk	Topical

Features: Intro to Leading a Study, Intro to Study, Prayer Helps, Ldr's Notes
  ★★★ Personal Application   Preparation Time: Low   ISBN: 0-8308-1065-X
  ★★ Relationship Building   Ldr. Guide Avail.: No   Size: 5.50 x 8.25
Subjects: God, Psychology, Self-esteem
Comments: This nine-week study on self-esteem helps participants gain a biblically balanced vision of who they are in Christ. The first five studies provide a foundation for healthy self-esteem. The next four reveal the multifaceted and sometimes contradictory nature of Christians: old yet new, weak yet strong, poor yet rich, dying yet alive. This guide is not intended to be a resource for those seeking recovery from badly wounded self-esteem.

Author: Kunz, Marilyn & Catherine Schnell   **615**
Series: Neighborhood Bible Studies
Title: *Acts*
Publisher: Tyndale House, 1961

Num. Sess.	Group Time	Num. Pgs.	Avg. Qst.	Price	Audience	Format	Bible Study
18	60-75	78	16	2.95	New Christian	Workbk	Book

Features: Intro to Leading a Study, Intro to Study, Maps
  ★★ Personal Application   Preparation Time: Med   ISBN: 0-8423-0030-9
  ★★ Relationship Building   Ldr. Guide Avail.: No   Size: 5.0 x 7.50
Subjects: Acts, Church Life, Holy Spirit
Comments: This chapter-by-chapter study of Acts explains how the Christian church began, and considers the connection between the apostolic letters and the gospel accounts. The events span about thirty years, immediately following Christ's resurrection and ascension. The study describes Christianity's geographical spread from Jerusalem to Rome, and its cultural spread from Jew to Gentile. A separate notebook is required.

Author: Kunz, Marilyn & Catherine Schnell   **616**
Series: Neighborhood Bible Studies
Title: *Bible Leaders Who Coped with Stress*
Publisher: Tyndale House, 1988

Num. Sess.	Group Time	Num. Pgs.	Avg. Qst.	Price	Audience	Format	Bible Study
12	60-75	65	21	2.95	Beginner	Workbk	Topical

Features: Intro to Leading a Study, Intro to Study, Scrpt Memory Helps, Summary
  ★★ Personal Application   Preparation Time: Med   ISBN: 0-8423-0375-8
  ★★ Relationship Building   Ldr. Guide Avail.: No   Size: 5.0 x 7.50
Subjects: Bible Personalities, Stress
Comments: This study focuses on twelve Old Testament leaders who faced moments of particular stress. It begins with Abraham and continues with Joseph, Moses, Gideon, David, Elijah, Jehoshaphat, Jeremiah, Daniel, Esther, Ezra, and Nehemiah. The format includes a brief introduction of each chapter followed by questions on specific verses. It closes with a summary, prayer, and memory verse. A separate notebook is required for responding to questions.

Author: Kunz, Marilyn & Catherine Schnell   **617**
Series: Neighborhood Bible Studies
Title: *Coming of the Lord, The*
Publisher: Tyndale House, 1982

Num. Sess.	Group Time	Num. Pgs.	Avg. Qst.	Price	Audience	Format	Bible Study
11	60-75	64	19	2.95	New Christian	Workbk	Topical

Features: Intro to Leading a Study, Intro to Study, Prayer Helps, Study Overview, Summary, Ldr's Notes, Maps
  ★★ Personal Application   Preparation Time: Med   ISBN: 0-8423-0424-X
  ★★ Relationship Building   Ldr. Guide Avail.: No   Size: 5.0 x 7.50
Subjects: Church Life, Holiness, Hope, Suffering, 1 & 2 Thessalonians, 1, 2 & 3 John/Jude
Comments: This is a chapter-by-chapter study of 1 and 2 Thessalonians, 2 and 3 John, and Jude. Its format includes a brief introduction to the book, followed by questions on specific verses. It closes with summary questions and a prayer. The advanced nature of the questions requires prior, careful reading of the scriptures. The closing lesson of each book offers additional overview questions, and a separate notebook is required for responding to questions. First John is not covered in this study.

Author: Kunz, Marilyn & Catherine Schnell   **618**
Series: Neighborhood Bible Studies
Title: *Courage to Cope*
Publisher: Tyndale House, 1984

Num. Sess.	Group Time	Num. Pgs.	Avg. Qst.	Price	Audience	Format	Bible Study
10	60-75	60	20	2.95	Mature Chrstn	Workbk	Topical

Features: Intro to Leading a Study, Intro to Study, Prayer Helps, Summary
  ★★ Personal Application   Preparation Time: Med   ISBN: 0-8423-0446-0
  ★★ Relationship Building   Ldr. Guide Avail.: No   Size: 5.0 x 7.50
Subjects: Christian Living, Emotions, Faith, Family, Prayer, Stress
Comments: This study teaches participants to cope with some of life's difficult problems, such as choices, leadership, persecution, family problems, oppression, and loneliness. Men and women from the Bible demonstrated courage in the face of trying circumstances. That courage was enhanced by persistent faith and prayer, as ultimately they realized the ability to cope is a gift from God. Each lesson includes summary questions and closes with a prayer. A separate notebook is required.

Author: Kunz, Marilyn & Catherine Schnell   **619**
Series: Neighborhood Bible Studies
Title: *Four Men of God: Abraham, Joseph, Moses, David*
Publisher: Tyndale House, 1965

Num. Sess.	Group Time	Num. Pgs.	Avg. Qst.	Price	Audience	Format	Bible Study
17	60-75	90	17	3.95	Beginner	Workbk	Charctr

Features: Intro to Leading a Study, Intro to Study, Prayer Helps, Summary
  ★★ Personal Application   Preparation Time: Med   ISBN: 0-8423-0900-4
  ★★ Relationship Building   Ldr. Guide Avail.: No   Size: 5.0 x 7.50
Subjects: Bible Personalities, Exodus, Faith, Genesis, God, Love, Marriage, Obedience, 1 & 2 Samuel
Comments: This is a study of four men who hold strategic places in history and who faced challenges and temptations which tested and developed them. Each is noted for an attribute found perfected in Jesus Christ: Abraham for obedient faith; Joseph for mercy toward those who betrayed him; Moses for meekness and sacrificial love for his rebellious people; and David for humility as God's anointed king. A notebook is required for responding to questions.

Author: Kunz, Marilyn & Catherine Schnell   **620**
Series: Neighborhood Bible Studies
Title: *Genesis*
Publisher: Tyndale House, 1981

Num. Sess.	Group Time	Num. Pgs.	Avg. Qst.	Price	Audience	Format	Bible Study
12	60-75	77	21	2.95	New Christian	Workbk	Book

Features: Intro to Leading a Study, Intro to Study, Summary, Maps
  ★★ Personal Application   Preparation Time: Med   ISBN: 0-8423-0995-0
  ★★ Relationship Building   Ldr. Guide Avail.: No   Size: 5.0 x 7.50
Subjects: Genesis, God
Comments: This chapter-by-chapter study of Genesis, chapters 1-13, describes the creation of the universe and the earth. Genesis 1-11, sometimes called the Bible's prologue, deals with primeval history through the time of Noah. Chapters 12 and 13 begin the first act of the redemption drama. The selection from Psalms included in each lesson helps participants recognize the implications of the Genesis events. A separate notebook is required.

Author: Kunz, Marilyn & Catherine Schnell   **621**
Series: Neighborhood Bible Studies
Title: *Hebrews*
Publisher: Tyndale House, 1967

Num. Sess.	Group Time	Num. Pgs.	Avg. Qst.	Price	Audience	Format	Bible Study
13	60-75	59	18	3.95	Mature Chrstn	Workbk	Book

Features: Intro to Leading a Study, Intro to Study, Scrpt Memory Helps, Summary, Charts
  ★★ Personal Application   Preparation Time: Med   ISBN: 0-8423-1410-5
  ★★ Relationship Building   Ldr. Guide Avail.: No   Size: 5.0 x 7.50
Subjects: Faith, God, Hebrews
Comments: This chapter-by-chapter study of Hebrews helps show participants that Old Testament Jewish religion is fulfilled by Christ and described in the New Testament. It states that the only access to God, through the blood of Christ, is a faith response. The format includes a brief introduction of each chapter followed by questions on specific verses. It closes with summary questions, an application exercise, and a memory verse.

Author: Kunz, Marilyn & Catherine Schnell   **622**
Series: Neighborhood Bible Studies
Title: *How to Start a Neighborhood Bible Study*
Publisher: Tyndale House, 1966

Num. Sess.	Group Time	Num. Pgs.	Avg. Qst.	Price	Audience	Format	Bible Study
-		28	N/A	3.95	New Christian	Book	Topical

Features: Intro to Leading a Study, Drawings
  ★★ Personal Application   Preparation Time: Low   ISBN: 0-8423-1530-6
  ★★ Relationship Building   Ldr. Guide Avail.: No   Size: 5.0 x 7.50
Subjects: Small Group Resource
Comments: This handbook shows what to do and what not to do in a discussion Bible study. Chapters include: "How to Begin," "Presenting the Idea," "Sample Study," "More Advice for Hosts and Discussion Leaders," "Inductive Bible Study," "Format of Neighborhood Bible Studies Guides," and "Recommended Order of Study." The chapters are short and could be used to supplement leadership training.

Author: Kunz, Marilyn & Catherine Schnell   **623**
Series: Neighborhood Bible Studies
Title: *Isaiah*
Publisher: Tyndale House, 1988

Num. Sess.	Group Time	Num. Pgs.	Avg. Qst.	Price	Audience	Format	Bible Study
13	60-75	81	20	2.95	New Christian	Workbk	Book

Features: Intro to Leading a Study, Intro to Study, Prayer Helps, Scrpt Memory Helps, Summary
  ★★ Personal Application   Preparation Time: Med   ISBN: 0-8423-1752-X
  ★★ Relationship Building   Ldr. Guide Avail.: No   Size: 5.0 x 7.50
Subjects: God, Isaiah/Jeremiah, Major Prophets, Prophecy
Comments: The chapter-by-chapter study examines Isaiah's history, prophecy, and central themes. God's beauty and majesty in dealing with His people come to life in the lessons. The format includes a brief introduction of each lesson, followed by questions, and closing with a summary, prayer, and memory verse. A separate notebook is required for responding to questions.

Author: Kunz, Marilyn & Catherine Schnell   **624**
Series: Neighborhood Bible Studies
Title: *John (Book 1)*
Publisher: Tyndale House, 1965

Num. Sess.	Group Time	Num. Pgs.	Avg. Qst.	Price	Audience	Format	Bible Study
12	60-75	61	22	3.95	Beginner	Workbk	Book

Features: Intro to Leading a Study, Intro to Study, Summary, Maps
  ★★ Personal Application   Preparation Time: Med   ISBN: 0-8423-1895-X
  ★★ Relationship Building   Ldr. Guide Avail.: No   Size: 5.0 x 7.50
Subjects: Baptism, Jesus: Life/Teaching, John
Comments: This chapter-by-chapter study of John 1-10 covers Jesus' ministry from His baptism by John the Baptist through conflict with the Jewish religious leaders in Jerusalem. The format includes a brief introduction of each chapter, followed by questions on specific verses. It closes with a summary and a section titled "Afterthoughts." A separate notebook is required for responding to questions.

Author: Kunz, Marilyn & Catherine Schnell   **625**
Series: Neighborhood Bible Studies
Title: *John (Book 2)*
Publisher: Tyndale House, 1979

Num. Sess.	Group Time	Num. Pgs.	Avg. Qst.	Price	Audience	Format	Bible Study
11	60-75	55	21	3.50	Beginner	Workbk	Book

Features: Intro to Leading a Study, Intro to Study, Summary, Maps
   ★★ Personal Application   Preparation Time: Med   ISBN: 0-8423-1896-8
   ★★ Relationship Building   Ldr. Guide Avail.: No   Size: 5.0 x 7.50
Subjects: Jesus: Life/Teaching, John
Comments: This chapter-by-chapter study of John 11-21 covers the events leading up to and including the passion, death, and resurrection of Christ. A brief introduction opens each chapter, followed by questions on specific verses, a summary, and a section titled "Afterthoughts." A separate notebook is required for responding to questions.

Author: Kunz, Marilyn & Catherine Schnell   **626**
Series: Neighborhood Bible Studies
Title: *Mark*
Publisher: Tyndale House, 1963

Num. Sess.	Group Time	Num. Pgs.	Avg. Qst.	Price	Audience	Format	Bible Study
17	60-75	63	20	2.95	Beginner	Workbk	Book

Features: Intro to Leading a Study, Intro to Study, Summary, Ldr's Notes, Maps
   ★★ Personal Application   Preparation Time: Med   ISBN: 0-8423-4101-3
   ★★ Relationship Building   Ldr. Guide Avail.: No   Size: 5.0 x 7.50
Subjects: Jesus: Life/Teaching, Mark
Comments: This chapter-by-chapter study of Mark raises and answers questions about who Jesus is. A brief introduction of each chapter is followed by questions on specific verses, summary questions, and a conclusion. Lesson 9 reviews Mark 1-8; the closing lesson 17 covers Mark 16:1-8 and Luke 24 on the "Resurrection." A brief conclusion follows the study, and a separate notebook is required for responding to questions.

Author: Kunz, Marilyn & Catherine Schnell   **627**
Series: Neighborhood Bible Studies
Title: *Matthew (Book 1)*
Publisher: Tyndale House, 1980

Num. Sess.	Group Time	Num. Pgs.	Avg. Qst.	Price	Audience	Format	Bible Study
12	60-75	57	21	3.95	New Christian	Workbk	Book

Features: Intro to Leading a Study, Intro to Study, Prayer Helps, Summary, Charts, Maps
   ★★ Personal Application   Preparation Time: Med   ISBN: 0-8423-4188-9
   ★★ Relationship Building   Ldr. Guide Avail.: No   Size: 5.0 x 7.50
Subjects: Jesus: Life/Teaching, Matthew
Comments: This chapter-by-chapter study of Matthew, chapters 1-16, begins with events surrounding Jesus' birth and ends with his disciples recognizing Him as the Christ. The format includes a brief introduction of each chapter followed by questions on specific verses. It closes with summary questions and a prayer. A conclusion wraps up the study. A separate notebook is required for responding to questions, and a large foldout chart of the Gospel of Matthew is included.

Author: Kunz, Marilyn & Catherine Schnell   **628**
Series: Neighborhood Bible Studies
Title: *Philippians & Colossians: Letters from Prison*
Publisher: Tyndale House, 1972

Num. Sess.	Group Time	Num. Pgs.	Avg. Qst.	Price	Audience	Format	Bible Study
12	60-75	61	17	2.95	New Christian	Workbk	Book

Features: Intro to Leading a Study, Intro to Study
   ★★ Personal Application   Preparation Time: Med   ISBN: 0-8423-4825-5
   ★★ Relationship Building   Ldr. Guide Avail.: No   Size: 5.0 x 7.50
Subjects: Colossians/Philemon, False Teachers, Forgiveness, Joy, Philippians, Prison Epistles, Suffering
Comments: This chapter-by-chapter study covers two letters Paul sent from prison to thank his followers for their gifts, to express his affection for them, and to update his current situation. Philippians has a bittersweet flavor of suffering and joy, as Paul expresses his concern about teaching that undermines and divides the church at Philippi. In Colossians Paul responds to the danger of certain heresies, especially false teachings. He seeks to protect Christians.

Author: Kunz, Marilyn & Catherine Schnell   **629**
Series: Neighborhood Bible Studies
Title: *Promises from God*
Publisher: Tyndale House, 1988

Num. Sess.	Group Time	Num. Pgs.	Avg. Qst.	Price	Audience	Format	Bible Study
8	60-75	48	18	2.95	Mature Chrstn	Workbk	Topical

Features: Intro to Leading a Study, Intro to Study, Prayer Helps, Scrpt Memory Helps, Summary, Ldr's Notes
   ★★ Personal Application   Preparation Time: Med   ISBN: 0-8423-4981-2
   ★★ Relationship Building   Ldr. Guide Avail.: No   Size: 5.0 x 7.50
Subjects: Christian Living, God's Promises
Comments: This study focuses on eight of God's promises from the Old and New Testaments. It begins with the Israelites entering the Promised Land in Genesis, and concludes with the promised return of Christ in Revelation. Each chapter begins with a brief introduction, followed by questions on specific verses. Each closes with a summary, prayer, and memory verse. A separate notebook is required for responding to questions.

Author: Kunz, Marilyn & Catherine Schnell   **630**
Series: Neighborhood Bible Studies
Title: *Psalms & Proverbs*
Publisher: Tyndale House, 1963

Num. Sess.	Group Time	Num. Pgs.	Avg. Qst.	Price	Audience	Format	Bible Study
23	60-75	62	14	2.95	New Christian	Workbk	Book

Features: Intro to Leading a Study, Intro to Study, Summary
   ★★ Personal Application   Preparation Time: Med   ISBN: 0-8423-4991-X
   ★★ Relationship Building   Ldr. Guide Avail.: No   Size: 5.0 x 7.50
Subjects: God, Proverbs, Psalms, Wisdom
Comments: This is a study of sixteen selected psalms and seven topical studies from Proverbs. Each discussion forms a complete unit and is suitable for biweekly or monthly group meetings. The Psalms, Israel's hymnbook and prayer book, reveals human character and the nature of God. Proverbs, a collection of wise sayings in poetic form, is a book of discipline which shows God's direct interest in every facet of human life. Notebooks are required.

Coming Soon to a Neighborhood Near You

A DRAMATICALLY DIFFERENT LOOK AT LIFESTYLE EVANGELISM.

When's the last time you went out with friends to see an evangelism flick? Probably not something you've had the occasion to do lately. Evangelism movies aren't advertised in the entertainment section. And, let's face it, the topic would not exactly be a box office smash.

An evangelism movie may never hit the silver screen. But a new feature-length video on lifestyle evangelism is about to hit viewers all over the country—right where they live!

The Difference Between Show and Tell

Living Proof is a 2 1/2 hour video that approaches one of the toughest subjects for Christians in the 90s in a way that's never been done before— entirely through drama!

Divided into 12 sessions, *Living Proof* was specifically designed to meet the needs of

small groups. There's not one second of dull lecture. The moment the tape rolls, viewers are instantly transported into the lives of twelve men and women who are struggling to share their faith with unbelieving friends and neighbors—creating the opportunity to learn from their successes and failures alike!

The Story Behind the Story

Drama is not the only thing that sets *Living Proof* apart. The project was distinctive from its beginnings over five years ago when the Christian Business Men's Committee (CBMC) and NavPress decided to coproduce a video that would help Christians overcome their biggest fears and insecurities about evangelism.

In the NavPress book by Jim Petersen, they found what they were

looking for. "Jim Petersen's approach to sharing the gospel *naturally* was refreshing," says NavPress Marketing Director Volney James. "His insights on conversion as a process were unique. And his emphasis that the task of evangelism is *not* to get unbelievers to accept western Christianity—but to introduce them to a relationship with Christ—was liberating."

A Labor of Love

So in the spring of 1990, after four script rewrites and innumerable brainstorming sessions, the filming of *Living Proof* began. And its real testimony was demonstrated during those 21 days on the set. "We had Christians and nonChristians who didn't know each other," says Jeff Valdez, one of the twelve principal actors. "And, given the subject matter, the unbelievers wondered, 'Will they try to convert me?' But as we began to work together toward this common goal, genuine friendships developed. We still keep in touch."

"*Living Proof* had a powerful impact on *everyone* who worked on it—cast, crew, and sponsors alike," says Paul Franklin, the director and cameraman. Professional actors came to work on *Living Proof* for the minimum screen actors guild salary (they normally make 2 to 3 times that much). One member of Franklin's crew gave his life to Christ during that time. "And *Living*

Proof has changed my life as well," Paul says.

The Proof Is in the Picture.

When all was said and done, *Living Proof* took five years of prayer and work, cost more than half a million dollars, built hundreds of new relationships, and set a new standard for Christian film and video.

Specially filmed sequences graphically explore the unconscious attitudes, fears, and feelings of believers and unbelievers. The depiction of the battle between the emotions, the intellect, and the will prior to conversion is truly inspired. Several scenes memorably portray conflict and resolution between characters. And feature-film lighting and photography make it all spring to life.

"You can't watch *Living Proof*," says Paul Franklin, "without being struck by its realism. The point is that these imperfect people are called to carry the message of Christ to their friends and neighbors."

And so are we.

LIVING PROOF VIDEO PACKAGE

(includes Jim Petersen's book, discussion guide, 2 video cassettes)
#39825 $199.00   Extra Discussion Guides #93494 $8.95
Available at your local Christian bookstore.
Or call **1-800-366-7788** and mention offer **#999.**

When Your Group Looks to You, Look to Us.

⊙ NAVPRESS SMALL GROUP VIDEO

Serving the Church for 20 years with audio, video and curriculum resources through the ministry of Dr. R.C. Sproul.

Ligonier Ministries

For a FREE catalog or video promotion, call
1-800-435-4343
In Canada, call 1-800-344-9499

SAVE YOUR CHURCH MONEY

with Group's Active Bible Curriculum™...

Spend less money—but teach kids more! Group's Active Bible Curriculum actually costs less—because there are no separate student books to buy. Simply photocopy the student handouts you need from the included masters.
Plus, your kids will learn more! You'll teach unforgettable lessons using **active learning**—where kids learn by doing.

Act now to learn how you can save your church money on this NEW, fast-to-prepare and fun-to-teach curriculum. 36 topics are now available—each perfect for Sunday school, religious education and all youth ministry meetings!

So order from your local bookstore or call toll-FREE today for full no-obligation information—on this new scripture-based curriculum that blasts away Sunday school boredom!

800-747-6060, ext. 427

Group • Box 481 • Loveland, CO 80539

Offer #1425

WHEN GROUP LEADERS LOOK TO YOU, LOOK TO US.'

NavPress Small Group Videos are specifically designed to give groups an experience they'll never forget—without pressuring the leader!

Each video package has everything a group needs for an exciting series of 60- to 90-minute discussion sessions, including:

- Powerful video segments, some including drama
- A viewer's discussion guide
- Leader's notes
- The popular book on which the video series is based

So when group leaders turn to you for a fresh, creative approach to discussion, turn to us.

◗ NavPress Small Group Videos
- Special preview videos available for churches
- Regular book discounts apply   • Easy return policy

NavPress ◗
HELPING CHRISTIANS GROW
1-800-366-7788

Author: Kunz, Marilyn & Catherine Schnell   **631**
Series: Neighborhood Bible Studies
Title: *Romans*
Publisher: Tyndale House, 1962

Num. Sess.	Group Time	Num. Pgs.	Avg. Qst.	Price	Audience	Format	Bible Study
16	60-75	47	14	2.95	Beginner	Workbk	Book

Features: Intro to Leading a Study, Intro to Study, Bibliography, Summary
    ★★ Personal Application   Preparation Time: Med   ISBN: 0-8423-5701-7
    ★★ Relationship Building   Ldr. Guide Avail.: No   Size: 5.0 x 7.50
Subjects: Faith, Grace, Romans
Comments: This chapter-by-chapter study traces basic issues of Christian faith as set forth in Paul's letter to the Romans. Paul cites reasons for alienation between God and humanity. The format includes a brief introduction of each chapter, followed by questions on specific verses, and closes with summary questions and a conclusion. A wrap-up conclusion follows the sixteenth study. A separate notebook is required for responding to questions.

Author: Kunz, Marilyn & Catherine Schnell   **632**
Series: Neighborhood Bible Studies
Title: *They Met Jesus*
Publisher: Tyndale House, 1968

Num. Sess.	Group Time	Num. Pgs.	Avg. Qst.	Price	Audience	Format	Bible Study
8	60-75	48	19	3.95	New Christian	Workbk	Charctr

Features: Intro to Leading a Study, Intro to Study
    ★★ Personal Application   Preparation Time: Med   ISBN: 0-8423-7080-3
    ★★ Relationship Building   Ldr. Guide Avail.: No   Size: 5.0 x 7.50
Subjects: Bible Personalities, Jesus: Life/Teaching
Comments: In this study of eight New Testament characters, selected episodes cover a wide range of situations from the lives of the blind man (John 9), James and John, Peter, Pilate, and others. It moves chronologically through the life of Christ, following a format which includes a brief introduction of each lesson followed by questions, summary, and conclusion. A separate notebook is required for responding to questions.

Author: Kunz, Marilyn & Catherine Schnell   **633**
Series: Neighborhood Bible Studies
Title: *1 John & James*
Publisher: Tyndale House, 1965

Num. Sess.	Group Time	Num. Pgs.	Avg. Qst.	Price	Audience	Format	Bible Study
15	60-75	56	16	3.95	New Christian	Workbk	Book

Features: Intro to Leading a Study, Intro to Study, Summary
    ★★ Personal Application   Preparation Time: Med   ISBN: 0-8423-1930-1
    ★★ Relationship Building   Ldr. Guide Avail.: No   Size: 5.0 x 7.50
Subjects: Faith, James, 1, 2 & 3 John/Jude
Comments: This chapter-by-chapter study of 1 John and James helps participants understand the assurance of salvation, the importance of faith, and the need for works as an expression of that faith. A brief introduction of each chapter is followed by questions on specific verses. Each lesson closes with summary questions. Review lessons for 1 John and James are provided, and a separate notebook is required for responding to questions.

Author: Kunz, Marilyn & Catherine Schnell   **634**
Series: Neighborhood Bible Studies
Title: *1 & 2 Peter: Letters to People in Trouble*
Publisher: Tyndale House, 1971

Num. Sess.	Group Time	Num. Pgs.	Avg. Qst.	Price	Audience	Format	Bible Study
10	60-75	51	20	3.95	Beginner	Workbk	Book

Features: Intro to Leading a Study, Intro to Study, Summary, Charts
    ★★ Personal Application   Preparation Time: Med   ISBN: 0-8423-4820-4
    ★★ Relationship Building   Ldr. Guide Avail.: No   Size: 5.0 x 7.50
Subjects: Discipleship, Faith, Suffering, 1 & 2 Peter
Comments: This chapter-by-chapter study of 1 and 2 Peter deals with suffering, attacks against one's faith, the need for spiritual maturity, and the growth of Christian character. A brief introduction opens each chapter, followed by questions on specific verses, summary questions, and a section titled "So What?" Review lessons for 1 and 2 Peter are provided. A separate notebook is required for responding to questions.

Author: Kunz, Marilyn & Catherine Schnell   **635**
Series: Neighborhood Bible Studies
Title: *2 Corinthians and Galatians*
Publisher: Tyndale House, 1975

Num. Sess.	Group Time	Num. Pgs.	Avg. Qst.	Price	Audience	Format	Bible Study
14	60-75	69	21	2.95	New Christian	Workbk	Book

Features: Intro to Leading a Study, Intro to Study, Scrpt Memory Helps, Summary, Maps
    ★★ Personal Application   Preparation Time: Med   ISBN: 0-8423-0442-8
    ★★ Relationship Building   Ldr. Guide Avail.: No   Size: 5.0 x 7.50
Subjects: Galatians, Hope, Integrity, Reconciliation, Repentance, Service, Suffering, Victorious Living, 2 Corinthians
Comments: This chapter-by-chapter study of 2 Corinthians and Galatians covers Paul's writing about God's comfort, the New Covenant, reconciliation, His providing for physical need, and spiritual freedom in Christ. The format includes a brief introduction of each chapter followed by questions on specific verses, summary questions, and a memory verse. A brief review closes each study, and a separate notebook is required for responding to questions.

Author: LaHaye, Tim   **636**
Series: Living Studies
Title: *Spirit-Controlled Temperament*
Publisher: Tyndale House, 1966

Num. Sess.	Group Time	Num. Pgs.	Avg. Qst.	Price	Audience	Format	Bible Study
12	60-75	143	N/A	6.95	New Christian	Book	Topical

Features: No Grp Discussion Quest, Drawings, Cartoons, Charts
    ★★ Personal Application   Preparation Time: Low   ISBN: 0-8423-6405-6
    ★★ Relationship Building   Ldr. Guide Avail.: No   Size: 5.0 x 8.0
Subjects: Holy Spirit, Leadership, Psychology, Relationships, Small Group Resource
Comments: This book was written to help explain the four temperaments—sanguine, choleric, melancholy, and phlegmatic. Each is characterized as having a mixture of strengths and weaknesses, and understanding them can help leaders facilitate small groups. The study helps participants understand how the Holy Spirit can help them overcome weaknesses after they have identified their temperament.

Author: Lake, Vicki　　　　　　　　　　637
Series: A Bible Study for Women
Title: *Firming Up Your Flabby Faith*
Publisher: Victor Books, 1990

Num. Sess.	Group Time	Num. Pgs.	Avg. Qst.	Price	Audience	Format	Bible Study
8	60-75	95	10	5.99	New Christian	Workbk	Topical

Features: Intro to Study, Prayer Helps, Scrpt Memory Helps, Follow Up, Ldr's Notes
★★★★ Personal Application　Preparation Time: Med　ISBN: 0-89693-783-6
★★★★ Relationship Building　Ldr. Guide Avail.: No　Size: 6.0 x 9.0
Subjects: Faith, James, Women's Issues
Comments: This study on firming up faith helps participants recognize that their spiritual fitness needs shaping up. By applying the practical principles of James, they can restore spiritual health by daily discipline of reading, applying, and memorizing God's Word. Each lesson contains a series of inductive questions, a narrative section, and a journaling section.

Author: Larsen, Dale & Sandy　　　　　　638
Series:
Title: *Blinded by the Lies: Discerning Truth in Distorted Times*
Publisher: Victor Books, 1989

Num. Sess.	Group Time	Num. Pgs.	Avg. Qst.	Price	Audience	Format	Bible Study
13	45-60	144	N/A	7.99	Beginner	Book	Topical

Features: Intro to Study
★★★ Personal Application　Preparation Time: Low　ISBN: 0-89693-680-5
★★★ Relationship Building　Ldr. Guide Avail.: Yes　Size: 5.50 x 8.0
Subjects: Christian Life, Cults
Comments: This book examines some subtle lies of modern culture, compares them to Scripture, and suggests a positive Christian response. The lies include indulgence, self-control versus Spirit control, total comfort, and making up one's own rules. The study also challenges participants to help others identify their worldviews and encourage them toward Christian worldviews. A leader's guide provides reproducible student response sheets and assignments.

Author: Larsen, Dale & Sandy　　　　　　639
Series: Fisherman Bible Studyguide
Title: *One Body, One Spirit*
Publisher: Shaw, 1988

Num. Sess.	Group Time	Num. Pgs.	Avg. Qst.	Price	Audience	Format	Bible Study
12	45-60	64	10	3.95	New Christian	Workbk	Topical

Features: Intro to Leading a Study, Intro to Study, Prayer Helps, Follow Up, Ldr's Notes
★★ Personal Application　Preparation Time: None　ISBN: 0-87788-619-9
★★ Relationship Building　Ldr. Guide Avail.: No　Size: 5.0 x 8.25
Subjects: Christian Living, Church Life, Holy Spirit
Comments: These studies explore how Christians can discern the difference between Christian unity and simple conformity to practices within the church. They also demonstrate how the Holy Spirit can break through barriers of difference to bring people together as the Body of Christ. Concepts regarding "unity among Christians" include: merging into one superchurch, celebrating communion exactly the same way, saying identical prayers, singing the same kind of music, meeting in the same building, and more.

Author: Larsen, Dale & Sandy　　　　　　640
Series: NetWork Discussion Guide
Title: *Tending Creation*
Publisher: Shaw, 1991

Num. Sess.	Group Time	Num. Pgs.	Avg. Qst.	Price	Audience	Format	Bible Study
8	30-45	48	5	3.50	Beginner	Workbk	Topical

Features: Intro to Leading a Study, Intro to Study, Bibliography, Follow Up, Ldr's Notes
★★★★ Personal Application　Preparation Time: Low　ISBN: 0-87788-806-X
★★★ Relationship Building　Ldr. Guide Avail.: No　Size: 5.25 x 8.25
Subjects: Social Issues
Comments: Eight short lessons help participants become more aware of their responsibilities for tending the earth. Questions include: What is our responsibility toward God's world? What does it mean to have dominion over the earth? and How can we enjoy creation without exploiting it? As a result of this study, participants will question years of silence, pollution, and waste.

Author: Larsen, Sandy　　　　　　641
Series: Any Old Time
Title: *Any Old Time (Book 9)*
Publisher: Victor Books, 1988

Num. Sess.	Group Time	Num. Pgs.	Avg. Qst.	Price	Audience	Format	Bible Study
15	30-45	80	Vry	9.99	New Christian	Book	Topical

Features: Intro to Study, Objectives, Bibliography, Prayer Helps, Study Overview, Digging Deeper Quest, Ldr's Notes
★★★★ Personal Application　Preparation Time: None　ISBN: 0-89693-360-1
★★★★ Relationship Building　Ldr. Guide Avail.: No　Size: 8.50 x 11.0
Subjects: Teens: Christian Liv, Teens: Evangelism, Teens: Junior High, Teens: Peer Pressure, Teens: Senior High
Comments: The fifteen sessions in this book help teenagers sharpen their servant skills. Topics include defining service, Jesus' example, serving without self-pity, a willing attitude, rewards for service, ways to serve God, looking for needs, the cost of serving, helping peers, serving people of a different age, serving through witnessing, and meeting physical needs. Each session has a warm-up activity, Bible study, and application ideas.

Author: Larsen, Sandy & Dale　　　　　　642
Series: Young Fisherman Bible
Title: *Forgiveness: No Guilt, No Grudges*
Publisher: Shaw, 1984

Num. Sess.	Group Time	Num. Pgs.	Avg. Qst.	Price	Audience	Format	Bible Study
13	50-60	74	12	2.95	Beginner	Workbk	Topical

Features: Intro to Study, Prayer Helps, Scrpt Memory Helps, Drawings, Exam
★★ Personal Application　Preparation Time: Low　ISBN: 0-87788-277-0
★★ Relationship Building　Ldr. Guide Avail.: Yes　Size: 6.0 x 8.0
Subjects: Teens: Christian Liv, Teens: Emotions
Comments: This study draws principles of lasting friendship from examples of relationships of Bible characters. It helps teens discover how God's forgiveness can turn life right-side up. Questions covered include: What do you do when somebody hurts you and it won't go away? Plan revenge? Keep it all inside while you turn bitter? Go smash a wall? Hate yourself? Or how about when you hurt someone else? How do you get rid of the guilt you feel? The answer is forgiveness.

Author: Larsen, Sandy **643**
Series: Young Teen Feedback Elective
Title: *For Real People Only (Leader's Book)*
Publisher: Victor Books, 1986

Num. Sess.	Group Time	Num. Pgs.	Avg. Qst.	Price	Audience	Format	Bible Study
12	30-45	76	Vry	12.99	New Christian	Book	Topical

Features: Intro to Study, Prayer Helps, Handouts
★★★★ Personal Application Preparation Time: None ISBN: 0-89693-513-2
★★★★ Relationship Building Ldr. Guide Avail.: Yes Size: 8.50 x 11.0
Subjects: Teens: New Testament, Teens: Prayer, Teens: Relationships
Comments: This twelve-lesson study challenges young teens to see that Jesus calls for real attitudes, real relationships, and real worship. Each session is based on interviews with youth and includes their feedback on personal needs and concerns. The format offers three four-week studies with reproducible student sheets. They can be used separately as short studies, or consecutively as a twelve-week elective. A student book is available.

Author: Larsen, Sandy & Dale **644**
Series: Young Fisherman Bible
Title: *Galatians: Free At Last*
Publisher: Shaw, 1982

Num. Sess.	Group Time	Num. Pgs.	Avg. Qst.	Price	Audience	Format	Bible Study
13	50-60	73	12	2.95	New Christian	Workbk	Book

Features: Intro to Study, Prayer Helps, Scrpt Memory Helps, Worship Helps, Drawings, Maps, Exam
★★★ Personal Application Preparation Time: Low ISBN: 0-87788-293-2
★★ Relationship Building Ldr. Guide Avail.: Yes Size: 6.0 x 8.0
Subjects: Teens: New Testament
Comments: This chapter-by-chapter study of Galatians helps teach young people what Paul wrote the church in Galatia about rules: what rules can and cannot do, how to respond to them, and what it means to be free in Jesus. An inductive study, it places the bulk of responsibility for understanding the Bible on the participant.

Author: Larsen, Sandy **645**
Series: Young Fisherman Bible
Title: *Joseph: Non-Stop Faith*
Publisher: Shaw, 1987

Num. Sess.	Group Time	Num. Pgs.	Avg. Qst.	Price	Audience	Format	Bible Study
13	50-60	57	10	2.95	Beginner	Workbk	Charctr

Features: Intro to Study, Scrpt Memory Helps, Drawings
★★ Personal Application Preparation Time: Low ISBN: 0-87788-437-4
★★ Relationship Building Ldr. Guide Avail.: Yes Size: 6.0 x 8.0
Subjects: Bible Personalities, Faith, Family
Comments: In this study, Joseph serves as an influential spiritual role model for young people who struggle with many of the same problems and temptations he faced. Joseph's struggles include family problems, legal hassles, responsibility, and being hurt by others. That the Lord can use anything, any circumstance, any person, is the message of Joseph's life. In good times or bad times, Joseph is an example of faith that won't quit.

Author: Larsen, Sandy **646**
Series: Young Fisherman Bible
Title: *Running the Race: Keeping the Faith*
Publisher: Shaw, 1986

Num. Sess.	Group Time	Num. Pgs.	Avg. Qst.	Price	Audience	Format	Bible Study
13	50-60	60	10	2.95	Beginner	Workbk	Topical

Features: Intro to Study, Scrpt Memory Helps, Drawings, Exam
★★ Personal Application Preparation Time: Low ISBN: 0-87788-740-3
★★ Relationship Building Ldr. Guide Avail.: Yes Size: 6.0 x 8.0
Subjects: Teens: Christian Liv, Teens: Discipleship
Comments: This study deals with the basics of Christian growth—assurance of salvation, the Holy Spirit, prayer, Bible study, fellowship, and witnessing. Teens will learn that the quest for Christian maturity requires endurance and commitment to Christ. A separate leader's guide uses the same page format, with added margin notes. Leaders are encouraged to help students keep moving by offering "trophies"—an extra word of kindness, a note in the mail, a smile—during the study.

Author: Larson, Bruce **647**
Series: Video Curriculum Resource
Title: *Faith Alive*
Publisher: Word, 1987

Num. Sess.	Group Time	Num. Pgs.	Avg. Qst.	Price	Audience	Format	Bible Study
4	50-60	N/A	7	159.99	New Christian	Video	Topical

Features: Intro to Leading a Study, Prayer Helps, Video Study Guide
★★ Personal Application Preparation Time: None ISBN: 8-01-880079-0
★★ Relationship Building Ldr. Guide Avail.: No Size: 10.25 x 12.50
Subjects: Church Life, Faith, Hope, Joy, Relationships
Comments: This four-part, two-cassette video study emphasizes that faith, hope, love, and joy characterize Christianity. It urges Christians to risk redefining the church in more biblical terms. Through conversations and filmed activities, it shows Christians coming alive in four different areas: local community, church family, global community, and personal growth. The study guide is divided into two sections: group questions based on the video segment; and a brief Bible study.

Author: Larson, Ellen E. & David V. Esterline **648**
Series: Tapestry Collection
Title: *More Than a Story*
Publisher: Victor Books, 1991

Num. Sess.	Group Time	Num. Pgs.	Avg. Qst.	Price	Audience	Format	Bible Study
9	60-90	96	Vry	5.99	New Christian	Workbk	Topical

Features: Intro to Leading a Study, Intro to Study, Prayer Helps, Digging Deeper Quest, Follow Up, Ldr's Notes, Persnl Study Quest
★★★★ Personal Application Preparation Time: Low ISBN: 0-89693-813-1
★★★ Relationship Building Ldr. Guide Avail.: No Size: 6.0 x 9.0
Subjects: Parables, Prayer, Women's Issues
Comments: This inductive Bible study for women examines eight parables of Jesus. Each lesson includes a narrative, application questions, and exercises in prayer. These parables challenge women at every stage of life, and every level of Christian maturity.

Author: Lawrence, Rick   **649**
Series: Group's Active Bible Curriculum
Title: *Evil and the Occult*
Publisher: Group Publishing, 1990

Num. Sess.	Group Time	Num. Pgs.	Avg. Qst.	Price	Audience	Format	Bible Study
4	35-60	46	Vry	6.95	Beginner	Workbk	Topical

Features: Intro to Leading a Study, Intro to Study, Objectives, Study Overview, Ldr's Notes, Handouts, Agenda, Publicity Ideas
  ★★★ Personal Application   Preparation Time: None   ISBN: 1-559-45102-5
  ★★★ Relationship Building   Ldr. Guide Avail.: No   Size: 8.50 x 11.0
Subjects: Teens: Junior High, Teens: Occult
Comments: In this study, teenagers will learn to protect themselves against the trap of satanism, and discover how to draw strength from God to overcome fears of evil and the unknown. Four lessons outline the attraction of the occult and warning signs of occult involvement, and recognize the differences between Christianity and the occult. It can be adapted for a Bible class or youth meeting. Activities and Bible studies are included as separate sheets that can be reproduced. The instructions are easy to follow.

Author: Lee, Harris W.   **650**
Series: Small Group Bible Studies
Title: *That You May Have Life*
Publisher: Augsburg Publishing House, 1976

Num. Sess.	Group Time	Num. Pgs.	Avg. Qst.	Price	Audience	Format	Bible Study
8	60-75	32	Vry	1.25	New Christian	Book	Topical

Features: Intro to Study, Prayer Helps
  ★★★ Personal Application   Preparation Time: None   ISBN:
  ★★★ Relationship Building   Ldr. Guide Avail.: No   Size: 8.50 x 5.50
Subjects: Jesus: Life/Teaching, John
Comments: This small pamphlet contains eight lessons taken from the book of John. Among the unique features of this gospel are Jesus' "I am" sayings: "I am the door . . . the way, the truth, and the life . . . the light of the world . . . the vine . . . the bread of life . . . the good shepherd . . . the resurrection and the life." Participants are reminded, as they pursue these sayings' meanings for today, of the promise of "life" which runs through John's entire book.

Author: Le Peau, Andrew T. & Phyllis J.   **651**
Series: LifeGuide Bible Study
Title: *Ephesians: Wholeness for a Broken World*
Publisher: InterVarsity, 1985

Num. Sess.	Group Time	Num. Pgs.	Avg. Qst.	Price	Audience	Format	Bible Study
13	45-60	64	13	3.95	Beginner	Workbk	Book

Features: Intro to Leading a Study, Intro to Study, Ldr's Notes
  ★ Personal Application   Preparation Time: Low   ISBN: 0-8308-1012-9
  ★ Relationship Building   Ldr. Guide Avail.: No   Size: 5.50 x 8.25
Subjects: Ephesians, Friendships, Marriage, Prison Epistles, Relationships, Wholeness
Comments: Broken marriages, shattered friendships, racial divisions, rifts between nations—we live in a fractured world. How can the pieces be put back together? In Ephesians Paul lifts the veil of the future to show God's new creation; His plan to right everyone and everything in Christ. This study helps people handle the present by putting their problems and lives in the context of eternity. The thirteenth lesson is a review.

Author: Le Peau, Andrew T. & Phyllis J.   **652**
Series: LifeGuide Bible Study
Title: *James: Faith That Works*
Publisher: InterVarsity, 1987

Num. Sess.	Group Time	Num. Pgs.	Avg. Qst.	Price	Audience	Format	Bible Study
11	45-60	62	12	3.95	New Christian	Workbk	Book

Features: Intro to Leading a Study, Intro to Study, Ldr's Notes
  ★ Personal Application   Preparation Time: Low   ISBN: 0-8308-1018-8
  ★ Relationship Building   Ldr. Guide Avail.: No   Size: 5.50 x 8.25
Subjects: Christian Living, Faith, James, Money, Time
Comments: James is a practical study built around life's imperfections. How does one handle trouble when it hits? In terminology easy to understand, James treats subjects like "words"—how to talk to others; "money"—how to handle it; and "time"—the use of it. The opening study, an overview, helps put the next nine studies in perspective; while the final chapter adds cohesion. James calls for living a consistent Christian life and developing a practical faith.

Author: Le Peau, Andrew T. & Phyllis J.   **653**
Series:
Title: *One Plus One Equals One*
Publisher: InterVarsity, 1981

Num. Sess.	Group Time	Num. Pgs.	Avg. Qst.	Price	Audience	Format	Bible Study
16	60-75	130	11	6.95	Beginner	Workbk	Topical

Features: Intro to Study, Ldr's Notes, Appendix
  ★★★ Personal Application   Preparation Time: Med   ISBN: 0-87784-803-3
  ★★★ Relationship Building   Ldr. Guide Avail.: No   Size: 5.50 x 8.25
Subjects: Divorce, Family, Love, Marriage, Sexual Issues
Comments: This sixteen-week study helps couples or small groups of couples work to improve their marriages. Topics covered include expectations, self-image, sex, family life, submission, communication, forgiveness, divorce, children, possessions, and priorities. An appendix offers practical suggestions for planning in marriage. The final part focuses on love, which binds an entire marriage together. Leader's notes include objectives and questions for each lesson.

Author: Le Peau, Phyllis J.   **654**
Series: Caring People Bible Study
Title: *Caring for Emotional Needs*
Publisher: InterVarsity, 1991

Num. Sess.	Group Time	Num. Pgs.	Avg. Qst.	Price	Audience	Format	Bible Study
9	45-60	64	12	3.95	New Christian	Workbk	Topical

Features: Intro to Leading a Study, Intro to Study, Ldr's Notes
  ★★★ Personal Application   Preparation Time: Low   ISBN: 0-8308-1195-8
  ★★★ Relationship Building   Ldr. Guide Avail.: No   Size: 5.50 x 8.50
Subjects: Caring, Emotions, Loneliness, Support
Comments: This inductive nine-week study helps participants understand there's nothing unspiritual about recognizing their own emotional needs, such as fear, loneliness, and depression. They will find that increased openness will attract people to them and to Christ through them. A series of questions leads participants to discover what the Bible says about this issue. Participants are challenged to make a commitment at the end of the study.

Author: Le Peau, Phyllis J.   **655**
Series: Caring People Bible Study
Title: *Caring for People in Grief*
Publisher: InterVarsity, 1991

Num. Sess.	Group Time	Num. Pgs.	Avg. Qst.	Price	Audience	Format	Bible Study
9	45-60	64	12	3.95	New Christian	Workbk	Topical

Features: Intro to Leading a Study, Intro to Study, Ldr's Notes
  ★★★Personal Application Preparation Time: Low ISBN: 0-8308-1193-1
  ★★★Relationship Building Ldr. Guide Avail.: No Size: 5.50 x 8.50
Subjects: Caring, Emotions, Grace, Grief, Hope, Support
Comments: This nine-week study helps participants understand the conflicting thoughts and emotions that consume the grieving. It considers fear, peace, grace, hope, comfort, and more. Participants learn to find genuine comfort for their own pain and to offer that comfort to others. This inductive study's format is a series of questions which lead participants to discover what the Bible says. Participants are challenged to make a commitment at the end of the study.

Author: Le Peau, Phyllis J.   **656**
Series: Caring People Bible Study
Title: *Caring for People in Conflict*
Publisher: InterVarsity, 1991

Num. Sess.	Group Time	Num. Pgs.	Avg. Qst.	Price	Audience	Format	Bible Study
9	45-60	64	12	3.95	New Christian	Workbk	Topical

Features: Intro to Leading a Study, Intro to Study, Ldr's Notes
  ★★★Personal Application Preparation Time: Low ISBN: 0-8308-1192-3
  ★★★Relationship Building Ldr. Guide Avail.: No Size: 5.50 x 8.50
Subjects: Caring, Marriage, Parenting, Reconciliation, Relationships, Support
Comments: This nine-week study examines conflict in divided churches, broken friendships, angry children, and damaged marriages. It helps participants approach conflict in a godly way by showing how God can bring healing and reconciliation to their lives and to the lives of their loved ones. In this inductive study a series of questions leads participants to discover what the Bible says. Participants are challenged to make a commitment at the end of the study.

Author: Le Peau, Phyllis J.   **657**
Series: Caring People Bible Study
Title: *Caring for Physical Needs*
Publisher: InterVarsity, 1991

Num. Sess.	Group Time	Num. Pgs.	Avg. Qst.	Price	Audience	Format	Bible Study
8	45-60	64	12	3.95	New Christian	Workbk	Topical

Features: Intro to Leading a Study, Intro to Study, Ldr's Notes
  ★★★Personal Application Preparation Time: Low ISBN: 0-8308-1196-6
  ★★★Relationship Building Ldr. Guide Avail.: No Size: 5.50 x 8.50
Subjects: Caring, Medical Issues, Support
Comments: This inductive eight-week study helps participants learn to be effective caregivers to the poor and the sick. God cares about our physical needs—food, clothing, shelter, and medical treatment. As participants attend to the physical needs of others, they show God's care and learn how He cares for them. A series of questions leads participants to discover what the Bible says about this issue. Participants are challenged to make a commitment at the end of the study.

Author: Le Peau, Phyllis J.   **658**
Series: Caring People Bible Study
Title: *Caring for Spiritual Needs*
Publisher: InterVarsity, 1991

Num. Sess.	Group Time	Num. Pgs.	Avg. Qst.	Price	Audience	Format	Bible Study
9	45-60	64	12	3.95	New Christian	Workbk	Topical

Features: Intro to Leading a Study, Intro to Study, Ldr's Notes
  ★★★Personal Application Preparation Time: Low ISBN: 0-8308-1194-X
  ★★★Relationship Building Ldr. Guide Avail.: No Size: 5.50 x 8.50
Subjects: Caring, Support
Comments: This nine-week study helps participants discover how God meets their spiritual needs and how He helps them minister to others' spiritual needs. Purpose, assurance, belonging, and love are some of the spiritual needs addressed which are common to every person. This inductive study's format is a series of questions which lead participants to discover what the Bible says. Participants are challenged to make a commitment at the end of the study.

Author: Le Peau, Phyllis J.   **659**
Series: Caring People Bible Study
Title: *Character of Caring People, The*
Publisher: InterVarsity, 1991

Num. Sess.	Group Time	Num. Pgs.	Avg. Qst.	Price	Audience	Format	Bible Study
8	45-60	64	12	3.95	New Christian	Workbk	Topical

Features: Intro to Leading a Study, Intro to Study, Ldr's Notes
  ★★★Personal Application Preparation Time: Low ISBN: 0-8308-1197-4
  ★★★Relationship Building Ldr. Guide Avail.: No Size: 5.50 x 8.50
Subjects: Caring, Service, Support
Comments: This eight-week study helps participants identify character traits of caring people and develop them in their own lives. It covers hospitality, generosity, encouragment, and more. This inductive study's format is a series of questions which lead participants to discover what the Bible says. Participants are challenged to make a commitment at the end of the study.

Author: Le Peau, Phyllis J.   **660**
Series: Fruit of the Spirit
Title: *Gentleness: The Strength of Being Tender*
Publisher: Zondervan, 1991

Num. Sess.	Group Time	Num. Pgs.	Avg. Qst.	Price	Audience	Format	Bible Study
6	45-60	48	12	3.95	New Christian	Workbk	Topical

Features: Intro to Study, Ldr's Notes
  ★★★Personal Application Preparation Time: None ISBN: 0-310-53691-X
  ★★Relationship Building Ldr. Guide Avail.: No Size: 5.50 x 8.50
Subjects: Caring, Christian Living, Fruit of the Spirit
Comments: This six-week study, using passages from Proverbs and the New Testament, helps participants discover the strength of being tender. It dispels the myth that gentle people are weak. They would rather persuade than force, are self-giving rather than self-assertive, and prefer a kind word more than a cutting remark; these qualities reveal quiet power. A strong person may not be gentle, but a gentle person must be strong.

Author: Le Peau, Phyllis J. & Bonnie J. Miller   **661**
Series: Caring People Bible Study
Title: *Handbook for Caring People*
Publisher: InterVarsity, 1991

Num. Sess.	Group Time	Num. Pgs.	Avg. Qst.	Price	Audience	Format	Bible Study
10	45-60	64	12	3.95	New Christian	Book	Topical

Features: Intro to Leading a Study, Intro to Study, Bibliography, Ldr's Notes

    Personal Application Preparation Time: ISBN: 0-8308-1198-2
    Relationship Building Ldr. Guide Avail.: No   Size: 5.50 x 8.50
Subjects: Caring, Grief, Loneliness, Medical Issues, Relationships, Small Group Resource, Support, Work
Comments: This ten-chapter book covers principles of care and communication that help participants minister to friends and neighbors. It takes away fears by providing simple, time-tested principles for dealing with people's pain. It addresses what one should say to a friend who just lost a job or to people torn apart by conflict or to someone who is terminally ill. It provides do's and don'ts for visiting the sick at home or in a hospital.

Author: Le Peau, Phyllis J.   **662**
Series: Fruit of the Spirit
Title: *Joy: How to Rejoice in Any Situation*
Publisher: Zondervan, 1991

Num. Sess.	Group Time	Num. Pgs.	Avg. Qst.	Price	Audience	Format	Bible Study
6	45-60	48	12	3.95	New Christian	Workbk	Topical

Features: Intro to Study, Ldr's Notes

    ★★★ Personal Application Preparation Time: None ISBN: 0-310-53711-8
    ★★ Relationship Building Ldr. Guide Avail.: No   Size: 5.50 x 8.50
Subjects: Christian Living, Fruit of the Spirit, Joy
Comments: This six-week study helps participants discover how to rejoice in any situation. Lessons use Psalms and New Testament passages and deal with joy in trials and in weakness, God's Word, the gospel, and God's discipline. Although hospital rooms, work around the house, and announcements of bad news are seldom "fun," they can be occasions of joy.

Author: Le Peau, Phyllis J.   **663**
Series: Fruit of the Spirit
Title: *Kindness: Reaching Out to Others*
Publisher: Zondervan, 1991

Num. Sess.	Group Time	Num. Pgs.	Avg. Qst.	Price	Audience	Format	Bible Study
6	45-60	48	12	3.95	New Christian	Workbk	Topical

Features: Intro to Study, Ldr's Notes

    ★★★ Personal Application Preparation Time: None ISBN: 0-310-53701-0
    ★★ Relationship Building Ldr. Guide Avail.: No   Size: 5.50 x 8.50
Subjects: Bible Personalities, Caring, Christian Living, Fruit of the Spirit, Relationships
Comments: This six-week study on kindness helps participants appreciate God's kindness to them so that they will be motivated to show kindness to others. The lessons illustrate kindness through the lives of Boaz and Ruth, and David and Mephibosheth. A lesson on reaching out to the poor and needy makes participants aware of the many modern opportunities to reach out in kindness to others—whether it is a family with car trouble, a homeless person, or a panhandler asking for change.

Author: Le Peau, Phyllis J.   **664**
Series: Caring People Bible Study
Title: *Resources for Caring People*
Publisher: InterVarsity, 1991

Num. Sess.	Group Time	Num. Pgs.	Avg. Qst.	Price	Audience	Format	Bible Study
8	45-60	64	12	3.95	New Christian	Workbk	Topical

Features: Intro to Leading a Study, Intro to Study, Ldr's Notes

    ★★★ Personal Application Preparation Time: Low ISBN: 0-8308-1191-5
    ★★★ Relationship Building Ldr. Guide Avail.: No   Size: 5.50 x 8.50
Subjects: Caring, Emotions, Support
Comments: This inductive eight-week study guide uncovers God's many resources for ministering to people. Participants learn that healing comes when God works through them, and not from their own wisdom or strength. God works through them even though they don't have all the answers. A series of questions leads participants to discover what the Bible says. Participants are challenged to make a commitment at the end of the study.

Author: Lewis, Robert   **665**
Series: Homebuilders Couples
Title: *Building Teamwork in Marriage*
Publisher: Word, 1989

Num. Sess.	Group Time	Num. Pgs.	Avg. Qst.	Price	Audience	Format	Bible Study
7	60-90	125	Vry	8.99	Beginner	Workbk	Topical

Features: Summary, Charts

    ★★★★ Personal Application Preparation Time: Low ISBN: 0-8499-8342-8
    ★★★ Relationship Building Ldr. Guide Avail.: Yes Size: 5.50 x 8.50
Subjects: Family, Marriage, Women's Issues
Comments: This study helps married participants understand their different but complementary roles by discerning and meeting a mate's unique needs, learning why honor and praise are important to a woman's role in marriage, understanding what a husband needs from his wife in order to feel like a man, learning about true equality in a marriage, and discovering special gifts to give one's children to improve their marriages.

Author: Limburg, James   **666**
Series: Friendship Bible Study
Title: *Jonah and Ruth*
Publisher: Augsburg Publishing House, 1989

Num. Sess.	Group Time	Num. Pgs.	Avg. Qst.	Price	Audience	Format	Bible Study
8	60-75	48	13	3.0	New Christian	Workbk	Book

Features: Intro to Study, Prayer Helps, Study Overview

    ★★★★ Personal Application Preparation Time: Low ISBN:
    ★★★★ Relationship Building Ldr. Guide Avail.: Yes Size: 5.50 x 8.50
Subjects: Bible Personalities, God, Jonah, Ruth
Comments: This eight-lesson study prompts adults to study two of the best-known stories from the Bible. The stories of Ruth and of Jonah are different in many ways, but they share a common theme: God's love is for all people, even those outside the chosen people of God. Specific suggestions in the introduction show how to approach the study. The lesson format includes an overview, an opening, a responsive reading, Bible background, questions for reflection, a key verse, prayer response, and more.

Author: Lindsley, Art   **667**
Series:
Title: *Against the Night: Study Guide*
Publisher: Servant Publications, 1989

Num. Sess.	Group Time	Num. Pgs.	Avg. Qst.	Price	Audience	Format	Bible Study
13	60-75	89	12	4.95	New Christian	Workbk	Topical

Features: Intro to Leading a Study, Intro to Study, Prayer Helps, Digging Deeper Quest, Summary
★★★★ Personal Application Preparation Time: Med ISBN: 0-89283-652-0
★★★★ Relationship Building Ldr. Guide Avail.: No Size: 5.25 x 8.0
Subjects: Cults, Faith, Hope, Obedience, Satan
Comments: This book challenges Christians to regain a vision of what it means to be God's people in the new dark ages. It offers a penetrating look at the crisis of character that besets our age. The primary message is an exhortation to courage, faithfulness, obedience, and hope. The study guide helps participants absorb this message as it rekindles a spiritual passion for goodness, justice, righteousness, and living as a light in a darkening world.

Author: Littauer, Florence   **668**
Series:
Title: *Your Personality Tree*
Publisher: Word, 1988

Num. Sess.	Group Time	Num. Pgs.	Avg. Qst.	Price	Audience	Format	Bible Study
8	60-75	N/A	Vry	159.99	Begi nner	Video	Topical

Features: Intro to Leading a Study, Intro to Study, Book Incl, Video Study Guide
★★★★ Personal Application Preparation Time: Low ISBN: 8-01-970079-X
★★★ Relationship Building Ldr. Guide Avail.: No Size: 10.0 x 12.50
Subjects: Leadership, Psychology, Relationships, Small Group Resource
Comments: This eight-week video study—a filmed lecture— takes a look at four personality types. It is not theology, but a tool to use in helping people, as the Bible says, "Let a man examine himself" (1 Corinthians 11:28). It enables participants to understand themselves and their offensive ways, but it also helps them obey God by understanding, and therefore accepting, others. Two video cassettes contain a total of the eight thirty-minute sessions. The study guide is reproducible.

Author: Little, Paul E.   **669**
Series:
Title: *How to Give Away Your Faith*
Publisher: InterVarsity, 1988

Num. Sess.	Group Time	Num. Pgs.	Avg. Qst.	Price	Audience	Format	Bible Study
10	60-75	190	10	7.95	New Christian	Book	Topical

Features: Intro to Study, Ldr's Notes, Drawings, Cassette Avail
★★★★ Personal Application Preparation Time: Med ISBN: 0-8308-1217-2
★★★★ Relationship Building Ldr. Guide Avail.: No Size: 5.50 x 8.25
Subjects: Apologetics, Evangelism, Small Group Resource
Comments: The down-to-earth approach of this ten-week study helps participants show how friendly and natural evangelism can really be. The study has been updated and expanded, making it more practical and contemporary. Chapters are followed by probing questions and suggestions for a group leader. Two chapters—"Hurdling Social Barriers," and "Christ Is Relevant Today"—deal with many questions Christians face when witnessing today.

Author: Little, Paul E.   **670**
Series:
Title: *Know What You Believe*
Publisher: Victor Books, 1970

Num. Sess.	Group Time	Num. Pgs.	Avg. Qst.	Price	Audience	Format	Bible Study
13	60-75	139	N/A	7.99	New Christian	Book	Topical

Features: Intro to Study
★★★★ Personal Application Preparation Time: Low ISBN: 0-89693-045-9
★★★★ Relationship Building Ldr. Guide Avail.: Yes Size: 5.50 x 8.0
Subjects: Angels, Church Life, Faith, God, Holy Spirit, Jesus: Life/Teaching, Satan, Theology
Comments: This thirteen-week study helps participants understand the basic truths of Christian faith. The lessons describe God, Jesus Christ, Christ's death and resurrection, man and sin, the Holy Spirit, the Church, God's Word, angels, Satan, demons, salvation, and coming events. The leader's guide offers many helps and reproducible transparency masters.

Author: Little, Paul E.   **671**
Series:
Title: *Know Why You Believe*
Publisher: Victor Books, 1967

Num. Sess.	Group Time	Num. Pgs.	Avg. Qst.	Price	Audience	Format	Bible Study
13	60-75	144	N/A	7.99	New Christian	Book	Topical

Features: Intro to Study
★★★★ Personal Application Preparation Time: Low ISBN: 0-89693-080-7
★★★★ Relationship Building Ldr. Guide Avail.: Yes Size: 5.50 x 8.0
Subjects: Faith, God, Miracles, Psychology, Theology
Comments: This thirteen-week study helps participants examine the claims of Christian faith. It responds to such questions as: "How do I know there's a God?" "Are miracles really possible?" "Why is there pain and evil?" "Did Christ really rise from the dead?" "Do science and Scripture conflict?" and "How can I know the truth, since some claim that Christian experience is psychological?" The leader's guide offers many helps and reproducible transparency masters.

Author: Littleton, Mark R.   **672**
Series: SonPower Elective Series
Title: *Cool Characters with Sweaty Palms*
Publisher: Victor Books, 1989

Num. Sess.	Group Time	Num. Pgs.	Avg. Qst.	Price	Audience	Format	Bible Study
12	60-75	158	N/A	5.99	New Christian	Book	Topical

Features: Intro to Study, Cartoons
★★★★ Personal Application Preparation Time: Low ISBN: 0-89693-639-2
★★★ Relationship Building Ldr. Guide Avail.: Yes Size: 4.25 x 7.0
Subjects: Teens: Bible/Pers., Teens: Senior High
Comments: This study for youth introduces fifteen biblical characters—Solomon, Joseph, Moses, Joshua, Paul, Mary, and others—who were "regular people" thrust into perilous but common situations. Participants will examine the steps they took when they faced difficult circumstances; modern Christians can take these same steps. It is written in a contemporary, vibrant manner. Student activity booklets and a leader's guide with transparency masters are available.

Author: Loddigs, Herbert   **673**
Series: Small Group Bible Studies
Title: *Repentance*
Publisher: Augsburg Publishing House, 1982

Num. Sess.	Group Time	Num. Pgs.	Avg. Qst.	Price	Audience	Format	Bible Study
4	60-75	16	20	0.95	New Christian	Book	Topical

Features: Intro to Study, Prayer Helps
★★★★ Personal Application   Preparation Time: None   ISBN:
★★★★ Relationship Building   Ldr. Guide Avail.: No   Size: 8.50 x 5.50
Subjects: Jesus: Life/Teaching, New Testament, Old Testament, Repentance
Comments: This short, four-session study focuses on two aspects of repentance: how repentance affects the lives of individuals, and how the word *repentance* is discussed and interpreted in the Bible. These four sessions consider how repentance was used by various people in the Bible (Peter, David, John, Paul); the difference in the Old and New Testament view; what place repentance has in a believer's life; and how repentance should be used in personal daily witness.

Author: Lum, Ada   **674**
Series:
Title: *How to Begin an Evangelistic Bible Study*
Publisher: InterVarsity, 1971

Num. Sess.	Group Time	Num. Pgs.	Avg. Qst.	Price	Audience	Format	Bible Study
9	-	33	N/A	3.95		Book	No

Features:
    Personal Application   Preparation Time: ISBN: 0-87784-317-1
    Relationship Building   Ldr. Guide Avail.:   Size: 4.75 x 6.75
Subjects: Evangelism, Small Group Resource
Comments: This short "how-to" guide, wise and highly practical, tells how Christians can initiate and lead an evangelistic Bible study for nonChristian friends. It defines an evangelistic study, outlines what techniques work and don't work, shows how to spread the "good news," and offers evaluation and suggestions for improving a study.

Author: Lunde, Ann   **675**
Series: Encourager Series
Title: *When You Hurt: A Study of God's Comfort*
Publisher: Aglow, 1987

Num. Sess.	Group Time	Num. Pgs.	Avg. Qst.	Price	Audience	Format	Bible Study
4	45-60	29	18	2.25	New Christian	Workbk	Topical

Features: Intro to Study, Prayer Helps, Scrpt Memory Helps, Persnl Study Quest
★★★★ Personal Application   Preparation Time: Med   ISBN: 0-932305-48-2
★★★★ Relationship Building   Ldr. Guide Avail.: No   Size: 5.25 x 8.25
Subjects: Charismatic Interest, Emotions, God, Grief, Women's Issues
Comments: This four-week study helps Christians understand that God is their comforter. Lessons assure participants that God cares even when one person is bruised and emotionally wounded. He is concerned about never-ending problems; He offers relief from the pain; and He is the Counselor. Participants are reminded how compassionately Jesus dealt with people who came to Him for help. The study format includes specific personal application questions.

Author: Lutzer, Erwin W.   **676**
Series:
Title: *How to Have a Whole Heart in a Broken World*
Publisher: Victor Books, 1987

Num. Sess.	Group Time	Num. Pgs.	Avg. Qst.	Price	Audience	Format	Bible Study
13	60-75	155	N/A	7.99	New Christian	Book	Topical

Features: Intro to Study
★★★ Personal Application   Preparation Time: Low   ISBN: 0-89693-025-4
★★★ Relationship Building   Ldr. Guide Avail.: Yes   Size: 5.50 x 8.0
Subjects: Caring, Christian Living, Commitments, Joy, Prayer, Wholeness
Comments: This thirteen-week study discusses twelve traits of a heart that is well equipped to meet the pressures of a world of broken values, broken vows, broken people. These traits include: clearness, calmness, prayer, courage, joy, care, discernment, fulfillment, and committment. The relevance of Christ's upper-room discourse—having a healthy, whole heart—is revealed to participants. A leader's guide includes reproducible transparency masters.

Author: Lutzer, Erwin W.   **677**
Series:
Title: *How to Say No to a Stubborn Habit*
Publisher: Victor Books, 1979

Num. Sess.	Group Time	Num. Pgs.	Avg. Qst.	Price	Audience	Format	Bible Study
13	60-75	143	5	7.99	New Christian	Book	Topical

Features: Intro to Study
★★★★ Personal Application   Preparation Time: Low   ISBN: 0-88207-787-2
★★★★ Relationship Building   Ldr. Guide Avail.: Yes   Size: 5.50 x 8.0
Subjects: Addictions, Christian Living, Satan, Self-help
Comments: This thirteen-week study helps participants fight stubborn, trouble-causing habits. It offers the good news that people can say no to sin and yes to God. Issues discussed include why temptation is so powerful and attractive; why God doesn't always curtail Satan's power; what to do when a temptation turns into a sin; and why God doesn't dull your passions. A leader's guide includes reproducible transparency masters.

Author: Lutzer, Erwin W.   **678**
Series: Critical Issues Series
Title: *Living with Your Passions: A Christian's Guide to Sexual Purity*
Publisher: Victor Books, 1983

Num. Sess.	Group Time	Num. Pgs.	Avg. Qst.	Price	Audience	Format	Bible Study
13	60-75	151	5	7.99	New Christian	Book	Topical

Features:
★★★ Personal Application   Preparation Time: Med   ISBN: 0-88207-294-3
★★ Relationship Building   Ldr. Guide Avail.: Yes   Size: 5.50 x 8.0
Subjects: Counseling, Psychology, Sexual Issues, Support
Comments: This book provides a strong rationale for sexual purity, from the Christian perspective. Questions answered include: "What happens when passion gets out of control?" "How do we reconcile sexual sin?" and "Are there legitimate expressions of passion?" Adultery, lust, homosexuality, and masturbation are dealt with specifically. Some areas should not be discussed in a group setting. Leaders must be sensitive to participants who have experienced, or been victims of, sexual sin.

Author: Lutzer, Erwin W.   **679**
Series:
Title: *Managing Your Emotions*
Publisher: Victor Books, 1983

Num. Sess.	Group Time	Num. Pgs.	Avg. Qst.	Price	Audience	Format	Bible Study
13	60-75	152	6	7.99	New Christian	Book	Topical

Features:
  ★★★ Personal Application Preparation Time: Med ISBN: 0-88207-386-9
  ★★ Relationship Building Ldr. Guide Avail.: Yes Size: 5.50 x 8.0
Subjects: Emotions, Psychology, Wholeness
Comments: This study shows participants how to regain emotional control by finding God's answer for emotional needs. They will learn how to defeat depression, survive sorrow, control anger, conquer fear, and enjoy life to its fullest. They will also learn why only God can completely heal emotional wounds and put people back on the road to emotional wholeness. Each chapter concludes with several application questions. A leader's guide with transparency masters is available.

Author: Lutzer, Erwin W.   **680**
Series:
Title: *When a Good Man Falls*
Publisher: Victor Books, 1985

Num. Sess.	Group Time	Num. Pgs.	Avg. Qst.	Price	Audience	Format	Bible Study
13	60-75	132	N/A	6.99	New Christian	Book	Topical

Features: Intro to Study
  ★★★★ Personal Application Preparation Time: Low ISBN: 0-89693-361-X
  ★★★ Relationship Building Ldr. Guide Avail.: Yes Size: 5.50 x 8.0
Subjects: Bible Personalities, Caring, Christian Life, Failure, Leadership, Men's Issues
Comments: This thirteen-week study examines the lives of some of the great men of the Bible who at some point took a fall, including Moses, Jonah, David, and Peter. Their experiences demonstrate God's great love and how He opens His arms to erring children. The study helps participants discover how to come back, or how to help loved ones recover. Transparency masters are included in the leader's guide.

Author: MacArthur, John, Jr.   **681**
Series: John MacArthur's
Title: *Adding to Your Faith*
Publisher: Moody Press, 1987

Num. Sess.	Group Time	Num. Pgs.	Avg. Qst.	Price	Audience	Format	Bible Study
4	45-60	80	17	4.25	New Christian	Book	Topical

Features: Intro to Study, Scrpt Index, Study Overview, Summary, Topical Index, Cassette Avail
  ★★★ Personal Application Preparation Time: Med ISBN: 0-8024-5351-1
  ★ Relationship Building Ldr. Guide Avail.: No Size: 5.50 x 8.50
Subjects: Faith, 1 & 2 Peter
Comments: This study of 2 Peter concerns the apostle's reminder to Christians of the basic qualities they should strive to attain and perfect. The apostle wrote, "For if these qualities are yours and are increasing, they render you neither useless nor unfruitful in the true knowledge of our Lord Jesus Christ" (2 Peter 1:8, NASB). Each lesson has an introduction, questions focusing on the lesson, and two statements that reflect on the lesson's principles.

Author: MacArthur, John, Jr.   **682**
Series: John MacArthur's
Title: *Advice to a Young Disciple*
Publisher: Moody Press, 1990

Num. Sess.	Group Time	Num. Pgs.	Avg. Qst.	Price	Audience	Format	Bible Study
4	45-60	68	18	4.99	New Christian	Book	Book

Features: Intro to Study, Scrpt Index, Study Overview, Summary, Topical Index, Cassette Avail
  ★★★ Personal Application Preparation Time: Med ISBN: 0-8024-5327-9
  ★ Relationship Building Ldr. Guide Avail.: No Size: 5.50 x 8.50
Subjects: Discipleship, Pastoral Epistles, 1 & 2 Timothy/Titus
Comments: This study of 2 Timothy serves as a reminder to participants that Christians' sole source of strength is the omnipotent Christ, and that they can live confidently and boldly in Him. It uses the examples of soldiers, athletes, and farmers to show how to be strong in the Lord in every instance. Each lesson has an introduction, questions focusing on the lesson, and two statements that reflect on the lesson's principles. Optional companion tape messages are available.

Author: MacArthur, John, Jr.   **683**
Series: John MacArthur's
Title: *Assurance of Victory*
Publisher: Moody Press, 1986

Num. Sess.	Group Time	Num. Pgs.	Avg. Qst.	Price	Audience	Format	Bible Study
4	45-60	80	24	4.25	New Christian	Book	Topical

Features: Intro to Study, Scrpt Index, Study Overview, Summary, Topical Index, Cassette Avail
  ★★★ Personal Application Preparation Time: Med ISBN: 0-8024-5130-6
  ★ Relationship Building Ldr. Guide Avail.: No Size: 5.50 x 8.50
Subjects: Victorious Living, 1, 2 & 3 John/Jude
Comments: This study of 1 John covers the Christian victory, one assured by both "internal and external" witnesses. It offers participants five things for certain: (1) eternal life, (2) that God answers prayer, (3) that Christians have victory over sin and Satan, (4) that each Christian belongs to God, and (5) that Christ is the true God. Each lesson has an introduction, questions focusing on the lesson, and two statements that reflect on the lesson's principles.

Author: MacArthur, John, Jr.   **684**
Series: John MacArthur's
Title: *Avoiding Spiritual Counterfeiters*
Publisher: Moody Press, 1988

Num. Sess.	Group Time	Num. Pgs.	Avg. Qst.	Price	Audience	Format	Bible Study
4	45-60	80	20	4.25	New Christian	Book	Topical

Features: Intro to Study, Scrpt Index, Study Overview, Summary, Topical Index, Cassette Avail
  ★★★ Personal Application Preparation Time: Med ISBN: 0-8024-5375-9
  ★ Relationship Building Ldr. Guide Avail.: No Size: 5.50 x 8.50
Subjects: Faith, False Teachers, Pastoral Epistles, 1 & 2 Timothy/Titus
Comments: This study of 1 and 2 Timothy discusses what must be done to stop false teachers. False teaching ruins the hearers, shames its teachers, leads to sin, is contagious, can overturn people's faith, and characterizes the unsaved. Christians must understand the error of false teachers if they are to successfully struggle against them. Each lesson has an introduction, questions focusing on the lesson, and two statements that reflect on the lesson's principles.

Author: MacArthur, John, Jr.　　　　　　　　　　**685**
Series: John MacArthur's
Title: *Believer's Armor, The*
Publisher: Moody Press, 1981

Num. Sess.	Group Time	Num. Pgs.	Avg. Qst.	Price	Audience	Format	Bible Study
12	60-75	230	19	5.99	Mature Chrstn	Book	Topical

Features: Intro to Study, Scrpt Index, Study Overview, Cassette Avail
　★★ Personal Application　Preparation Time: Med　ISBN: 0-8024-5092-X
　★ Relationship Building　Ldr. Guide Avail.: No　Size: 5.50 x 8.50
Subjects: Ephesians, Satan
Comments: This study describes every piece of the believer's armor. Participants will explore the Apostle Paul's teaching that Christians who live as believers should will be severly tempted. Paul concludes Ephesians with an impressive list of armor to protect believers in the battle against Satan. Each lesson has an introduction, the lesson, questions about the lesson, and two statements that reflect on the lesson's principles. Optional companion tape messages are available.

Author: MacArthur, John, Jr.　　　　　　　　　　**686**
Series: John MacArthur's
Title: *Believer's Life in Christ, The*
Publisher: Moody Press, 1989

Num. Sess.	Group Time	Num. Pgs.	Avg. Qst.	Price	Audience	Format	Bible Study
8	45-60	144	18	5.99	New Christian	Book	Topical

Features: Intro to Study, Scrpt Index, Study Overview, Summary, Topical Index, Cassette Avail
　★★★ Personal Application　Preparation Time: Med　ISBN: 0-8024-5382-1
　★ Relationship Building　Ldr. Guide Avail.: No　Size: 5.50 x 8.50
Subjects: Ephesians, Jesus: Life/Teaching
Comments: The eight chapters of this study of Ephesians examine the mystery of the Church; redemption through Christ's blood; divine, guaranteed promises; resources in Christ; coming alive in Christ; and a two-lesson study of the body formed in eternity past. Each lesson has an introduction, questions focusing on the lesson, and two statements that reflect on the lesson's principles. Optional companion tape messages are available.

Author: MacArthur, John, Jr.　　　　　　　　　　**687**
Series: John MacArthur's
Title: *Believer's Privileges, The*
Publisher: Moody Press, 1990

Num. Sess.	Group Time	Num. Pgs.	Avg. Qst.	Price	Audience	Format	Bible Study
6	45-60	105	17	4.99	New Christian	Book	Topical

Features: Intro to Study, Scrpt Index, Study Overview, Summary, Topical Index, Cassette Avail
　★★★ Personal Application　Preparation Time: Med　ISBN: 0-8024-5335-X
　★ Relationship Building　Ldr. Guide Avail.: No　Size: 5.50 x 8.50
Subjects: Forgiveness, Holy Spirit, 1 & 2 Peter
Comments: This study of 1 Peter concerns the eternal benefits of becoming a Christian. It covers forgiveness of sins; acceptance by God, and the gift of the Holy Spirit. Participants will learn how a child of God receives union with, dominion with, possession by, illumination in, and compassion for, the Lord. Each lesson has an introduction, questions focusing on the lesson, and two statements that reflect on the lesson's principles. Optional companion tape messages are available.

Author: MacArthur, John, Jr.　　　　　　　　　　**688**
Series: John MacArthur's
Title: *Benefiting from Life's Trials*
Publisher: Moody Press, 1988

Num. Sess.	Group Time	Num. Pgs.	Avg. Qst.	Price	Audience	Format	Bible Study
6	60-75	107	17	4.99	Mature Chrstn	Book	Topical

Features: Intro to Study, Scrpt Index, Study Overview, Topical Index, Cassette Avail
　★★ Personal Application　Preparation Time: Med　ISBN: 0-8024-5356-2
　★ Relationship Building　Ldr. Guide Avail.: No　Size: 5.50 x 8.50
Subjects: Faith, James, Joy, Suffering
Comments: This verse-by-verse study of James 1:2-18 offers a deeper understanding of why and how participants face trials, and how they actually benefit from them. As they study, participants should ask: Do I endure trials and hardships without losing faith? Do I keep a joyous attitude, a submissive will, and a contented spirit? Each lesson consists of an introduction, questions focusing on the lesson, and two statements that reflect on the lesson's principles. Optional companion tape messages are available.

Author: MacArthur, John, Jr.　　　　　　　　　　**689**
Series:
Title: *Body Dynamics*
Publisher: Victor Books, 1982

Num. Sess.	Group Time	Num. Pgs.	Avg. Qst.	Price	Audience	Format	Bible Study
13	60-90	155	N/A	7.99	Mature Chrstn	Book	Topical

Features: Intro to Study
　★★★ Personal Application　Preparation Time: Med　ISBN: 0-88207-360-5
　★★★ Relationship Building　Ldr. Guide Avail.: Yes　Size: 5.50 x 8.0
Subjects: Church Life, Theology
Comments: This study presents a basic and definitive examination of the personality and properties of a truly effective church body. Participants will find answers to: "What is this 'body' concept?" "Who is part of the body?" "How does the body grow?" "What are the responsibilities of each member of the body?" "Will the concept work in your local church?" and "How is the individual involved?" A leader's guide with transparency masters is available.

Author: MacArthur, John, Jr.　　　　　　　　　　**690**
Series: John MacArthur's
Title: *Caring for Widows*
Publisher: Moody Press, 1991

Num. Sess.	Group Time	Num. Pgs.	Avg. Qst.	Price	Audience	Format	Bible Study
4	45-60	56	18	4.99	New Christian	Book	Topical

Features: Intro to Study, Study Overview, Summary, Full Scrpt Printed, Topical Index
　★★★ Personal Application　Preparation Time: Med　ISBN: 0-8024-5326-0
　★ Relationship Building　Ldr. Guide Avail.: No　Size: 5.50 x 8.50
Subjects: Caring, Women's Issues, 1 & 2 Timothy/Titus
Comments: This study of 1 Timothy considers a widow's special place in God's family. As part of His church, participants are called by God to make sure widows are cared for, supported, and encouraged to serve. The study helps participants understand widows' needs and roles. Each lesson has an introduction, questions focusing on the lesson, and two statements that reflect on the lesson's principles. Optional companion tape messages are available.

Author: MacArthur, John, Jr.   **691**
Series: John MacArthur's
Title: *Chosen for Eternity: A Study of Election*
Publisher: Moody Press, 1989

Num. Sess.	Group Time	Num. Pgs.	Avg. Qst.	Price	Audience	Format	Bible Study
4	45-60	70	14	4.25	New Christian	Book	Topical

Features: Intro to Study, Scrpt Index, Study Overview, Summary, Topical Index, Cassette Avail
★★★ Personal Application   Preparation Time: Med   ISBN: 0-8024-5386-4
★ Relationship Building   Ldr. Guide Avail.: No   Size: 5.50 x 8.50
Subjects: Holy Spirit, Theology, 1 & 2 Peter
Comments: This study of 1 Peter helps participants understand the richness of election by God. It helps them learn how the triune God chooses us by "foreknowledge of God the Father" via "the sanctifying work of the Spirit," in order that we "obey Christ and be sprinkled with His blood." Each lesson has an introduction, questions focusing on the lesson, and two statements that reflect on the lesson's principles. Optional companion tape messages are available.

Author: MacArthur, John, Jr.   **692**
Series: John MacArthur's
Title: *Christian and Government, The*
Publisher: Moody Press, 1986

Num. Sess.	Group Time	Num. Pgs.	Avg. Qst.	Price	Audience	Format	Bible Study
5	45-60	91	20	4.25	New Christian	Book	Topical

Features: Intro to Study, Scrpt Index, Study Overview, Summary, Cassette Avail
★★★ Personal Application   Preparation Time: Med   ISBN: 0-8024-5095-4
★ Relationship Building   Ldr. Guide Avail.: No   Size: 5.50 x 8.50
Subjects: Money, Romans, Social Issues
Comments: This study of Romans deals with Christians' response to government, a key issue. It concludes the following: government is decreed by God; to resist is to resist an institution of God; rebellion will be punished; governments are to resist evil and promote good; and rulers are empowered to inflict severe punishment. It also discusses Christians' responsibility to pay taxes. Each lesson has an introduction, questions focusing on the lesson, and two statements that reflect on the lesson's principles.

Author: MacArthur, John, Jr.   **693**
Series: John MacArthur's
Title: *Church Leadership: A Study of Elders and Deacons*
Publisher: Moody Press, 1989

Num. Sess.	Group Time	Num. Pgs.	Avg. Qst.	Price	Audience	Format	Bible Study
9	45-60	171	22	5.99	New Christian	Book	Topical

Features: Intro to Study, Scrpt Index, Study Overview, Summary, Topical Index, Cassette Avail
★★★ Personal Application   Preparation Time: Med   ISBN: 0-8024-5384-8
★ Relationship Building   Ldr. Guide Avail.: No   Size: 5.50 x 8.50
Subjects: Church Life, Leadership, Pastoral Epistles, 1 & 2 Timothy/Titus
Comments: This study of 1 Timothy brings the character qualities God requires of spiritual leaders in the local church into sharp focus. It examines the offices of deacon and elder, highlighting moral, spiritual, ethical, and familial requirements. And it points out the urgent need to follow the guidelines. Each lesson has an introduction, questions focusing on the lesson, and two statements that reflect on the lesson's principles. Optional companion tape messages are available.

Author: MacArthur, John, Jr.   **694**
Series: John MacArthur's
Title: *Confession of Sin*
Publisher: Moody Press, 1986

Num. Sess.	Group Time	Num. Pgs.	Avg. Qst.	Price	Audience	Format	Bible Study
4	45-60	77	27	4.25	New Christian	Book	Topical

Features: Intro to Study, Study Overview, Summary, Cassette Avail
★★★ Personal Application   Preparation Time: Med   ISBN: 0-8024-5093-8
★ Relationship Building   Ldr. Guide Avail.: No   Size: 5.50 x 8.50
Subjects: Forgiveness, Repentance, Sexual Issues, 1, 2 & 3 John/Jude
Comments: In this study of 1 John, participants are offered a proper perspective of Christ, sin, and God. Christians realize the existence of sin in their lives, and their need for mercy and forgiveness. The study ends with Psalm 51, in which David confesses his sin of adultery, realizing that sin deserves judgment. Each lesson has an introduction, questions focusing on the lesson, and two statements that reflect on the lesson's principles.

Author: MacArthur, John, Jr.   **695**
Series: John MacArthur's
Title: *Convicting Ministry of the Holy Spirit, The*
Publisher: Moody Press, 1989

Num. Sess.	Group Time	Num. Pgs.	Avg. Qst.	Price	Audience	Format	Bible Study
4	45-60	63	14	4.25	New Christian	Book	Topical

Features: Intro to Study, Scrpt Index, Study Overview, Summary, Topical Index, Cassette Avail
★★★ Personal Application   Preparation Time: Med   ISBN: 0-8024-5374-0
★ Relationship Building   Ldr. Guide Avail.: No   Size: 5.50 x 8.50
Subjects: Holy Spirit, John
Comments: This study of John discusses the ministry of the Holy Spirit as it confronts the world's hatred; He's the only One who can break that hatred. The Spirit's ministry involves convicting people of sin and witnessing to the Person of Jesus Christ. The study shows that the Holy Spirit is the vehicle through which God gave the world His Word. Each lesson has an introduction, questions focusing on the lesson, and two statements that reflect on the lesson's principles.

Author: MacArthur, John, Jr.   **696**
Series: John MacArthur's
Title: *Danger of Loving Money, The*
Publisher: Moody Press, 1989

Num. Sess.	Group Time	Num. Pgs.	Avg. Qst.	Price	Audience	Format	Bible Study
8	45-60	157	21	5.99	New Christian	Book	Topical

Features: Intro to Study, Scrpt Index, Study Overview, Summary, Cassette Avail
★★★ Personal Application   Preparation Time: Med   ISBN: 0-8024-5380-5
★ Relationship Building   Ldr. Guide Avail.: No   Size: 5.50 x 8.50
Subjects: Ethics, James, Money, 1 & 2 Timothy/Titus
Comments: This study of 1 Timothy and James concerns Christians' attitudes toward money and calls for a return to the biblical view. It contrasts wrongful extremes—finances themselves as evil and hope in the "uncertainty of riches"—and calls for a balanced hope in God, who richly meets needs. Each lesson has an introduction, questions focusing on the lesson, and two statements that reflect on the lesson's principles. Optional companion tape messages are available.

Author: MacArthur, John, Jr. 697
Series: John MacArthur's
Title: *Elements of True Prayer*
Publisher: Moody Press, 1988

Num. Sess.	Group Time	Num. Pgs.	Avg. Qst.	Price	Audience	Format	Bible Study
4	45-60	80	17	4.25	New Christian	Book	Topical

Features: Intro to Study, Scrpt Index, Study Overview, Summary, Topical Index, Cassette Avail
★★★ Personal Application   Preparation Time: Med   ISBN: 0-8024-5367-8
★ Relationship Building   Ldr. Guide Avail.: No   Size: 5.50 x 8.50
Subjects: Daniel, Major Prophets, Prayer
Comments: This study of Daniel examines the prophet's intercessory prayer for Jerusalem, one of the Bible's greatest model prayers. In it Daniel associates himself with the sin of his people, confesses that sin, acknowledges God's sovereignty and love, and asks God for mercy. This study is designed to help participants understand and apply these prayer elements. Each lesson has an introduction, questions focusing on the lesson, and two statements that reflect on the lesson's principles.

Author: MacArthur, John, Jr. 698
Series: John MacArthur's
Title: *Eternal Security*
Publisher: Moody Press, 1989

Num. Sess.	Group Time	Num. Pgs.	Avg. Qst.	Price	Audience	Format	Bible Study
4	45-60	77	18	4.99	New Christian	Book	Topical

Features: Intro to Study, Scrpt Index, Study Overview, Summary, Topical Index, Cassette Avail
★★★ Personal Application   Preparation Time: Med   ISBN: 0-8024-5373-2
★ Relationship Building   Ldr. Guide Avail.: No   Size: 5.50 x 8.50
Subjects: Grace, Joy, Romans, Theology
Comments: This study of Romans discusses several topics: believers' peace with God; standing in grace; hope of glory; possession of love; certainty of deliverance; and joy in God. It tests and affirms God's assurances for Christians. Each lesson has an introduction, questions focusing on the lesson, and two statements that reflect on the lesson's principles. Optional companion tape messages are available.

Author: MacArthur, John, Jr. 699
Series: John MacArthur's
Title: *Exposing False Spiritual Leaders*
Publisher: Moody Press, 1986

Num. Sess.	Group Time	Num. Pgs.	Avg. Qst.	Price	Audience	Format	Bible Study
6	45-60	124	16	4.25	New Christian	Book	Topical

Features: Intro to Study, Scrpt Index, Study Overview, Summary, Topical Index, Cassette Avail
★★★ Personal Application   Preparation Time: Med   ISBN: 0-8024-5345-7
★ Relationship Building   Ldr. Guide Avail.: No   Size: 5.50 x 8.50
Subjects: Cults, False Teachers, Matthew
Comments: This study of Matthew 23 covers Jesus' condemnation of false spiritual leaders, a condemnation which is as valid today as when Jesus made it. Participants will learn the characteristics of false leaders, and why they are cursed by God. This study is especially pertinent in light of the large number of contemporary cults and pseudo-Christian groups. Each lesson has an introduction, questions focusing on the lesson, and two statements that reflect on the lesson's principles.

Author: MacArthur, John, Jr. 700
Series: John MacArthur's
Title: *Fulfilled Family, The*
Publisher: Moody Press, 1981

Num. Sess.	Group Time	Num. Pgs.	Avg. Qst.	Price	Audience	Format	Bible Study
8	60-75	146	19	5.99	Mature Chrstn	Book	Topical

Features: Intro to Study, Scrpt Index, Study Overview, Cassette Avail
★★ Personal Application   Preparation Time: Med   ISBN: 0-8024-5318-X
★ Relationship Building   Ldr. Guide Avail.: No   Size: 5.50 x 8.50
Subjects: Ephesians, Family, Marriage, Relationships
Comments: This verse-by-verse study of Ephesians 5:21-6:4 clearly presents the divine pattern of authority, submission, and godly love that should guide family relationships. Participants will learn how to understand and apply that pattern to achieve more meaningful, rewarding, and fulfilling family life. Preceding each lesson is an introduction, and succeeding each are questions and summarizing statements. Optional companion tape messages are available.

Author: MacArthur, John, Jr. 701
Series: John MacArthur's
Title: *God, Satan, and Angels*
Publisher: Moody Press, 1989

Num. Sess.	Group Time	Num. Pgs.	Avg. Qst.	Price	Audience	Format	Bible Study
9	45-60	190	17	5.99	New Christian	Book	Topical

Features: Intro to Study, Scrpt Index, Study Overview, Summary, Topical Index, Cassette Avail
★★★ Personal Application   Preparation Time: Med   ISBN: 0-8024-5385-6
★ Relationship Building   Ldr. Guide Avail.: No   Size: 5.50 x 8.50
Subjects: Angels, God, Satan
Comments: This study of selected scriptures focuses on God: His existence; who He is; and what He's like. Then it focuses on Satan, dealing with the rebellion of his angels, who he is, what he's like, and how he operates. Finally, it examines God's angels, their existence, their origins, nature, and ministry. Each lesson has an introduction, questions focusing on the lesson, and two statements that reflect on the lesson's principles. Optional companion tape messages are available.

Author: MacArthur, John, Jr. 702
Series: John MacArthur's
Title: *God's High Calling for Women*
Publisher: Moody Press, 1987

Num. Sess.	Group Time	Num. Pgs.	Avg. Qst.	Price	Audience	Format	Bible Study
4	45-60	57	13	4.99	Mature Chrstn	Book	Topical

Features: Intro to Study, Scrpt Index, Study Overview, Topical Index, Cassette Avail
★★ Personal Application   Preparation Time: Med   ISBN: 0-8024-5308-2
★ Relationship Building   Ldr. Guide Avail.: No   Size: 5.50 x 8.50
Subjects: Theology, Women's Issues, 1 & 2 Timothy/Titus
Comments: This verse-by-verse study of 1 Timothy 2:9-15 covers major concerns for women in the church as outlined by the Apostle Paul: attitude, appearance, testimony, roles, design, and contribution. Each lesson opens with an introduction, followed by the lesson itself, questions focusing on the facts, and two statements that reflect on the lesson's principles. Optional companion tape messages are available.

Author: MacArthur, John, Jr.   703
Series: John MacArthur's
Title: *God's Plan for Giving*
Publisher: Moody Press, 1982

Num. Sess.	Group Time	Num. Pgs.	Avg. Qst.	Price	Audience	Format	Bible Study
6	60-75	100	16	4.99	Mature Chrstn	Book	Topical

Features: Intro to Study, Scrpt Index, Study Overview, Cassette Avail
★★ Personal Application   Preparation Time: Med   ISBN: 0-8024-5107-1
★ Relationship Building   Ldr. Guide Avail.: No   Size: 5.50 x 8.50
Subjects: Christian Living, Money, Stewardship
Comments: This study helps participants discover what the Bible says about giving. It says that people spend their lives making money so they can afford to live. Money itself is amoral; it becomes good or bad depending on how people use it. Each lesson includes an introduction, follow-up questions, and concluding statements. Optional companion tape messages are available.

Author: MacArthur, John, Jr.   704
Series: John MacArthur's
Title: *Heaven*
Publisher: Moody Press, 1988

Num. Sess.	Group Time	Num. Pgs.	Avg. Qst.	Price	Audience	Format	Bible Study
8	45-60	128	16	5.99	New Christian	Book	Topical

Features: Intro to Study, Scrpt Index, Study Overview, Summary, Topical Index
★★★ Personal Application   Preparation Time: Med   ISBN: 0-8024-5383-X
★ Relationship Building   Ldr. Guide Avail.: No   Size: 5.50 x 8.50
Subjects: Heaven/Hell
Comments: This study of selected scriptures presents a comprehensive viewpoint of Heaven. It shows what Heaven is; where it is; what it is like; what people will be like there; how they'll relate with one another; what God will be like; and what saints will do. Each lesson has an introduction, questions focusing on the lesson, and two statements that reflect on the lesson's principles. Optional companion tape messages are available.

Author: MacArthur, John, Jr.   705
Series: John MacArthur's
Title: *How to Study The Bible*
Publisher: Moody Press, 1982

Num. Sess.	Group Time	Num. Pgs.	Avg. Qst.	Price	Audience	Format	Bible Study
4	60-75	82	27	4.99	New Christian	Book	Topical

Features: Intro to Leading a Study, Scrpt Index, Study Overview, Cassette Avail
★★ Personal Application   Preparation Time: Med   ISBN: 0-8024-5105-5
★ Relationship Building   Ldr. Guide Avail.: No   Size: 5.50 x 8.50
Subjects: Bible Study, Small Group Resource
Comments: This study examines not only how to study the Bible, but why Bible study is so important in every believer's life. Participants will learn that the Bible offers the Word of life, as well as hope in death. Each lesson consists of an introduction, the lesson, questions focusing on the facts, and two statements that reflect on the lesson's principles. Optional companion tape messages are available.

Author: MacArthur, John, Jr.   706
Series: John MacArthur's
Title: *Jesus on Trial*
Publisher: Moody Press, 1988

Num. Sess.	Group Time	Num. Pgs.	Avg. Qst.	Price	Audience	Format	Bible Study
8	45-60	159	21	5.25	New Christian	Book	Charctr

Features: Intro to Study, Scrpt Index, Study Overview, Summary, Topical Index, Cassette Avail
★★★ Personal Application   Preparation Time: Med   ISBN: 0-8024-5355-4
★ Relationship Building   Ldr. Guide Avail.: No   Size: 5.50 x 8.50
Subjects: Jesus: Life/Teaching, Matthew
Comments: This study of Matthew portrays Jesus, a "man of sorrows," as One who knew what it was to suffer. It details His greatest ordeal, betrayed by a disciple and abandoned by others, mocked and beaten in an unjust trial. It's a great study to unveil Jesus' true character. Each lesson has an introduction, questions focusing on the lesson, and two statements that reflect on the lesson's principles. Optional companion tape messages are available.

Author: MacArthur, John, Jr.   707
Series: John MacArthur's
Title: *Keys to Effective Evangelism*
Publisher: Moody Press, 1988

Num. Sess.	Group Time	Num. Pgs.	Avg. Qst.	Price	Audience	Format	Bible Study
4	45-60	83	18	4.25	New Christian	Book	Topical

Features: Intro to Study, Scrpt Index, Study Overview, Summary, Topical Index, Cassette Avail
★★★ Personal Application   Preparation Time: Med   ISBN: 0-8024-5361-9
★ Relationship Building   Ldr. Guide Avail.: No   Size: 5.50 x 8.50
Subjects: Acts, Church Life, Evangelism
Comments: This study of Acts shows participants that after Christ's ascension, the disciples didn't let anything stop them from evangelizing—not even beatings or imprisonment. The study lays out the pattern of evangelism set by the early Church, and it helps participants improve their outreach efforts. Each lesson has an introduction, questions focusing on the lesson, and two statements that reflect on the lesson's principles. Optional companion tape messages are available.

Author: MacArthur, John, Jr.   708
Series: John MacArthur's
Title: *Living Sacrifice, A*
Publisher: Moody Press, 1987

Num. Sess.	Group Time	Num. Pgs.	Avg. Qst.	Price	Audience	Format	Bible Study
4	45-60	75	15	4.25	New Christian	Book	Topical

Features: Intro to Study, Scrpt Index, Study Overview, Summary, Topical Index, Cassette Avail
★★★ Personal Application   Preparation Time: Med   ISBN: 0-8024-5354-6
★ Relationship Building   Ldr. Guide Avail.: No   Size: 5.50 x 8.50
Subjects: Romans, Spiritual Gifts, Worship
Comments: This study of Romans shows participants that it is Christians' spiritual service of worship to present their bodies as living and holy sacrifices, acceptable to God. It covers the supreme act of spiritual worship and the ministry of spiritual gifts. Each lesson has an introduction, questions focusing on the lesson, and two statements that reflect on the lesson's principles. Optional companion tape messages are available.

Author: MacArthur, John, Jr.　　　　　　　**709**
Series: John MacArthur's
Title: *Love Not the World*
Publisher: Moody Press, 1986

Num. Sess.	Group Time	Num. Pgs.	Avg. Qst.	Price	Audience	Format	Bible Study
4	45-60	69	23	4.25	New Christian	Book	Topical

Features: Intro to Study, Scrpt Index, Study Overview, Summary, Cassette Avail

★★★ Personal Application　Preparation Time: Med　ISBN: 0-8024-5098-9
★ Relationship Building　Ldr. Guide Avail.: No　Size: 5.50 x 8.50

Subjects: 1, 2 & 3 John/Jude
Comments: This study of 1 John describes appropriate behavior for believers, as well as reasons not to love by the world's standards. Participants learn that the saying "Actions speak louder than words" is especially true for Christians; that people who truly love God will behave accordingly, avoiding the world's pitfalls. Each lesson has an introduction, questions focusing on the lesson, and two statements that reflect on the lesson's principles.

Author: MacArthur, John, Jr.　　　　　　　**710**
Series: John MacArthur's
Title: *Making Disciples*
Publisher: Moody Press, 1991

Num. Sess.	Group Time	Num. Pgs.	Avg. Qst.	Price	Audience	Format	Bible Study
6	45-60	78	16	4.99	New Christian	Book	Topical

Features: Intro to Study, Scrpt Index, Study Overview, Summary, Topical Index, Cassette Avail

★★★ Personal Application　Preparation Time: Med　ISBN: 0-8024-5379-1
★ Relationship Building　Ldr. Guide Avail.: No　Size: 5.50 x 8.50

Subjects: Bible Personalities, Discipleship
Comments: This study uses selected scriptures to challenge participants seeking their ultimate goal—becoming positive witnesses for Christ—and provides a useful tool for the task. Through the study, Christians understand how they can be used to communicate God's truth to others. It uses Zacchaeus and Jonah as examples of different but effective witnesses. Each lesson has an introduction, questions focusing on the lesson, and two statements that reflect on the lesson's principles.

Author: MacArthur, John, Jr.　　　　　　　**711**
Series: John MacArthur's
Title: *Marks of a Healthy Church*
Publisher: Moody Press, 1990

Num. Sess.	Group Time	Num. Pgs.	Avg. Qst.	Price	Audience	Format	Bible Study
8	45-60	151	21	5.99	New Christian	Book	Topical

Features: Intro to Study, Scrpt Index, Study Overview, Summary, Topical Index, Cassette Avail

★★★ Personal Application　Preparation Time: Med　ISBN: 0-8024-5338-4
★ Relationship Building　Ldr. Guide Avail.: No　Size: 5.50 x 8.50

Subjects: Church Life, Leadership
Comments: This study uses selected scriptures to show participants how the modern church should comply with Christ's mandate for church conduct. It also focuses on their roles as leaders and workers trying to make a difference in their local congregations. It offers six necessary factors for effective church leadership, including specific guidelines for Christian men and women. Each lesson has an introduction, questions focusing on the lesson, and two statements that reflect on the lesson's principles.

Author: MacArthur, John, Jr.　　　　　　　**712**
Series: John MacArthur's
Title: *On Divorce*
Publisher: Moody Press, 1983

Num. Sess.	Group Time	Num. Pgs.	Avg. Qst.	Price	Audience	Format	Bible Study
6	60-75	103	28	4.99	Mature Chrstn	Book	Topical

Features: Intro to Study, Scrpt Index, Study Overview, Cassette Avail

★★ Personal Application　Preparation Time: Med　ISBN: 0-8024-5111-X
★ Relationship Building　Ldr. Guide Avail.: No　Size: 5.50 x 8.50

Subjects: Divorce, Marriage, Matthew
Comments: This verse-by-verse study of Matthew 19:1-12 takes a thorough, practical look at Jesus' teachings on divorce. It also covers Paul's commentary on divorce, as written in 1 Corinthians 7:1-40. Each lesson includes an introduction, questions focusing on the lesson, and two statements that summarize the lesson's principles. Optional companion tape messages are available.

Author: MacArthur, John, Jr.　　　　　　　**713**
Series: John MacArthur's
Title: *Parables of the Kingdom, The*
Publisher: Moody Press, 1984

Num. Sess.	Group Time	Num. Pgs.	Avg. Qst.	Price	Audience	Format	Bible Study
8	60-75	134	23	5.99	Mature Chrstn	Book	Topical

Features: Intro to Study, Scrpt Index, Study Overview, Cassette Avail

★★ Personal Application　Preparation Time: Med　ISBN: 0-8024-5112-8
★ Relationship Building　Ldr. Guide Avail.: No　Size: 5.50 x 8.50

Subjects: Matthew, Parables
Comments: This study of Matthew 13:1-52 concerns seven parables in which Jesus describes how and what believers are to do during the interim period between His first and second appearances on earth. Each lesson opens with an introduction, followed by the lesson itself, questions on the lesson, and two statements that reflect on the lesson's principles. Optional companion tape messages are available.

Author: MacArthur, John, Jr.　　　　　　　**714**
Series: John MacArthur's
Title: *Resurrection of Jesus Christ, The*
Publisher: Moody Press, 1989

Num. Sess.	Group Time	Num. Pgs.	Avg. Qst.	Price	Audience	Format	Bible Study
5	45-60	101	17	4.25	New Christian	Book	Topical

Features: Intro to Study, Scrpt Index, Study Overview, Summary, Topical Index, Cassette Avail

★★★ Personal Application　Preparation Time: Med　ISBN: 0-8024-5376-7
★ Relationship Building　Ldr. Guide Avail.: No　Size: 5.50 x 8.50

Subjects: Jesus: Life/Teaching, Matthew
Comments: This study of Matthew first covers the amazing burial of Christ, itself a supernatural event. Then, it views the Resurrection through the attitudes and emotions of the women who faithfully attended His crucifixion and burial. It finally looks at the bribing of the Roman soldiers by Jewish leaders, and how the subsequent lie proves the reality of the Resurrection. Each lesson has an introduction, questions focusing on the lesson, and two statements that reflect on the lesson's principles.

Author: MacArthur, John, Jr.　　　　　　**715**
Series: John MacArthur's
Title: *Rise and Fall of World Powers, The*
Publisher: Moody Press, 1989

Num. Sess.	Group Time	Num. Pgs.	Avg. Qst.	Price	Audience	Format	Bible Study
6	45-60	118	21	4.99	New Christian	Book	Topical

Features: Intro to Study, Scrpt Index, Study Overview, Summary, Topical Index, Cassette Avail
★★★Personal Application　Preparation Time: Med　ISBN: 0-8024-5377-5
　★Relationship Building　Ldr. Guide Avail.: No　Size: 5.50 x 8.50
Subjects: Daniel, Major Prophets
Comments: This study of Daniel first discusses the prophet's interpretation of Nebuchadnezzar's dream concerning a huge statue of gold, silver, bronze, iron, and clay. It next deals with Nebuchadnezzar's humiliation and restoration, then follows the events surrounding mysterious writing that appeared on the wall during Belshazzar's great feast. Each lesson has an introduction, questions focusing on the lesson, and two statements that reflect on the lesson's principles.

Author: MacArthur, John, Jr.　　　　　　**716**
Series: John MacArthur's
Title: *Signs of Christ's Return*
Publisher: Moody Press, 1987

Num. Sess.	Group Time	Num. Pgs.	Avg. Qst.	Price	Audience	Format	Bible Study
15	60-75	240	14	6.99	Mature Chrstn	Book	Topical

Features: Intro to Study, Scrpt Index, Study Overview, Topical Index, Cassette Avail
★★Personal Application　Preparation Time: Med　ISBN: 0-8024-5311-2
　★Relationship Building　Ldr. Guide Avail.: No　Size: 5.50 x 8.50
Subjects: Eschatology, Matthew
Comments: In this verse-by-verse study of Matthew 24-25, participants see the disciples' eagerness for details of Christ's triumphant return. The disciples wanted to know when and how. This study covers signs that will precede His return, outlining the calamity, confusion, and corruption. It also discusses the results Christ's return will have on people and nations. Participants are challenged to "be ready," just as Christ called His disciples to be constantly ready and faithful. A scripture index is provided.

Author: MacArthur, John, Jr.　　　　　　**717**
Series: John MacArthur's
Title: *Spiritual Gifts*
Publisher: Moody Press, 1983

Num. Sess.	Group Time	Num. Pgs.	Avg. Qst.	Price	Audience	Format	Bible Study
14	60-75	270	22	6.0	Mature Chrstn	Book	Topical

Features: Intro to Study, Scrpt Index, Study Overview, Cassette Avail
★★Personal Application　Preparation Time: Med　ISBN: 0-8024-5121-7
　★Relationship Building　Ldr. Guide Avail.: No　Size: 5.50 x 8.50
Subjects: Spiritual Gifts, 1 Corinthians
Comments: This verse-by-verse study of 1 Corinthians 12 provides participants with a thorough understanding of the various kinds of gifts, how to use them, and the characteristics of each, because each believer's gifts must be used to glorify God. Each lesson includes an introduction, follow-up questions, and concluding statements. Optional companion tape messages are available.

Author: MacArthur, John, Jr.　　　　　　**718**
Series: John MacArthur's
Title: *Spiritual Warfare: Fighting to Win*
Publisher: Moody Press, 1988

Num. Sess.	Group Time	Num. Pgs.	Avg. Qst.	Price	Audience	Format	Bible Study
4	45-60	75	10	4.25	Mature Chrstn	Book	Topical

Features: Intro to Study, Scrpt Index, Study Overview, Topical Index, Cassette Avail
★★Personal Application　Preparation Time: Med　ISBN: 0-8024-5368-6
　★Relationship Building　Ldr. Guide Avail.: No　Size: 5.50 x 8.50
Subjects: Accountability, Church Life, Pastoral Epistles, Victorious Living, 1 & 2 Timothy/Titus
Comments: This study of 1 Timothy explores the spiritual battles believers face. Participants will see why Paul exhorts Timothy to maximum effort. He tells Timothy that in order to be victorious in spiritual warfare, one must understand three things: responsibility to the church, accountability to the Lord, and how to deal with the enemy. Each lesson has an introduction, questions focusing on the lesson, and two statements that reflect on the lesson's principles. Optional companion tape messages are available.

Author: MacArthur, John, Jr.　　　　　　**719**
Series: John MacArthur's
Title: *Transforming Power of Scripture, The*
Publisher: Moody Press, 1989

Num. Sess.	Group Time	Num. Pgs.	Avg. Qst.	Price	Audience	Format	Bible Study
4	45-60	79	18	4.25	New Christian	Book	Topical

Features: Intro to Study, Scrpt Index, Study Overview, Summary, Topical Index, Cassette Avail
★★★Personal Application　Preparation Time: Med　ISBN: 0-8024-5372-4
　★Relationship Building　Ldr. Guide Avail.: No　Size: 5.50 x 8.50
Subjects: Pastoral Epistles, 1 & 2 Timothy/Titus
Comments: This study of 2 Timothy discusses the use of God's Word in salvation, teaching, reproof, correction, and training in righteousness. Participants are shown the nature and transmission of the Scriptures, and gain inspiration from the Bible. Each lesson has an introduction, questions focusing on the lesson, and two statements that reflect on the lesson's principles.

Author: MacArthur, John, Jr.　　　　　　**720**
Series: John MacArthur's
Title: *True Faith*
Publisher: Moody Press, 1989

Num. Sess.	Group Time	Num. Pgs.	Avg. Qst.	Price	Audience	Format	Bible Study
8	45-60	141	18	5.25	New Christian	Book	Topical

Features: Intro to Study, Scrpt Index, Study Overview, Summary, Cassette Avail
★★★Personal Application　Preparation Time: Med　ISBN: 0-8024-5381-3
　★Relationship Building　Ldr. Guide Avail.: No　Size: 5.50 x 8.50
Subjects: Faith, James, Obedience
Comments: This study of James is filled with tests that determine whether or not a participant's faith is genuine. It shows that true belief means hearing and obeying God's Word. The study closes with a discussion of dead faith contrasted with living faith. Each lesson has an introduction, questions focusing on the lesson, and two statements that reflect on the lesson's principles. Optional companion tape messages are available.

Author: MacArthur, John, Jr.   **721**
Series: John MacArthur's
Title: *True Worship*
Publisher: Moody Press, 1982

Num. Sess.	Group Time	Num. Pgs.	Avg. Qst.	Price	Audience	Format	Bible Study
8	60-75	111	19	4.99	Mature Chrstn	Book	Topical

Features: Intro to Study, Scrpt Index, Study Overview, Cassette Avail
★★ Personal Application   Preparation Time: Med   ISBN: 0-8024-5108-X
★ Relationship Building   Ldr. Guide Avail.: No   Size: 5.50 x 8.50
Subjects: Church Life, Worship
Comments: This study of selected scriptures helps participants examine their attitude toward worship. This hard-hitting study shows what it means to really worship the living God. Worship is not "getting" something from the sermon or the music, or just "getting" blessed. It is "giving" ourselves to Him. Preceding each lesson is an introduction, and following it are questions and summarizing statements. Optional companion tape messages are available.

Author: MacArthur, John, Jr.   **722**
Series: John MacArthur's
Title: *Walk Worthy*
Publisher: Moody Press, 1989

Num. Sess.	Group Time	Num. Pgs.	Avg. Qst.	Price	Audience	Format	Bible Study
6	45-60	110	18	4.25	New Christian	Book	Topical

Features: Intro to Study, Scrpt Index, Study Overview, Summary, Topical Index, Cassette Avail
★★★ Personal Application   Preparation Time: Med   ISBN: 0-8024-5378-3
★ Relationship Building   Ldr. Guide Avail.: No   Size: 5.50 x 8.50
Subjects: Ephesians, Fruit of the Spirit
Comments: This study of Ephesians discusses the basis of Christians' duty to "walk worthy" of their great blessings. It describes characteristics of that walk—humility, meekness, patience, love, and unity—and offers encouragement to participants. Each lesson has an introduction, questions focusing on the lesson, and two statements that reflect on the lesson's principles.

Author: MacArthur, John, Jr.   **723**
Series: John MacArthur's
Title: *Whatever Happened to the Holy Spirit?*
Publisher: Moody Press, 1989

Num. Sess.	Group Time	Num. Pgs.	Avg. Qst.	Price	Audience	Format	Bible Study
6	45-60	107	16	4.99	New Christian	Book	Topical

Features: Intro to Study, Scrpt Index, Study Overview, Summary, Topical Index
★★★ Personal Application   Preparation Time: Med   ISBN: 0-8024-5387-2
★ Relationship Building   Ldr. Guide Avail.: No   Size: 5.50 x 8.50
Subjects: Charismatic Interest, Galatians, Holy Spirit
Comments: This study uses selected scriptures to unveil the Holy Spirit and examines the tremendous confusion that exists in the modern church regarding the Spirit. It attributes the confusion to the impact of the charismatic movement, an overwrought American emphasis on pragmatism, and a distortion of the Spirit's role in sanctification. Each lesson has an introduction, questions on the lesson, and two statements that reflect on the lesson's principles. Optional companion tape messages are available.

Author: Mahoney, Ralph & JoAnne Sakowsky   **724**
Series: Basic Bible Study Series
Title: *Drawing Closer to God: A Study of Ruth*
Publisher: Aglow, 1982

Num. Sess.	Group Time	Num. Pgs.	Avg. Qst.	Price	Audience	Format	Bible Study
9	75-90	60	24	2.95	New Christian	Workbk	Book

Features: Intro to Study, Prayer Helps, Scrpt Memory Helps, Persnl Study Quest
★★★ Personal Application   Preparation Time: Med   ISBN: 0-930756-72-X
★★★ Relationship Building   Ldr. Guide Avail.: No   Size: 5.25 x 8.25
Subjects: Charismatic Interest, Joy, Ruth
Comments: This nine-week study presents biblical truths that will bring joy to the spirit, and provides a clear pattern of a Christian's growing relationship with the Lord. The book of Ruth contains all the elements of old-fashioned drama: pathos, loyalty, romance, and suspense.

Author: Mallison, John   **725**
Series:
Title: *Growing Christians in Small Groups*
Publisher: Scripture Union Books, 1989

Num. Sess.	Group Time	Num. Pgs.	Avg. Qst.	Price	Audience	Format	Bible Study
17	-	168	N/A	14.95		Book	No

Features: Intro to Study, Drawings, Charts, Index, Appendix
Personal Application   Preparation Time: ISBN: 0-85892-407-2
Relationship Building   Ldr. Guide Avail.:   Size: 9.0 x 8.50
Subjects: Small Group Resource
Comments: This comprehensive study, a resource for clergy and laypeople, is a compilation of the experiences of pioneers and leaders in the small group movement. It describes different types of groups, and offers insights on how to set them up, select leaders, and expand and diversify a church's ministry while avoiding fragmentation. It stresses the need for small groups to function as launching pads for missions. Many creative program ideas are included in the appendices.

Author: Marcum, Walt   **726**
Series: Group's Active Bible Curriculum
Title: *Sex: A Christian Perspective*
Publisher: Group Publishing, 1990

Num. Sess.	Group Time	Num. Pgs.	Avg. Qst.	Price	Audience	Format	Bible Study
4	35-60	46	Vry	6.95	New Christian	Workbk	Topical

Features: Intro to Leading a Study, Intro to Study, Objectives, Study Overview, Ldr's Notes, Drawings, Handouts, Agenda, Publicity Ideas
★★★★ Personal Application   Preparation Time: None   ISBN: 1-559-45206-4
★★★★ Relationship Building   Ldr. Guide Avail.: No   Size: 8.50 x 11.0
Subjects: Teens: Senior High, Teens: Sexuality
Comments: This study provides biblical guidance for senior high students living in a sexually confused world. Its four lessons discuss the Bible's view of premarital sex, sexuality as a gift from God, creative ways to resist sexual pressure, and how to avoid the negative consequences of sex outside marriage. Instructions are easy to follow and provide multiple options for teachers. No student books are required.

Author: Martin, George & Paul Thigpen   **727**
Series: Catholic Bible Study Guide
Title: *Praying the Scriptures: A Guide to Talking with God*
Publisher: Servant Publications, 1990

Num. Sess.	Group Time	Num. Pgs.	Avg. Qst.	Price	Audience	Format	Bible Study
9	60-75	84	10	4.95	Beginner	Workbk	Topical

Features: Intro to Leading a Study, Intro to Study, Prayer Helps, Scrpt Memory Helps, Summary, Charts
★★★★ Personal Application   Preparation Time: Low   ISBN: 0-89283-647-4
★★★ Relationship Building   Ldr. Guide Avail.: No   Size: 5.25 x 8.0
Subjects: God, Prayer
Comments: The focus of this nine-lesson study is not on what Scripture teaches about prayer; rather, it's on passages of Scripture used as the basis for different types of prayer. Its subject matter varies from prayers of thanksgiving to stories of Jesus' life to theological statements of mystery. The approach is the unifying thread—not the subject matter. It's divided into three topical areas: "praying prayers of scripture"; "scriptural conversation starters"; and "praying beyond the words."

Author: Mauney, Jim   **728**
Series: Small Group Bible Studies
Title: *First Peter*
Publisher: Augsburg Publishing House, 1988

Num. Sess.	Group Time	Num. Pgs.	Avg. Qst.	Price	Audience	Format	Bible Study
4	60-75	22	22	0.95	New Christian	Book	Book

Features: Intro to Study, Prayer Helps
★★★ Personal Application   Preparation Time: None   ISBN:
★★★ Relationship Building   Ldr. Guide Avail.: No   Size: 8.50 x 5.50
Subjects: Baptism, Relationships, Suffering, 1 & 2 Peter
Comments: This short, four-session study on 1 Peter helps participants discover the baptismal imagery and understand the rite of baptism and its meaning for their lives. Secondly, it deals with references to suffering. Thirdly, it wrestles with 1 Peter's constant theme of being "sojourners." Finally, it speaks to relationships, then leads participants to redefine and recovenant their own relationships.

Author: Mayhue, Richard   **729**
Series:
Title: *Unmasking Satan*
Publisher: Victor Books, 1988

Num. Sess.	Group Time	Num. Pgs.	Avg. Qst.	Price	Audience	Format	Bible Study
13	60-75	166	N/A	7.99	New Christian	Book	Charctr

Features: Intro to Study, Bibliography
★★★★ Personal Application   Preparation Time: Low   ISBN: 0-89693-603-1
★★★ Relationship Building   Ldr. Guide Avail.: Yes   Size: 5.50 x 8.0
Subjects: Cults, Satan
Comments: This thirteen-week study unmasks the Adversary and exposes the tricks of the temptation trade. For each devilish tactic, biblical countertactics are given to combat schemes of sensationalism, ecumenicism, rationalism, situationalism, individualism, isolationism, pessimism, negativism, defeatism, cultism, egoism, and antagonism. This study can properly arm participants to triumph over Satan. A leader's guide includes reproducible transparency masters.

Author: McAllister, Dawson & Jim Lamb   **730**
Series:
Title: *Discussion Manual for Student Relationships (Volume 2)*
Publisher: Shepherd Ministries, 1976

Num. Sess.	Group Time	Num. Pgs.	Avg. Qst.	Price	Audience	Format	Bible Study
26	45-60	210	Vry	8.75	New Christian	Workbk	Topical

Features: Intro to Study, Drawings, Cartoons
★★★★ Personal Application   Preparation Time: None   ISBN: 0-86606-402-8
★★★ Relationship Building   Ldr. Guide Avail.: Yes   Size: 8.50 x 11.0
Subjects: Teens: Discipleship, Teens: Friends, Teens: Peer Pressure, Teens: Psychology, Teens: Relationships, Teens: Sexuality
Comments: This study, second in a series of three youth-oriented discussion manuals, is appealing and relevant to the needs of youth. Topics covered include glorifying God, discipleship, love, what's not love, dating, peer pressure, making friends, and honesty. The format is discussion-oriented, contemporary, and uses cartoon characters. It can be used one-on-one or with a large or small group. A leader's guide is easy to follow and includes transparency masters.

Author: McAllister, Dawson & Dan Webster   **731**
Series:
Title: *Discussion Manual for Student Relationships (Volume 1)*
Publisher: Shepherd Ministries, 1975

Num. Sess.	Group Time	Num. Pgs.	Avg. Qst.	Price	Audience	Format	Bible Study
26	45-60	174	Vry	8.75	New Christian	Workbk	Topical

Features: Intro to Study, Drawings, Cartoons
★★★★ Personal Application   Preparation Time: None   ISBN: 0-86606-400-1
★★ Relationship Building   Ldr. Guide Avail.: Yes   Size: 8.50 x 11.0
Subjects: Teens: Christian Liv, Teens: Discipleship, Teens: Peer Pressure, Teens: Psychology, Teens: Relationships, Teens: Self-image, Teens: Sexuality
Comments: This study, first in a series of three youth-oriented discussion manuals, is appealing and relevant to the needs of youth. Topics include the Bible, God's will, self-image, loneliness, parents, sex, dating, love, clearing the mind, and temptation. The format promotes discussion, is contemporary, and uses cartoon characters. It can be used one-on-one or with a large or small group. A leader's guide is easy to follow and includes transparency masters.

Author: McAllister, Dawson & Jim Lamb   **732**
Series:
Title: *Discussion Manual for Student Relationships (Volume 3)*
Publisher: Shepherd Ministries, 1978

Num. Sess.	Group Time	Num. Pgs.	Avg. Qst.	Price	Audience	Format	Bible Study
26	45-60	240	Vry	8.75	New Christian	Workbk	Topical

Features: Intro to Study, Drawings, Cartoons
★★★★ Personal Application   Preparation Time: None   ISBN: 0-86606-404-4
★★ Relationship Building   Ldr. Guide Avail.: Yes   Size: 8.50 x 11.0
Subjects: Teens: Christian Liv, Teens:Drugs/Drinking, Teens: Family, Teens: Friends, Teens: Music, Teens: Peer Pressure, Teens: Psychology, Teens: Relationships, Teens: Self-image
Comments: This study, third in a series of three youth-oriented discussion manuals, is appealing and relevant to the needs of youth. Topics include dealing with cliques, breaking up, drugs and alcohol, bad habits, healthy habits, broken homes, guilt, rock music, using time, and death. The format is discussion-oriented, contemporary, and uses cartoon characters. It can be used one-on-one or with a large or small group. A leader's guide is easy to follow and includes transparency masters.

Author: McAllister, Dawson   **733**
Series:
Title: *Discussion Manual for Student Discipleship (Volume 2)*
Publisher: Shepherd Ministries, 1978

Num. Sess.	Group Time	Num. Pgs.	Avg. Qst.	Price	Audience	Format	Bible Study
8	45-60	162	Vry	8.50	New Christian	Workbk	Topical

Features: Intro to Study, Cartoons, Index
★★★★ Personal Application   Preparation Time: None   ISBN: 0-86606-407-9
  ★★ Relationship Building   Ldr. Guide Avail.: No   Size: 8.50 x 11.0
Subjects: Teens: Discipleship, Teens: Youth Life
Comments: This study, second in a two-volume series for new Christians, is formatted in easy-to-use, discussion-oriented, fill-in-the-blank style. Material is presented in a concise, interesting manner and includes cartoon characters. Topics covered include the importance of obedience, learning to obey God, worship, the Christian and the lordship of Christ, the Christian life and endurance, and more. This study of basic biblical principles is designed for new Christians.

Author: McAllister, Dawson & Dan Webster   **734**
Series:
Title: *Discussion Manual for Student Discipleship (Volume 1)*
Publisher: Shepherd Ministries, 1975

Num. Sess.	Group Time	Num. Pgs.	Avg. Qst.	Price	Audience	Format	Bible Study
10	45-60	200	Vry	8.50	New Christian	Workbk	Topical

Features: Intro to Study, Drawings, Cartoons
★★★★ Personal Application   Preparation Time: None   ISBN: 0-86606-406-0
  ★★ Relationship Building   Ldr. Guide Avail.: No   Size: 8.50 x 11.0
Subjects: Teens: Discipleship, Teens: Prayer, Teens: Relationships, Teens: Youth Life
Comments: This study, first in a two-volume series for new Christians, is formatted in easy-to-use, discussion-oriented, fill-in-the-blank style. Material is presented in a concise, interesting manner and includes cartoon characters. Chapter titles include: "Your New Life," "God's Love and Forgiveness," "Your Trials," "Your Quiet Time," "The Word," "Your Prayer," and more. Designed for use in small groups of new Christians, this study presents basic biblical principles in an inductive manner.

Author: McAllister, Dawson   **735**
Series:
Title: *How to Get Along with Your Parents*
Publisher: Word, 1983

Num. Sess.	Group Time	Num. Pgs.	Avg. Qst.	Price	Audience	Format	Bible Study
4	45-60	33	20	1.95	Beginner	Workbk	Topical

Features: Worship Helps, Full Scrpt Printed, Cartoons
★★★ Personal Application   Preparation Time: None   ISBN: 0-8499-8249-9
★★★ Relationship Building   Ldr. Guide Avail.: No   Size: 8.50 x 11.0
Subjects: Teens: Family
Comments: This discussion manual is a tool designed to be used with a four-part videocassette series, which was created by American Student Ministries in conjunction with Western Bible College. The four-part study includes: "Seeing God Through Your Parents' Eyes," "Being a Peacemaker in Your Home," "Learning How to Obey Your Parents," and "Seeing Life from Your Parents' Points of View." Each section ends with discussion questions. The four-part video costs $159.95; the student workbooks (set of five), $9.75.

Author: McAllister, Dawson   **736**
Series:
Title: *Preparing Your Teenager for Sexuality*
Publisher: Shepherd Ministries, 1988

Num. Sess.	Group Time	Num. Pgs.	Avg. Qst.	Price	Audience	Format	Bible Study
6	45-60	61	Vry	6.95	Beginner	Workbk	Topical

Features: Intro to Study, Prayer Helps, Full Scrpt Printed, Drawings
★★★ Personal Application   Preparation Time: None   ISBN: 0-923417-00-1
★★★ Relationship Building   Ldr. Guide Avail.: No   Size: 8.50 x 11.0
Subjects: Parenting, Teens: Ethics, Teens: Peer Pressure, Teens: Relationships, Teens: Sexuality
Comments: This study is a resource to help parents communicate an often neglected topic, sexual morality. Unit 1, directed toward the parent, discusses the need for preparing children for adulthood, the common barriers, and biblical principles to help break down those barriers. Unit 2, directed toward youth, points out God's positive viewpoint on sex. Each son or daughter should have his or her own book. A companion six-part video is available for $189.95.

Author: McAllister, Dawson & Robert S. McGee   **737**
Series:
Title: *Search for Significance: Youth Edition*
Publisher: Shepherd Ministries, 1990

Num. Sess.	Group Time	Num. Pgs.	Avg. Qst.	Price	Audience	Format	Bible Study
7	60-90	147	Vry	7.95	Beginner	Workbk	Topical

Features: Intro to Study, Full Scrpt Printed, Drawings
★★★ Personal Application   Preparation Time: None   ISBN: 0-923417-12-5
  ★★ Relationship Building   Ldr. Guide Avail.: No   Size: 8.50 x 11.0
Subjects: Teens: Emotions, Teens: Psychology, Teens: Relationships, Teens: Self-esteem
Comments: This seven-lesson study on low self-esteem concerns one of the most critical problems students face today. How people perceive themselves affects their abilities and relationships. The study goes beyond theory and offers practical work projects to bring about positive results. Four specific areas covered include: the performance, approval, blame game, and shame trap. The questions are designed to motivate thoughtful discussion and to make significant points clearly understandable and applicable.

Author: McAllister, Dawson   **738**
Series: Word LifeWare Video
Title: *Straight Talk About Friends and Peer Pressure*
Publisher: Word, 1986

Num. Sess.	Group Time	Num. Pgs.	Avg. Qst.	Price	Audience	Format	Bible Study
5	45-75	N/A	10	169.99	Begi nner	Video	Topical

Features: Drawings, Video Study Guide
★★★ Personal Application   Preparation Time: None   ISBN: 8-01-810079-9
★★★ Relationship Building   Ldr. Guide Avail.: No   Size: 10.25 x 12.50
Subjects: Teens: Family, Teens: Friends, Teens: Peer Pressure, Teens: Relationships
Comments: This two-cassette video study helps teens take a hard yet humorous look at themselves and their relationships with other young people. It is divided into five sections, two on friends, and three on peer pressure. Participants will explore the how's and why's of friends, parents, and the world. They are reminded that a relationship with Christ is the foundation for relationships with others. The discussion guide is brief, and no homework or pat answers are given.

Author: McAllister, Dawson — **739**
Series:
Title: *Walk with Christ Through the Resurrection, A*
Publisher: Shepherd Ministries, 1981

Num. Sess.	Group Time	Num. Pgs.	Avg. Qst.	Price	Audience	Format	Bible Study
9	60-75	220	Vry	8.95	Beginner	Workbk	Charctr

Features: Bibliography, Full Scrpt Printed, Drawings
★★★ Personal Application Preparation Time: None ISBN: 0-923417-14-1
★★ Relationship Building Ldr. Guide Avail.: No Size: 8.50 x 11.0
Subjects: Teens: Christian Liv, Teens: Jesus' Life, Teens: Theology
Comments: This nine-part study describes the profound story of God's victory over death, as Jesus Christ arose from the darkness of a tomb to the glory of Heaven. It traces Christ's walk, from the intense agony of the Cross, through the exciting moments of the Resurrection, to the glorious event of the Ascension.

Author: McAllister, Dawson — **740**
Series:
Title: *Walk with Christ to the Cross, A*
Publisher: Shepherd Ministries, 1980

Num. Sess.	Group Time	Num. Pgs.	Avg. Qst.	Price	Audience	Format	Bible Study
12	60-75	270	Vry	8.95	Beginner	Workbk	Charctr

Features: Bibliography, Full Scrpt Printed, Drawings
★★★ Personal Application Preparation Time: None ISBN: 0-923417-09-5
★★ Relationship Building Ldr. Guide Avail.: Yes Size: 8.50 x 11.0
Subjects: Teens: Jesus' Life, Teens: Theology
Comments: This twelve-lesson study takes a close look at the last thirteen hours of Christ's life and the suffering and humiliation He endured. It does so in order to help participants understand why Jesus should be put at the center of people's lives. A six-part video is available for $189.95. Transparency masters are also available for $24.95.

Author: McAllister, Dawson & Rich Miller — **741**
Series:
Title: *Who Are You, God? and What Are You Like?*
Publisher: Shepherd Ministries, 1988

Num. Sess.	Group Time	Num. Pgs.	Avg. Qst.	Price	Audience	Format	Bible Study
11	45-60	112	Vry	7.95	Beginner	Workbk	Topical

Features: Intro to Study, Full Scrpt Printed, Drawings
★★★ Personal Application Preparation Time: None ISBN: 0-923417-11-7
★★ Relationship Building Ldr. Guide Avail.: Yes Size: 8.50 x 11.0
Subjects: Teens: Christian Liv, Teens: Peer Pressure, Teens: Theology
Comments: This study provides biblical answers that stand the test, practical answers that probe the heart, and realistic answers that satisfy youth's search for the identify of God. Titles include "False ideas people have about God"; "Your God must be strong, know everything, be big, be in control, be holy, be loving, be merciful and gracious, and be trustworthy"; and "Your God must be a person." The closing lesson calls for youth to make up their minds about God's place in their lives.

Author: McAllister, Dawson — **742**
Series:
Title: *Who Are You Jesus?*
Publisher: Shepherd Ministries, 1986

Num. Sess.	Group Time	Num. Pgs.	Avg. Qst.	Price	Audience	Format	Bible Study
10	45-60	141	Vry	7.95	Beginner	Workbk	Charctr

Features: Intro to Study, Full Scrpt Printed, Drawings
★★★ Personal Application Preparation Time: None ISBN: 0-923417-05-2
★★ Relationship Building Ldr. Guide Avail.: Yes Size: 8.50 x 11.0
Subjects: Teens: Family, Teens: Friends, Teens: Jesus' Life, Teens: Relationships, Teens: Theology, Teens: Youth Life
Comments: This study introduces Jesus Christ as the answer to one of America's top problems—teenage suicides. It challenges searching students to consider Christ as the provider of purpose, hope, and satisfaction. The format consists of simple, basic, and hard-hitting discussions for which American students are looking.

Author: McAllister, Dawson — **743**
Series:
Title: *You, God, and Your Sexuality*
Publisher: Shepherd Ministries, 1988

Num. Sess.	Group Time	Num. Pgs.	Avg. Qst.	Price	Audience	Format	Bible Study
4	45-60	61	Vry	3.95	Beginner	Workbk	Topical

Features: Intro to Study, Prayer Helps, Full Scrpt Printed, Drawings
★★★ Personal Application Preparation Time: None ISBN: 0-923417-01-X
★★★ Relationship Building Ldr. Guide Avail.: No Size: 8.50 x 11.0
Subjects: Teens: Ethics, Teens: Peer Pressure, Teens: Relationships, Teens: Sexuality
Comments: This study, which helps students understand an often neglected topic—sexual morality—demonstrates God's positive viewpoint on sex. It also helps participants understand the counterfeit being portrayed as love, and offers practical steps to a life of real love. At the conclusion, participants will understand how God protects their dignity, shields them from lust, and guards their future marriage. It provides straight answers about God's view of sex in the context of discussion with others.

Author: McBride, Neil F. — **744**
Series:
Title: *How to Lead Small Groups*
Publisher: NavPress, 1990

Num. Sess.	Group Time	Num. Pgs.	Avg. Qst.	Price	Audience	Format	Bible Study
7	-	141	N/A	5.95		Book	No

Features: Intro to Study
Personal Application Preparation Time: ISBN: 0-89109-303-6
Relationship Building Ldr. Guide Avail.: Size: 5.25 x 8.0
Subjects: Small Group Resource
Comments: This book studies leadership skills for all types of small groups—Bible study, fellowship, task, and support groups—and offers guidance in a step-by-step format. It includes practical exercises to help readers group the critical aspects of small group leadership and dynamics, including: defining your group's purpose; covenanting; understanding group stages; evaluating your group; handling conflict; asking good discussion questions; and stimulating healthy fellowship, sharing, and prayer.

Author: McCann, Michael D. **745**
Series: Standard Bible Studies
Title: *Hebrews*
Publisher: Standard Publishing, 1986

Num. Sess.	Group Time	Num. Pgs.	Avg. Qst.	Price	Audience	Format	Bible Study
13	60-80	61	Vry	3.50	New Christian	Workbk	Book

Features: Intro to Leading a Study, Objectives, Digging Deeper Quest, Drawings, Charts
★★ Personal Application Preparation Time: Low ISBN: 0-87403-191-5
★★ Relationship Building Ldr. Guide Avail.: Yes Size: 8.50 x 11.0
Subjects: Faith, God's Promises, Hebrews
Comments: This thirteen-lesson workbook, companion to David Eubank's and Robert Shannon's study of Hebrews, focuses on main Scripture ideas. Chapter titles include: "Resting on the Promises," "The Balanced Life," and "Faith's Hall of Fame." Each lesson features a main truth and learning goals, and includes a series of questions leading to application. Only the leader in a small group setting needs this companion book.

Author: McCann, Mike, & Hal Stallings **746**
Series: Standard Bible Studies
Title: *Galatians/Ephesians*
Publisher: Standard Publishing, 1987

Num. Sess.	Group Time	Num. Pgs.	Avg. Qst.	Price	Audience	Format	Bible Study
13	60-80	80	Vry	3.50	New Christian	Workbk	Book

Features: Intro to Leading a Study, Objectives, Digging Deeper Quest, Charts
★★ Personal Application Preparation Time: Low ISBN: 0-87403-189-3
★★ Relationship Building Ldr. Guide Avail.: Yes Size: 8.50 x 11.0
Subjects: Christian Living, Ephesians, Galatians, Grace
Comments: This thirteen-lesson workbook, a companion to LeRoy Lawson's study of Galatians and Ephesians, focuses on main Scripture ideas and includes chapter titles like, "The Evidence of Grace," "The Law Is No Flaw," and "Living in Freedom." Each lesson includes an outline, Bible study, and summary and application questions. Only the leader in a small group setting needs this companion book.

Author: McCullough, Donald W. **747**
Series:
Title: *Waking from the American Dream: Growing Through Your Disappointments*
Publisher: InterVarsity, 1988

Num. Sess.	Group Time	Num. Pgs.	Avg. Qst.	Price	Audience	Format	Bible Study
13	60-75	210	5	8.95	Beginner	Book	Topical

Features:
★★★★ Personal Application Preparation Time: Low ISBN: 0-8308-1702-6
★★ Relationship Building Ldr. Guide Avail.: No Size: 5.50 x 8.25
Subjects: Christian Life, Failure, Grief, Joy
Comments: This study proves that "trying harder" doesn't offer a fully satisfying way of life and explains how only a Christian outlook prepares people for dealing with life's joys and disappointments. Topics covered include false gods, the good news of brokenness, beyond positive thinking, and dreaming. Case studies, personal stories, and biblical references encourage those who fight despair and seek comfort. A brief list of questions follows each chapter.

Author: McCullough, Steven **748**
Series: Group's Active Bible Curriculum
Title: *Becoming Responsible*
Publisher: Group Publishing, 1991

Num. Sess.	Group Time	Num. Pgs.	Avg. Qst.	Price	Audience	Format	Bible Study
4	35-60	48	Vry	6.95	New Christian	Workbk	Topical

Features: Intro to Leading a Study, Intro to Study, Objectives, Study Overview, Ldr's Notes, Drawings, Handouts, Agenda, Publicity Ideas
★★★★ Personal Application Preparation Time: None ISBN: 1-559-45109-2
★★★★ Relationship Building Ldr. Guide Avail.: No Size: 8.50 x 11.0
Subjects: Teens: Junior High, Teens: Relationships
Comments: This study helps junior high students discover the importance of being responsible. Its four lessons examine the following topics: how being responsible can build trust in relationships; how it can result in positive ways of gaining independence; learn biblical reasons why youth should submit to proper authority; and how they can grow in faith as they learn the importance of honesty in relationships. Instructions are easy to follow and provide multiple options for teachers. No student books are required.

Author: McDowell, Clyde B. **749**
Series: Lay Action Ministry
Title: *How to Discover Your Spiritual Gifts*
Publisher: Lay Action Ministry Program, 1988

Num. Sess.	Group Time	Num. Pgs.	Avg. Qst.	Price	Audience	Format	Bible Study
12	60-90	112	Vry	5.95	New Christian	Workbk	Topical

Features: Objectives, Prayer Helps, Ldr's Notes
★★★ Personal Application Preparation Time: Low ISBN: 1-555-13016-X
★★ Relationship Building Ldr. Guide Avail.: Yes Size: 5.25 x 8.25
Subjects: Church Life, Service, Spiritual Gifts
Comments: This practical study helps Christians identify who they are in the Body of Christ—and how their spiritual gifts contribute to the ongoing life of the Church. Participants learn how the speaking, serving, and sign gifts differ from their natural talents, and identify the gifts God blesses in their life. They learn which areas of service and ministry match their spiritual gifts. Homework is required.

Author: McDowell, Josh **750**
Series: Video Curriculum Resource
Title: *Evidence for Faith*
Publisher: Word, 1984

Num. Sess.	Group Time	Num. Pgs.	Avg. Qst.	Price	Audience	Format	Bible Study
13	60-75	N/A	Vry	179.99	New Christian	Video	Topical

Features: Prayer Helps, Study Overview, Appendix, Video Study Guide
★★★★ Personal Application Preparation Time: Low ISBN: 8-01-910079-2
★★ Relationship Building Ldr. Guide Avail.: Yes Size: 11.0 x 12.0
Subjects: Apologetics, Christian Life, Faith, God
Comments: This thirteen-session video study addresses uncertainty over the reliability of Scripture. Archaeological discoveries, physical and historical findings, and easy-to-understand proof are quoted to reinforce faith. Participants learn that the Bible is reliable, that God is trustworthy and will meet their basic needs for love, acceptance, and security. The kit includes two audio cassettes, a book, *Unlocking the Secrets of Being Loved, Accepted and Secure,* and a leader's study guide.

Author: McDowell, Josh   **751**
Series: Video Curriculum Resource
Title: *How to Help Your Child Say "No" to Sexual Pressure*
Publisher: Word, 1987

Num. Sess.	Group Time	Num. Pgs.	Avg. Qst.	Price	Audience	Format	Bible Study
8	50-60	N/A	Vry	159.99	Begi nner	Video	Topical

Features: Intro to Leading a Study, Prayer Helps, Study Overview, Publicity Ideas, Book Incl, Video Study Guide
★★★★ Personal Application   Preparation Time: Low   ISBN: 8-01-890079-5
 ★★★ Relationship Building   Ldr. Guide Avail.: Yes   Size: 11.0 x 12.0
Subjects: Parenting, Sexual Issues
Comments: This eight-session video study for parents of preteens and teens is designed to help them provide their children with a Christian understanding of sexuality. This video curriculum kit contains eight video segments on two video cassettes, a leader's guide, a paperback book with the same title as the video, a third video containing a twenty-two-minute promotional program, and an audio cassette of popular Christian music. Each participant should have a copy of the book.

Author: McDowell, Josh   **752**
Series: Video Curriculum Resource
Title: *Let's Talk About Love & Sex*
Publisher: Word, 1988

Num. Sess.	Group Time	Num. Pgs.	Avg. Qst.	Price	Audience	Format	Bible Study
3	45-60	N/A	Vry	39.99	Beginner	Video	Topical

Features: Book Incl
★★★★ Personal Application   Preparation Time: None   ISBN: 8-01-506079-6
★★★★ Relationship Building   Ldr. Guide Avail.: Yes   Size: 7.50 x 10.50
Subjects: Parenting, Teens: Junior High, Teens: Psychology, Teens: Self-image, Teens: Senior High, Teens: Sexuality
Comments: This fast-paced thirty-five-minute video study is designed to be used as a conversation tool by parents, teens, and preteens. It covers three important issues regarding sexuality: forming a healthy self-image, adopting biblical values, and establishing rules and standards; and is a modern approach to presenting traditional values. A companion book, *Love, Dad*, a collection of personal letters, will be eagerly read by teens. A parent instruction guide provides guidelines for conversation.

Author: McDowell, Josh   **753**
Series: Video Curriculum Resource
Title: *No! The Positive Answer*
Publisher: Word, 1987

Num. Sess.	Group Time	Num. Pgs.	Avg. Qst.	Price	Audience	Format	Bible Study
4	45-60	N/A	Vry	79.99	Beginner	Video	Topical

Features: Intro to Leading a Study, Bibliography, Handouts, Publicity Ideas
★★★★ Personal Application   Preparation Time: None   ISBN: 8-01-930079-1
 ★★★ Relationship Building   Ldr. Guide Avail.: Yes   Size: 10.0 x 12.50
Subjects: Teens: Ethics, Teens: Junior High, Teens: Senior High, Teens: Sexuality
Comments: This four-session video study helps young people reject premature sexual involvement, and opt to wait for the relationship God intends for marriage. Teens view hard-hitting, entertaining, musical, dramatic, thought-provoking vignettes designed to help them open up about both problems and solutions in the teen sexual puzzle. They learn to say no in a comfortable, unintimidating, fun environment. The kit includes a video with four twelve- to fifteen-minute segments, and more.

Author: McGee, Robert S.   **754**
Series:
Title: *Search for Significance, The*
Publisher: Rapha Publishing, 1985

Num. Sess.	Group Time	Num. Pgs.	Avg. Qst.	Price	Audience	Format	Bible Study
25	60-90	480	Vry	10.0	Beginner	Workbk	Topical

Features: Intro to Study
★★★ Personal Application   Preparation Time: Med   ISBN: 0-945276-07-9
 ★★ Relationship Building   Ldr. Guide Avail.: No   Size: 6.0 x 9.0
Subjects: Beliefs, Emotions, Psychology, Support
Comments: This combination book and workbook brings participants face to face with a Christ-centered therapeutic program that has achieved success in many lives. The book examines self-worth, what brings lasting happiness, and striving for Christlike love. The workbook provides a self-analysis exercise that focuses attention on Christ, shows how to get off the performance treadmill, and how to trace harmful emotions back to their root false beliefs and replace them with God's Word.

Author: McNulty, Edward N.   **755**
Series:
Title: *Controversial Topics for Youth Groups*
Publisher: Group Publishing, 1988

Num. Sess.	Group Time	Num. Pgs.	Avg. Qst.	Price	Audience	Format	Bible Study
40	45-60	360	N/A	13.95	New Christian	Book	Topical

Features: Intro to Study, Charts, Appendix
★★★ Personal Application   Preparation Time: None   ISBN: 0-931529-51-4
 ★★★ Relationship Building   Ldr. Guide Avail.: No   Size: 6.0 x 9.0
Subjects: Teens: Decisions, Teens:Drugs/Drinking, Teens: Music, Teens: Sexuality, Teens: Youth Life, Youth Life
Comments: Forty programs provide tools for teaching young people how to examine facts, hear opposing views, apply scriptural values, and then make faith-based decisions. The issues include reincarnation, abortion, rock music, pornography, premarital sex, drugs and drinking, and capital punishment. Each issue begins with two vignettes presenting opposite positions. The purpose is to help kids and leaders decide where they stand. A helpful appendix shows leaders "How to Conduct a Debate."

Author: McNulty, Edward N.   **756**
Series: Group's Active Bible Curriculum
Title: *Hazardous to Your Health*
Publisher: Group Publishing, 1990

Num. Sess.	Group Time	Num. Pgs.	Avg. Qst.	Price	Audience	Format	Bible Study
4	35-60	46	Vry	6.95	Beginner	Workbk	Topical

Features: Intro to Leading a Study, Intro to Study, Objectives, Study Overview, Ldr's Notes, Handouts, Agenda, Publicity Ideas
★★★★ Personal Application   Preparation Time: None   ISBN: 1-559-45200-5
★★★★ Relationship Building   Ldr. Guide Avail.: No   Size: 8.50 x 11.0
Subjects: Teens: Decisions, Teens: Discipleship, Teens: Senior High
Comments: This study helps young people learn, from a Christian perspective, to avoid destructive lifestyles. The four lessons, which explore the AIDS crisis, the dangers of steroids, eating disorders, and the importance of a healthy physical and spiritual life, can be used in a Bible class or youth meeting. Activities and Bible studies are included as separate reproducible sheets. The instructions are easy to follow and provide multiple options for teachers. No student books are required.

Author: McQuay, Earl P.   **757**
Series: Lay Action Ministry
Title: *Panorama of the Bible, A*
Publisher: Lay Action Ministry Program, 1988

Num. Sess.	Group Time	Num. Pgs.	Avg. Qst.	Price	Audience	Format	Bible Study
12	60-90	128	Vry	5.95	New Christian	Workbk	Topical

Features: Prayer Helps, Ldr's Notes, Maps
  ★★★ Personal Application   Preparation Time: Low   ISBN: 0-89191-511-7
  ★★★ Relationship Building   Ldr. Guide Avail.: Yes   Size: 5.25 x 8.25
Subjects: Bible Study, Church Life
Comments: This study helps participants trace God's dealings with humankind through the ages, from Genesis to Revelation. Participants will be encouraged to follow God's call to Christian living and service as they study His work in the lives of faithful men and women before them. A visual memory system helps participants understand and remember twelve important segments of Bible history. The final lesson includes a test on the material and symbols covered over the twelve weeks. Homework is required.

Author: Mehl, Gary L.   **758**
Series: Small Group Bible Studies
Title: *Fellowship*
Publisher: Augsburg Publishing House, 1984

Num. Sess.	Group Time	Num. Pgs.	Avg. Qst.	Price	Audience	Format	Bible Study
8	60-75	24	8	1.25	New Christian	Book	Topical

Features: Intro to Study, Prayer Helps
  ★★★★ Personal Application   Preparation Time: None   ISBN:
  ★★★★ Relationship Building   Ldr. Guide Avail.: No   Size: 8.50 x 5.50
Subjects: Relationships
Comments: This small eight-session study helps participants explore in detail the biblical understanding of fellowship. It addresses why they can have fellowship, with whom, and how fellowship can be strengthened. It emphasizes that because God has reached out to us, our priority should be to reach out and extend fellowship to others. The study provides a fresh look at fellowship in the contemporary church.

Author: Menconi, Peter, et al.   **759**
Series: Lifestyle Small Group
Title: *Career: Take This Job and Love It*
Publisher: Serendipity House, 1989

Num. Sess.	Group Time	Num. Pgs.	Avg. Qst.	Price	Audience	Format	Bible Study
7	40-120	61	Vry	4.95	Beginner	Workbk	Topical

Features: Intro to Leading a Study, Intro to Study, Bibliography, Digging Deeper Quest, Summary, Full Scrpt Printed
  ★★★★ Personal Application   Preparation Time: None   ISBN: 0-89109-582-9
  ★★★ Relationship Building   Ldr. Guide Avail.: No   Size: 6.50 x 9.25
Subjects: Work
Comments: This study considers six aspects of planning a career: choice, planning, advancement, change, workaholics, and meaningful work. It uses a verse-by-verse study of selected gospel and epistle passages. The first lesson is an introductory, get-acquainted session. Then, three study tracks are followed by a gospel study (basic entry level), an epistle study (advanced study groups), or both. Reference notes help participants understand difficult words and contexts of the Bible passages.

Author: Menconi, Peter, et al.   **760**
Series: Lifestyle Small Group
Title: *Family: Living Under the Same Leaky Roof*
Publisher: Serendipity House, 1989

Num. Sess.	Group Time	Num. Pgs.	Avg. Qst.	Price	Audience	Format	Bible Study
7	40-120	64	Vry	4.95	Beginner	Workbk	Topical

Features: Intro to Leading a Study, Intro to Study, Bibliography, Digging Deeper Quest, Summary, Full Scrpt Printed
  ★★★★ Personal Application   Preparation Time: None   ISBN: 0-89109-583-7
  ★★★ Relationship Building   Ldr. Guide Avail.: No   Size: 6.50 x 9.25
Subjects: Christian Living, Family, Stress
Comments: This study considers six topics of interest to families: marriage, becoming parents, parents and children, family conflicts, family stress, and family of God. It studies selected gospel and epistle passages verse by verse. The first lesson is an introductory, get-acquainted session. Then, three study tracks are followed by a gospel study (basic entry level), an epistle study (advanced study groups), or both. Reference notes help participants understand difficult words and contexts.

Author: Menconi, Peter, et al.   **761**
Series: Lifestyle Small Group
Title: *Lifestyles: Going In Style*
Publisher: Serendipity House, 1988

Num. Sess.	Group Time	Num. Pgs.	Avg. Qst.	Price	Audience	Format	Bible Study
7	40-120	62	Vry	4.95	Beginner	Workbk	Topical

Features: Intro to Leading a Study, Intro to Study, Bibliography, Digging Deeper Quest, Summary, Full Scrpt Printed
  ★★★★ Personal Application   Preparation Time: None   ISBN: 0-89109-584-5
  ★★★ Relationship Building   Ldr. Guide Avail.: No   Size: 6.50 x 9.25
Subjects: Christian Living, Social Issues
Comments: This study considers six kinds of "lifestyles": the fast tracker, the risk taker, the perfectionist, the nonconformist, the confident, and the committed. It uses a verse-by-verse study of selected gospel and epistle passages. The first lesson is an introductory, get-acquainted session. Then, three study tracks are followed by a gospel study (basic entry level), an epistle study (advanced study groups), or both. Reference notes help participants understand difficult words and contexts.

Author: Menconi, Peter   **762**
Series: Serendipity Support Group
Title: *Mid Life: The Crisis That Brings Renewal*
Publisher: Serendipity House, 1990

Num. Sess.	Group Time	Num. Pgs.	Avg. Qst.	Price	Audience	Format	Bible Study
14	60-90	80	12	5.45	Beginner	Workbk	Topical

Features: Intro to Leading a Study, Objectives, Bibliography, Prayer Helps, Full Scrpt Printed, Ldr's Notes, Cartoons, Agenda
  ★★★★ Personal Application   Preparation Time: None   ISBN:
  ★★★★ Relationship Building   Ldr. Guide Avail.: No   Size: 6.50 x 9.0
Subjects: Men's Issues, Renewal, Social Issues, Women's Issues
Comments: This study is written for anyone approaching, in, or just through midlife. The book of Ecclesiastes is the source of insights into the nature and dynamics of midlife. Everyone has to face midlife questions of mortality, crazy decisions, dumb moves, and crises of all sorts. This study leads participants through reevaluation, rediscovery, reaffirmation, and redirection. Midlife can be less a crisis and more an opportunity.

Author: Menconi, Peter, et al.   **763**
Series: Lifestyle Small Group
Title: *Money: Handling the Bucks*
Publisher: Serendipity House, 1989

Num. Sess.	Group Time	Num. Pgs.	Avg. Qst.	Price	Audience	Format	Bible Study
7	40-120	58	Vry	4.95	Beginner	Workbk	Topical

Features: Intro to Leading a Study, Intro to Study, Bibliography, Digging Deeper Quest, Summary, Full Scrpt Printed
★★★★ Personal Application   Preparation Time: None   ISBN: 0-89109-585-3
★★★ Relationship Building   Ldr. Guide Avail.: No   Size: 6.50 x 9.25
Subjects: Christian Living, Money, Work
Comments: This study considers six views on finance: high finance, low finance, belly-up finance, good investment, bad investment, and best investment. It uses a verse-by-verse study of selected gospel and epistle passages. The first lesson is an introductory, get-acquainted session. Then, three study tracks are followed by a gospel study (basic entry level), an epistle study (advanced study groups), or both. Reference notes help participants understand difficult words and contexts of the Bible passages.

Author: Menconi, Peter, et al.   **764**
Series: Lifestyle Small Group
Title: *Singles: Looking Out for Number One*
Publisher: Serendipity House, 1988

Num. Sess.	Group Time	Num. Pgs.	Avg. Qst.	Price	Audience	Format	Bible Study
7	40-120	64	Vry	4.95	Beginner	Workbk	Topical

Features: Intro to Leading a Study, Intro to Study, Bibliography, Digging Deeper Quest, Summary, Full Scrpt Printed
★★★★ Personal Application   Preparation Time: None   ISBN:
★★★ Relationship Building   Ldr. Guide Avail.: No   Size: 6.50 x 9.25
Subjects: Christian Living, Loneliness, Sexual Issues, Singles Issues
Comments: This study considers six topics of interest to singles: friendship, intimacy, sexuality, rejection, loneliness, and lifestyle. It uses a verse-by-verse study of selected gospel and epistle passages. The first lesson is an introductory, get-acquainted session. Then, three study tracks are followed by a gospel study (basic entry level), an epistle study (advanced study groups), or both. Reference notes help participants understand difficult words and contexts of the Bible passages.

Author: Menconi, Peter, et al.   **765**
Series: Lifestyle Small Group
Title: *Stressed-Out: Keeping It Together When It's Falling Apart*
Publisher: Serendipity House, 1988

Num. Sess.	Group Time	Num. Pgs.	Avg. Qst.	Price	Audience	Format	Bible Study
7	40-120	64	Vry	4.95	Beginner	Workbk	Topical

Features: Intro to Leading a Study, Intro to Study, Bibliography, Digging Deeper Quest, Summary, Full Scrpt Printed
★★★★ Personal Application   Preparation Time: None   ISBN: 0-89109-588-8
★★★ Relationship Building   Ldr. Guide Avail.: No   Size: 6.50 x 9.25
Subjects: Christian Living, Emotions, Failure, Stress, Work
Comments: This study considers six causes of stress: worry, over-work, failure, conflict, loss, and burnout. It studies selected gospel and epistle passages verse by verse. The first lesson is an introductory, get-acquainted session. Then, three study tracks are followed by a gospel study (basic entry level), an epistle study (advanced study groups), or both. Reference notes help participants understand difficult words and contexts of the Bible passages.

Author: Menconi, Peter, et al.   **766**
Series: Lifestyle Small Group
Title: *Success: Does the One with the Most Toys Win?*
Publisher: Serendipity House, 1988

Num. Sess.	Group Time	Num. Pgs.	Avg. Qst.	Price	Audience	Format	Bible Study
7	40-120	64	Vry	4.95	Beginner	Workbk	Topical

Features: Intro to Leading a Study, Intro to Study, Bibliography, Digging Deeper Quest, Summary, Full Scrpt Printed
★★★★ Personal Application   Preparation Time: None   ISBN:
★★★ Relationship Building   Ldr. Guide Avail.: No   Size: 6.50 x 9.25
Subjects: Christian Living, Money, Service, Success, Work
Comments: This study considers six definitions of "success": success in power, wealth, status, happiness, self-fulfillment, and service. It uses a verse-by-verse study of selected gospel and epistle passages. The first lesson is an introductory, get-acquainted session. Then, three study tracks are followed by a gospel study (basic entry level), an epistle study (advanced study groups), or both. Reference notes help participants understand difficult words and the contexts of the Bible passages.

Author: Menconi, Peter, et al.   **767**
Series: Lifestyle Small Group
Title: *Transitions: Savoring the Seasons of Life*
Publisher: Serendipity House, 1988

Num. Sess.	Group Time	Num. Pgs.	Avg. Qst.	Price	Audience	Format	Bible Study
7	40-120	64	Vry	4.95	Beginner	Workbk	Topical

Features: Intro to Leading a Study, Intro to Study, Bibliography, Digging Deeper Quest, Summary, Full Scrpt Printed
★★★★ Personal Application   Preparation Time: None   ISBN: 0-89109-591-8
★★★ Relationship Building   Ldr. Guide Avail.: No   Size: 6.50 x 9.25
Subjects: Christian Living, Loneliness
Comments: This study considers several causes of transition: end of childhood, on your own, mid-life, becoming empty nesters, and aging. It studies selected gospel and epistle passages verse by verse. The first lesson is an introductory, get-acquainted session. Then, three study tracks are followed by a gospel study (basic entry level), an epistle study (advanced study groups), or both. Reference notes help participants understand difficult words and contexts of the Bible passages.

Author: Menconi, Peter, et al.   **768**
Series: Lifestyle Small Group
Title: *Wholeness: Putting the Pieces Together*
Publisher: Serendipity House, 1989

Num. Sess.	Group Time	Num. Pgs.	Avg. Qst.	Price	Audience	Format	Bible Study
7	40-120	60	Vry	4.95	Beginner	Workbk	Topical

Features: Intro to Leading a Study, Intro to Study, Bibliography, Digging Deeper Quest, Summary, Full Scrpt Printed
★★★★ Personal Application   Preparation Time: None   ISBN: 0-89109-592-6
★★★ Relationship Building   Ldr. Guide Avail.: No   Size: 6.50 x 9.25
Subjects: Christian Living, Relationships, Wholeness, Wisdom, Work
Comments: This study considers the physical, mental, emotional, relational, vocational, and spiritual components of wholeness. It uses a verse-by-verse study of selected gospel and epistle passages. The first lesson is an introductory, get-acquainted session. Then, three study tracks are followed by a gospel study (basic entry level), an epistle study (advanced study groups), or both. Reference notes help participants understand difficult words and the contexts of the Bible passages.

Author: Mercer, Jerry   **769**
Series: Spiritual Formation Series
Title: *Cry Joy!*
Publisher: Victor Books, 1987

Num. Sess.	Group Time	Num. Pgs.	Avg. Qst.	Price	Audience	Format	Bible Study
13	60-75	156	N/A	7.99	New Christian	Book	Topical

Features: Intro to Study, Bibliography
★★★★ Personal Application Preparation Time: Low ISBN: 0-89693-316-4
  ★★★ Relationship Building Ldr. Guide Avail.: Yes Size: 5.50 x 8.0
Subjects: Discipleship, Holiness, Joy, Matthew, Relationships, Sermon on the Mount
Comments: This thirteen-week study on the Beatitudes helps participants set standards for spiritual foundation, a stability which helps shape their understanding of what matters most in life. Discipleship is presented as a friendship with God; lifestyle, not program; a relationship, not a system; a journey, not a roadmap. Participants are called to a holy partnership with God. A leader's guide includes reproducible transparency masters.

Author: Miller, J. Keith   **770**
Series:
Title: *Secrets of a Best Seller: How to Write the Non-Fiction Book*
Publisher: Word, 1989

Num. Sess.	Group Time	Num. Pgs.	Avg. Qst.	Price	Audience	Format	Bible Study
7	60-90	N/A	Vry	99.99	Beginner	Video	No

Features: Intro to Study, Video Study Guide
★★★★ Personal Application Preparation Time: Low ISBN: 8-01-504079-5
  ★ Relationship Building Ldr. Guide Avail.: No Size: 10.0 x 12.50
Subjects: Small Group Resource
Comments: This three-hour video study teaches the mechanics of writing an inspirational book—from the idea stage to getting the book sold. Time during the lecture is allowed for viewers to participate, and cues indicate the breaks. Actual viewing time of each session can be determined by how quickly the group responds. This is excellent for a church-sponsored writer's group.

Author: Moberg, Frederick J.   **771**
Series: Small Group Bible Studies
Title: *Parables*
Publisher: Augsburg Publishing House, 1978

Num. Sess.	Group Time	Num. Pgs.	Avg. Qst.	Price	Audience	Format	Bible Study
6	60-75	24	20	1.10	New Christian	Book	Topical

Features: Intro to Study, Prayer Helps
★★★ Personal Application Preparation Time: None ISBN:
★★★ Relationship Building Ldr. Guide Avail.: No Size: 8.50 x 5.50
Subjects: Parables
Comments: This short, six-session study looks at the parables of Jesus in three ways. It determines the real-life situation Jesus addressed in a particular parable; what question He answered, to which audience He spoke, and their need. It determines the parable's central idea and how it is related to the audience and the situation. Finally, it examines the parables in light of modern problems or needs.

Author: Money, Royce   **772**
Series:
Title: *Building Stronger Families*
Publisher: Victor Books, 1984

Num. Sess.	Group Time	Num. Pgs.	Avg. Qst.	Price	Audience	Format	Bible Study
13	60-90	165	N/A	7.99	Beginner	Book	Topical

Features:
★★★★ Personal Application Preparation Time: Med ISBN: 0-88207-244-7
★★★★ Relationship Building Ldr. Guide Avail.: Yes Size: 5.50 x 8.0
Subjects: Church Life, Family, Parenting, Relationships
Comments: This book helps families develop good communication patterns, spend time togther, express appreciation, affirm spiritual values, and deal positively with crises. The same principles that strengthen family relationships also strengthen the church family. The second part of the book shows how a church can develop a family ministry, so that church and family can work together. A thorough leader's guide with transparency masters is available.

Author: Moore, James W.   **773**
Series: Bible Study for Christian
Title: *1 Corinthians (Volumes 1-3)*
Publisher: Cokesbury, 1989

Num. Sess.	Group Time	Num. Pgs.	Avg. Qst.	Price	Audience	Format	Bible Study
9	45-60	N/A	Vry	29.95	New Christian	Video	Book

Features: Intro to Leading a Study, Intro to Study, Ldr's Notes, Video Study Guide
★★★ Personal Application Preparation Time: Low ISBN: 0-687-76138-7
★★★ Relationship Building Ldr. Guide Avail.: Yes Size: 4.75 x 8.0
Subjects: Christian Living, 1 Corinthians
Comments: This three-volume video lecture study covers Paul's first letter to the Corinthian Christians, rugged individualists eager to be free of the apostle's traditional standards of personal conduct. He knew that if the church were to mature, the individualists would have to share one Lord, and one common life. It's valid, relevant subject matter for contemporary Christians. A leader's guide contains helpful insights and questions for a group; the study is also effective for personal use.

Author: Moravec, Marilyn   **774**
Series: Growing Together Studies
Title: *Balancing Your Priorities*
Publisher: David C. Cook Publishing Co., 1989

Num. Sess.	Group Time	Num. Pgs.	Avg. Qst.	Price	Audience	Format	Bible Study
6	50-60	64	10	3.95	Beginner	Workbk	Topical

Features: Intro to Leading a Study, Intro to Study, Bibliography, Prayer Helps, Drawings
★★★ Personal Application Preparation Time: None ISBN: 1-555-13189-1
★★★★ Relationship Building Ldr. Guide Avail.: No Size: 5.25 x 8.25
Subjects: Caring, Christian Living, Wisdom
Comments: This study, part of a four-book series, shows participants how to balance priorities by: deciding what's really important; listening to God in a noisy world; understanding personal needs without being self-centered; and taking time to express love to others. Warm, genuine fellowship will result. Complete with easy-to-follow instructions for leaders and group members, the study can last from six to twelve weeks. It is appropriate for new or established classes, neighborhood small groups, and for any age.

Author: Moravec, Marilyn 775
Series: Growing Together Studies
Title: *Getting Along with People You Love*
Publisher: David C. Cook Publishing Co., 1989

Num. Sess.	Group Time	Num. Pgs.	Avg. Qst.	Price	Audience	Format	Bible Study
6	50-60	64	8	3.95	Beginner	Workbk	Topical

Features: Intro to Leading a Study, Intro to Study, Bibliography, Prayer Helps, Drawings
★★★ Personal Application   Preparation Time: None ISBN: 1-555-13195-6
★★★★ Relationship Building Ldr. Guide Avail.: No   Size: 5.25 x 8.25
Subjects: Christian Living, Commitments, Relationships
Comments: This study, part of a four-book series, shows participants how to get along with loved ones by: easing tension in relationships; understanding what loved ones really mean; accepting and comforting loved ones; and letting commitment to Christ change relationships with loved ones. Complete with easy-to-follow instructions for leaders and group members, the study can last from six to twelve weeks. It is appropriate for new or established classes, neighborhood small groups, and for any age.

Author: Moravec, Marilyn 776
Series: Growing Together Studies
Title: *Getting Your Act Together*
Publisher: David C. Cook Publishing Co., 1989

Num. Sess.	Group Time	Num. Pgs.	Avg. Qst.	Price	Audience	Format	Bible Study
6	50-60	66	12	3.95	Beginner	Workbk	Topical

Features: Intro to Leading a Study, Intro to Study, Bibliography, Prayer Helps, Drawings
★★★ Personal Application   Preparation Time: None ISBN: 1-555-13194-8
★★★★ Relationship Building Ldr. Guide Avail.: No   Size: 5.25 x 8.25
Subjects: Christian Living, Emotions, Stress, Success
Comments: This study, part of a four-book series, shows participants how to get their acts together by: achieving goals through self-management; overcoming disabling fears; counting the cost of achievement; and caring for the "inner world" of biblical self-management. Complete with easy-to-follow instructions for leaders and group members, the study can last from six to twelve weeks. It is appropriate for new or established classes, neighborhood small groups, and for any age.

Author: Moravec, Marilyn 777
Series: Growing Together Studies
Title: *Living in Harmony*
Publisher: David C. Cook Publishing Co., 1989

Num. Sess.	Group Time	Num. Pgs.	Avg. Qst.	Price	Audience	Format	Bible Study
6	50-60	61	8	3.95	Beginner	Workbk	Topical

Features: Intro to Leading a Study, Intro to Study, Bibliography, Prayer Helps, Drawings
★★★ Personal Application   Preparation Time: None ISBN: 1-555-13190-5
★★★★ Relationship Building Ldr. Guide Avail.: No   Size: 5.25 x 8.25
Subjects: Christian Living, Emotions, Relationships, Stress
Comments: This study, part of a four-book series, shows participants how to live in harmony by: identifying their style for handling conflicts; taming their anger; stating needs clearly and competing fairly; and turning conflict into spiritual growth instead of revenge. Complete with easy-to-follow instructions for leaders and group members, the study can last from six to twelve weeks. It is appropriate for new or established classes, neighborhood small groups, and for any age.

Author: Mork, Carol J. 778
Series: Friendship Bible Study
Title: *Sermon on the Mount*
Publisher: Augsburg Publishing House, 1987

Num. Sess.	Group Time	Num. Pgs.	Avg. Qst.	Price	Audience	Format	Bible Study
8	60-75	48	13	3.0	New Christian	Workbk	Topical

Features: Intro to Study, Prayer Helps, Study Overview
★★★★ Personal Application   Preparation Time: Low   ISBN:
★★★★ Relationship Building Ldr. Guide Avail.: Yes   Size: 5.50 x 8.0
Subjects: Matthew, Sermon on the Mount
Comments: This eight-lesson study challenges contemporary participants to explore what Jesus' Sermon on the Mount means for them as Christians in North America. They are confronted time and again with an inability to be perfect. The first lesson consists of the first ten verses of Jesus' sermon called the Beatitudes. The lesson format includes an overview, an opening, a responsive reading, Bible background, questions for reflection, a key verse, a prayer response, and an "our faith" response.

Author: Morrissey, Kirkie 779
Series: Woman's Workshop Series
Title: *Designed by God: Studies on Healing & Wholeness*
Publisher: Zondervan, 1985

Num. Sess.	Group Time	Num. Pgs.	Avg. Qst.	Price	Audience	Format	Bible Study
13	60-90	156	36	6.95	New Christian	Workbk	Topical

Features: Intro to Study, Scrpt Memory Helps, Glossary, Appendix
★★★ Personal Application   Preparation Time: High ISBN: 0-310-45011-X
★★★ Relationship Building Ldr. Guide Avail.: No   Size: 5.25 x 8.0
Subjects: Christian Living, Emotions, Spiritual Gifts, Victorious Living, Wholeness, Women's Issues
Comments: This study on healing and wholeness helps participants identify gifts and abilities, remove hindrances, and become all God designs them to be. The first half deals with "inner healing," eliminating things that produce poor self-image, deep hurts, anger, and guilt. The second half explores God-given potential, including how to use "gifts," how to overcome fear that hinders their use, and how to plug into God's power to use them to the fullest.

Author: Morrissey, Kirkie 780
Series: Woman's Workshop Series
Title: *Forgiveness*
Publisher: Zondervan, 1982

Num. Sess.	Group Time	Num. Pgs.	Avg. Qst.	Price	Audience	Format	Bible Study
13	60-90	159	22	6.95	New Christian	Workbk	Topical

Features: Intro to Leading a Study, Intro to Study, Scrpt Memory Helps, Ldr's Notes
★★★ Personal Application   Preparation Time: Med ISBN: 0-310-44931-6
★★★ Relationship Building Ldr. Guide Avail.: No   Size: 5.25 x 8.0
Subjects: Christian Living, Forgiveness, Women's Issues
Comments: This study examines forgiveness—what it's like, how it comes, and how it is given. Through the examples of Christ and other biblical characters, it helps participants deal with life's difficult circumstances, to restore and renew relationships. Each chapter is divided into suggested daily portions, a format that helps participants establish patterns of daily meditation. Due to the quantity of questions, those most beneficial for group study are starred.

Author: Mouat, Linda **781**
Series: Basic Bible Study Series
Title: *Making a Difference: The Power of Servant Love*
Publisher: Aglow, 1989

Num. Sess.	Group Time	Num. Pgs.	Avg. Qst.	Price	Audience	Format	Bible Study
10	75-90	61	21	2.95	New Christian	Workbk	Topical

Features: Intro to Study, Prayer Helps, Scrpt Memory Helps, Persnl Study Quest
★★★ Personal Application Preparation Time: Med ISBN: 0-932305-74-1
★★★ Relationship Building Ldr. Guide Avail.: No Size: 5.25 x 8.25
Subjects: Charismatic Interest, Service
Comments: This ten-week study defines servanthood in light of the Bible. It examines: Christ's example as servant; our calling to be servants; the cost of servanthood; the role of the servant as catalyst for change; the rewards of a servant lifestyle; and right and wrong reasons to serve. It answers the questions "Why should someone care about servant love?" and "What does the Bible say about being a servant?" Participants are led to understand Christ as servant, to know Him more fully, and become more like Him.

Author: Mouser, William **782**
Series: LifeGuide Bible Study
Title: *Proverbs*
Publisher: InterVarsity, 1990

Num. Sess.	Group Time	Num. Pgs.	Avg. Qst.	Price	Audience	Format	Bible Study
13	45-60	95	11	3.95	Beginner	Workbk	Topical

Features: Intro to Leading a Study, Intro to Study, Ldr's Notes
★★★ Personal Application Preparation Time: Low ISBN: 0-8308-1026-9
★★★ Relationship Building Ldr. Guide Avail.: No Size: 5.50 x 8.25
Subjects: Family, Friendships, Proverbs, Relationships, Wisdom, Work
Comments: This thirteen-week study introduces participants to selected proverbs from Solomon's collection, grouped together under thirteen different themes. They teach how to be successful and prosperous in work, in dealings with family and friends, and in a relationship with God. Direction and guidance from Proverbs is practical, concrete, reasonable, and fruitful; it will teach participants to live more wisely.

Author: Mowchan, Carolyn M. **783**
Series: Friendship Bible Study
Title: *Prayer*
Publisher: Augsburg Publishing House, 1989

Num. Sess.	Group Time	Num. Pgs.	Avg. Qst.	Price	Audience	Format	Bible Study
8	60-75	48	14	3.0	New Christian	Workbk	Topical

Features: Intro to Study, Prayer Helps, Study Overview
★★★★ Personal Application Preparation Time: Low ISBN:
★★★★ Relationship Building Ldr. Guide Avail.: Yes Size: 5.50 x 8.50
Subjects: Faith, Prayer
Comments: This eight-lesson study helps participants explore issues of prayer and spirituality. It encourages the practice of individual and corporate prayer, which deepen faith and enrich spiritual life. The lesson format includes an overview, an opening, a responsive reading, Bible background, questions for reflection, a key verse, a prayer response, and an "our faith" response.

Author: Mullins, Terence Y. **784**
Series: Friendship Bible Study
Title: *Isaiah*
Publisher: Augsburg Publishing House, 1988

Num. Sess.	Group Time	Num. Pgs.	Avg. Qst.	Price	Audience	Format	Bible Study
8	60-75	48	10	3.0	New Christian	Workbk	Book

Features: Intro to Study, Prayer Helps, Study Overview
★★★★ Personal Application Preparation Time: Low ISBN:
★★★★ Relationship Building Ldr. Guide Avail.: Yes Size: 5.50 x 8.50
Subjects: Isaiah/Jeremiah, Major Prophets, Prophecy
Comments: This eight-lesson study examines the Old Testament prophecy of Isaiah. Three sections are viewed. The first (chapters 1-39) is about the acts and words of the prophet; the second (chapters 40-55) speaks of "comfort, comfort my people, says your God" (40:1); and the third (chapters 56-66) emphasizes righteousness. The lesson format includes an overview, an opening, a responsive reading, Bible background, questions for reflection, a key verse, a prayer response, and more.

Author: Munson, Barbara **785**
Series:
Title: *Life & Ministry of Jesus Christ, The (Book 2)*
Publisher: NavPress, 1987

Num. Sess.	Group Time	Num. Pgs.	Avg. Qst.	Price	Audience	Format	Bible Study
9	90-120	141	25	6.95	New Christian	Workbk	Charctr

Features: Intro to Study, Bibliography, Charts, Maps
★★★ Personal Application Preparation Time: Med ISBN: 0-89109-554-3
★★ Relationship Building Ldr. Guide Avail.: No Size: 8.50 x 11.50
Subjects: Commitments, Forgiveness, Jesus: Life/Teaching, Service
Comments: This second in a two-book study focuses on the accomplishment of Jesus' mission on earth: death on a cross, burial, resurrection, ascension, and leaving a commission to Christians to take His good news to all the world. Christian character qualities emphasized include serving others, getting to know God through meditation, being a disciple of Jesus, gratefulness, commitment, giving, forgiveness, and more. The "Bridge to Life" illustration, a simple gospel presentation, is included.

Author: Munson, Barbara **786**
Series:
Title: *Life & Ministry of Jesus Christ, The (Book 1)*
Publisher: NavPress, 1987

Num. Sess.	Group Time	Num. Pgs.	Avg. Qst.	Price	Audience	Format	Bible Study
9	90-120	123	26	6.95	New Christian	Workbk	Charctr

Features: Intro to Study, Bibliography, Summary, Charts, Maps
★★★ Personal Application Preparation Time: Med ISBN: 0-89109-553-5
★★ Relationship Building Ldr. Guide Avail.: No Size: 8.50 x 11.50
Subjects: Evangelism, Faith, Jesus: Life/Teaching, Obedience, Prayer, Sermon on the Mount
Comments: This two-book study helps participants learn more about Jesus, His teachings, actions, and character qualities. This first book traces Jesus' life and ministry from preexistence and birth to the Sermon on the Mount, then through a period of healing and teaching. Christian character qualities emphasized include a worshipful attitude, obedience, endurance, witnessing, prayer, faith, doing God's will, and love for the Lord. The "Bridge to Life" illustration, a simple gospel presentation, is included.

Author: Myers, Bill   **787**
Series: SonPower Elective Series
Title: *Hot Topics, Tough Questions*
Publisher: Victor Books, 1987

Num. Sess.	Group Time	Num. Pgs.	Avg. Qst.	Price	Audience	Format	Bible Study
13	60-75	159	Vry	5.99	Beginner	Book	Topical

Features: Drawings
★★★★ Personal Application Preparation Time: None ISBN: 0-89693-517-5
★★★★ Relationship Building Ldr. Guide Avail.: Yes   Size: 4.25 x 7.0
Subjects: Teens: Christian Liv, Teens: Emotions, Teens: Senior High
Comments: This book responds to a series of tough questions asked by teenagers, such as: "How do I find God's will?" "Sex—why not?" "How do I handle anger, fear, depression?" Answers are found in the Bible. A leader's guide with transparency masters is available. Rip-out sheets for students are also available.

Author: Myers, Bill   **788**
Series: SonPower Elective Series
Title: *More Hot Topics*
Publisher: Victor Books, 1989

Num. Sess.	Group Time	Num. Pgs.	Avg. Qst.	Price	Audience	Format	Bible Study
13	60-75	142	N/A	5.99	Beginner	Book	Topical

Features:
★★★★ Personal Application Preparation Time: Low ISBN: 0-89693-670-8
★★★★ Relationship Building Ldr. Guide Avail.: Yes   Size: 4.25 x 7.0
Subjects: Teens: Christian Liv, Teens: Cults, Teens: Sexuality
Comments: This book digs deep for biblical answers to teenage questions like, What is God really like? Sex—how far is too far? Why do good people suffer? What is the "new age"? and more. A leader's guide with transparency masters and rip-out sheets for students are available.

Author: Mylander, Charles   **789**
Series:
Title: *Supernatural Energy for the Struggle: Daily Action For Busy People*
Publisher: Regal Books, 1989

Num. Sess.	Group Time	Num. Pgs.	Avg. Qst.	Price	Audience	Format	Bible Study
13	30-45	210	7	7.95	New Christian	Book	Topical

Features: Intro to Study, Prayer Helps
★★ Personal Application Preparation Time: Low ISBN: 0-8307-1363-8
★★ Relationship Building Ldr. Guide Avail.: No   Size: 5.50 x 8.50
Subjects: Charismatic Interest, Christian Life, Devotionals, Success, Work
Comments: This book allows a reader to spend five minutes a day reading an essay. It can be read at bedtime, at the breakfast table, or at the reader's desk. Monday through Saturday, readings are assigned. For Sunday there are small group questions for the previous week's review. This book is for the busy person who wants to maintain an inspired mind.

Author: Nelson, Wayne S.   **790**
Series: The Lifechange Series
Title: *Exodus*
Publisher: NavPress, 1989

Num. Sess.	Group Time	Num. Pgs.	Avg. Qst.	Price	Audience	Format	Bible Study
18	60-90	166	17	5.95	New Christian	Workbk	Book

Features: Intro to Leading a Study, Intro to Study, Bibliography, Prayer Helps, Worship Helps, Study Overview, Digging Deeper Quest, Summary, Maps, Cross Ref, Word Study
★★★ Personal Application Preparation Time: Med ISBN: 0-89109-283-8
★★★ Relationship Building Ldr. Guide Avail.: No   Size: 5.50 x 8.50
Subjects: Exodus, God, Worship
Comments: This verse-by-verse study of Exodus offers valuable insights for participants, including God's methods for dealing with rebellion, His shaping of Moses into a leader, governing principles for just treatment of others, and guidelines for pure and wholehearted worship. It covers part two in the story of humanity's redemption, showing how God brought Israel out of slavery to become His servants. Participants will see how, through God's covenant law, the Redeemer is revealed.

Author: Nelson, Wayne S.   **791**
Series: The Lifechange Series
Title: *1 Samuel*
Publisher: NavPress, 1989

Num. Sess.	Group Time	Num. Pgs.	Avg. Qst.	Price	Audience	Format	Bible Study
16	60-90	168	17	5.95	New Christian	Workbk	Book

Features: Intro to Leading a Study, Intro to Study, Bibliography, Prayer Helps, Worship Helps, Study Overview, Digging Deeper Quest, Summary, Maps, Cross Ref, Word Study
★★★ Personal Application Preparation Time: Med ISBN: 0-89109-277-3
★★★ Relationship Building Ldr. Guide Avail.: No   Size: 5.50 x 8.50
Subjects: Bible Personalities, Commitments, Leadership, 1 & 2 Samuel
Comments: This verse-by-verse study of 1 Samuel looks at three men chosen by God to guide Israel's military attacks on moral corruption. The three are Samuel, a prophet who directs Israel's transition from judgeship to monarchy; Saul, Israel's first king, who epitomizes what God doesn't want in a leader; and David, a man after God's own heart. These men offer participants perfect examples both of godliness and halfhearted commitment.

Author: Niguette, Alan & Beth   **792**
Series: Building Books
Title: *Building Your Christian Defense System*
Publisher: Bethany House, 1988

Num. Sess.	Group Time	Num. Pgs.	Avg. Qst.	Price	Audience	Format	Bible Study
34	45-60	54	Vry	4.95	New Christian	Workbk	Topical

Features: Intro to Study
★★ Personal Application Preparation Time: Low ISBN: 1-556-61015-7
★★ Relationship Building Ldr. Guide Avail.: Yes   Size: 8.50 x 11.0
Subjects: Teens: Cults
Comments: This thirty-four-lesson study is designed to train young people to think biblically and uncover the subtle tactics of cults. It helps equip participants to discern truth from falsehood by treating six major topics: deception of the cults, warning signs of deception, four common threads of deception, how counterfeit things look real, the attractive but deadly nature of cults, and how to overcome error with truth.

Author: Nilsen, Mary Y.   **793**
Series: Friendship Bible Study
Title: *Proverbs*
Publisher: Augsburg Publishing House, 1987

Num. Sess.	Group Time	Num. Pgs.	Avg. Qst.	Price	Audience	Format	Bible Study
8	60-75	48	10	3.0	New Christian	Workbk	Book

Features: Intro to Study, Prayer Helps, Study Overview
★★★★ Personal Application   Preparation Time: Low   ISBN:
★★★★ Relationship Building   Ldr. Guide Avail.: Yes   Size: 5.50 x 8.50
Subjects: Proverbs, Wisdom
Comments: This eight-lesson study enhances Christian growth and friendship. A study of Proverbs helps participants "recognize wisdom . . .and live intelligently" (1:2-3, TEV). It can make them "clever" and "resourceful," and even add knowledge to those already wise or educated (1:5-6, TEV). The lesson format includes an overview, an opening, a responsive reading, Bible background, questions for reflection, a key verse, a prayer response, and an "our faith" response.

Author: Nyquist, James F. & Jack Kuhatschek   **794**
Series: LifeGuide Bible Study
Title: *Leading Bible Discussion*
Publisher: InterVarsity, 1985

Num. Sess.	Group Time	Num. Pgs.	Avg. Qst.	Price	Audience	Format	Bible Study
9	-	64	N/A	3.95	New Christian	Book	No

Features: Intro to Study, Appendix
   Personal Application   Preparation Time: ISBN: 0-8308-1000-5
   Relationship Building   Ldr. Guide Avail.:   Size: 5.50 x 8.25
Subjects: Leadership, Small Group Resource
Comments: The suggestions in this book can enable potential leaders to effectively and enjoyably fulfill their leadership roles. Subjects covered include how to: start a group, decide what to study, prepare to lead, study the Bible, use a study guide, write your own questions, lead a discussion, and evaluate a study. An appendix reviews a model study on humility.

Author: Nysse, Richard W.   **795**
Series: Men's Bible Study Series
Title: *Daniel*
Publisher: Augsburg Publishing House, 1987

Num. Sess.	Group Time	Num. Pgs.	Avg. Qst.	Price	Audience	Format	Bible Study
10	30-45	48	13	3.0	New Christian	Workbk	Book

Features: Intro to Study, Prayer Helps, Summary
★★★★ Personal Application   Preparation Time: None   ISBN:
★★★★ Relationship Building   Ldr. Guide Avail.: Yes   Size: 4.50 x 9.50
Subjects: Daniel, Faith, Major Prophets, Men's Issues
Comments: This ten-lesson study of Daniel, written to inspire faith, allows participants to strengthen and renew their own faith. Speculation on Daniel's visions threatens to drown out the book's encouraging character; but while the visions have twists, they all end on encouraging notes. The book shows there's a limit to even the worst forms of evil, and the Kingdom of God will prevail. The study may be used at prayer breakfasts, men's Bible study groups, or any other men's meetings.

Author: Nystrom, Carolyn   **796**
Series: Young Fisherman Bible
Title: *Mark: God on the Move*
Publisher: Shaw, 1978

Num. Sess.	Group Time	Num. Pgs.	Avg. Qst.	Price	Audience	Format	Bible Study
16	50-60	96	16	2.95	New Christian	Workbk	Book

Features: Intro to Study, Prayer Helps, Drawings, Maps
★★ Personal Application   Preparation Time: Low   ISBN: 0-87788-311-4
★★ Relationship Building   Ldr. Guide Avail.: Yes   Size: 6.0 x 8.0
Subjects: Teens: Family, Teens: Jesus' Life, Teens: New Testament, Teens: Peer Pressure, Teens: Prayer, Teens: Theology
Comments: This chapter-by-chapter analysis of Mark's gospel reveals breathtaking miracles, brillant teaching, plots against Jesus, and the triumph of an empty grave; it's an exciting study for teens. Questions considered include: Should I follow Jesus? Who is Jesus? Am I in Christ's family? Will God help me believe? What makes me "dirty"? What does it cost to follow Jesus? How can I pray with power?

Author: Nystrom, Carolyn & Margaret Fromer   **797**
Series:
Title: *People in Turmoil: A Woman's Workshop on 1 Corinthians*
Publisher: Zondervan, 1985

Num. Sess.	Group Time	Num. Pgs.	Avg. Qst.	Price	Audience	Format	Bible Study
16	60-90	127	12	2.95	Beginner	Workbk	Book

Features: Intro to Leading a Study, Intro to Study, Bibliography, Ldr's Notes
★★ Personal Application   Preparation Time: None   ISBN: 0-310-41891-7
★★ Relationship Building   Ldr. Guide Avail.: No   Size: 5.25 x 8.0
Subjects: Christian Living, Sexual Issues, Wisdom, 1 Corinthians
Comments: This study of 1 Corinthians examines the church in Corinth, as it struggles to find harmony among its members and encounters tough questions about what is godly behavior. This guide leads a group through questions such as: "How can we balance secular education and spiritual wisdom?" "What should the church do about members who commit sexual sins?" "Is our conscience always a safe guide?" "May a Christian wife leave her nonChristian husband?" and "Is the Christian life worth the hassle?"

Author: Nystrom, Carolyn & Matthew Floding   **798**
Series: Young Fisherman Bible
Title: *Relationships: Face to Face*
Publisher: Shaw, 1986

Num. Sess.	Group Time	Num. Pgs.	Avg. Qst.	Price	Audience	Format	Bible Study
11	50-60	59	10	2.95	Beginner	Workbk	Topical

Features: Intro to Study, Scrpt Memory Helps, Drawings
★★ Personal Application   Preparation Time: Low   ISBN: 0-87788-722-5
★★ Relationship Building   Ldr. Guide Avail.: Yes   Size: 6.0 x 8.0
Subjects: Teens: Relationships, Teens: Youth Life
Comments: This study leads teens to the Bible for guidance in relating with God, peers, parents, and the needy. It outlines God's design for marriage at a time when teens are facing the realities of dating, and it encourages a face-to-face look at the Bible's fascinating network of relationships.

Author: Nystrom, Carolyn   **799**
Series: Young Fisherman Bible
Title: *Romans: Christianity on Trial*
Publisher: Shaw, 1980

Num. Sess.	Group Time	Num. Pgs.	Avg. Qst.	Price	Audience	Format	Bible Study
16	50-60	124	16	3.95	New Christian	Workbk	Book

Features: Intro to Study, Bibliography, Prayer Helps, Scrpt Memory Helps, Worship Helps, Full Scrpt Printed, Glossary, Exam
  ★★ Personal Application   Preparation Time: Low   ISBN: 0-87788-898-1
  ★★★ Relationship Building   Ldr. Guide Avail.: Yes   Size: 6.0 x 8.0
Subjects: Teens: Christian Liv, Teens: Discipleship, Teens: New Testament, Teens: Relationships, Teens: Theology
Comments: Stimulating questions and creative exercises help Paul's theology in Romans come alive for young adults senior high and up. Each lesson addresses a chapter dealing with contemporary themes such as: "Is God fair?" "Am I a snob?" "Do I get what I deserve?" and "Why do I have to take orders?" Paul's letter reveals the basis for Christian belief and deals with whether belief in Christ can make a difference in the contemporary world.

Author: Nystrom, Carolyn & Matthew Floding   **800**
Series: Young Fisherman Bible
Title: *Sexuality: God's Good Idea*
Publisher: Shaw, 1988

Num. Sess.	Group Time	Num. Pgs.	Avg. Qst.	Price	Audience	Format	Bible Study
12	50-60	71	13	2.95	Beginner	Workbk	Topical

Features: Intro to Study, Drawings
  ★★ Personal Application   Preparation Time: Low   ISBN: 0-87788-764-0
  ★★ Relationship Building   Ldr. Guide Avail.: Yes   Size: 6.0 x 8.0
Subjects: Teens: Sexuality, Teens: Youth Life
Comments: This study helps teens view sexuality from a biblical perspective and offers practical answers to questions about sexuality. Topics include dating, marriage, homosexuality, sexual violence, faithfulness, and whether making love is more than just sex. Leaders are encouraged to present this information with freedom, sensitivity, and good judgment; especially homosexuality and abuse, topics seldom discussed in the church context.

Author: Nystrom, Carolyn   **801**
Series: Workshop Series
Title: *Workshop on David and His Psalms, A*
Publisher: Zondervan, 1982

Num. Sess.	Group Time	Num. Pgs.	Avg. Qst.	Price	Audience	Format	Bible Study
16	60-75	159	14	6.95	New Christian	Workbk	Book

Features: Intro to Leading a Study, Intro to Study, Bibliography, Ldr's Notes, Maps, Agenda
  ★★ Personal Application   Preparation Time: Med   ISBN: 0-310-41931-X
  ★★ Relationship Building   Ldr. Guide Avail.: No   Size: 5.25 x 8.0
Subjects: Bible Personalities, Kings/Chronicles, Psalms, 1 & 2 Samuel
Comments: In this study of David, participants will see his heart through his prayers, now known as psalms. Taken from the books of Samuel and Chronicles, this guide provides the narrative history that served as backdrop for the Psalms. Through seventy-three psalms, participants will observe David speaking to, pleading with, and worshiping God. Each lesson has a brief introduction followed by a scripture reading and group questions. "Through the Week" sections provide daily study.

Author: Nystrom, Carolyn   **802**
Series: Workshop Series
Title: *Workshop on the Christian Faith, A*
Publisher: Zondervan, 1986

Num. Sess.	Group Time	Num. Pgs.	Avg. Qst.	Price	Audience	Format	Bible Study
12	60-75	102	14	4.95	Beginner	Workbk	Topical

Features: Intro to Leading a Study, Intro to Study, Ldr's Notes
  ★★ Personal Application   Preparation Time: Low   ISBN: 0-310-41971-9
  ★★ Relationship Building   Ldr. Guide Avail.: No   Size: 5.25 x 8.0
Subjects: Apologetics, Discipleship, Faith, Repentance
Comments: This study presents central issues and questions on faith as discussed in Scripture. Old and New Testaments reveal key points: Luke 11:1-13 explains why we should pray; Acts 3 and Isaiah 53 offer insight on repentance; John 3:1-21 describes what it means to be "born again." Two basic questions from which others stem are: "What difference does being a Christian make?" and "What difference does it make between you and your unbelieving neighbor?"

Author: Nystrom, Carolyn   **803**
Series: Workshop Series
Title: *Workshop on the Book of John, A*
Publisher: Zondervan, 1989

Num. Sess.	Group Time	Num. Pgs.	Avg. Qst.	Price	Audience	Format	Bible Study
26	60-75	144	14	6.95	Beginner	Workbk	Book

Features: Intro to Leading a Study, Intro to Study, Bibliography, Follow Up, Ldr's Notes
  ★★ Personal Application   Preparation Time: None   ISBN: 0-310-41841-0
  ★★ Relationship Building   Ldr. Guide Avail.: No   Size: 5.25 x 8.0
Subjects: Jesus: Life/Teaching, John, Miracles
Comments: This study of John points to one inescapable fact: It's impossible to study John and remain neutral. Readers must ask, "Who is this man called Jesus?" and, "If Jesus is all this book claims, what must I do about His claim on me?" John's Gospel is a personal account of Christ's life. He records only seven of Christ's miracles and writes that these are included that all may believe that Jesus is the Christ, and that believing in Him brings everlasting life.

Author: Nystrom, Carolyn & Margaret Fromer   **804**
Series: Workshop Series
Title: *Workshop on the Book of James, A*
Publisher: Zondervan, 1980

Num. Sess.	Group Time	Num. Pgs.	Avg. Qst.	Price	Audience	Format	Bible Study
12	60-90	122	12	5.95	New Christian	Workbk	Book

Features: Intro to Leading a Study, Intro to Study, Prayer Helps, Worship Helps, Ldr's Notes
  ★★★ Personal Application   Preparation Time: Low   ISBN: 0-310-41901-8
  ★★★ Relationship Building   Ldr. Guide Avail.: No   Size: 5.25 x 8.0
Subjects: Faith, James, Suffering
Comments: This study of James covers timeless issues, such as taming the tongue, patience in suffering, faith and deeds, listening and doing, and favoritism. James, thought to be the first New Testament book written, reminds participants today, just as in the past, that believers' hearts must be prepared for the second coming of the Lord.

Author: Nystrom, Carolyn   **805**
Series: Workshop Series
Title: *Workshop on the Book of Romans, A*
Publisher: Zondervan, 1982

Num. Sess.	Group Time	Num. Pgs.	Avg. Qst.	Price	Audience	Format	Bible Study
16	60-75	128	13	5.95	Beginner	Workbk	Book

Features: Intro to Leading a Study, Intro to Study, Bibliography, Scrpt Memory Helps, Worship Helps, Charts
  ★★★ Personal Application Preparation Time: Low ISBN: 0-310-41921-2
  ★★★ Relationship Building Ldr. Guide Avail.: Yes Size: 5.25 x 8.0
Subjects: Faith, Grace, Romans
Comments: This chapter-by-chapter study of Romans—like the biblical book itself—presents a thorough defense of Christian faith. It also addresses significant questions such as "Are the heathen lost?" and rationalizations such as "If God knows I can't stop sinning, why should I try?" The study moves from the general to the specific, and participants will discover how to control personal sin, whether anyone has a corner on God, and how to become the people God intends them to be.

Author: O'Donnell, Peter, et al.   **806**
Series: Life Application
Title: *Philippians & Colossians*
Publisher: Tyndale House, 1989

Num. Sess.	Group Time	Num. Pgs.	Avg. Qst.	Price	Audience	Format	Bible Study
13	60-90	82	12	4.95	New Christian	Workbk	Book

Features: Intro to Leading a Study, Intro to Study, Study Overview, Digging Deeper Quest, Full Scrpt Printed, Drawings, Charts, Maps, Cross Ref
  ★★★ Personal Application Preparation Time: Med ISBN: 0-8423-2733-9
  ★★★ Relationship Building Ldr. Guide Avail.: No Size: 6.50 x 9.0
Subjects: Church Life, Colossians/Philemon, False Teachers, Forgiveness, Joy, Philippians, Prison Epistles, Service, Suffering
Comments: This study contains the complete texts of Philippians and Colossians. Although Paul wrote from prison, joy is the dominant theme of Philippians; lessons cover joy in suffering, serving, believing, and giving. Colossians was written to combat errors in the church, and to show that believers have everything they need in Christ. The lessons cover what Christ has done and what Christians should do. Questions lead to application of biblical truth and action plans.

Author: O'Donnell, Peter, et al.   **807**
Series: Life Application
Title: *Romans*
Publisher: Tyndale House, 1989

Num. Sess.	Group Time	Num. Pgs.	Avg. Qst.	Price	Audience	Format	Bible Study
13	60-90	88	13	4.95	New Christian	Workbk	Book

Features: Intro to Leading a Study, Intro to Study, Study Overview, Digging Deeper Quest, Full Scrpt Printed, Drawings, Charts, Maps, Cross Ref
  ★★★ Personal Application Preparation Time: Med ISBN: 0-8423-2718-5
  ★★★ Relationship Building Ldr. Guide Avail.: No Size: 6.50 x 9.0
Subjects: Commitments, Faith, Relationships, Romans
Comments: In this study, which contains the complete text of Romans, Paul clearly sets forth the foundations of Christian faith. He also provides clear, practical guidelines for believers in Rome. The study allows participants to reexamine their commitments to Christ and reconfirm their relationships with other believers. Questions lead to application of biblical truth and action plans.

Author: Offner, Hazel   **808**
Series: LifeGuide Bible Study
Title: *Fruit of the Spirit*
Publisher: InterVarsity, 1987

Num. Sess.	Group Time	Num. Pgs.	Avg. Qst.	Price	Audience	Format	Bible Study
9	45-60	57	10	3.95	New Christian	Workbk	Topical

Features: Intro to Leading a Study, Intro to Study, Ldr's Notes
  ★ Personal Application Preparation Time: Low ISBN: 0-8308-1058-7
  ★ Relationship Building Ldr. Guide Avail.: No Size: 5.50 x 8.25
Subjects: Christian Living, Discipleship, Fruit of the Spirit
Comments: This study draws on Old and New Testament verses to define, describe, and challenge believers to a Christlike maturity, and help them display the fruits of the Spirit, including love, joy, peace, patience, kindness, goodness, faithfulness, gentleness, and self-control. Strong emphasis is given to God's meaning of the "fruits of the Spirit" and the way each fruit can be worked out in our own lives. Optional passages are included for further study.

Author: Ogilvie, Lloyd John   **809**
Series: Proven Word
Title: *Ask Him Anything: God Can Handle Your Hardest Questions*
Publisher: Word, 1981

Num. Sess.	Group Time	Num. Pgs.	Avg. Qst.	Price	Audience	Format	Bible Study
20	45-60	270	7	8.99	New Christian	Book	Topical

Features: Intro to Leading a Study, Intro to Study, Ldr's Notes
  ★★★ Personal Application Preparation Time: Low ISBN: 0-8499-2982-2
  ★★ Relationship Building Ldr. Guide Avail.: No Size: 5.50 x 8.0
Subjects: Apologetics, Faith, Forgiveness, Prayer, Spiritual Gifts, Suffering
Comments: The study offers reassurance that God can handle the hardest questions—Where is He when I suffer? If God knows everything, why pray? What can I do with my moods? How do I forgive and forget? How do I discover my gifts? It encourages believers to seek God's answers to questions that lurk beneath the surface of faith, and includes study questions for small groups.

Author: Ogilvie, Lloyd John   **810**
Series: Proven Word
Title: *Bush Is Still Burning, The: The Christ Who Makes Things Happen*
Publisher: Word, 1980

Num. Sess.	Group Time	Num. Pgs.	Avg. Qst.	Price	Audience	Format	Bible Study
21	45-60	300	7	8.99	New Christian	Book	Topical

Features: Intro to Leading a Study, Intro to Study, Ldr's Notes
  ★★ Personal Application Preparation Time: Low ISBN: 0-8499-3031-6
  ★★ Relationship Building Ldr. Guide Avail.: No Size: 5.50 x 8.0
Subjects: Christian Living, John, Joy
Comments: The theme of this study is that the New Testament Jesus made several "I am" statements that tell who He is and what He can do in participants' lives. The study relates to twenty-one of the deepest needs people experience, as revealed in a nationwide survey. Questions in a built-in study guide are designed to help participants identify needs in their lives and pinpoint ways Jesus can satisfy these needs and offer the opportunity to live a joyful, free life.

Author: Ogilvie, Lloyd John   **811**
Series: Proven Word
Title: *Making Stress Work for You: Ten Proven Principles*
Publisher: Word, 1984

Num. Sess.	Group Time	Num. Pgs.	Avg. Qst.	Price	Audience	Format	Bible Study
10	45-60	220	6	8.99	Beginner	Book	Topical

Features: Ldr's Notes
★★ Personal Application   Preparation Time: Low   ISBN: 0-8499-3039-1
★★ Relationship Building   Ldr. Guide Avail.: No   Size: 5.50 x 8.0
Subjects: Emotions, James, Psychology, Stress
Comments: This study examines the problem of stress from medical and psychological perspectives, then uses the book of James as a biblical guide to its cure. It pinpoints ten antidotes to stress. Everything James wrote was to encourage early Christians to release the power of God in their lives. This power, available to modern Christians as well, includes the ability to cope with debilitating stress. The study includes a topical listing of biblical assurances for times of stress, and a study guide.

Author: Olson, Dennis T.   **812**
Series: Men's Bible Study Series
Title: *Bible, The: Ten Words for Today*
Publisher: Augsburg Publishing House, 1986

Num. Sess.	Group Time	Num. Pgs.	Avg. Qst.	Price	Audience	Format	Bible Study
10	30-45	48	11	3.0	New Christian	Workbk	Topical

Features: Intro to Study, Prayer Helps, Summary
★★★★ Personal Application   Preparation Time: None   ISBN:
★★★★ Relationship Building   Ldr. Guide Avail.: Yes   Size: 4.50 x 9.50
Subjects: Christian Living, Faith, Men's Issues, Wisdom
Comments: This ten-lesson study is for Christian men of any denomination who wish to better understand their faith. The lessons cover ten major scriptural themes: creation, stewardship, guidance, justice, praise, lament, wisdom, Jesus' good news, community, and resurrection. The lessons are brief and include an opening, Bible background, thought questions, summary, and prayer. The study may be used at prayer breakfasts, men's Bible study groups, or any other men's meetings.

Author: Olson, Dennis T.   **813**
Series: Men's Bible Study Series
Title: *Ethics for Living*
Publisher: Augsburg Publishing House, 1986

Num. Sess.	Group Time	Num. Pgs.	Avg. Qst.	Price	Audience	Format	Bible Study
10	30-45	48	9	3.0	New Christian	Workbk	Topical

Features: Intro to Study, Prayer Helps, Summary
★★★★ Personal Application   Preparation Time: None   ISBN:
★★★★ Relationship Building   Ldr. Guide Avail.: Yes   Size: 4.50 x 9.50
Subjects: Ethics, Faith, Men's Issues, Ten Commandments
Comments: This ten-lesson study encourages participants to consider how their faith affects their daily ethics. Concerning the Ten Commandments, it shows participants how the commands flow from a loving Creator. It may be used at prayer breakfasts, men's Bible study groups, or any other men's meetings.

Author: Olson, Edmund E.   **814**
Series: Small Group Bible Studies
Title: *Open the Door*
Publisher: Augsburg Publishing House, 1975

Num. Sess.	Group Time	Num. Pgs.	Avg. Qst.	Price	Audience	Format	Bible Study
4	60-75	16	13	0.95	New Christian	Book	Topical

Features: Intro to Study, Prayer Helps
★★★ Personal Application   Preparation Time: None   ISBN:
★★★ Relationship Building   Ldr. Guide Avail.: No   Size: 8.50 x 5.50
Subjects: Prayer
Comments: This short, four-session study on prayer begins with a personal evaluation of participants' prayer ideas and experiences. Session 2 examines the Lord's Prayer in different versions, Matthew 6:9-13 and Luke 11:1-4. Session 3 reviews Jesus in prayer, using John 17—sometimes called the "High Priestly Prayer." Jesus prays not just for Himself, but also for His own disciples and for the Church. The final lesson deals with the development of personal prayer life.

Author: Olson, Stanley N.   **815**
Series: Friendship Bible Study
Title: *Romans*
Publisher: Augsburg Publishing House, 1986

Num. Sess.	Group Time	Num. Pgs.	Avg. Qst.	Price	Audience	Format	Bible Study
8	60-75	48	10	3.0	New Christian	Workbk	Book

Features: Intro to Study, Prayer Helps, Study Overview
★★★★ Personal Application   Preparation Time: Low   ISBN:
★★★★ Relationship Building   Ldr. Guide Avail.: Yes   Size: 5.50 x 8.50
Subjects: Christian Living, God, Grace, Relationships, Romans
Comments: This eight-week study of Romans stresses justification by faith, not law, and emphasizes the interplay between Christian freedom and concern for others. The lesson format includes an overview, an opening, a responsive reading, Bible background, questions for reflection, a key verse, a prayer response, and an "our faith" response. Lesson titles include: "At Peace and Free," "Unbelief and the Promise of God," "Confident in the Gospel," and "God Creates Trust."

Author: Orr, Robert D., et al.   **816**
Series:
Title: *Life & Death Decisions*
Publisher: NavPress, 1990

Num. Sess.	Group Time	Num. Pgs.	Avg. Qst.	Price	Audience	Format	Bible Study
11	60-90	210	5	9.95	Beginner	Book	Topical

Features: Bibliography, Glossary, Appendix
★★★ Personal Application   Preparation Time: Med   ISBN: 0-89109-295-1
★★★ Relationship Building   Ldr. Guide Avail.: No   Size: 5.50 x 8.50
Subjects: Christian Living, Ethics, Grief, Medical Issues
Comments: This study helps participants make informed decisions about emotionally charged issues society faces, such as an infertile spouse, a severely handicapped newborn, a suffering aged parent, or a comatose teenager. The study, biblically based and medically reliable, uses case studies and discussion questions to help Christians face these kinds of issues. Of the three authors, two are medical experts and one has fourteen years of pastoral experience.

Author: Ortland, Ray & Anne   **817**
Series: Influencer Discussion
Title: *Renewal*
Publisher: NavPress, 1989

Num. Sess.	Group Time	Num. Pgs.	Avg. Qst.	Price	Audience	Format	Bible Study
9	90-120	84	10	5.95	New Christian	Workbk	Topical

Features: Intro to Study, Prayer Helps, Follow Up, Ldr's Notes
★★★★ Personal Application   Preparation Time: Low   ISBN: 0-89109-546-2
★★★★ Relationship Building   Ldr. Guide Avail.: No   Size: 5.50 x 8.50
Subjects: Evangelism, Relationships, Renewal
Comments: This study helps participants grow stronger in their relationship with God, with the Body of Christ, and with the unchurched. The lessons focus on practicing God's presence, developing lifestyles that reach the lost, and living in complete Christian liberty. A strong emphasis is placed on practicing renewal, as participants are challenged to set priorities and be determined to live a renewed life.

Author: Ortlund, Anne   **818**
Series: Proven Word
Title: *Disciplines of the Beautiful Woman*
Publisher: Word, 1977

Num. Sess.	Group Time	Num. Pgs.	Avg. Qst.	Price	Audience	Format	Bible Study
14	45-60	144	6	7.99	Beginner	Book	Topical

Features: Intro to Leading a Study, Intro to Study, Ldr's Notes
★★★ Personal Application   Preparation Time: Low   ISBN: 0-8499-2983-0
★★ Relationship Building   Ldr. Guide Avail.: No   Size: 5.50 x 8.0
Subjects: Prayer, Time, Women's Issues
Comments: This study is for every woman who wants to be truly beautiful, from the inside out. It offers practical, specific suggestions: hints for managing schedules, maintaining wardrobes, organizing personal notebooks. Sections on prayer, meditation, and discipline combine practical "hows" with thoughtful and considered "whys." Young and old, homemakers and career women, all can profit from this sound advice on living beautifully.

Author: Packer, J. I.   **819**
Series:
Title: *Knowing God*
Publisher: InterVarsity, 1975

Num. Sess.	Group Time	Num. Pgs.	Avg. Qst.	Price	Audience	Format	Bible Study
22	30-60	47	Vry	4.95	Beginner	Book	Charctr

Features: Intro to Study, Bibliography, Summary
★★★★ Personal Application   Preparation Time: Low   ISBN: 0-87784-413-5
★★★★ Relationship Building   Ldr. Guide Avail.: No   Size: 5.50 x 8.25
Subjects: God, Theology
Comments: This guide contains twenty-two studies, one for each chapter of the book by the same title. Christians can use the entire book or various chapters, according to their purposes, interest, and time limitations. Each study includes a purpose sentence, a series of questions, and summary questions. Participants will learn both who God is and how a human being can relate to Him. Three sections describe the hows and whys of knowing God, His attributes, and the benefits of being a child of God.

Author: Packer, J. I.   **820**
Series: LifeGuide Bible Study
Title: *Meeting God*
Publisher: InterVarsity, 1986

Num. Sess.	Group Time	Num. Pgs.	Avg. Qst.	Price	Audience	Format	Bible Study
12	45-60	64	11	3.95	New Christian	Workbk	Topical

Features: Intro to Leading a Study, Intro to Study, Ldr's Notes
★ Personal Application   Preparation Time: Low   ISBN: 0-8308-1057-9
★ Relationship Building   Ldr. Guide Avail.: No   Size: 5.50 x 8.25
Subjects: God, Holiness, Marriage, Theology
Comments: Twelve key Bible passages are explored which enlarge humanity's vision of God. The studies help refocus attention on God whenever the Bible is read, not on the principles of daily personal godliness. Exodus offers a fresh vision of God's glory and goodness. In John the Father is known through the Son. The remaining lessons challenge humanity's tiny thoughts of God's greatness, love, holiness, delivering power, comfort, control, mercy, and triumph.

Author: Packer, J. I.   **821**
Series: Living Studies
Title: *Ten Commandments, The*
Publisher: Tyndale House, 1977

Num. Sess.	Group Time	Num. Pgs.	Avg. Qst.	Price	Audience	Format	Bible Study
16	45-60	80	3	4.95	Beginner	Book	Topical

Features: Intro to Study, Digging Deeper Quest
★★ Personal Application   Preparation Time: Low   ISBN: 0-8423-7004-8
★★ Relationship Building   Ldr. Guide Avail.: No   Size: 5.0 x 8.0
Subjects: Christian Living, God, Ten Commandments
Comments: This companion study to the book *Knowing God* (1972) offers a series of brief outlines, or "sprints," designed to open discussion, with questions and Bible passages for further study. It explores various aspects of the Ten Commandments, God's directives for a successful life. In particular, it shows how the commandments reflect God's own nature, as well as His desire for people to turn to Him for a life well lived.

Author: Parker, Margaret   **822**
Series:
Title: *Unlocking the Power of God's Word*
Publisher: InterVarsity, 1991

Num. Sess.	Group Time	Num. Pgs.	Avg. Qst.	Price	Audience	Format	Bible Study
8	45-60	178	8	8.95	Beginner	Book	Topical

Features: Appendix
★★★ Personal Application   Preparation Time: Low   ISBN: 0-8308-1722-0
★★ Relationship Building   Ldr. Guide Avail.: No   Size: 5.50 x 8.25
Subjects: Bible Study
Comments: This eight-week study helps participants discover the excitement and enjoyment of Scripture. It provides beginning readers (and people who find the Bible dry and boring) with the right tools for bringing the images, poetry, and stories of Scripture to life. Each of the eight chapters is followed by a Bible study, and homework is optional.

Author: Parolini, Stephen   **823**
Series: Group's Active Bible Curriculum
Title: *Today's Music: Good or Bad?*
Publisher: Group Publishing, 1990

Num. Sess.	Group Time	Num. Pgs.	Avg. Qst.	Price	Audience	Format	Bible Study
4	35-60	45	Vry	6.95	Beginner	Workbk	Topical

Features: Intro to Leading a Study, Intro to Study, Objectives, Study Overview, Ldr's Notes, Handouts, Agenda, Publicity Ideas
  ★★★ Personal Application Preparation Time: None ISBN: 1-559-45101-7
  ★★★ Relationship Building Ldr. Guide Avail.: No Size: 8.50 x 11.0
Subjects: Teens: Junior High, Teens: Music
Comments: This study helps teenagers understand and evaluate contemporary music, and learn how their music can help them build a stronger relationship with God. It takes a look at the messages and controversy in music, alternative types of music, accepting opposing music tastes, and how to talk with parents and become selective listeners. It could be adapted for use in a Bible class or youth meeting, and activities and Bible studies are included as separate sheets that can be reproduced.

Author: Parrish, Archie & John Parrish   **824**
Series: Word LifeWare Video
Title: *Best Friends*
Publisher: Word, 1986

Num. Sess.	Group Time	Num. Pgs.	Avg. Qst.	Price	Audience	Format	Bible Study
13	45-60	N/A	Vry	179.99	New Christian	Video	Topical

Features: Intro to Leading a Study, Intro to Study, Bibliography, Drawings, Photos, Transpcy Masters, Publicity Ideas, Book Incl, Video Study Guide
  ★★★★ Personal Application Preparation Time: Low ISBN: 8-01-870079-6
  ★★★★ Relationship Building Ldr. Guide Avail.: Yes Size: 11.0 x 12.0
Subjects: Discipleship, Friendships, Obedience, Relationships
Comments: This video study helps Christians develop a renewed intimate relationship with God through loving, obedient means of growth. This intimate relationship equips Christians with spiritual strength and motivation to share the gospel with family and friends. The video begins as a television newscast, using personal interviews with people calling Jesus a friend closer than a brother. The diversified segments of the sessions keep the presentation interesting to view, and practical.

Author: Peace, Richard   **825**
Series:
Title: *Small Group Evangelism*
Publisher: InterVarsity, 1985

Num. Sess.	Group Time	Num. Pgs.	Avg. Qst.	Price	Audience	Format	Bible Study
13	60-75	190	N/A	8.95	New Christian	Book	Topical

Features: Ldr's Notes
  ★★★★ Personal Application Preparation Time: ISBN: 0-87784-329-5
  ★★★★ Relationship Building Ldr. Guide Avail.: No Size: 5.50 x 8.25
Subjects: Evangelism, Small Group Resource
Comments: This study combines theory and practice by explaining both the "ins and outs" of group dynamics, and how they affect presentation of the gospel. This nine- to thirteen-week program for training in small group evangelism includes a full set of guidelines to help leaders of training groups make the experience work. Timelines are given for both the eight chapters on "concept" and the eight sessions on "the experience."

Author: Peace, Richard & Lyman Coleman   **826**
Series: Mastering the Basics
Title: *1 John*
Publisher: Serendipity House, 1988

Num. Sess.	Group Time	Num. Pgs.	Avg. Qst.	Price	Audience	Format	Bible Study
7	60-75	64	Vry	5.95	Beginner	Workbk	Book

Features: Intro to Leading a Study, Intro to Study, Digging Deeper Quest, Summary, Full Scrpt Printed, Photos, Maps, Agenda
  ★★★ Personal Application Preparation Time: Low ISBN:
  ★★★ Relationship Building Ldr. Guide Avail.: Yes Size: 9.50 x 8.0
Subjects: 1, 2 & 3 John/Jude
Comments: The book of 1 John is John's record of his final thoughts on the nature of faith. It's written so that those leaning toward strange doctrine can, once and for all, get it straight. It records the essentials of Christianity as seen by the last of the twelve disciples. This verse-by-verse, seven- or thirteen-week study is part of "Mastering the Basics," a comprehensive, integrated program for personal or small group study. It features expository teaching with a master teacher.

Author: Peace, Richard   **827**
Series: Serendipity Support Group
Title: *12 Steps: The Path to Wholeness*
Publisher: Serendipity House, 1990

Num. Sess.	Group Time	Num. Pgs.	Avg. Qst.	Price	Audience	Format	Bible Study
7	60-90	96	Vry	5.45	Beginner	Workbk	Topical

Features: Intro to Leading a Study, Objectives, Bibliography, Full Scrpt Printed, Cartoons, Agenda
  ★★★★ Personal Application Preparation Time: None ISBN:
  ★★★★ Relationship Building Ldr. Guide Avail.: No Size: 6.50 x 9.25
Subjects: Addictions, God, Repentance, Support, Wholeness
Comments: This study offers a path to wholeness using the twelve step program. The first lesson defines the twelve step approach. Others include: "Naming the Addiction," "Naming the Higher Power," "Coming to God," "Being Open," "Being Repentant," and "Living Addiction-free." The format includes icebreakers, Bible study, and prayer. Timelines are provided for each lesson.

Author: Petersen, William J.   **828**
Series:
Title: *Jeremiah: The Prophet Who Wouldn't Quit*
Publisher: Victor Books, 1984

Num. Sess.	Group Time	Num. Pgs.	Avg. Qst.	Price	Audience	Format	Bible Study
13	60-75	155	N/A	7.99	New Christian	Book	Book

Features: Intro to Study, Bibliography
  ★★★ Personal Application Preparation Time: Low ISBN: 0-88207-243-9
  ★★ Relationship Building Ldr. Guide Avail.: Yes Size: 5.50 x 8.0
Subjects: Bible Personalities, Failure, Isaiah/Jeremiah, Major Prophets, Obedience, Prophecy
Comments: This thirteen-week study of the Old Testament prophet Jeremiah helps participants turn even the most trying times into spiritual stepping-stones. Jeremiah was thrust into a job he didn't want; he was often misunderstood; he was unsuccessful in his mission; and he complained frequently to God about his problems. He felt like giving up, but he didn't. Participants learn as Jeremiah did that a beliver grows through trials. A leader's guide includes transparency masters.

Author: Peterson, Eugene H.   **829**
Series: LifeGuide Bible Study
Title: *Psalms: Prayers of the Heart*
Publisher: InterVarsity, 1987

Num. Sess.	Group Time	Num. Pgs.	Avg. Qst.	Price	Audience	Format	Bible Study
12	45-60	64	11	3.95	New Christian	Workbk	Book

Features: Intro to Leading a Study, Intro to Study, Ldr's Notes
   ★ Personal Application   Preparation Time: Low   ISBN: 0-8308-1034-X
   ★ Relationship Building   Ldr. Guide Avail.: No   Size: 5.50 x 8.25
Subjects: Emotions, Prayer, Psalms
Comments: This is a book of poetry and prayer: the poetry exposes and sharpens what it means to be a human being before God; prayer is the language used to relate to and communicate with God. The Psalms do not teach about God but train response to Him. Areas dealt with include inattention, intimidation, trouble, creation, sin, salvation, fear, hate, tears, doubt, death, and praise. This introspective study allows growth in personal prayer life and dependence on God.

Author: Peterson, Lorraine   **830**
Series:
Title: *If God Loves Me, Why Can't I Get My Locker Open?*
Publisher: Bethany House, 1980

Num. Sess.	Group Time	Num. Pgs.	Avg. Qst.	Price	Audience	Format	Bible Study
13	45-60	153	N/A	6.95	New Christian	Book	Topical

Features: Intro to Leading a Study, Prayer Helps, Scrpt Memory Helps, Drawings
   ★★★ Personal Application   Preparation Time: Med   ISBN: 0-87123-251-0
   ★★ Relationship Building   Ldr. Guide Avail.: Yes   Size: 5.50 x 8.50
Subjects: Teens: Devotionals, Teens: Junior High, Teens: Psychology, Teens: Self-image, Teens: Senior High
Comments: This teen devotional has been adapted for group study through use of a companion teacher's guide. Twenty-five lessons incorporate ninety-one devotionals from the book for use during two quarters of a Sunday school class or weekly Bible study. The devotionals squarely face issues confronting teens in junior and senior high school. Examples include: "Do I Have to Forgive My Sister For Ruining My Good Jeans?" and "How Can I Get Rid of Self-Consciousness?"

Author: Phillips, John L.   **831**
Series: Teach Yourself the Bible
Title: *How to Live Forever*
Publisher: Moody Press, 1964

Num. Sess.	Group Time	Num. Pgs.	Avg. Qst.	Price	Audience	Format	Bible Study
8	45-60	48	18	3.99	Beginner	Workbk	Topical

Features: Intro to Leading a Study, Exam
   ★★ Personal Application   Preparation Time: Low   ISBN: 0-8024-3700-1
   ★★ Relationship Building   Ldr. Guide Avail.: No   Size: 5.50 x 8.50
Subjects: Evangelism, Theology
Comments: This study on how to live forever—part of a twenty-five-book series—is a step-by-step study of God's nature. Participants will learn that eternal life is a gift from God, and learn why to accept that gift. The format includes a series of fill-in-the-blank questions, and checkups to test participants' grasp of scriptural truths. The series is designed for self-study; however, suggestions for group study, and a four-year plan for using the series, are included.

Author: Pippert, Rebecca & Ruth Siemens   **832**
Series: LifeGuide Bible Study
Title: *Evangelism: A Way of Life*
Publisher: InterVarsity, 1985

Num. Sess.	Group Time	Num. Pgs.	Avg. Qst.	Price	Audience	Format	Bible Study
12	45-60	75	11	3.95	Mature Chrstn	Workbk	Topical

Features: Intro to Leading a Study, Intro to Study, Ldr's Notes
   ★ Personal Application   Preparation Time: Low   ISBN: 0-8308-1050-1
   ★ Relationship Building   Ldr. Guide Avail.: No   Size: 5.50 x 8.25
Subjects: Commitments, Evangelism
Comments: This is a practical guide for communicating the gospel. Evangelism can be intimidating for Christians as well as nonChristians, but with proper understanding it can be a natural and exciting way of life. Topics covered include the "why" of sharing, reluctant evangelists, seeking the lost, getting people interested, creative communication, friendship evangelism, talking with strangers, cross-cultural evangelism, presenting the cost of commitment, facing opposition, and balanced expectations.

Author: Pippert, Rebecca   **833**
Series:
Title: *Hope Has Its Reasons*
Publisher: NavPress, 1991

Num. Sess.	Group Time	Num. Pgs.	Avg. Qst.	Price	Audience	Format	Bible Study
6	60-90	32	10	139.0	New Christian	Video	No

Features: Intro to Leading a Study, Intro to Study, Objectives, Prayer Helps, Pre-discussion Quest, Follow Up, Full Scrpt Printed, Ldr's Notes, Glossary, Video Study Guide
   ★★★★ Personal Application   Preparation Time: None   ISBN: 9-900738-04-7
   ★★★★ Relationship Building   Ldr. Guide Avail.: No   Size: 8.50 x 11.0
Subjects: Christian Living, Emotions, Hope, Relationships
Comments: Does being a Christian make a practical difference to our lives? In six thirty-minute talks, Pippert shows how the Cross and the Resurrection are vitally relevant to modern life, and how to live in light of them. We are forgiven people, and resurrection power to overcome our bondages is available to us. The guide is geared toward helping viewers get to know each other, examine their own lives, and support one another in putting their insights into practice.

Author: Pippert, Rebecca   **834**
Series:
Title: *Out of the Saltshaker & into the World*
Publisher: InterVarsity, 1979

Num. Sess.	Group Time	Num. Pgs.	Avg. Qst.	Price	Audience	Format	Bible Study
12	60-90	31	10	4.95	New Christian	Workbk	Topical

Features: Intro to Study, Bibliography, Prayer Helps
   ★★★★ Personal Application   Preparation Time: Med   ISBN: 0-87784-532-8
   ★★★ Relationship Building   Ldr. Guide Avail.: Yes   Size: 5.50 x 8.25
Subjects: Evangelism
Comments: This study demonstrates how to make evangelism a way of life. Its stories, biblical insight, and plain common sense will help participants feel relaxed and enthusiastic about sharing their faith. Each lesson in the parallel is divided into three sections: purpose, understanding, and application. The lessons suggest how group members can support each other as they witness, and provide opportunities for practicing witnessing skills and developing the ability to be open without being pushy.

Author: Plueddemann, Carol　　　　**835**
Series: Fisherman Bible Studyguide
Title: *Great Passages of the Bible*
Publisher: Shaw, 1987

Num. Sess.	Group Time	Num. Pgs.	Avg. Qst.	Price	Audience	Format	Bible Study
14	45-60	76	12	3.95	Beginner	Workbk	Topical

Features: Intro to Leading a Study, Intro to Study, Prayer Helps
　★★ Personal Application　Preparation Time: None　ISBN: 0-87788-332-7
　★★ Relationship Building　Ldr. Guide Avail.: No　Size: 5.0 x 8.25
Subjects: Jesus: Life/Teaching, New Testament, Old Testament, Ten Commandments
Comments: This study, which presents an overview of main themes of the Bible, focuses on fourteen individual, chronological passages from the Old and New Testaments. They include the Ten Commandments, Psalm 23, and the birth, death, and resurrection of Christ among others. God's plan for all people and each person's part in that design is made clearer by this study.

Author: Plueddemann, Carol, et al.　　**836**
Series: Fisherman Bible Studyguide
Title: *Great People of the Bible*
Publisher: Shaw, 1988

Num. Sess.	Group Time	Num. Pgs.	Avg. Qst.	Price	Audience	Format	Bible Study
15	45-60	77	11	3.95	Beginner	Workbk	Charctr

Features: Intro to Leading a Study, Intro to Study, Prayer Helps, Follow Up
　★★ Personal Application　Preparation Time: None　ISBN: 0-87788-333-5
　★★ Relationship Building　Ldr. Guide Avail.: No　Size: 5.0 x 8.25
Subjects: Bible Personalities, Failure, God, Hope, Loneliness, Relationships
Comments: These fifteen character studies look into the lives of well-known Bible characters, including Adam and Eve, Moses, Ruth, Mary, Peter, and Barnabas. The great heroes of the past struggled with difficult family relationships, failure, illness, poverty, death, war, temptation, and loneliness—the same challenges we face today. Whether they conquered or failed, they always experienced God's faithfulness. Studying the trials and tribulations of Bible characters offers Christians encouragement and hope.

Author: Plueddemann, Carol　　　　**837**
Series: Fisherman Bible Studyguide
Title: *Great Prayers of the Bible*
Publisher: Shaw, 1991

Num. Sess.	Group Time	Num. Pgs.	Avg. Qst.	Price	Audience	Format	Bible Study
13	45-60	64	12	3.95	New Christian	Workbk	Topical

Features: Intro to Leading a Study, Intro to Study, Prayer Helps, Follow Up
　★★★ Personal Application　Preparation Time: None　ISBN: 0-87788-334-3
　★★★ Relationship Building　Ldr. Guide Avail.: No　Size: 5.0 x 8.25
Subjects: Bible Personalities, Prayer
Comments: These lessons help participants understand the discipline of prayer and God's character, through the lives of His praying people throughout history. Participants see how people like David, Daniel, and Mary talked to God and what can be learned from their examples. Through the prayers of Hannah, Job, and Paul, they will discover much about God's character. The great prayers recorded in Scripture offer Christians models for their own prayer lives.

Author: Plueddemann, Jim & Carol　　**838**
Series:
Title: *Pilgrims in Progress*
Publisher: Shaw, 1990

Num. Sess.	Group Time	Num. Pgs.	Avg. Qst.	Price	Audience	Format	Bible Study
12	-	165	N/A	7.95		Book	No

Features: Intro to Study, Bibliography, Index, Appendix
　Personal Application　Preparation Time:　ISBN: 0-87788-647-4
　Relationship Building　Ldr. Guide Avail.:　Size: 5.25 x 8.25
Subjects: Leadership, Small Group Resource
Comments: This book concerns why small groups work and how they can be most effective. It provides a historical perspective; speaks to the purpose, nature, and aim, of small groups; and discusses the methods by which Christians (pilgrims) form them. "Pilgrim" leaders are discussed in a narrow context, as only authoritarian and laissez-faire styles are addressed. Remaining chapters include "Benefits and Pitfalls," "Profiles of Pilgrim Groups," and "Strengthening Pilgrim Groups." Questions are provided.

Author: Plueddemann, Jim　　　　**839**
Series: Fisherman Bible Studyguide
Title: *Strengthened to Serve: 2 Corinthians*
Publisher: Shaw, 1991

Num. Sess.	Group Time	Num. Pgs.	Avg. Qst.	Price	Audience	Format	Bible Study
12	45-60	64	12	3.95	New Christian	Workbk	Book

Features: Intro to Leading a Study, Intro to Study, Prayer Helps, Follow Up
　★★★ Personal Application　Preparation Time: None　ISBN: 0-87788-783-7
　★★ Relationship Building　Ldr. Guide Avail.: No　Size: 5.0 x 8.25
Subjects: Service, Success, 2 Corinthians
Comments: These lessons discuss service, a great theme of Paul's second letter to the Corinthian Christians. It helps participants sort out society's concepts of success and develop biblical views of successful ministry and service to a needy world.

Author: Plunkett, Mark W.　　　　**840**
Series: Standard Bible Studies
Title: *John*
Publisher: Standard Publishing, 1987

Num. Sess.	Group Time	Num. Pgs.	Avg. Qst.	Price	Audience	Format	Bible Study
13	60-80	80	Vry	3.50	New Christian	Workbk	Book

Features: Intro to Leading a Study, Objectives, Digging Deeper Quest
　★★ Personal Application　Preparation Time: Low　ISBN: 0-87403-184-2
　★★ Relationship Building　Ldr. Guide Avail.: Yes　Size: 8.50 x 11.0
Subjects: Jesus: Life/Teaching, John
Comments: This thirteen-lesson workbook, a companion to Lewis Foster's study of John, focuses on "The Way," "The Truth," and "The Life." Each lesson features training goals, lesson aims, and key ideas. Each lesson begins with introductory activities, followed by Bible study, "Digging Deeper" questions, and "What do you think?" questions. Only the leader in a small group setting needs this companion book.

Author: Pollinger, Eileen   **841**
Series: Building Books
Title: *Building Christian Discipline*
Publisher: Bethany House, 1986

Num. Sess.	Group Time	Num. Pgs.	Avg. Qst.	Price	Audience	Format	Bible Study
34	45-60	48	Vry	4.95	New Christian	Workbk	Topical

Features: Intro to Study, Scrpt Memory Helps, Charts
  ★★ Personal Application   Preparation Time: Low   ISBN: 0-87123-877-2
  ★★ Relationship Building   Ldr. Guide Avail.: Yes   Size: 8.50 x 11.0
Subjects: Teens: Discipleship, Teens: Prayer
Comments: This thirty-four-lesson study shows young people how to apply Christian discipline through prayer, praise, confession, thanksgiving, and Bible reading. It encourages them to examine their lives in the light of biblical standards, asking: "What are my strengths?" "In what areas do I fall short?" and "Where can I begin to improve in disciplining my life?"

Author: Powell, Terry D.   **842**
Series: Lay Action Ministry
Title: *Learning to Serve: Jesus As Role Model*
Publisher: Lay Action Ministry Program, 1989

Num. Sess.	Group Time	Num. Pgs.	Avg. Qst.	Price	Audience	Format	Bible Study
12	60-90	112	Vry	5.95	New Christian	Workbk	Topical

Features: Prayer Helps, Ldr's Notes
  ★★★ Personal Application   Preparation Time: Low   ISBN: 0-89191-489-7
  ★★★ Relationship Building   Ldr. Guide Avail.: Yes   Size: 5.25 x 8.25
Subjects: Accountability, Church Life, Jesus: Life/Teaching, Service
Comments: This study helps participants understand and follow the example of Jesus, the greatest servant. They discover how servanthood begins in the heart; how a true servant prays, loves, trusts, and faces temptation; and how to be accountable to others, who can help them grow. The leader's guide includes perspectives and objectives for each lesson, suggestions for accountability, a focusing activity, and a discovering and responding to the Word section. Homework is required.

Author: Powell, Terry D.   **843**
Series: Lay Action Ministry
Title: *Welcome to the Church*
Publisher: Lay Action Ministry Program, 1987

Num. Sess.	Group Time	Num. Pgs.	Avg. Qst.	Price	Audience	Format	Bible Study
12	60-90	96	Vry	5.95	New Christian	Workbk	Topical

Features: Prayer Helps, Scrpt Memory Helps
  ★★★ Personal Application   Preparation Time: Low   ISBN: 0-89191-514-1
  ★★★ Relationship Building   Ldr. Guide Avail.: Yes   Size: 5.25 x 8.25
Subjects: Church Life, Prayer, Service
Comments: This practical study helps participants respond to several questions: How do I tell others about salvation? How can I know God better? How do I tap the power of prayer? How do I "fit in" at my church? Answers to these questions are explored as participants learn how to search Scripture for guidance. A Christian service inventory is included. Homework is required. An accompanying book, *Daily Time with God,* focuses on scheduled Bible reading, Bible memory, prayer, and notetaking from sermons.

Author: Powell, Terry D.   **844**
Series: Lay Action Ministry
Title: *Welcome to Your Ministry*
Publisher: Lay Action Ministry Program, 1987

Num. Sess.	Group Time	Num. Pgs.	Avg. Qst.	Price	Audience	Format	Bible Study
12	60-90	96	Vry	5.95	New Christian	Workbk	Topical

Features:
  ★★★ Personal Application   Preparation Time: Low   ISBN: 0-89191-515-X
  ★★★ Relationship Building   Ldr. Guide Avail.: Yes   Size: 5.25 x 8.25
Subjects: Church Life, Service, Spiritual Gifts
Comments: This practical study helps participants identify and develop their spiritual gifts. They learn that God has called them—not just pastors and church leaders—to minister on His behalf and leave distinctive marks for Christ wherever they go. The study provides biblical foundations for lay ministry; students will be excited by the opportunities and rewards of serving Christ. The ministries of encouragement, intercession, and evangelism are among subjects covered. Homework is required.

Author: Raguse, Dan   **845**
Series: Group's Active Bible Curriculum
Title: *Prayer*
Publisher: Group Publishing, 1990

Num. Sess.	Group Time	Num. Pgs.	Avg. Qst.	Price	Audience	Format	Bible Study
4	35-60	45	Vry	6.95	Beginner	Workbk	Topical

Features: Intro to Leading a Study, Intro to Study, Objectives, Study Overview, Ldr's Notes, Handouts, Agenda, Publicity Ideas
  ★★★ Personal Application   Preparation Time: None   ISBN: 1-559-45104-1
  ★★★ Relationship Building   Ldr. Guide Avail.: No   Size: 8.50 x 11.0
Subjects: Teens: Junior High, Teens: Prayer
Comments: Christian teenagers will learn how to unleash the power of prayer and develop active prayer lives. This study explores topics like "Why Pray?" "How to Pray," "God's Answer to Prayer," and "Developing a Prayer Attitude." This course can be adapted for use in a Bible class or youth meeting. Activities and Bible studies are included as separate sheets that can be reproduced. The instructions are easy to follow, and there are multiple options for teachers.

Author: Rainey, Barbara & Dennis   **846**
Series: Homebuilders Couples
Title: *Strengthening Your Mate's Self-Esteem*
Publisher: Word, 1989

Num. Sess.	Group Time	Num. Pgs.	Avg. Qst.	Price	Audience	Format	Bible Study
8	60-90	180	Vry	8.99	Beginner	Workbk	Topical

Features: Prayer Helps, Charts
  ★★★★ Personal Application   Preparation Time: Low   ISBN: 0-8499-8339-8
  ★★★ Relationship Building   Ldr. Guide Avail.: Yes   Size: 5.50 x 8.50
Subjects: Family, Marriage, Self-esteem
Comments: This study helps participants focus on practical ways to strengthen marriage by building up and encouraging one another. Sessions include: learning practical and effective ways to love and support one's mate; repairing past hurts in a spouse's life; building intimacy through unconditional acceptance; and communicating freely by working together on sixteen practical projects.

Author: Rainey, Dennis   **847**
Series: Homebuilders Couples
Title: *Building Your Marriage*
Publisher: Word, 1989

Num. Sess.	Group Time	Num. Pgs.	Avg. Qst.	Price	Audience	Format	Bible Study
7	60-90	148	Vry	8.99	Beginner	Workbk	Topical

Features: Summary, Charts
  ★★★★ Personal Application   Preparation Time: Low   ISBN: 0-8499-8336-3
   ★★★ Relationship Building   Ldr. Guide Avail.: Yes   Size: 5.50 x 8.50
Subjects: Family, Marriage
Comments: This study helps participants discover many ways to apply God's blueprint for a strong marriage. These include learning to express and experience real love; rekindling romance by sharing feelings, hopes, and dreams; working together to solve annoying, persistent marital problems; and growing together with other couples. A "Make a Date" segment is a between-session, joy-filled assignment that can lead to better communication, deeper commitment, and a stronger family.

Author: Reapsome, James & Martha   **848**
Series: Fisherman Bible Studyguide
Title: *Discipleship: The Growing Christian's Lifestyle*
Publisher: Shaw, 1984

Num. Sess.	Group Time	Num. Pgs.	Avg. Qst.	Price	Audience	Format	Bible Study
12	45-60	57	14	3.95	New Christian	Workbk	Topical

Features: Intro to Leading a Study, Intro to Study, Prayer Helps
  ★★ Personal Application   Preparation Time: None   ISBN: 0-87788-175-8
  ★★ Relationship Building   Ldr. Guide Avail.: No   Size: 5.0 x 8.25
Subjects: Bible Personalities, Discipleship
Comments: This study explores Jesus' requirements of those who want to be His disciples. Selected passages address the life of discipleship under the lordship of Jesus Christ. Ten studies discuss principles of discipleship, while two studies show how New Testament personalities demonstrate the characteristics of discipleship. In total, the study explores ways to become a true follower of Jesus, by identifying with His character, attitudes, and priorities, and by drawing on His resources.

Author: Reapsome, James   **849**
Series: LifeGuide Bible Study
Title: *Exodus: Learning to Trust God*
Publisher: InterVarsity, 1989

Num. Sess.	Group Time	Num. Pgs.	Avg. Qst.	Price	Audience	Format	Bible Study
24	45-75	110	14	3.95	New Christian	Workbk	Book

Features: Intro to Leading a Study, Intro to Study, Ldr's Notes
  ★ Personal Application   Preparation Time: Low   ISBN: 0-8308-1023-4
  ★ Relationship Building   Ldr. Guide Avail.: No   Size: 5.50 x 8.25
Subjects: Exodus, God
Comments: This study shows how Israel's struggle to trust God mirrors that of modern man. It's divided into two parts: the first twelve lessons concern liberating God's people (Exodus 1-19); the second twelve lessons teach God's people (Exodus 20-40). The study covers one hundred years of Hebrew history and is organized around major events, their significance for Israel and the insights and practical values relevant today. It is a good study for those with only a basic knowledge of Hebrew history.

Author: Reapsome, James & Martha   **850**
Series: LifeGuide Bible Study
Title: *Marriage: God's Design for Intimacy*
Publisher: InterVarsity, 1986

Num. Sess.	Group Time	Num. Pgs.	Avg. Qst.	Price	Audience	Format	Bible Study
12	45-60	63	11	3.95	New Christian	Workbk	Topical

Features: Intro to Leading a Study, Intro to Study, Ldr's Notes
  ★★★ Personal Application   Preparation Time: Med   ISBN: 0-8308-1056-0
  ★★ Relationship Building   Ldr. Guide Avail.: No   Size: 5.50 x 8.25
Subjects: God, Marriage, Money, Relationships
Comments: This study begins with the view of God's purpose and plan for marriage, as well as the source of broken relationship between husband and wife as shown in Genesis. In Galatians, God's design is restored. In Ephesians, the role of the man and woman is explored. The remaining lessons deal with God's design for communication, conflict, and handling money. The final study explores God's demand for faithfulness and love in marriage. "Between study" assignments are effective.

Author: Reapsome, James   **851**
Series: Fisherman Bible Studyguide
Title: *Romans: The Christian Story*
Publisher: Shaw, 1989

Num. Sess.	Group Time	Num. Pgs.	Avg. Qst.	Price	Audience	Format	Bible Study
16	45-60	75	10	3.95	Beginner	Workbk	Book

Features: Intro to Leading a Study, Intro to Study, Ldr's Notes
  ★★ Personal Application   Preparation Time: Low   ISBN: 0-87788-734-9
  ★★ Relationship Building   Ldr. Guide Avail.: No   Size: 5.0 x 8.25
Subjects: Romans
Comments: This study inseparably binds theology and practice. After Paul drills theology into the minds and hearts of his readers, he calls them to transformed living. The study includes justification, reconciliation, righteousness, sin, and redemption. Other topics covered are how to be holy in daily conduct, how to live under government, and how to get along with fellow believers in church and unbelieving neighbors across the street. The chapter-by-chapter treatment includes topical subjects.

Author: Reapsome, Martha   **852**
Series: LifeGuide Bible Study
Title: *Colossians & Philemon*
Publisher: InterVarsity, 1989

Num. Sess.	Group Time	Num. Pgs.	Avg. Qst.	Price	Audience	Format	Bible Study
10	45-60	63	12	3.95	New Christian	Workbk	Book

Features: Intro to Leading a Study, Intro to Study, Ldr's Notes
  ★ Personal Application   Preparation Time: Low   ISBN: 0-8308-1014-5
  ★ Relationship Building   Ldr. Guide Avail.: No   Size: 5.50 x 8.25
Subjects: Church Life, Colossians/Philemon, False Teachers, Forgiveness, Hope, Prison Epistles, Relationships, Service, Suffering
Comments: The twentieth century teaches "more" is better—more wisdom, maturity, power, faith, and material goods. People seek "more" in secular ways: seminars, concerts, books, horoscopes, even gurus. Paul responded to Colossian Christians with similar longings by pointing to the fullness in Christ—which they had—and away from false teachers. The study of Colossians defines the scope, reality, and implications of fullness of life in Christ. Philemon offers principles for mending relationships.

Author: Reeder, W. Donald 853
Series: Teach Yourself the Bible
Title: *Letters of John and Jude, The*
Publisher: Moody Press, 1965

Num. Sess.	Group Time	Num. Pgs.	Avg. Qst.	Price	Audience	Format	Bible Study
8	60-75	64	37	3.99	New Christian	Workbk	Book

Features: Intro to Leading a Study, Exam
★★ Personal Application   Preparation Time: Low   ISBN: 0-8024-4674-4
★★ Relationship Building   Ldr. Guide Avail.: No   Size: 5.50 x 8.50
Subjects: Church Life, False Teachers, 1, 2 & 3 John/Jude
Comments: This study is part of a twenty-five-book series and concerns four letters addressed to members of the early Church. Their problems, similar to those faced by contemporary Christians, include struggling with false teachers, heresy, and intrachurch personalities. The format includes a series of fill-in-the-blank questions, and checkups to test participants' grasp of scriptural truths. The series is designed for self-study; however, suggestions for group study are included.

Author: Reuss, Edith A. 854
Series: Small Group Bible Studies
Title: *Mary*
Publisher: Augsburg Publishing House, 1978

Num. Sess.	Group Time	Num. Pgs.	Avg. Qst.	Price	Audience	Format	Bible Study
4	60-75	16	18	0.95	New Christian	Book	Charctr

Features: Intro to Study, Prayer Helps
★★★ Personal Application   Preparation Time: None   ISBN:
★★ Relationship Building   Ldr. Guide Avail.: No   Size: 8.50 x 5.50
Subjects: Bible Personalities, Faith, Jesus: Life/Teaching, Prophecy
Comments: This small pamphlet includes four sessions on Mary, the Lord's mother. The study portrays the unfolding drama of Jesus' birth and life from her point of view. It gives a clearer picture of Mary as a real person. Sessions include: "Mary, an Example of Faith"; "Mary, Fulfiller of Prophecy"; "Mary, the Mother of the Christ"; and "Mary, Follower of the Christ." Starred questions are especially recommended for group discussion.

Author: Reynolds, Randy 855
Series: Serendipity Support Group
Title: *Compassion Fatigue: Worn Out from Caring*
Publisher: Serendipity House, 1990

Num. Sess.	Group Time	Num. Pgs.	Avg. Qst.	Price	Audience	Format	Bible Study
7	60-90	80	Vry	5.45	Beginner	Workbk	Topical

Features: Intro to Leading a Study, Objectives, Bibliography, Prayer Helps, Full Scrpt Printed, Cartoons, Agenda
★★★★ Personal Application   Preparation Time: None   ISBN:
★★★★ Relationship Building   Ldr. Guide Avail.: No   Size: 6.50 x 9.25
Subjects: Caring, Stress, Support
Comments: This study is for caregivers who face the danger of burnout from giving of themselves. Issues covered include: the gift of caring, the causes of burnout, dependency, self-protection, recovery, and how to handle the feeling of being indispensable. The format includes icebreakers, Bible study, and prayer. Timelines are provided for each lesson.

Author: Rhodes, Ron 856
Series: The Lifechange Series
Title: *Hebrews*
Publisher: NavPress, 1989

Num. Sess.	Group Time	Num. Pgs.	Avg. Qst.	Price	Audience	Format	Bible Study
19	60-90	190	18	5.95	New Christian	Workbk	Book

Features: Intro to Leading a Study, Intro to Study, Bibliography, Prayer Helps, Worship Helps, Study Overview, Digging Deeper Quest, Summary, Cross Ref, Word Study
★★★ Personal Application   Preparation Time: Med   ISBN: 0-89109-272-2
★★★ Relationship Building   Ldr. Guide Avail.: No   Size: 5.50 x 8.50
Subjects: Faith, Hebrews, Obedience
Comments: This is a study of Hebrews, which reigns unchallenged as the New Testament's finest commentary on the relationship between Christ and the Old Testament. Its message challenges participants to live wholeheartedly for Christ in every situation. They see Jewish Christians faced with hostility and loss of jobs and tempted to revert to Jewish customs. Then they see a trusted mentor remind them that Christ is far superior to anything Judaism offers.

Author: Rhodes, Ron 857
Series: The Lifechange Series
Title: *Proverbs*
Publisher: NavPress, 1990

Num. Sess.	Group Time	Num. Pgs.	Avg. Qst.	Price	Audience	Format	Bible Study
15	60-90	149	15	5.95	New Christian	Workbk	Book

Features: Intro to Leading a Study, Intro to Study, Bibliography, Prayer Helps, Worship Helps, Study Overview, Digging Deeper Quest, Summary, Charts, Cross Ref, Word Study
★★★ Personal Application   Preparation Time: Med   ISBN: 0-89109-348-6
★★★ Relationship Building   Ldr. Guide Avail.: No   Size: 5.50 x 8.50
Subjects: Christian Living, Proverbs, Wisdom
Comments: This verse-by-verse study of Proverbs offers participants a wealth of practical wisdom for everyday living. Its timeless teachings provide helpful advice on nearly every aspect—both good and bad—of personal conduct imaginable, including goodness, folly, sin, wealth and poverty, the tongue, pride and humility, justice, vengeance, strife, gluttony, love, lust, laziness, friendship, the family, life, and death.

Author: Richards, Lawrence O. 858
Series:
Title: *Creative Personal Bible Study*
Publisher: Zondervan, 1987

Num. Sess.	Group Time	Num. Pgs.	Avg. Qst.	Price	Audience	Format	Bible Study
10	-	123	N/A	7.95	Beginner	Book	Topical

Features: Full Scrpt Printed
　　Personal Application   Preparation Time: ISBN: 0-310-31891-2
　　Relationship Building   Ldr. Guide Avail.:   Size: 5.25 x 8.0
Subjects: Bible Study, Small Group Resource
Comments: This study can be effectively used to transform potential leaders' personal time with God. It deals with ideas, feelings, attitudes, and assumptions that people bring to Scripture—matters that can cloud their understanding of the Bible's intended message. Selected biblical passages, reader exercises, and new concepts are used to develop a dynamic, creative, personal Bible study.

Author: Richards, Lawrence O.   **859**
Series:
Title: *99 Ways to Start a Study Group and Keep It Growing*
Publisher: Zondervan, 1987

Num. Sess.	Group Time	Num. Pgs.	Avg. Qst.	Price	Audience	Format	Bible Study
6	-	158	N/A	6.95		Book	No

Features:
    Personal Application   Preparation Time: ISBN: 0-310-31921-8
    Relationship Building Ldr. Guide Avail.:   Size: 5.50 x 8.0
Subjects: Small Group Resource
Comments: This book offers five principles for properly balancing Bible study and fellowship in groups: identification, affirmation, exploration, concentration, and adoration. Then it outlines ninety-nine ways to start groups and keep them growing. Some areas covered include creative ideas for group involvement, affirmation, fresh ideas on studying Scripture, and worship.

Author: Rickerson, Wayne   **860**
Series:
Title: *This Is the Thanks I Get? A Guide to Raising Teenagers*
Publisher: Standard Publishing, 1988

Num. Sess.	Group Time	Num. Pgs.	Avg. Qst.	Price	Audience	Format	Bible Study
13	60-120	142	10	5.99	Beginner	Book	Topical

Features: Intro to Leading a Study, Intro to Study, Drawings
  ★★★ Personal Application Preparation Time: Low   ISBN: 0-87403-406-X
  ★★ Relationship Building Ldr. Guide Avail.: Yes   Size: 5.25 x 8.50
Subjects: Parenting, Relationships, Support
Comments: This study, part of a two-book series on rearing children, is designed to prepare parents, through Bible-inspired instruction and by encouraging the development of parenting support groups, for the task of parenting teenagers. Three sections take participants from laying a firm foundation for understanding and preparation, to developing a structure and skills for dealing with teens, to building a positive relationship involving give-and-take and communication. Discussion questions follow each section.

Author: Rickerson, Wayne   **861**
Series:
Title: *What Should I Do Now? A Guide to Raising Children*
Publisher: Standard Publishing, 1988

Num. Sess.	Group Time	Num. Pgs.	Avg. Qst.	Price	Audience	Format	Bible Study
13	60-120	176	10	5.99	Beginner	Book	Topical

Features: Intro to Study, Drawings
  ★★★ Personal Application Preparation Time: Low   ISBN: 0-87403-405-1
  ★★ Relationship Building Ldr. Guide Avail.: Yes   Size: 5.25 x 8.50
Subjects: Ethics, Family, Parenting, Relationships, Support
Comments: This study, part of a two-book series on rearing children, is designed to prepare parents for parenting, through Bible-inspired instruction and by encouraging the development of parenting support groups. Three sections take participants through the following topics: family foundations, Christian values, and family togetherness; the basics of parenting, dealing with authority; and what to do when the kids fight. Discussion questions follow each section. This is ideal for individuals or groups.

Author: Ridenour, Fritz   **862**
Series: LifeTouch
Title: *How to Be a Christian and Still Enjoy Life*
Publisher: Regal Books, 1988

Num. Sess.	Group Time	Num. Pgs.	Avg. Qst.	Price	Audience	Format	Bible Study
13	60-75	190	Vry	7.95	New Christian	Book	Topical

Features: Prayer Helps, Drawings
  ★★★★ Personal Application Preparation Time: Med   ISBN: 0-8307-1218-6
  ★★★★ Relationship Building Ldr. Guide Avail.: Yes   Size: 5.50 x 8.50
Subjects: Christian Life, Integrity, Joy, Philippians, Prison Epistles, Success, Victorious Living
Comments: This study examines what Paul's letter to the Philippians says about integrity, perseverance, and true success. Philippians shows participants why life can be joyous. The format combines Bible commentary with life-related questions to challenge participants to incorporate their spiritual discoveries into daily living. The separate leader's guide offers an eight- to thirteen-week study format. A lesson handout section which can be reproduced for Bible study is included.

Author: Robbins, Duffy   **863**
Series: Any Old Time
Title: *Any Old Time (Book 8)*
Publisher: Victor Books, 1987

Num. Sess.	Group Time	Num. Pgs.	Avg. Qst.	Price	Audience	Format	Bible Study
15	30-45	80	Vry	9.99	New Christian	Book	Topical

Features: Intro to Study, Objectives, Bibliography, Prayer Helps, Study Overview, Digging Deeper Quest, Ldr's Notes, Charts
  ★★★★ Personal Application Preparation Time: None   ISBN: 0-89693-514-0
  ★★★★ Relationship Building Ldr. Guide Avail.: No   Size: 8.50 x 11.0
Subjects: Teens: Bible/Pers., Teens: Discipleship, Teens: Junior High, Teens: Senior High
Comments: This book includes fifteen topical sessions strong on content and short on preparation time. Each contains opening games, warm-up activities, biblical application, and a wrap-up section. There are three parts on growth: as a person, as a disciple, and as a fellowship. Growth as a person includes studing Bible characters like Pharaoh, Peter, and Samson. Growth as a disciple includes studies of "The Complete Man" (2 Timothy 3:1-17) and "A Man for All Seasons" (2 Timothy 4: 1-18).

Author: Roecker, Ann   **864**
Series: Workshop Series
Title: *Workshop on Time Management, A*
Publisher: Zondervan, 1988

Num. Sess.	Group Time	Num. Pgs.	Avg. Qst.	Price	Audience	Format	Bible Study
10	60-90	88	Vry	4.95	Beginner	Workbk	Topical

Features: Intro to Study
  ★★ Personal Application Preparation Time: None   ISBN: 0-310-37931-8
  ★★ Relationship Building Ldr. Guide Avail.: No   Size: 5.25 x 8.0
Subjects: Men's Issues, Time, Women's Issues, Work
Comments: This is a workable Bible study on time management. In addition to the Old and New Testaments, it quotes many other sources, such as Martin Luther, Albert Einstein, and Carl Sagan. Participants will determine ways to establish priorities, plan schedules, and learn to say no without feeling guilty. The role model is "Jesus Christ . . .never frenzied, never anxious, never unorganized, nor out of control."

Author: Roen, Scott D. 865
Series: Lay Action Ministry
Title: *Outreach As a Life-Style*
Publisher: Lay Action Ministry Program, 1989

Num. Sess.	Group Time	Num. Pgs.	Avg. Qst.	Price	Audience	Format	Bible Study
12	60-90	142	Vry	5.95	New Christian	Workbk	Topical

Features: Intro to Study, Prayer Helps, Scrpt Memory Helps, Ldr's Notes
★★★ Personal Application   Preparation Time: Low   ISBN: 0-89191-484-6
★★★ Relationship Building   Ldr. Guide Avail.: Yes   Size: 5.25 x 8.25
Subjects: Accountability, Evangelism
Comments: This study shows Christians how to take the terror out of sharing their faith. Participants discover how to listen to nonbelievers, sense their needs, and gauge their levels of interest. They also learn how to clarify their own personal testimony, explain the gospel, and handle objections. The leaders's guide includes perspectives and objectives for each lesson, suggestion for accountability, a focusing activity, and a section on responding to the Word.

Author: Root, Jerry & Claudia 866
Series: NetWork Discussion Guide
Title: *Friendship Evangelism*
Publisher: Shaw, 1990

Num. Sess.	Group Time	Num. Pgs.	Avg. Qst.	Price	Audience	Format	Bible Study
8	30-45	48	5	3.50	Beginner	Workbk	Topical

Features: Intro to Leading a Study, Intro to Study, Bibliography, Follow Up, Ldr's Notes
★★★★ Personal Application   Preparation Time: Low   ISBN: 0-87788-273-8
★★★ Relationship Building   Ldr. Guide Avail.: No   Size: 5.25 x 8.25
Subjects: Christian Life, Evangelism
Comments: A practical short study on friendship evangelism, this guide will prepare participants for reaching out to coworkers or neighbors with the good news of Jesus. Helpful sections include: a list of suggestions for starting conversations about Christ, components of an effective testimony, suggestions for using a church for evangelism, and the three essential elements of a Christian life. A closing journal entry helps reinforce the principles of each lesson.

Author: Roper, Harlin J. 867
Series: Through the Bible
Title: *And You Shall Be Witnesses: Acts (Youth)*
Publisher: Roper Press, 1978

Num. Sess.	Group Time	Num. Pgs.	Avg. Qst.	Price	Audience	Format	Bible Study
26	30-45	64	10	4.50	New Christian	Workbk	Book

Features: Intro to Leading a Study, Intro to Study, Scrpt Memory Helps, Maps
★★★ Personal Application   Preparation Time: Low   ISBN: 0-86606-370-6
★★ Relationship Building   Ldr. Guide Avail.: Yes   Size: 5.50 x 8.0
Subjects: Teens: Evangelism, Teens: New Testament
Comments: This chapter-by-chapter study encourages youth to develop inductive Bible study skills by answering questions, thus learning to interpret the Word and discover its message. This study covers Acts, the great bridge between fulfillment of Old Testament prophecy about Christ, and the commission following His death and resurrection. Crossword puzzles enhance the study.

Author: Roper, Harlin J. 868
Series: Through the Bible
Title: *And You Shall Be Witnesses*
Publisher: Roper Press, 1978

Num. Sess.	Group Time	Num. Pgs.	Avg. Qst.	Price	Audience	Format	Bible Study
26	45-60	52	20	4.50	New Christian	Workbk	Book

Features: Intro to Study, Scrpt Memory Helps, Maps
★★★ Personal Application   Preparation Time: Med   ISBN: 0-86606-358-7
★ Relationship Building   Ldr. Guide Avail.: Yes   Size: 5.50 x 8.25
Subjects: Acts, Church Life, Evangelism
Comments: In this chapter-by-chapter study of Acts, participants will develop inductive Bible study skills by answering questions, thus learning to interpret the Word and discover its message. This study, the tenth of a thirteen-unit series, covers Acts, which serves as a bridge between the fulfillment of Old Testament prophecy about Christ and His commission following death and resurrection. An in-depth leader's guide is available.

Author: Roper, Harlin J. 869
Series: Through the Bible
Title: *Consider Jesus: Hebrews–Revelation (Youth)*
Publisher: Roper Press, 1988

Num. Sess.	Group Time	Num. Pgs.	Avg. Qst.	Price	Audience	Format	Bible Study
26	30-45	64	10	4.50	New Christian	Workbk	Book

Features: Intro to Leading a Study, Intro to Study, Scrpt Memory Helps, Maps
★★★ Personal Application   Preparation Time: Low   ISBN: 0-86606-373-0
★★ Relationship Building   Ldr. Guide Avail.: Yes   Size: 5.50 x 8.0
Subjects: Teens: Jesus' Life, Teens: New Testament
Comments: This chapter-by-chapter study encourages participants to develop inductive Bible study skills by responding to true/false, fill-in-the-blank, and application questions, thus learning to interpret the Word and discover its message. This study covers the last nine books of the New Testament—Hebrews, James, 1 and 2 Peter, 1, 2, and 3 John, Jude and Revelation. Revelation is both the final book of Scripture and the summation of all revealed truth.

Author: Roper, Harlin J. 870
Series: Through the Bible
Title: *Consider Jesus: Hebrews–Revelation*
Publisher: Roper Press, 1988

Num. Sess.	Group Time	Num. Pgs.	Avg. Qst.	Price	Audience	Format	Bible Study
26	45-60	52	20	4.50	New Christian	Workbk	Book

Features: Intro to Study, Scrpt Memory Helps, Maps
★★★ Personal Application   Preparation Time: Med   ISBN: 0-86606-361-7
★ Relationship Building   Ldr. Guide Avail.: Yes   Size: 5.50 x 8.25
Subjects: Faith, Hebrews, James, Jesus: Life/Teaching, Revelation, 1 & 2 Peter, 1, 2 & 3 John/Jude
Comments: This chapter-by-chapter study encourages participants to develop inductive Bible study skills by answering questions, thus learning to interpret the Word and discover its message. The last in a thirteen-unit series, this study covers the last nine books of the New Testament—Hebrews, James, 1 and 2 Peter, 1, 2, and 3 John, Jude, and Revelation. Revelation is both the final book of Scripture and the summation of all revealed truth. An in-depth leader's guide is available.

Author: Roper, Harlin J.   **871**
Series: Through the Bible
Title: *Declaring His Deity: John*
Publisher: Roper Press, 1978

Num. Sess.	Group Time	Num. Pgs.	Avg. Qst.	Price	Audience	Format	Bible Study
26	45-60	52	20	4.50	New Christian	Workbk	Book

Features: Intro to Study, Scrpt Memory Helps, Maps
  ★★★ Personal Application   Preparation Time: Med   ISBN: 0-86606-357-9
  ★ Relationship Building   Ldr. Guide Avail.: Yes   Size: 5.50 x 8.25
Subjects: Jesus: Life/Teaching, John
Comments: This chapter-by-chapter study of John encourages participants to develop inductive Bible study skills by answering questions, thus learning to interpret the Word and discover its message. The ninth of a thirteen-unit series, this study covers the Gospel of John, a book different from Matthew, Mark, and Luke, being theological and interpretive rather than historical and factual. John deals with Jesus' humanity, using his human name 247 times. An in-depth leader's guide is available.

Author: Roper, Harlin J.   **872**
Series: Through the Bible
Title: *Declaring His Deity: John—Part 1 (Youth)*
Publisher: Roper Press, 1978

Num. Sess.	Group Time	Num. Pgs.	Avg. Qst.	Price	Audience	Format	Bible Study
13	30-45	40	10	4.50	New Christian	Workbk	Book

Features: Intro to Leading a Study, Intro to Study, Scrpt Memory Helps, Maps
  ★★★ Personal Application   Preparation Time: Low   ISBN: 0-86606-062-6
  ★★ Relationship Building   Ldr. Guide Avail.: Yes   Size: 5.50 x 8.0
Subjects: Teens: Jesus' Life, Teens: New Testament
Comments: This chapter-by-chapter study of John encourages youth to develop inductive Bible study skills. They will respond to true/false, fill-in-the-blank, and application questions to learn to interpret the Word and discover its message. This study covers the first part of John's gospel. The book is different from Matthew, Mark, and Luke, being theological and interpretive rather than historical and factual. John deals with Jesus' humanity, using his human name 247 times. Crossword puzzles enhance the study.

Author: Roper, Harlin J.   **873**
Series: Through the Bible
Title: *Declaring His Deity: John—Part 2 (Youth)*
Publisher: Roper Press, 1978

Num. Sess.	Group Time	Num. Pgs.	Avg. Qst.	Price	Audience	Format	Bible Study
13	30-45	40	10	4.50	New Christian	Workbk	Book

Features: Intro to Leading a Study, Intro to Study, Scrpt Memory Helps, Maps
  ★★★ Personal Application   Preparation Time: Low   ISBN: 0-86606-063-4
  ★★ Relationship Building   Ldr. Guide Avail.: Yes   Size: 5.50 x 8.0
Subjects: Teens: Jesus' Life, Teens: New Testament
Comments: This chapter-by-chapter study of John encourages youth to develop inductive Bible study skills by responding to true/false, fill-in-the-blank and application questions. Thus they will learn to interpret the Word and discover its message. This study covers John 12 through 21, concentrating on the story of Jesus' humanity. Crossword puzzles enhance the study.

Author: Roper, Harlin J.   **874**
Series: Through the Bible
Title: *Disruption and Dispersion: 1 Kings 9–2 Chronicles (Youth)*
Publisher: Roper Press, 1978

Num. Sess.	Group Time	Num. Pgs.	Avg. Qst.	Price	Audience	Format	Bible Study
13	30-45	40	10	4.50	New Christian	Workbk	Book

Features: Intro to Leading a Study, Intro to Study, Scrpt Memory Helps, Maps
  ★★★ Personal Application   Preparation Time: Low   ISBN: 0-86606-054-5
  ★★ Relationship Building   Ldr. Guide Avail.: Yes   Size: 5.50 x 8.0
Subjects: Teens: Bible/Pers., Teens: Old Testament
Comments: This chapter-by-chapter study encourages youth to develop inductive Bible study skills by responding to true/false, fill-in-the-blank and application questions. This will teach them to interpret the Word and discover its message. This study covers 1 and 2 Kings, showing that, despite warnings, sin brings ruin without remedy; and 1 and 2 Chronicles, covering similar ground and showing all in light of God's Temple and divine government. Crossword puzzles enhance the study.

Author: Roper, Harlin J.   **875**
Series: Through the Bible
Title: *Disruption, Dispersion & Restoration: 1 Kings 9–Job*
Publisher: Roper Press, 1978

Num. Sess.	Group Time	Num. Pgs.	Avg. Qst.	Price	Audience	Format	Bible Study
26	45-60	52	20	4.50	New Christian	Workbk	Book

Features: Intro to Study, Scrpt Memory Helps, Maps
  ★★★ Personal Application   Preparation Time: Med   ISBN: 0-86606-353-6
  ★ Relationship Building   Ldr. Guide Avail.: Yes   Size: 5.50 x 8.25
Subjects: Bible Personalities, Esther, Ezra/Nehemiah, Job, Kings/Chronicles
Comments: This chapter-by-chapter study of 1 Kings 9 through Job encourages participants to develop inductive Bible study skills by answering questions to interpret the Word and discover its message. This study, fourth in a thirteen-unit series, deals with the great Bible truths of these books. An in-depth leader's guide is available.

Author: Roper, Harlin J.   **876**
Series: Through the Bible
Title: *God Leads His People: Exodus 19–Deuteronomy (Youth)*
Publisher: Roper Press, 1978

Num. Sess.	Group Time	Num. Pgs.	Avg. Qst.	Price	Audience	Format	Bible Study
26	30-45	64	10	4.50	New Christian	Workbk	Book

Features: Intro to Leading a Study, Intro to Study, Scrpt Memory Helps, Maps
  ★★★ Personal Application   Preparation Time: Low   ISBN: 0-86606-363-3
  ★★ Relationship Building   Ldr. Guide Avail.: Yes   Size: 5.50 x 8.0
Subjects: Teens: Bible/Pers., Teens: Old Testament
Comments: This chapter-by-chapter study of Exodus 19 through Deuteronomy encourages youth to develop inductive Bible Study skills by responding to true/false, fill-in-the-blank, and application questions. Thus they will learn to interpret the Word and discover its message. This study shows the Israelites preparing for the Promised Land and receiving the Law from Moses. Crossword puzzles enhance the study.

Author: Roper, Harlin J. 877
Series: Through the Bible
Title: *God Leads His People: Exodus 19–Deuteronomy*
Publisher: Roper Press, 1978

Num. Sess.	Group Time	Num. Pgs.	Avg. Qst.	Price	Audience	Format	Bible Study
26	45-60	52	20	4.50	New Christian	Workbk	Book

Features: Intro to Study, Scrpt Memory Helps, Maps
★★★ Personal Application Preparation Time: Med ISBN: 0-86606-351-X
★ Relationship Building Ldr. Guide Avail.: Yes Size: 5.50 x 8.25
Subjects: Bible Personalities, Exodus, God, Leviticus, Numbers/Deuteronomy
Comments: This chapter-by-chapter study, the second of a thirteen-unit series, covers the last half of Exodus and all of Leviticus, Numbers, and Deuteronomy, the Israelites prepare for the Promised Land and gain the Law from Moses. Participants are encouraged to develop inductive Bible study skills by answering questions, thus learning to interpret the Word and discover its message. An in-depth leader's guide is available.

Author: Roper, Harlin J. 878
Series: Through the Bible
Title: *God's Salvation and Grace: Romans–Galatians (Youth)*
Publisher: Roper Press, 1978

Num. Sess.	Group Time	Num. Pgs.	Avg. Qst.	Price	Audience	Format	Bible Study
26	30-45	64	10	4.50	New Christian	Workbk	Book

Features: Intro to Leading a Study, Intro to Study, Scrpt Memory Helps, Maps
★★★ Personal Application Preparation Time: Low ISBN: 0-86606-371-4
★★ Relationship Building Ldr. Guide Avail.: Yes Size: 5.50 x 8.0
Subjects: Teens: Evangelism, Teens: Jesus' Life, Teens: New Testament
Comments: This chapter-by-chapter study encourages youth to develop inductive Bible study skills by answering questions, thus learning to interpret the Word and discover its message. This study covers Romans, 1 and 2 Corinthians, and Galatians. It deals with the Apostle Paul's letters to Christians in those cities, supports the gospel, and lifts up Christ as the only true example. Crossword puzzles enhance the study.

Author: Roper, Harlin J. 879
Series: Through the Bible
Title: *God's Salvation and Grace: Romans–Galatians*
Publisher: Roper Press, 1978

Num. Sess.	Group Time	Num. Pgs.	Avg. Qst.	Price	Audience	Format	Bible Study
26	45-60	52	20	4.50	New Christian	Workbk	Book

Features: Intro to Study, Scrpt Memory Helps, Maps
★★★ Personal Application Preparation Time: Med ISBN: 0-86606-359-5
★ Relationship Building Ldr. Guide Avail.: Yes Size: 5.50 x 8.25
Subjects: Galatians, Grace, Repentance, Romans, Service, Suffering, 1 Corinthians, 2 Corinthians
Comments: This chapter-by-chapter study of Romans through Galatians encourages participants to develop inductive Bible study skills by answering questions, thus learning to interpret the Word and discover its message. This study, the eleventh of a thirteen-unit series, deals with four of the Apostle Paul's letters that support the gospel and lifting up Christ as the only true example. An in-depth leader's guide is available.

Author: Roper, Harlin J. 880
Series: Through the Bible
Title: *Golden Years of the Kingdom, The: 1 Samuel 13–1 Kings 8 (Youth)*
Publisher: Roper Press, 1978

Num. Sess.	Group Time	Num. Pgs.	Avg. Qst.	Price	Audience	Format	Bible Study
13	30-45	40	10	4.50	New Christian	Workbk	Book

Features: Intro to Leading a Study, Intro to Study, Scrpt Memory Helps, Maps
★★★ Personal Application Preparation Time: Low ISBN: 0-86606-053-7
★★ Relationship Building Ldr. Guide Avail.: Yes Size: 5.50 x 8.0
Subjects: Teens: Bible/Pers., Teens: Old Testament
Comments: This chapter-by-chapter study of 1 Samuel through 1 Kings 8 encourages youth to develop inductive Bible study skills by responding to true/false, fill-in-the-blank, and application questions. Thus they will learn to interpret the Word and discover its message. This study shows the people of Israel demanding a new king; the rule of David, God's king; the record of David's last days; and the glory of Solomon's reign. Crossword puzzles enhance the study.

Author: Roper, Harlin J. 881
Series: Through the Bible
Title: *In the Beginning God: Genesis–Exodus 18*
Publisher: Roper Press, 1978

Num. Sess.	Group Time	Num. Pgs.	Avg. Qst.	Price	Audience	Format	Bible Study
26	45-60	52	20	4.50	New Christian	Workbk	Book

Features: Intro to Study, Objectives, Scrpt Memory Helps, Maps
★★★ Personal Application Preparation Time: Med ISBN: 0-86606-350-1
★ Relationship Building Ldr. Guide Avail.: Yes Size: 5.50 x 8.25
Subjects: Exodus, Genesis, God
Comments: This chapter-by-chapter study of Genesis 1 through Exodus 18 encourages participants to develop inductive Bible study skills. By answering questions, participants will learn to interpret the Word and discover its message. This study, the first of thirteen units in the series, deals with the Creation, the Flood, the tower of Babel, Abraham and the Jewish nation, Joseph, and the Exodus. An in-depth leader's guide is available.

Author: Roper, Harlin J. 882
Series: Through the Bible
Title: *In the Beginning God: Genesis–Exodus 18 (Youth)*
Publisher: Roper Press, 1988

Num. Sess.	Group Time	Num. Pgs.	Avg. Qst.	Price	Audience	Format	Bible Study
26	30-45	64	10	4.50	New Christian	Workbk	Book

Features: Intro to Leading a Study, Intro to Study, Scrpt Memory Helps, Maps
★★★ Personal Application Preparation Time: Low ISBN: 0-86606-362-5
★★ Relationship Building Ldr. Guide Avail.: Yes Size: 5.50 x 8.0
Subjects: Teens: Bible/Pers., Teens: Old Testament
Comments: This chapter-by-chapter study encourages youth to develop inductive Bible study skills. They will respond to true/false, fill-in-the-blank, and application questions and learn to interpret the Word and discover its message. This study deals with Genesis—the Creation, the Flood, the tower of Babel, Abraham and the Jewish nation, Joseph—and Exodus—the deliverance from Egypt. Crossword puzzles enhance the study.

Author: Roper, Harlin J. **883**
Series: Through the Bible
Title: *Jesus Christ the Son of God: Matthew thru Luke—Part 2*
(Youth)
Publisher: Roper Press, 1978

Num. Sess.	Group Time	Num. Pgs.	Avg. Qst.	Price	Audience	Format	Bible Study
13	30-45	40	10	4.50	New Christian	Workbk	Book

Features: Intro to Leading a Study, Intro to Study, Scrpt Memory Helps, Maps
  ★★★ Personal Application   Preparation Time: Low   ISBN:
   ★★ Relationship Building Ldr. Guide Avail.: Yes   Size: 5.50 x 8.0
Subjects: Teens: Jesus' Life, Teens: New Testament
Comments: This chapter-by-chapter study encourages youth to develop inductive Bible study skills by responding to true/false, fill-in-the-blank, and application questions, thus learning to interpret the Word and discover its message. This study covers the synoptic gospels, leading up to and including the final days of Christ's earthly ministry—the trial, Crucifixion, and Resurrection. Crossword puzzles enhance the study.

Author: Roper, Harlin J. **884**
Series: Through the Bible
Title: *Jesus Christ the Son of God: Matthew thru Luke—Part 1*
(Youth)
Publisher: Roper Press, 1978

Num. Sess.	Group Time	Num. Pgs.	Avg. Qst.	Price	Audience	Format	Bible Study
13	30-45	40	10	4.50	New Christian	Workbk	Book

Features: Intro to Leading a Study, Intro to Study, Scrpt Memory Helps, Maps
  ★★★ Personal Application   Preparation Time: Low   ISBN: 0-86606-060-X
   ★★ Relationship Building Ldr. Guide Avail.: Yes   Size: 5.50 x 8.0
Subjects: Teens: Jesus' Life, Teens: New Testament
Comments: This chapter-by-chapter study of Matthew, Mark, and Luke encourages youth to interpret the Word and discover its message by responding to true/false, fill-in-the-blank, and application questions. This study is the first of two units covering the three synoptic gospels. It covers Luke chronologically, interweaving Matthew and Mark when appropriate. Crossword puzzles enhance the study.

Author: Roper, Harlin J. **885**
Series: Through the Bible
Title: *Jesus Christ the Son of God: Matthew thru Luke—Part 1*
Publisher: Roper Press, 1978

Num. Sess.	Group Time	Num. Pgs.	Avg. Qst.	Price	Audience	Format	Bible Study
13	45-60	48	20	4.50	New Christian	Workbk	Book

Features: Intro to Study, Scrpt Memory Helps, Maps
  ★★★ Personal Application   Preparation Time: Med   ISBN: 0-86606-012-X
   ★ Relationship Building Ldr. Guide Avail.: Yes   Size: 5.50 x 8.25
Subjects: Jesus: Life/Teaching, Luke, Mark, Matthew
Comments: This chapter-by-chapter study of Matthew through Luke encourages participants to develop inductive Bible study skills by answering questions, thus learning to interpret the Word and discover its message. This study, the seventh in a thirteen-unit series, is the first of two units covering the synoptic gospels. It covers Luke chronologically, interweaving Matthew and Mark when appropriate. An in-depth leader's guide is available.

Author: Roper, Harlin J. **886**
Series: Through the Bible
Title: *Jesus Christ the Son of God: Matthew thru Luke—Part 2*
Publisher: Roper Press, 1978

Num. Sess.	Group Time	Num. Pgs.	Avg. Qst.	Price	Audience	Format	Bible Study
13	45-60	48	20	4.50	New Christian	Workbk	Book

Features: Intro to Study, Scrpt Memory Helps, Maps
  ★★★ Personal Application   Preparation Time: Med   ISBN: 0-86606-013-8
   ★ Relationship Building Ldr. Guide Avail.: Yes   Size: 5.50 x 8.25
Subjects: Luke, Mark, Matthew
Comments: This chapter-by-chapter study of Matthew through Luke encourages participants to develop inductive Bible study skills by answering questions, thus learning to interpret the Word and discover its message. This study, eighth of a thirteen-unit series, covers the synoptic gospels leading up to and including the final days of Christ's earthly ministry—the trial, Crucifixion, and Resurrection. An in-depth leader's guide is available.

Author: Roper, Harlin J. **887**
Series: Through the Bible
Title: *Land and the Kingdom, The: Joshua–1 Kings 8*
Publisher: Roper Press, 1978

Num. Sess.	Group Time	Num. Pgs.	Avg. Qst.	Price	Audience	Format	Bible Study
26	45-60	52	20	4.50	New Christian	Workbk	Book

Features: Intro to Study, Scrpt Memory Helps, Maps
  ★★★ Personal Application   Preparation Time: Med   ISBN: 0-86606-352-8
   ★ Relationship Building Ldr. Guide Avail.: Yes   Size: 5.50 x 8.25
Subjects: Bible Personalities, Joshua, Judges, Kings/Chronicles, Ruth, 1 & 2 Samuel
Comments: This chapter-by-chapter study of Joshua through 1 Kings 8 encourages participants to develop inductive Bible study skills. By answering questions, students will learn to interpret the Word and discover its message. This study, third of a thirteen-unit series, covers the Israelites gaining the Promised Land and the great lessons in Judges, Ruth, 1 and 2 Samuel, and the first half of Kings, from David to Solomon. An in-depth leader's guide is available.

Author: Roper, Harlin J. **888**
Series: Through the Bible
Title: *Letters To Believers: Ephesians–Titus (Youth)*
Publisher: Roper Press, 1978

Num. Sess.	Group Time	Num. Pgs.	Avg. Qst.	Price	Audience	Format	Bible Study
26	30-45	64	10	4.50	New Christian	Workbk	Book

Features: Intro to Leading a Study, Intro to Study, Scrpt Memory Helps, Maps
  ★★★ Personal Application   Preparation Time: Low   ISBN: 0-86606-372-2
   ★★ Relationship Building Ldr. Guide Avail.: Yes   Size: 5.50 x 8.0
Subjects: Teens: Christian Liv, Teens: New Testament
Comments: This chapter-by-chapter study encourages youth to develop inductive Bible study skills by answering questions, thus learning to interpret the Word and discover its message. This study covers Ephesians, Philippians, Colossians, Philemon, 1 and 2 Thessalonians, 1 and 2 Timothy, and Titus. It deals with the Apostle Paul's letters to churches and to his fellow Christian leaders. Crossword puzzles enhance the study.

Author: Roper, Harlin J. 889
Series: Through the Bible
Title: *Letters to Believers: Ephesians–Titus*
Publisher: Roper Press, 1978

Num. Sess.	Group Time	Num. Pgs.	Avg. Qst.	Price	Audience	Format	Bible Study
26	45-60	52	20	4.50	New Christian	Workbk	Book

Features: Intro to Study, Scrpt Memory Helps, Maps
★★★ Personal Application   Preparation Time: Med   ISBN: 0-86606-360-9
★ Relationship Building   Ldr. Guide Avail.: Yes   Size: 5.50 x 8.25
Subjects: Church Life, Colossians/Philemon, Ephesians, Leadership, Pastoral Epistles, Philippians, Prison Epistles, 1 & 2 Thessalonians, 1 & 2 Timothy/Titus
Comments: This chapter-by-chapter study encourages participants to develop inductive Bible study skills by answering questions, thus learning to interpret the Word and discover its message. This study, the twelfth in a thirteen-unit series, covers Ephesians, Philippians, Colossians, Philemon, 1 and 2 Thessalonians, 1 and 2 Timothy, and Titus. It deals with the Apostle Paul's letters to churches and to his fellow Christian leaders. An in-depth leader's guide is available.

Author: Roper, Harlin J. 890
Series: Through the Bible
Title: *Let the Wicked Be Warned: Joel–Malachi (Youth)*
Publisher: Roper Press, 1978

Num. Sess.	Group Time	Num. Pgs.	Avg. Qst.	Price	Audience	Format	Bible Study
13	30-45	40	10	4.50	New Christian	Workbk	Book

Features: Intro to Leading a Study, Intro to Study, Scrpt Memory Helps, Maps
★★★ Personal Application   Preparation Time: Low   ISBN: 0-86606-059-6
★★ Relationship Building   Ldr. Guide Avail.: Yes   Size: 5.50 x 8.0
Subjects: Teens: Bible/Pers., Teens: Old Testament
Comments: In this chapter-by-chapter study, youth are encouraged to develop inductive Bible study skills by responding to true/false, fill-in-the-blank, and application questions. Thus they learn to interpret the Word and discover its message. This study covers the writings of the minor prophets Joel, Amos, Obadiah, Jonah, Micah, Nahum, Habakkuk, Zephaniah, Haggai, Zechariah, and Malachi. Crossword puzzles enhance the study.

Author: Roper, Harlin J. 891
Series: Through the Bible
Title: *Let the Wicked Be Warned: Lamentations–Malachi*
Publisher: Roper Press, 1988

Num. Sess.	Group Time	Num. Pgs.	Avg. Qst.	Price	Audience	Format	Bible Study
26	45-60	52	20	4.50	New Christian	Workbk	Book

Features: Intro to Study, Scrpt Memory Helps, Maps
★★★ Personal Application   Preparation Time: Med   ISBN: 0-86606-355-2
★ Relationship Building   Ldr. Guide Avail.: Yes   Size: 5.50 x 8.25
Subjects: Bible Personalities, Daniel, Ezekiel, Lamentations, Major Prophets, Minor Prophets
Comments: This study, sixth in a thirteen-unit series, covers the remainder of the Old Testament—the major prophets Ezekiel and Daniel, and the remaining twelve minor prophets, from Hosea to Malachi. Participants will be encouraged to develop inductive Bible study skills by answering questions, thus learning to interpret the Word and discover its message. An in-depth leader's guide is available.

Author: Roper, Harlin J. 892
Series: Through the Bible
Title: *Occupying the Land: Joshua–1 Samuel 12 (Youth)*
Publisher: Roper Press, 1978

Num. Sess.	Group Time	Num. Pgs.	Avg. Qst.	Price	Audience	Format	Bible Study
13	30-45	40	10	4.50	New Christian	Workbk	Book

Features: Intro to Leading a Study, Intro to Study, Scrpt Memory Helps, Maps
★★★ Personal Application   Preparation Time: Low   ISBN: 0-86606-052-9
★★ Relationship Building   Ldr. Guide Avail.: Yes   Size: 5.50 x 8.0
Subjects: Teens: Bible/Pers., Teens: Old Testament
Comments: In this chapter-by-chapter study, youth are encouraged to develop inductive Bible study skills by responding to true/false, fill-in-the-blank, and application questions. This study covers Joshua—in which the Israelites gain the Promised Land—and the great lessons in Judges, Ruth, and 1 Samuel. Crossword puzzles enhance the study.

Author: Roper, Harlin J. 893
Series: Through the Bible
Title: *Predictions of Judgment and Glory: Isaiah–Jeremiah (Youth)*
Publisher: Roper Press, 1978

Num. Sess.	Group Time	Num. Pgs.	Avg. Qst.	Price	Audience	Format	Bible Study
13	30-45	40	10	4.50	New Christian	Workbk	Book

Features: Intro to Leading a Study, Intro to Study, Scrpt Memory Helps, Maps
★★★ Personal Application   Preparation Time: Low   ISBN: 0-86606-057-X
★★ Relationship Building   Ldr. Guide Avail.: Yes   Size: 5.50 x 8.0
Subjects: Teens: Bible/Pers., Teens: Old Testament
Comments: This chapter-by-chapter study of Isaiah and Jeremiah encourages youth to develop inductive Bible study skills by responding to true/false, fill-in-the-blank, and application questions. Thus they will learn to interpret the Word and discover its message. This study covers two major prophets, Isaiah and Jeremiah, and basic themes of prophecy. Crossword puzzles enhance the study.

Author: Roper, Harlin J. 894
Series: Through the Bible
Title: *Prophecy out of Captivity: Lamentations–Hosea (Youth)*
Publisher: Roper Press, 1978

Num. Sess.	Group Time	Num. Pgs.	Avg. Qst.	Price	Audience	Format	Bible Study
13	30-45	40	10	4.50	New Christian	Workbk	Book

Features: Intro to Leading a Study, Intro to Study, Scrpt Memory Helps, Maps
★★★ Personal Application   Preparation Time: Low   ISBN: 0-86606-058-8
★★ Relationship Building   Ldr. Guide Avail.: Yes   Size: 5.50 x 8.0
Subjects: Teens: Bible/Pers., Teens: Old Testament
Comments: This chapter-by-chapter study encourages youth to develop inductive Bible study skills. They will respond to true/false, fill-in-the-blank, and application questions and thus learn to interpret the Word and discover its message. This study covers Lamentations, Ezekiel, Daniel, and Hosea, completing study of the Major Prophets and introducing Hosea, the first in written order of the Minor Pprophets. Crossword puzzles enhance the study.

Author: Roper, Harlin J.   **895**
Series: Through the Bible
Title: *Return and Restoration: Ezra–Job (Youth)*
Publisher: Roper Press, 1978

Num. Sess.	Group Time	Num. Pgs.	Avg. Qst.	Price	Audience	Format	Bible Study
13	30-45	40	10	4.50	New Christian	Workbk	Book

Features: Intro to Leading a Study, Intro to Study, Scrpt Memory Helps, Maps
  ★★★ Personal Application   Preparation Time: Low   ISBN: 0-86606-055-3
   ★★ Relationship Building   Ldr. Guide Avail.: Yes   Size: 5.50 x 8.0
Subjects: Teens: Bible/Pers., Teens: Old Testament
Comments: This chapter-by-chapter study of Ezra through Job encourages youth to learn to interpret the Word and discover its message by responding to true/false, fill-in-the-blank, and application questions. This study covers Ezra, Nehemiah, Esther, and Job, dealing with great historical records in the Old Testament. Crossword puzzles enhance the study.

Author: Roper, Harlin J.   **896**
Series: Through the Bible
Title: *Songs, Sayings and Searches: Psalms–Song of Solomon (Youth)*
Publisher: Roper Press, 1978

Num. Sess.	Group Time	Num. Pgs.	Avg. Qst.	Price	Audience	Format	Bible Study
13	30-45	40	10	4.50	New Christian	Workbk	Book

Features: Intro to Leading a Study, Intro to Study, Scrpt Memory Helps, Maps
  ★★★ Personal Application   Preparation Time: Low   ISBN: 0-86606-056-1
   ★★ Relationship Building   Ldr. Guide Avail.: Yes   Size: 5.50 x 8.0
Subjects: Teens: Old Testament
Comments: In this chapter-by-chapter study, youth are encouraged to develop inductive Bible study skills by responding to true/false, fill-in-the-blank, and application questions, thus learning to interpret the Word and discover its message. This study covers the Psalms, Proverbs, Ecclesiastes, and Song of Solomon—a group of books generally called "the poetry." Crossword puzzles enhance the study.

Author: Roper, Harlin J.   **897**
Series: Through the Bible
Title: *Wisdom and Prophecy: Psalms–Jeremiah*
Publisher: Roper Press, 1978

Num. Sess.	Group Time	Num. Pgs.	Avg. Qst.	Price	Audience	Format	Bible Study
26	45-60	52	20	4.50	New Christian	Workbk	Book

Features: Intro to Study, Scrpt Memory Helps, Maps
  ★★★ Personal Application   Preparation Time: Med   ISBN: 0-86606-354-4
    ★ Relationship Building   Ldr. Guide Avail.: Yes   Size: 5.50 x 8.25
Subjects: Ecclesiastes, Isaiah/Jeremiah, Major Prophets, Prophecy, Proverbs, Psalms, Song of Solomon, Wisdom
Comments: This chapter-by-chapter study of Psalms through Jeremiah encourages participants to develop inductive Bible study skills by answering questions, thus learning to interpret the Word and discover its message. This study, fifth of a thirteen-unit series, covers Psalms, Proverbs, Ecclesiastes, Song of Solomon, Lamentations—a group of books generally called "the poetry"—and major prophets Isaiah and Jeremiah. An in-depth leader's guide is available.

Author: Rosenberger, Margaret   **898**
Series:
Title: *Issues in Focus*
Publisher: Regal Books, 1989

Num. Sess.	Group Time	Num. Pgs.	Avg. Qst.	Price	Audience	Format	Bible Study
15	60-90	230	Vry	6.95	Beginner	Book	Topical

Features: Bibliography, No Grp Discussion Quest, Appendix
  ★★★ Personal Application   Preparation Time: Low   ISBN: 0-8307-1332-8
  ★★★ Relationship Building   Ldr. Guide Avail.: Yes   Size: 5.0 x 8.0
Subjects: Divorce, Ethics, Medical Issues, Occult, Sexual Issues, Women's Issues
Comments: This study forces participants to take an informed stand on fifteen controversial contemporary topics. They will deal especially with what the Bible has to say about them. The topics, themselves clouded with emotion and controversy, include AIDS, drug abuse, sexual sin, the New Age movement, aging, divorce, and women in the church. The leader's material includes a study overview, insights and guide sheets, session plans and reproducible in-session handouts. The study can be adapted for fewer sessions.

Author: Rowlands, Gerald & JoAnne Sekowsky   **899**
Series: Basic Bible Study Series
Title: *Coming Alive in the Spirit: The Spirit-Led Life*
Publisher: Aglow, 1985

Num. Sess.	Group Time	Num. Pgs.	Avg. Qst.	Price	Audience	Format	Bible Study
8	75-90	63	20	2.95	New Christian	Workbk	Topical

Features: Intro to Study, Prayer Helps, Scrpt Memory Helps, Persnl Study Quest
  ★★★ Personal Application   Preparation Time: Med   ISBN: 0-930756-90-8
  ★★★ Relationship Building   Ldr. Guide Avail.: No   Size: 5.25 x 8.25
Subjects: Charismatic Interest, Fruit of the Spirit, Holy Spirit
Comments: This eight-week study reveals how the Holy Spirit renews believers. It teaches about the new life in Christ, the renewed mind, one's spiritual senses, and the fruit of the Spirit. Lessons include: "Possessing the Mind of Christ"; "Walking in the Spirit"; "Marching to Victory"; and more. It is not a theoretical study; rather, it is practical and calls for personal application.

Author: Rowlands, Gerald & JoAnne Sekowsky   **900**
Series: Basic Bible Study Series
Title: *Holy Spirit and His Gifts, The: A Study of the Spiritual Gifts*
Publisher: Aglow, 1984

Num. Sess.	Group Time	Num. Pgs.	Avg. Qst.	Price	Audience	Format	Bible Study
10	75-90	64	20	2.95	New Christian	Workbk	Topical

Features: Intro to Study, Prayer Helps, Scrpt Memory Helps, Persnl Study Quest
  ★★★ Personal Application   Preparation Time: Med   ISBN: 0-930756-83-5
  ★★★ Relationship Building   Ldr. Guide Avail.: No   Size: 5.25 x 8.25
Subjects: Charismatic Interest, Holy Spirit, Spiritual Gifts
Comments: This ten-week study leads participants to an understanding of the Holy Spirit, His work in the present age, and the spiritual gifts He makes available to every believer. Lessons include: "Who Is the Holy Spirit?"; "The Fullness of the Spirit Predicted"; "The Initial Evidence of the Holy Spirit"; "The Holy Spirit and the Believer"; "Why Speak in Tongues?"; "The Gifts of the Spirit"; "The Gift of Prophecy"; and more.

Author: Rudie, Carol Veldman   **901**
Series: Discover Your Bible
Title: *Discover: Genesis*
Publisher: Church Development Resources, 1987

Num. Sess.	Group Time	Num. Pgs.	Avg. Qst.	Price	Audience	Format	Bible Study
11	60-75	38	8	1.80	Beginner	Workbk	Book

Features: Intro to Study, Summary, Glossary
  ★★★ Personal Application   Preparation Time: None ISBN:
    ★★ Relationship Building Ldr. Guide Avail.: Yes   Size: 5.50 x 8.50
Subjects: Genesis, God
Comments: This inductive study of Genesis chapters 1-12 explores the creation of the world, the animal kingdom, and the first humans. It records humanity's fall into sin and God's first promise of a Savior. It tells of the spread of civilization and the birth of the Jewish nation, and leads participants up to Abraham, the "father of all believers." A comprehensive study guide is available.

Author: Rudie, Carol Veldman   **902**
Series: Discover Your Bible
Title: *Discover: Genesis–Abraham and Sarah*
Publisher: Church Development Resources, 1989

Num. Sess.	Group Time	Num. Pgs.	Avg. Qst.	Price	Audience	Format	Bible Study
13	60-75	38	8	2.10	Beginner	Workbk	Book

Features: Intro to Study, Glossary
  ★★★ Personal Application   Preparation Time: None ISBN:
    ★★ Relationship Building Ldr. Guide Avail.: Yes   Size: 5.50 x 8.50
Subjects: Bible Personalities, Faith, Genesis, God
Comments: This inductive study of Genesis 1-25 introduces participants to Abraham, "father" of the Jewish nation and of all who believe in God. Participants will study his weaknesses as well as his faith. They will learn about Abraham's God, who is loving and just and faithful, who understands weakness, and who calls people to faith in Him. A comprehensive leader's guide is available.

Author: Rudie, Carol Veldman   **903**
Series: Discover Your Bible
Title: *Discover: God in the Psalms*
Publisher: Church Development Resources, 1988

Num. Sess.	Group Time	Num. Pgs.	Avg. Qst.	Price	Audience	Format	Bible Study
7	60-75	23	9	1.25	Beginner	Workbk	Book

Features: Intro to Study, Summary, Glossary
  ★★★ Personal Application   Preparation Time: None ISBN:
    ★★ Relationship Building Ldr. Guide Avail.: Yes   Size: 5.50 x 8.50
Subjects: God, Holiness, Marriage, Psalms
Comments: This inductive study of Psalms explores the depths of the relationship between God and humankind. It focuses on psalms that teach the character of God, His holiness, power, majesty, and love. An underlying theme is God's continual pursuit of the human heart and His kindness to those who find Him. Using word pictures comparing God to things like thunderstorms, fathers with small children, kings, rocks, or refuge, they can enhance contemporary Christians' understanding.

Author: Rundstrom, G. B.   **904**
Series: Small Group Bible Studies
Title: *Lord's Prayer, The*
Publisher: Augsburg Publishing House, 1984

Num. Sess.	Group Time	Num. Pgs.	Avg. Qst.	Price	Audience	Format	Bible Study
6	60-75	24	12	1.15	New Christian	Book	Topical

Features: Intro to Study, Prayer Helps
  ★★★ Personal Application   Preparation Time: None ISBN:
    ★★ Relationship Building Ldr. Guide Avail.: No   Size: 8.50 x 5.50
Subjects: God, Prayer
Comments: This short, six-session study on the Lord's Prayer will enlarge participants' conception of the seven petitions that make up the prayer. Various passages of scripture are related to the different petitions. The Lord's Prayer is found in two forms in the Bible, but Matthew 6:9-13 is used for this study. The primary focus is on what it says to individuals, and the response to God as they pray the prayer.

Author: Ryan, Dale & Juanita   **905**
Series: Life Recovery Guides
Title: *Recovery from Bitterness*
Publisher: InterVarsity, 1990

Num. Sess.	Group Time	Num. Pgs.	Avg. Qst.	Price	Audience	Format	Bible Study
6	45-60	63	9	3.95	Beginner	Workbk	Topical

Features: Intro to Leading a Study, Intro to Study, Prayer Helps, Full Scrpt Printed, Ldr's Notes
  ★★★ Personal Application   Preparation Time: Low ISBN: 0-8308-1154-0
    ★★ Relationship Building Ldr. Guide Avail.: No   Size: 5.50 x 8.25
Subjects: Counseling, Emotions, Forgiveness, Support
Comments: This study is pertinent for those who have tried to forgive and become frustrated because they were unable to do so. Sometimes forgiveness is blocked, stuck, restrained, and entangled, and hearts turn to bitterness and revenge. The inability to forgive can result in a feeling of spiritual failure. This guide helps provide the strength to change bitterness into forgiveness. Each lesson includes an introduction, a personal reflection section with two or three questions, and a Bible study.

Author: Ryan, Dale & Juanita   **906**
Series: Life Recovery Guides
Title: *Recovery from Loss*
Publisher: InterVarsity, 1990

Num. Sess.	Group Time	Num. Pgs.	Avg. Qst.	Price	Audience	Format	Bible Study
6	45-60	63	8	3.95	Beginner	Workbk	Topical

Features: Intro to Leading a Study, Intro to Study, Prayer Helps, Full Scrpt Printed, Ldr's Notes
  ★★★★ Personal Application   Preparation Time: Low ISBN: 0-8308-1157-5
    ★★ Relationship Building Ldr. Guide Avail.: No   Size: 5.50 x 8.25
Subjects: Counseling, Emotions, Grief, Support
Comments: Disappointment, unmet expectations, physical or emotional illness, and death are all examples of losses. Working through grief does not help people forget what has been lost, but it does help people grow in understanding, compassion, and courage in the midst of loss. This study encourages participants to lean on God for comfort, strength, and purpose. An enclosed response card may be returned for networking purposes.

Author: Ryan, Dale & Juanita   **907**
Series: Life Recovery Guides
Title: *Recovery from Shame*
Publisher: InterVarsity, 1990

Num. Sess.	Group Time	Num. Pgs.	Avg. Qst.	Price	Audience	Format	Bible Study
6	45-60	64	9	3.95	Beginner	Workbk	Topical

Features: Intro to Leading a Study, Intro to Study, Prayer Helps, Full Scrpt Printed, Ldr's Notes
★★★★ Personal Application   Preparation Time: Low   ISBN: 0-8308-1153-2
★★ Relationship Building   Ldr. Guide Avail.: No   Size: 5.50 x 8.25
Subjects: Counseling, Emotions, Self-esteem, Support
Comments: This study has been written for people who have experienced shame and need to realize God's unconditional love. Whatever its source—public humiliation, personal rejection—shame affects self-image, producing feelings of being unlovable or unworthy. Because shame wounds deeply, recovery requires deep healing—the kind only God can provide. Each lesson includes an introduction, personal reflection, Bible study, and prayer. An enclosed response card may be returned for networking.

Author: Ryan, Dale & Juanita   **908**
Series: Life Recovery Guides
Title: *Recovery from Family Dysfunctions*
Publisher: InterVarsity, 1990

Num. Sess.	Group Time	Num. Pgs.	Avg. Qst.	Price	Audience	Format	Bible Study
6	45-60	64	8	3.95	Beginner	Workbk	Topical

Features: Intro to Leading a Study, Intro to Study, Prayer Helps, Full Scrpt Printed, Ldr's Notes
★★★★ Personal Application   Preparation Time: Low   ISBN: 0-8308-1151-6
★★ Relationship Building   Ldr. Guide Avail.: No   Size: 5.50 x 8.25
Subjects: Counseling, Family, Relationships, Support
Comments: Dysfunctional relationship patterns learned early in life can affect all future relationships. People can become guarded and defensive, talk little about what really matters, and become reluctant to trust others . . . and God. This study shows participants how to break these patterns and learn the vital skills of building relationships. It also offers healing from the pain of the past and acceptance into God's family. An enclosed response card may be returned for networking purposes.

Author: Ryan, Dale & Juanita   **909**
Series: Life Recovery Guides
Title: *Recovery from Abuse*
Publisher: InterVarsity, 1990

Num. Sess.	Group Time	Num. Pgs.	Avg. Qst.	Price	Audience	Format	Bible Study
6	45-60	63	9	3.95	Beginner	Workbk	Topical

Features: Intro to Leading a Study, Intro to Study, Prayer Helps, Full Scrpt Printed, Ldr's Notes
★★★★ Personal Application   Preparation Time: Low   ISBN: 0-8308-1158-3
★★ Relationship Building   Ldr. Guide Avail.: No   Size: 5.50 x 8.25
Subjects: Counseling, Emotions, Self-esteem, Sexual Issues, Support
Comments: This study presents a series of practical, positive steps from abuse to health and happiness. Fortunately, recovery, while often not easy or quick, is possible. Questions addressed include: Does the nightmare of abuse ever end? Is it possible to be called terrible names thoughout childhood and later develop a healthy self-esteem? Is it possible to be physically beaten by a loved one and later develop a capacity for intimacy? Is it possible to be sexually violated and later feel secure in a relationship?

Author: Ryan, Dale & Juanita   **910**
Series: Life Recovery Guides
Title: *Recovery from Addictions*
Publisher: InterVarsity, 1990

Num. Sess.	Group Time	Num. Pgs.	Avg. Qst.	Price	Audience	Format	Bible Study
6	45-60	63	8	3.95	Beginner	Workbk	Topical

Features: Intro to Leading a Study, Intro to Study, Prayer Helps, Full Scrpt Printed, Ldr's Notes
★★★★ Personal Application   Preparation Time: Low   ISBN: 0-8308-1155-9
★★ Relationship Building   Ldr. Guide Avail.: No   Size: 5.50 x 8.25
Subjects: Addictions, Counseling, Money, Psychology, Sexual Issues, Support
Comments: Addictions have always been a human predicament. Addiction to chemicals, food, sex, work, spending, gambling, religious practices, etc. can enslave and lead to spiritual, emotional or physical death. This guide is structured like the Alcoholics Anonymous Twelve Steps program; it explores biblical principles which are rich sources of help and healing for those struggling with addiction. An enclosed response card may be returned for networking purposes.

Author: Ryan, Dale & Juanita   **911**
Series: Life Recovery Guides
Title: *Recovery from Codependency*
Publisher: InterVarsity, 1990

Num. Sess.	Group Time	Num. Pgs.	Avg. Qst.	Price	Audience	Format	Bible Study
6	45-60	64	8	3.95	Beginner	Workbk	Topical

Features: Intro to Leading a Study, Intro to Study, Prayer Helps, Full Scrpt Printed, Ldr's Notes
★★★★ Personal Application   Preparation Time: Low   ISBN: 0-8308-1156-7
★★ Relationship Building   Ldr. Guide Avail.: No   Size: 5.50 x 8.25
Subjects: Addictions, Counseling, Psychology, Support
Comments: Fear, anger, and helplessness concerning an addicted loved one can lead a person to attempt to control that loved one. Both the addicted person's and codependent's behavior can become a destructive spiral of denial and blame. This study shows how to relinquish overresponsibility and entrust those one loves to God. An enclosed response card may be returned for networking purposes.

Author: Ryan, Dale & Juanita   **912**
Series: Life Recovery Guides
Title: *Recovery from Distorted Images of God*
Publisher: InterVarsity, 1990

Num. Sess.	Group Time	Num. Pgs.	Avg. Qst.	Price	Audience	Format	Bible Study
6	45-60	63	8	3.95	Beginner	Workbk	Topical

Features: Intro to Leading a Study, Intro to Study, Prayer Helps, Full Scrpt Printed, Ldr's Notes
★★★★ Personal Application   Preparation Time: Low   ISBN: 0-8308-1152-4
★★ Relationship Building   Ldr. Guide Avail.: No   Size: 5.50 x 8.25
Subjects: Counseling, Family, God, Psychology, Support
Comments: This study helps participants identify distorted images of God, meditate on true scriptural images of God, and exchange the distortions for biblically accurate portraits. The distortions interfere with the ability to talk honestly with God, express feelings to Him, and trust Him. Distorted images of God are often rooted in family and cultural backgrounds; this study can lead to recovery. An enclosed response card may be returned for networking purposes.

Author: Rydberg, Denny   **913**
Series:
Title: *Creating Quality Relationships in a Fast-Paced World*
(Study Guide)
Publisher: Group Publishing, 1988

Num. Sess.	Group Time	Num. Pgs.	Avg. Qst.	Price	Audience	Format	Bible Study
12	45-75	132	Vry	4.50	Beginner	Workbk	Topical

Features: Objectives, Bibliography, Prayer Helps, Drawings, Charts
★★★★ Personal Application Preparation Time: Low ISBN: 0-931529-35-2
★★★★ Relationship Building Ldr. Guide Avail.: Yes Size: 5.50 x 8.50
Subjects: Friendships, Marriage, Relationships, Singles Issues,
Work, Youth Life
Comments: This twelve-session course for young adults (ages
18-35) is a Christ-centered curriculum that helps both married and
single young adults build more satisfying relationships with friends,
family, coworkers, God, and themselves. Topics covered include living abundantly as a single, becoming one's own best friend, making
sense of the dating scene, and how not to lose one's individuality
in marriage. The leader's guide ($10.95) provides preparation tips,
session outlines, objectives, and more.

Author: Rydberg, Denny   **914**
Series:
Title: *Creative Bible Studies for Young Adults*
Publisher: Group Publishing, 1990

Num. Sess.	Group Time	Num. Pgs.	Avg. Qst.	Price	Audience	Format	Bible Study
20	45-60	154	Vry	11.95	New Christian	Book	Topical

Features: Intro to Leading a Study, Intro to Study, Prayer Helps,
Study Overview, Drawings,Handouts, Charts
★★★★ Personal Application Preparation Time: Low ISBN: 0-931529-99-9
★★★★ Relationship Building Ldr. Guide Avail.: No Size: 6.0 x 9.0
Subjects: Christian Living, Emotions, Faith, Sexual Issues, Singles
Issues, Stress, Success, Youth Life
Comments: This study provides twenty faith-building Bible studies
for people eighteen to thirty-five years old. Divided into five four-
week studies, topics include: "Handling Stress"; "Sex: God's Good
Idea"; "Christians and Success"; "Discipleship and God's Will"; and
"Growing in Faith." Each study is designed to address young adults'
daily needs. Each study includes reproducible creative handouts
to photocopy, simple preparation tips, time-saving Scripture background, and easy-to-follow study plans.

Author: Ryrie, Charles C.   **915**
Series:
Title: *So Great Salvation: What It Means to Believe in Jesus Christ*
Publisher: Victor Books, 1989

Num. Sess.	Group Time	Num. Pgs.	Avg. Qst.	Price	Audience	Format	Bible Study
13	60-90	166	N/A	6.99	New Christian	Book	Topical

Features: Scrpt Index
★★★ Personal Application Preparation Time: Med ISBN: 0-89693-127-7
★★★ Relationship Building Ldr. Guide Avail.: Yes Size: 5.50 x 8.0
Subjects: Evangelism, Jesus: Life/Teaching, Theology
Comments: This study clarifies the meaning and evidences of
salvation. It is clear, concise, and authoritative, when the tendency
today is to water down the gospel or add nonscriptural requirements
to it. It addresses specific questions, including: "What exactly is
the gospel?" "What is spiritual fruit?" "Can a born-again Christian
be carnal and, if so, for how long?" and "What is eternal security?"
Participants will find clear implications for their spiritual lives.

Author: Salerno, Tony, et al.   **916**
Series:
Title: *Life in Christ: A Manual for Disciples*
Publisher: Bethany House, 1983

Num. Sess.	Group Time	Num. Pgs.	Avg. Qst.	Price	Audience	Format	Bible Study
10	60-90	290	Vry	11.95	New Christian	Workbk	Topical

Features: Intro to Study, Bibliography, Prayer Helps, Scrpt Memory
Helps, Photos
★★ Personal Application Preparation Time: High ISBN: 0-87123-887-X
★★ Relationship Building Ldr. Guide Avail.: No Size: 8.50 x 11.0
Subjects: Baptism, Discipleship, Faith, God, Prayer, Repentance
Comments: This in-depth study helps new Christians understand
their faith, read the Word of God, and fellowship with other believers. Doctrinal truths of Scripture are introduced, then immediately
applied. Topics include repentance, faith, restitution, baptism, the
Church, prayer, the Word of God, love of God, witnessing, and
spiritual power. References to the teachings of well-known Christians, past and present, help illuminate the material. Illustrations are
elaborate.

Author: Samms, Robert L.   **917**
Series: Lay Action Ministry
Title: *How to Study the Bible (Part 2)*
Publisher: Lay Action Ministry Program, 1987

Num. Sess.	Group Time	Num. Pgs.	Avg. Qst.	Price	Audience	Format	Bible Study
12	60-90	112	Vry	5.95	New Christian	Workbk	Topical

Features: Full Scrpt Printed, Ldr's Notes
★★★ Personal Application Preparation Time: Low ISBN: 0-89191-517-6
★★★ Relationship Building Ldr. Guide Avail.: Yes Size: 5.25 x 8.25
Subjects: Bible Study, Ephesians, Small Group Resource
Comments: This study, the second of a two-part series on Bible
study, will improve participants' abilities to study Scripture inductively, and lead their own Bible studies. This continuation of an
in-depth look at Ephesians covers the following: looking for the big
ideas; observing the text; asking the text questions; studying the
context; using cross-references, concordances, Bible atlases, Bible
dictionaries, and commentaries; and more. Homework is required.
One leader's guide covers both parts 1 and 2.

Author: Samms, Robert L.   **918**
Series: Lay Action Ministry
Title: *How to Study the Bible (Part 1)*
Publisher: Lay Action Ministry Program, 1987

Num. Sess.	Group Time	Num. Pgs.	Avg. Qst.	Price	Audience	Format	Bible Study
12	60-90	90	Vry	5.95	New Christian	Workbk	Topical

Features: Prayer Helps, Full Scrpt Printed
★★★ Personal Application Preparation Time: Low ISBN: 0-89191-516-8
★★★ Relationship Building Ldr. Guide Avail.: Yes Size: 5.25 x 8.25
Subjects: Bible Study, Ephesians, Small Group Resource
Comments: This study, the first of a two-part series on Bible study,
introduces inductive study techniques and helps participants practice
them in examing Ephesians. This book includes the following: study
tools; guidelines for understanding, applying, and teaching Bible
portions; ideas for developing a personal study plan; and an in-depth
study of Ephesians 1. Homework is required. One leader's guide
covers both parts 1 and 2.

Author: Samms, Robert L.   **919**
Series: Lay Action Ministry
Title: *Truth That Transforms: A Study in Christian Doctrine*
Publisher: Lay Action Ministry Program, 1990

Num. Sess.	Group Time	Num. Pgs.	Avg. Qst.	Price	Audience	Format	Bible Study
12	60-90	142	Vry	5.95	New Christian	Workbk	Topical

Features: Intro to Study, Ldr's Notes
★★★ Personal Application Preparation Time: Low ISBN: 0-89191-486-2
★★★ Relationship Building Ldr. Guide Avail.: Yes Size: 5.25 x 8.25
Subjects: Beliefs, Faith, God, Theology, Worship
Comments: This study examines God: who He is, what He has done, and what He wants everyone to know through His Word. Participants will benefit from an explanation of the story upon which Christianity and its doctrines are founded: the story of Jesus Christ. Doctrine provides Christians common ground concerning faith, belief, and worship, and a study of doctrines provide a basis for the way they live. Homework is required.

Author: Samms, Robert L. & Maryann E.   **920**
Series: Lay Action Ministry
Title: *Your Ministry at Home*
Publisher: Lay Action Ministry Program, 1988

Num. Sess.	Group Time	Num. Pgs.	Avg. Qst.	Price	Audience	Format	Bible Study
12	60-90	112	Vry	5.95	New Christian	Workbk	Topical

Features: Prayer Helps, Scrpt Memory Helps, Ldr's Notes
★★★ Personal Application Preparation Time: Low ISBN: 0-89191-487-0
★★★ Relationship Building Ldr. Guide Avail.: Yes Size: 5.25 x 8.25
Subjects: Devotionals, Family, Money, Time
Comments: This study, designed for younger couples, provides many practical "how-to's" for establishing a Christian home. Included are instructions on developing family quiet times; improving communication at home; and managing time, money, and nutrition. Participants are asked to start, maintain, and be accountable for daily quiet times; begin a spiritual journal; memorize a key verse each week; and keep a prayer list.

Author: Sather, Verdie   **921**
Series: Enrichment Series
Title: *More Than Conquerors: The Christian's Spiritual Authority*
Publisher: Aglow, 1981

Num. Sess.	Group Time	Num. Pgs.	Avg. Qst.	Price	Audience	Format	Bible Study
10	60-75	80	27	2.95	New Christian	Workbk	Topical

Features: Intro to Study, Prayer Helps, Scrpt Memory Helps, Digging Deeper Quest, Persnl Study Quest
★★★★ Personal Application Preparation Time: Med ISBN: 0-930756-62-2
★★★★ Relationship Building Ldr. Guide Avail.: No Size: 5.25 x 8.25
Subjects: Charismatic Interest, Holy Spirit
Comments: This ten-week study considers the foundational truths on which spiritual authority is based. Believers are Christ's representatives on earth, and they have been given His authority to carry out His assignments. Before that authority can be exercised, believers who have a confused picture of spiritual authority must learn how it may be properly used. Believers must act in the power of the Holy Spirit to face the strength and opposition of Satan.

Author: Scanlon, Michael, T.O.R.   **922**
Series: Catholic Bible Study Guide
Title: *Repentance: A Guide to Receiving God's Forgiveness*
Publisher: Servant Publications, 1989

Num. Sess.	Group Time	Num. Pgs.	Avg. Qst.	Price	Audience	Format	Bible Study
9	60-75	85	10	4.95	Beginner	Workbk	Topical

Features: Intro to Leading a Study, Intro to Study, Scrpt Memory Helps, Summary, Charts
★★★★ Personal Application Preparation Time: Low ISBN: 0-89283-398-X
★★★ Relationship Building Ldr. Guide Avail.: No Size: 5.25 x 8.0
Subjects: Christian Life, Forgiveness, Repentance
Comments: This nine-lesson study shows participants how to turn away from sin and receive God's abundant mercy, even in moments of personal difficulty. It provides a biblical basis for the sacrament of reconciliation, including a practical tip on how to use Scripture to prepare for confession. The lessons are divided into three parts: "Responding to the Call to Repent"; "Common Pitfalls That Hinder Us from Repenting"; and "A Life of Ongoing Conversion."

Author: Scazzero, Peter   **923**
Series: Fruit of the Spirit
Title: *Love: Building Healthy Relationships*
Publisher: Zondervan, 1991

Num. Sess.	Group Time	Num. Pgs.	Avg. Qst.	Price	Audience	Format	Bible Study
6	45-60	48	12	3.95	New Christian	Workbk	Topical

Features: Intro to Study, Ldr's Notes
★★★ Personal Application Preparation Time: None ISBN: 0-310-53721-5
★★ Relationship Building Ldr. Guide Avail.: No Size: 5.50 x 8.50
Subjects: Christian Living, Forgiveness, Fruit of the Spirit, Love, Marriage, Relationships
Comments: This six-week study explores the "most excellent way" into the hearts of those we care about. It considers how to develop a love that affirms, that forgives, and that lasts. Using New Testament passages, lessons look at loving Jesus, God's family, our neighbors, and more.

Author: Scazzero, Peter   **924**
Series: LifeGuide Bible Study
Title: *Old Testament Characters*
Publisher: InterVarsity, 1988

Num. Sess.	Group Time	Num. Pgs.	Avg. Qst.	Price	Audience	Format	Bible Study
12	45-60	63	12	3.95	Beginner	Workbk	Topical

Features: Intro to Leading a Study, Intro to Study, Ldr's Notes, Charts, Maps
★★ Personal Application Preparation Time: Low ISBN: 0-8308-1059-5
★ Relationship Building Ldr. Guide Avail.: No Size: 5.50 x 8.25
Subjects: Bible Personalities, Marriage, Old Testament, Prayer
Comments: A study of real men and women of the Old Testament who, with both weaknesses and strengths, provide excellent role models. Studying biblical characters—including Jonah, Hannah, Samuel, Abraham, Caleb and Joshua, Elijah, Achan, King Saul, Daniel, Esther, David, and Moses—exemplifies different themes relevant to following Jesus today, including prayer, temptation, lordship, and unconditional love. The studies are not in chronological order, but may be arranged to meet groups' needs.

Author: Schaap, Mary Nelle　　　　　　　　**925**
Series: Challenge Bible Study
Title: *David's Lord: Seeing God in the Life of David*
Publisher: Baker Book House, 1989

Num. Sess.	Group Time	Num. Pgs.	Avg. Qst.	Price	Audience	Format	Bible Study
13	60-75	174	7	6.95	New Christian	Book	Charctr

Features: Intro to Study
　★★ Personal Application　Preparation Time: Med　ISBN: 0-8010-8295-1
　★★ Relationship Building　Ldr. Guide Avail.: No　Size: 5.25 x 7.50
Subjects: Bible Personalities, God, 1 & 2 Samuel
Comments: This thirteen-lesson study of David focuses on his life as he learned to rely on what he knew of God. The lessons view God, who chose, empowered, elevated, consoled, directed, softened, corrected, crowned, reassured, convicted, forgave, comforted, and completed David. In the study plan, questions precede each lesson and scripture passages, commentary, and directions for using the questions are included.

Author: Schaeffer, Dr. Francis A. & Dr. C. Everett Koop　　**926**
Series:
Title: *Whatever Happened to the Human Race?*
Publisher: Gospel Films, 1980

Num. Sess.	Group Time	Num. Pgs.	Avg. Qst.	Price	Audience	Format	Bible Study
6	90-120	62	Vry	149.95	Begi nner	Video	Topical

Features: Intro to Study, Digging Deeper Quest, Photos, Video Study Guide
　★★★★ Personal Application　Preparation Time: None　ISBN:
　★★★★ Relationship Building　Ldr. Guide Avail.: No　Size: 7.0 x 10.0
Subjects: Abortion, Medical Issues, Social Issues
Comments: This dramatic six-part comprehensive video study has a twofold purpose: to inform the public, whether Christian or not, of the actual facts of abortion on demand, infanticide, and euthanasia; and to encourage decisive, sacrificial action within the generous boundaries provided by the U.S. Constitution. The study guide clarifies the facts and arguments presented, and forces participants to think through the issues for themselves. There are five episodes on three tapes.

Author: Schaeffer, Dr. Francis A.　　　　　　　　**927**
Series:
Title: *Basic Bible Studies*
Publisher: Tyndale House, 1972

Num. Sess.	Group Time	Num. Pgs.	Avg. Qst.	Price	Audience	Format	Bible Study
25	45-60	86	N/A	3.95	Beginner	Book	Topical

Features: Intro to Study, No Grp Discussion Quest
　★ Personal Application　Preparation Time: None　ISBN: 0-8423-0103-8
　★ Relationship Building　Ldr. Guide Avail.: No　Size: 5.0 x 7.50
Subjects: Apologetics, Bible Study, Theology
Comments: This unusual study is more like a commentary which could become an effective study with trained leadership. Twenty-five lessons build an understanding of the whole system of Bible teaching. By maintaining a unified approach to studying the Bible, it reveals the relationship of all its parts. The many doctrinal studies include: "The God of the Bible," "Creation," "The Holy Spirit," and "Sanctification—Glorification."

Author: Schaller, Lyle E.　　　　　　　　**928**
Series:
Title: *Getting Things Done*
Publisher: Abingdon, 1986

Num. Sess.	Group Time	Num. Pgs.	Avg. Qst.	Price	Audience	Format	Bible Study
8	-	270	N/A	10.95		Book	No

Features: Drawings, Cartoons
　Personal Application　Preparation Time:　ISBN: 0-687-14142-7
　Relationship Building　Ldr. Guide Avail.:　Size: 5.25 x 8.50
Subjects: Leadership, Small Group Resource
Comments: This book proposes that "anyone" can learn to be a leader, and discusses various aspects about leadership: leadership can be learned; leaders know how to organize, accept responsibility, enlist allies, and institute change when necessary; authoritarian and laissez-faire leadership styles are obsolete; leaders share certain qualities; and it's never too late to learn to become a leader. Cartoons and a fictional character are used to illustrate assumptions about effective leadership.

Author: Scheidel, Thomas M. & Laura Crowell　　**929**
Series:
Title: *Discussing and Deciding: A Desk Book for Group Leaders and Members*
Publisher: Macmillan Publishing Co., 1979

Num. Sess.	Group Time	Num. Pgs.	Avg. Qst.	Price	Audience	Format	Bible Study
10	-	330	N/A	52.0		Book	No

Features: Intro to Study, Bibliography, Index
　Personal Application　Preparation Time:　ISBN: 0-02-406750-4
　Relationship Building　Ldr. Guide Avail.:　Size: 6.25 x 9.50
Subjects: Small Group Resource
Comments: This book is designed for continuing use by leaders and participants in deliberate discussions of small groups. It is useful for anyone concerned with improving groups' effectiveness, whether in a school, church, community, business, or other setting. Handy for quick reference, it is divided into three major parts: an overview of the group discussion process; a chronology of discussion concepts; and a description of special techniques and useful procedures.

Author: Schneider, Herbert, S. J.　　　　　　**930**
Series:
Title: *Catholic Bible Study Workbook, The: A Guide to the Gospel of John*
Publisher: Servant Publications, 1988

Num. Sess.	Group Time	Num. Pgs.	Avg. Qst.	Price	Audience	Format	Bible Study
9	60-75	120	Vry	8.95	Beginner	Workbk	Topical

Features: Intro to Study, Bibliography, Prayer Helps, Worship Helps, Charts
　★★★★ Personal Application　Preparation Time: Med　ISBN: 0-89283-332-7
　★★★★ Relationship Building　Ldr. Guide Avail.: No　Size: 6.0 x 9.0
Subjects: Bible Study, Jesus: Life/Teaching, John
Comments: This workbook, specifically for Catholics with little or no Bible study backgrounds, is for personal and group study and takes the beginner through the Gospel of John in nine chapters. Participants get hands-on experience learning important study skills and using valuable reference works. The study uses the "discovery" method, emphasizing development of skills to "discover" Scripture. Participants learn how to do overview studies of entire books of the Bible and a detailed study of a passage.

Author: Schoberg, Gerry & R. Paul Stevens   **931**
Series: NetWork Discussion Guide
Title: *Servant Leadership*
Publisher: Shaw, 1990

Num. Sess.	Group Time	Num. Pgs.	Avg. Qst.	Price	Audience	Format	Bible Study
8	30-45	48	5	3.50	Beginner	Workbk	Topical

Features: Intro to Leading a Study, Intro to Study, Bibliography, Follow Up, Ldr's Notes
  ★★★★ Personal Application   Preparation Time: Low   ISBN: 0-87788-755-1
  ★★★ Relationship Building   Ldr. Guide Avail.: No   Size: 5.25 x 8.25
Subjects: Christian Living, Church Life, Family, Leadership, Work
Comments: Eight short studies on mixing leader and servant qualities help participants focus on Christian response to everyday challenges of both. Qualities considered include what it means to be a servant in the marketplace, how to value oneself without becoming proud, and how to balance the competing agendas of work, family, church, and friends. This study is best suited for an office setting, either early morning or lunch time.

Author: Schrag, Dr. Lyle, et al.   **932**
Series: Life Application
Title: *Revelation*
Publisher: Tyndale House, 1989

Num. Sess.	Group Time	Num. Pgs.	Avg. Qst.	Price	Audience	Format	Bible Study
13	60-90	96	12	4.95	New Christian	Workbk	Book

Features: Intro to Leading a Study, Intro to Study, Study Overview, Digging Deeper Quest, Full Scrpt Printed, Drawings, Charts, Maps, Cross Ref
  ★★★ Personal Application   Preparation Time: Med   ISBN: 0-8423-2719-3
  ★★★ Relationship Building   Ldr. Guide Avail.: No   Size: 6.50 x 9.0
Subjects: Church Life, Hope, Revelation
Comments: This study contains the complete text of Revelation, a book of hope. Participants will marvel with John at the panorama of God's revealed plan, listen as Christ warns the churches, and root out any sin that blocks their relationships with Him. They are urged to have hope, knowing that God is in control, that Christ's victory is assured, and all who trust Him will be saved. Questions lead to application of biblical truth and action plans.

Author: Schramm, Mary   **933**
Series: Small Group Bible Studies
Title: *Peacemaking*
Publisher: Augsburg Publishing House, 1986

Num. Sess.	Group Time	Num. Pgs.	Avg. Qst.	Price	Audience	Format	Bible Study
8	60-75	32	11	1.25	New Christian	Book	Topical

Features: Intro to Study, Prayer Helps
  ★★★ Personal Application   Preparation Time: None   ISBN:
  ★★★ Relationship Building   Ldr. Guide Avail.: No   Size: 8.50 x 5.50
Subjects: Relationships, Wholeness
Comments: This small pamphlet includes eight sessions on peacemaking, using Scripture as a guide. Peacemaking begins with and is an integral part of the vision of shalom—God's plan for the world. This Hebrew word is a way to say hello and goodby. It means prosperity and health, security and well-being, but its best definition is "wholeness" or "completeness." God is interested in an inner peace. These sessions reflect peacemaking as a call upon Christians' lives, in relationships, and environment.

Author: Schreur, Tamera Veenstra   **934**
Series: Discover Your Bible
Title: *Discover: Ephesians*
Publisher: Church Development Resources, 1984

Num. Sess.	Group Time	Num. Pgs.	Avg. Qst.	Price	Audience	Format	Bible Study
12	60-75	43	5	1.95	Beginner	Workbk	Book

Features: Intro to Study, Summary, Glossary
  ★★★ Personal Application   Preparation Time: None   ISBN:
  ★★ Relationship Building   Ldr. Guide Avail.: Yes   Size: 5.50 x 8.50
Subjects: Ephesians, Marriage, Parenting, Relationships
Comments: This inductive study of Ephesians deals with the transformation from the "old self" to the "new." Paul offers contemporary participants practical, candid guidance on parenting, marriage, and other relationships. Ephesian Christians had previously lived to gratify their own selfish desires and thoughts. Their lifestyles had opposed God's will, but now they were alive in Christ. Participants will find the letter encouraging and relevant.

Author: Schreur, Tamera Veenstra   **935**
Series: Discover Your Bible
Title: *Discover: Galatians*
Publisher: Church Development Resources, 1986

Num. Sess.	Group Time	Num. Pgs.	Avg. Qst.	Price	Audience	Format	Bible Study
8	60-75	46	6	1.35	Beginner	Workbk	Book

Features: Intro to Study, Summary, Glossary
  ★★★ Personal Application   Preparation Time: None   ISBN:
  ★★ Relationship Building   Ldr. Guide Avail.: Yes   Size: 5.50 x 8.50
Subjects: Church Life, Faith, Galatians
Comments: This inductive study of Galatians discusses the issues and customs that concerned the early Church. It uncovers universal Christian principles that have become foundations of the Church's life, and shows their modern application. Paul's letter helps answer basic questions about Christian faith, such as: "How is one saved—by believing or by achieving?" "Does Jesus save us or do we save ourselves?" A comprehensive leader's guide is available.

Author: Schreur, Tamera Veenstra   **936**
Series: Discover Your Bible
Title: *Discover Luke: Jesus' Parables and Miracles*
Publisher: Church Development Resources, 1983

Num. Sess.	Group Time	Num. Pgs.	Avg. Qst.	Price	Audience	Format	Bible Study
9	60-75	35	6	1.50	Beginner	Workbk	Book

Features: Intro to Study, Summary, Glossary
  ★★★ Personal Application   Preparation Time: None   ISBN:
  ★★ Relationship Building   Ldr. Guide Avail.: Yes   Size: 5.50 x 8.50
Subjects: Jesus: Life/Teaching, Luke, Miracles, Parables
Comments: This study on Jesus' parables and miracles is second in a three-part series on Luke. An inductive study, it helps participants discover Bible truth themselves, in this case, verse by verse through Luke 13-19. Each of nine lessons consists of a series of questions which, when answered, give participants a clear, personal understanding of the scripture. Application of the message in their lives and sharing with others are encouraged.

Author: Schreur, Tamera Veenstra   **937**
Series: Discover Your Bible
Title: *Discover Luke: Jesus' Last Days*
Publisher: Church Development Resources, 1983

Num. Sess.	Group Time	Num. Pgs.	Avg. Qst.	Price	Audience	Format	Bible Study
9	60-75	36	6	1.50	Beginner	Workbk	Book

Features: Intro to Study, Summary
  ★★★ Personal Application   Preparation Time: None   ISBN:
  ★★ Relationship Building   Ldr. Guide Avail.: Yes   Size: 5.50 x 8.50
Subjects: Jesus: Life/Teaching, Luke
Comments: This study on Jesus' last days is last in a three-part series on Luke. An inductive study, it helps participants discover Bible truth themselves, in this case, verse by verse through Luke 19-24. Each of seven lessons consists of a series of questions which, when answered, give participants a clear, personal understanding of the scripture. Application of the message in their lives and sharing with others are encouraged.

Author: Schreur, Tamera Veenstra   **938**
Series: Discover Your Bible
Title: *Discover: The Sermon on the Mount*
Publisher: Church Development Resources, 1985

Num. Sess.	Group Time	Num. Pgs.	Avg. Qst.	Price	Audience	Format	Bible Study
8	60-75	31	6	1.35	Beginner	Workbk	Book

Features: Intro to Study, Summary, Glossary
  ★★★ Personal Application   Preparation Time: None   ISBN:
  ★★ Relationship Building   Ldr. Guide Avail.: Yes   Size: 5.50 x 8.50
Subjects: Christian Living, Sermon on the Mount, Ten Commandments
Comments: This inductive study of the Sermon on the Mount deals with murder, adultery, peacemaking, ambition, and righteousness. Putting the Ten Commandments into perspective, Jesus shows His listeners what God intended the Law to be. He presents it as a guide to a believer's new life that comes from a changed heart, not from following a set of rules. It is a practical study. A comprehensive leader's guide is available.

Author: Schultz, Thom & Joani   **939**
Series: Group's Active Bible Curriculum
Title: *Is Marriage in Your Future?*
Publisher: Group Publishing, 1990

Num. Sess.	Group Time	Num. Pgs.	Avg. Qst.	Price	Audience	Format	Bible Study
4	35-60	46	Vry	6.95	Beginner	Workbk	Topical

Features: Intro to Leading a Study, Intro to Study, Objectives, Study Overview, Ldr's Notes, Handouts, Agenda, Publicity Ideas
  ★★★ Personal Application   Preparation Time: None   ISBN: 1-559-45203-X
  ★★★ Relationship Building   Ldr. Guide Avail.: No   Size: 8.50 x 11.0
Subjects: Teens: Family, Teens: Relationships, Teens: Senior High
Comments: This study offers senior high students the secrets of a great marriage, how to have a continuing successful marriage and family life. It defines marriage, discusses how friendship builds a foundation for marriage, deals with God's idea of love, and outlines what makes a marriage work. It can be adapted for use in a Bible class or youth meeting. Activities and Bible studies are included as separate sheets that can be reproduced. The instructions are easy to follow, and offer many options.

Author: Schultz, Yvonne   **940**
Series: The Lifechange Series
Title: *Colossians & Philemon*
Publisher: NavPress, 1988

Num. Sess.	Group Time	Num. Pgs.	Avg. Qst.	Price	Audience	Format	Bible Study
11	60-90	139	15	5.95	New Christian	Workbk	Book

Features: Intro to Leading a Study, Intro to Study, Bibliography, Prayer Helps, Worship Helps, Study Overview, Digging Deeper Quest, Summary, Maps, Word Study
  ★★★ Personal Application   Preparation Time: Med   ISBN: 0-89109-119-X
  ★★★ Relationship Building   Ldr. Guide Avail.: No   Size: 5.50 x 8.50
Subjects: Church Life, Colossians/Philemon, False Teachers, Forgiveness, Prison Epistles
Comments: This verse-by-verse study of Colossians and Philemon addresses two crises in Colosse. Visitors to Paul in prison recount news of false teachers belittling Christ, laying down rules, and boasting of secret knowledge beyond the gospel. Then, a runaway slave begs Paul to ask his Christian master for mercy. The letters were written to show Colossian Christians how to handle these dilemmas. Paul's words exalt Christ, refocus the Colossians' attention, and affirm a Christian lifestyle.

Author: Sciacca, Fran & Jill   **941**
Series: Lifelines
Title: *Burger, Fries and a Friend to Go*
Publisher: NavPress, 1988

Num. Sess.	Group Time	Num. Pgs.	Avg. Qst.	Price	Audience	Format	Bible Study
6	45-60	45	4	3.95	Beginner	Workbk	Topical

Features: Intro to Leading a Study, Intro to Study, Scrpt Memory Helps, Persnl Study Quest
  ★★★★ Personal Application   Preparation Time: Low   ISBN: 0-89109-593-4
  ★★★ Relationship Building   Ldr. Guide Avail.: Yes   Size: 5.50 x 8.50
Subjects: Teens: Christian Liv, Teens: Friends
Comments: This study concerns young adults building friendships. Lessons deal with selecting friends, identifying genuine friends, ingredients in true friendships, nonChristian friends, conflict among friends, and the ultimate friend—Jesus. Each lesson begins with a true story from the life of a teenager. An inductive study approach is used, but no group-building activities are provided.

Author: Sciacca, Fran & Jill   **942**
Series: Lifelines
Title: *Caution: Contents Under Pressure*
Publisher: NavPress, 1990

Num. Sess.	Group Time	Num. Pgs.	Avg. Qst.	Price	Audience	Format	Bible Study
6	45-60	55	5	3.95	Beginner	Workbk	Topical

Features: Intro to Leading a Study, Intro to Study, Scrpt Memory Helps, Persnl Study Quest
  ★★★★ Personal Application   Preparation Time: Low   ISBN: 0-89109-374-5
  ★★★ Relationship Building   Ldr. Guide Avail.: Yes   Size: 5.50 x 8.50
Subjects: Teens: Emotions, Teens: Relationships
Comments: This contemporary study for young adults concerns anger. Lessons cover anger as a natural emotion; unrighteous, righteous, and unresolved anger; reaction to angry people; and things that anger God. Each lesson begins with a true story from the life of a teenager. An inductive study approach is used, but no group-building activities are provided.

Author: Sciacca, Fran & Jill   **943**
Series: Lifelines
Title: *Cliques and Clones*
Publisher: NavPress, 1988

Num. Sess.	Group Time	Num. Pgs.	Avg. Qst.	Price	Audience	Format	Bible Study
6	45-60	54	3	3.95	Beginner	Workbk	Topical

Features: Intro to Leading a Study, Intro to Study, Scrpt Memory Helps, Persnl Study Quest
★★★★ Personal Application   Preparation Time: Low   ISBN: 0-89109-594-2
★★★ Relationship Building   Ldr. Guide Avail.: Yes   Size: 5.50 x 8.50
Subjects: Teens: Decisions, Teens: Peer Pressure
Comments: This study deals with peer pressure on young adults. Lessons include: "Who's Pushing Me?—The Inner Response"; "When the Party's Over—Consequences of Choices"; "It's Your Choice—Choosing Friends"; "Why Won't God Help Me?—Things I Won't Do"; and "Surprise!—Get Out." Each lesson begins with a true story from the life of a teenager. An inductive study approach is used, but no group-building activities are provided.

Author: Sciacca, Fran & Jill   **944**
Series: Lifelines
Title: *Desperately Seeking Perfect Family*
Publisher: NavPress, 1988

Num. Sess.	Group Time	Num. Pgs.	Avg. Qst.	Price	Audience	Format	Bible Study
6	45-60	44	4	3.95	Beginner	Workbk	Topical

Features: Intro to Leading a Study, Intro to Study, Scrpt Memory Helps, Persnl Study Quest
★★★★ Personal Application   Preparation Time: Low   ISBN: 0-89109-595-0
★★★ Relationship Building   Ldr. Guide Avail.: Yes   Size: 5.50 x 8.50
Subjects: Teens: Family, Teens: Relationships
Comments: This contemporary study for young adults concerns family. Lessons include: "May I Speak to the Manager, Please?"—(God chooses parents); "I Can't Wait Until I Graduate!"—(obeying one's parents); "Technical Difficulties . . .Please Stand By"—("how" I talk to my parents); "Did You Hear Me?"—(listening); and "After the Bomb Drops"—(children of divorce). Each lesson begins with a true story from the life of a teenager. No group-building activities are provided.

Author: Sciacca, Fran & Jill   **945**
Series: Lifelines
Title: *Does Anyone Else Feel This Way?*
Publisher: NavPress, 1990

Num. Sess.	Group Time	Num. Pgs.	Avg. Qst.	Price	Audience	Format	Bible Study
6	45-60	59	5	3.95	Beginner	Workbk	Topical

Features: Intro to Leading a Study, Intro to Study, Scrpt Memory Helps, Persnl Study Quest
★★★★ Personal Application   Preparation Time: Low   ISBN: 0-89109-375-3
★★★ Relationship Building   Ldr. Guide Avail.: Yes   Size: 5.50 x 8.50
Subjects: Teens: Emotions, Teens: Psychology
Comments: This contemporary study for young adults concerns loneliness, depression, and thoughts of suicide. Lessons address honesty about loneliness, causes of loneliness and depression, understanding one's inner and outer focus, talking about thoughts of suicide, and why suicide is no solution. A chart titled "What to Say to a Suicidal Friend" outlines what to say and why, as well as what to do and why. Each lesson begins with a true story from the life of a teenager.

Author: Sciacca, Fran & Jill   **946**
Series: Lifelines
Title: *Does God Live Here Anymore?*
Publisher: NavPress, 1988

Num. Sess.	Group Time	Num. Pgs.	Avg. Qst.	Price	Audience	Format	Bible Study
6	45-60	53	6	3.95	Beginner	Workbk	Topical

Features: Intro to Leading a Study, Intro to Study, Scrpt Memory Helps, Persnl Study Quest
★★★★ Personal Application   Preparation Time: Low   ISBN: 0-89109-596-9
★★★ Relationship Building   Ldr. Guide Avail.: Yes   Size: 5.50 x 8.50
Subjects: Teens: Discipleship, Teens: Occult
Comments: This is a contemporary study on Christian perspective for young adults. Lessons include: "Natural and Supernatural Worlds," "The Christian's View of the World," "God's Holiness and Perfect Love," "The Christian's View of Respect," and "The Reality of Satan." Each lesson begins with a true story from the life of a teenager. An inductive study approach is used, but no group-building activities are provided.

Author: Sciacca, Fran & Jill   **947**
Series: Lifelines
Title: *Good News for a Bad News World*
Publisher: NavPress, 1988

Num. Sess.	Group Time	Num. Pgs.	Avg. Qst.	Price	Audience	Format	Bible Study
6	45-60	67	5	3.95	Beginner	Workbk	Topical

Features: Intro to Leading a Study, Intro to Study, Scrpt Memory Helps, Full Scrpt Printed,Drawings, Persnl Study Quest
★★★★ Personal Application   Preparation Time: Low   ISBN: 0-89109-597-7
★★★ Relationship Building   Ldr. Guide Avail.: Yes   Size: 5.50 x 8.50
Subjects: Teens: Discipleship, Teens: Evangelism
Comments: This contemporary study for young adults is subtitled "Jesus Christ Has a Plan for Your Life." Lessons include: "God's Image," "The Bad News," "The Good News," "The Gift of Salvation," and "The Security of My Salvation." A brief tract and some drawings in the back of the study review the steps to salvation. Each lesson begins with a true story from the life of a teenager. An inductive study approach is used, but no group-building activities are provided.

Author: Sciacca, Fran & Jill   **948**
Series: Lifelines
Title: *Is This the Real Thing?*
Publisher: NavPress, 1990

Num. Sess.	Group Time	Num. Pgs.	Avg. Qst.	Price	Audience	Format	Bible Study
6	45-60	59	5	3.95	Beginner	Workbk	Topical

Features: Intro to Leading a Study, Intro to Study, Scrpt Memory Helps, Drawings, Persnl Study Quest
★★★★ Personal Application   Preparation Time: Low   ISBN: 0-89109-376-1
★★★ Relationship Building   Ldr. Guide Avail.: Yes   Size: 5.50 x 8.50
Subjects: Teens: Emotions, Teens: Friends
Comments: This contemporary study for young adults concerns what love is and what it isn't. Lessons are entitled: "Why Love?," "Genuine Love Is a Choice," "Loving the Unlovable," "Love Between Friends," "The Growing Pattern of True Love," and "How Love Can Be Destroyed." Each lesson begins with a true story from the life of a teenager. An inductive study approach is used, but no group-building activities are provided.

Author: Sciacca, Fran & Jill   **949**
Series: Lifelines
Title: *Kick the Fear Habit*
Publisher: NavPress, 1990

Num. Sess.	Group Time	Num. Pgs.	Avg. Qst.	Price	Audience	Format	Bible Study
6	45-60	53	4	3.95	Beginner	Workbk	Topical

Features: Intro to Leading a Study, Intro to Study, Scrpt Memory Helps, Persnl Study Quest

★★★★ Personal Application   Preparation Time: Low   ISBN: 0-89109-373-7
★★★ Relationship Building   Ldr. Guide Avail.: Yes   Size: 5.50 x 8.50

Subjects: Teens: Emotions
Comments: This contemporary study on fear, for young adults, looks at why they should fear, good fear, fear "traps," fear of the future, fear of failure, and fear of death. Each lesson begins with a true story from the life of a teenager. An inductive study approach is used, but no group-building attivities are provided.

Author: Sciacca, Fran & Jill   **950**
Series: Lifelines
Title: *Learning to Hope in a Wish-Filled World*
Publisher: NavPress, 1988

Num. Sess.	Group Time	Num. Pgs.	Avg. Qst.	Price	Audience	Format	Bible Study
6	45-60	58	5	3.95	Beginner	Workbk	Topical

Features: Intro to Leading a Study, Intro to Study, Scrpt Memory Helps, Persnl Study Quest

★★★★ Personal Application   Preparation Time: Low   ISBN: 0-89109-598-5
★★★ Relationship Building   Ldr. Guide Avail.: Yes   Size: 5.50 x 8.50

Subjects: Teens: Christian Liv
Comments: This contemporary study for young adults concerns hope. Lessons address the hope necessary for meaningful life; hopelessness which is not terminal; hope for tomorrow; hope as security; shaping one's sense of hope; and hope which cannot be cultivated alone. Each lesson begins with a true story from the life of a teenager. An inductive study approach is used, but no group-building activities are provided.

Author: Sciacca, Fran & Jill   **951**
Series: Lifelines
Title: *No Pain, No Gain*
Publisher: NavPress, 1988

Num. Sess.	Group Time	Num. Pgs.	Avg. Qst.	Price	Audience	Format	Bible Study
6	45-60	58	5	3.95	Beginner	Workbk	Topical

Features: Intro to Leading a Study, Intro to Study, Scrpt Memory Helps, Persnl Study Quest

★★★★ Personal Application   Preparation Time: Low   ISBN: 0-89109-599-3
★★★ Relationship Building   Ldr. Guide Avail.: Yes   Size: 5.50 x 8.50

Subjects: Forgiveness, Obedience, Teens: Discipleship
Comments: This contemporary study teaches young adults to train for spiritual fitness and includes lessons addressing obedience, temptation, sonship, forgiveness, letting go, and violation of conscience. Each lesson begins with a true story from the life of a teenager. An inductive study approach is used, but no group-building activities are provided.

Author: Sciacca, Fran & Jill   **952**
Series: Lifelines
Title: *Sex: When to Say "Yes"*
Publisher: NavPress, 1988

Num. Sess.	Group Time	Num. Pgs.	Avg. Qst.	Price	Audience	Format	Bible Study
6	45-60	51	4	3.95	Beginner	Workbk	Topical

Features: Intro to Leading a Study, Intro to Study, Scrpt Memory Helps, Persnl Study Quest

★★★★ Personal Application   Preparation Time: Low   ISBN: 0-89109-600-0
★★★ Relationship Building   Ldr. Guide Avail.: Yes   Size: 5.50 x 8.50

Subjects: Teens: Christian Liv, Teens: Sexuality
Comments: This contemporary study for young adults concerns sex. Lessons deal with premarital sex, supply and demand of sex outside of marriage, sex in marriage, and dating a nonbeliever. Each lesson begins with a true story from the life of a teenager. Several true false quizzes help focus the study. An inductive study approach is used, but no group-building activities are provided.

Author: Sciacca, Fran & Jill   **953**
Series: Lifelines
Title: *Some Assembly Required*
Publisher: NavPress, 1988

Num. Sess.	Group Time	Num. Pgs.	Avg. Qst.	Price	Audience	Format	Bible Study
6	45-60	56	5	3.95	Beginner	Workbk	Topical

Features: Intro to Leading a Study, Intro to Study, Scrpt Memory Helps, Drawings, Persnl Study Quest

★★★★ Personal Application   Preparation Time: Low   ISBN: 0-89109-602-7
★★★ Relationship Building   Ldr. Guide Avail.: Yes   Size: 5.50 x 8.50

Subjects: Teens: Discipleship, Teens: Prayer
Comments: This contemporary study allows young adults to put together a new life in Christ. Lessons include: "The Old and New Self"; "God, a Friend in Normal and Crisis Times"; "The Bible's Authority"; "The Study of God's Word"; "The Power of Prayer"; and "The Necessity for Christian Friends." Each lesson begins with a true story from the life of a teenager. An inductive study approach is used, but no group-building activities are provided.

Author: Sciacca, Fran & Jill   **954**
Series: Lifelines
Title: *Some Things Are Never Discounted*
Publisher: NavPress, 1988

Num. Sess.	Group Time	Num. Pgs.	Avg. Qst.	Price	Audience	Format	Bible Study
6	45-60	50	6	3.95	Beginner	Workbk	Topical

Features: Intro to Leading a Study, Intro to Study, Scrpt Memory Helps, Persnl Study Quest

★★★★ Personal Application   Preparation Time: Low   ISBN: 0-89109-603-5
★★★ Relationship Building   Ldr. Guide Avail.: Yes   Size: 5.50 x 8.50

Subjects: Teens: Christian Liv
Comments: This contemporary study for young adults concerns values. Lessons include: "Things Treasured"; "Values 'Caught,' Not 'Taught'"; "God's Values"; "Preoccupation with Self"; and "Standing Alone." Each lesson begins with a true story from the life of a teenager. Several checklists and rating scales help direct the study. An inductive study approach is used, but no group-building activities are provided.

Author: Sciacca, Fran & Jill   **955**
Series: Lifelines
Title: *So What's Wrong with a Big Nose?*
Publisher: NavPress, 1988

Num. Sess.	Group Time	Num. Pgs.	Avg. Qst.	Price	Audience	Format	Bible Study
6	45-60	56	6	3.95	Beginner	Workbk	Topical

Features: Intro to Leading a Study, Intro to Study, Scrpt Memory Helps, Persnl Study Quest
  ★★★★ Personal Application   Preparation Time: Low   ISBN: 0-89109-601-9
  ★★★ Relationship Building   Ldr. Guide Avail.: Yes   Size: 5.50 x 8.50
Subjects: Teens: Psychology, Teens: Self-esteem
Comments: This contemporary study on self-esteem is for young adults. Lessons deal with subjects like the need for self-worth, where self-worth comes from, God's love, God's perfect plan, preoccupation with self, and self-sacrifice. Each lesson begins with a true story from the life of a teenager. An inductive study approach is used, but no group-building activities are provided.

Author: Sciacca, Fran   **956**
Series:
Title: *To Walk and Not Grow Weary*
Publisher: NavPress, 1985

Num. Sess.	Group Time	Num. Pgs.	Avg. Qst.	Price	Audience	Format	Bible Study
12	45-60	81	10	4.95	New Christian	Workbk	Topical

Features: Intro to Study, Bibliography, Scrpt Memory Helps, Digging Deeper Quest
  ★★★ Personal Application   Preparation Time: Low   ISBN: 0-89109-034-7
  ★★ Relationship Building   Ldr. Guide Avail.: No   Size: 5.50 x 8.50
Subjects: Bible Personalities, Emotions, Loneliness, Psychology, Success
Comments: This study presents cameos of twelve godly people under pressure. Each contrasts human problems with God's solutions, under chapter titles such as: "Job—When the Lights Go Out"; "David—Dealing with Guilt"; "Jesus—How to Handle Rejection"; and "Barnabas—Encouraging Others." The study is for people suffering from emotional fatigue, loneliness, discouragement, pressure to succeed, oppressive guilt, and adverse circumstances.

Author: Sciacca, Fran & Jill   **957**
Series: Lifelines
Title: *Warning: This Christian Is Highly Explosive!*
Publisher: NavPress, 1988

Num. Sess.	Group Time	Num. Pgs.	Avg. Qst.	Price	Audience	Format	Bible Study
6	45-60	58	6	3.95	Beginner	Workbk	Topical

Features: Intro to Leading a Study, Intro to Study, Scrpt Memory Helps, Persnl Study Quest
  ★★★★ Personal Application   Preparation Time: Low   ISBN: 0-89109-604-3
  ★★★ Relationship Building   Ldr. Guide Avail.: Yes   Size: 5.50 x 8.50
Subjects: Teens: Evangelism
Comments: This study encourages contemporary young adults to impact their world through their commitment to Christ. Lessons address topics such as following God's direction, becoming more like Jesus, representing God, developing a servant's attitude, and giving the gift of salvation. Each lesson begins with a true story from the life of a teenager. An inductive study approach is used, but no group-building activities are provided.

Author: Scott, Latayne C.   **958**
Series: Woman's Workshop Series
Title: *Open Up Your Life: A Woman's Workshop on Hospitality*
Publisher: Zondervan, 1984

Num. Sess.	Group Time	Num. Pgs.	Avg. Qst.	Price	Audience	Format	Bible Study
9	60-75	132	14	5.95	New Christian	Workbk	Topical

Features: Intro to Study, Bibliography, Prayer Helps, Ldr's Notes
  ★★★ Personal Application   Preparation Time: Med   ISBN: 0-310-38901-1
  ★★ Relationship Building   Ldr. Guide Avail.: No   Size: 5.25 x 8.0
Subjects: Caring, Christian Living, Women's Issues
Comments: This inductive study shows the biblical basis and model for hospitality. It consists of nine lessons, each divided into two-part questions for group discussion and daily devotion. The lessons explain that love for Christ motivates people to be hospitable, and that hospitality will teach them to love more deeply. Participants will realize through the Scripture that a Christian's life is incomplete if he or she is not practicing hospitality.

Author: Scott, Latayne C.   **959**
Series: Woman's Workshop Series
Title: *Time, Talents, Things: A Woman's Workshop on Christian Stewardship*
Publisher: Zondervan, 1987

Num. Sess.	Group Time	Num. Pgs.	Avg. Qst.	Price	Audience	Format	Bible Study
10	60-90	95	12	4.95	New Christian	Workbk	Topical

Features: Intro to Leading a Study, Intro to Study, Ldr's Notes, Persnl Study Quest, Charts, Appendix
  ★★★ Personal Application   Preparation Time: Low   ISBN: 0-310-38771-X
  ★★ Relationship Building   Ldr. Guide Avail.: No   Size: 5.25 x 8.0
Subjects: Christian Living, Stewardship, Time, Wisdom, Women's Issues
Comments: This study on Christian stewardship emphasizes that while each person's opportunities and resources are different, each is called to "a unique stewardship." Stewardship, traceable throughout the Bible, is a reflection of godly people's belief that God ultimately owns their possessions, abilities, and span of life. Participants will become aware that they are merely caretakers, not owners, of God's gifts; that He expects them to manage His resources effectively.

Author: Seamands, David A.   **960**
Series:
Title: *Putting Away Childish Things*
Publisher: Victor Books, 1982

Num. Sess.	Group Time	Num. Pgs.	Avg. Qst.	Price	Audience	Format	Bible Study
13	60-90	144	N/A	7.99	New Christian	Book	Topical

Features:
  ★★★★ Personal Application   Preparation Time: Med   ISBN: 0-88207-308-7
  ★★★ Relationship Building   Ldr. Guide Avail.: Yes   Size: 5.50 x 8.0
Subjects: Christian Living, Discipleship, Grace, Marriage, Psychology
Comments: This study helps participants progress toward the maturity God desires for all believers. These lessons identify outdated childish patterns and suggest ways of breaking their grip, so there can be growth in Christ. Lessons include: "The Hidden Child in Us All," "The Healing of the Memories," "Childish Ideas of Love and Marriage," "Childish Ideas of God and His Will," and "Reprogramming Grace." A leader's guide with transparency masters is available.

Author: Seemuth, David P.   **961**
Series: GroupBuilder Resources
Title: *Defeating Those Dragons*
Publisher: Victor Books, 1991

Num. Sess.	Group Time	Num. Pgs.	Avg. Qst.	Price	Audience	Format	Bible Study
8	75-90	144	Vry	5.99	New Christian	Workbk	Topical

Features: Intro to Leading a Study, Objectives, Pre-discussion Quest, Digging Deeper Quest, Full Scrpt Printed, Ldr's Notes, Cartoons, Persnl Study Quest

★★★ Personal Application   Preparation Time: Low   ISBN: 0-89693-924-3
★★★ Relationship Building   Ldr. Guide Avail.: No   Size: 6.0 x 9.0

Subjects: Emotions, Failure

Comments: This study helps small groups gain insight and support as they study how to put to death (or at least mortally wound) hindrances to their spiritual growth. Sessions deal with such dragons as anxiety, doubt, temptation, discouragement, hopelessness, fear, bitterness, and failure. Optional activities, hints for leaders, and answers to questions can be found in the leader's guide at the back of the book.

Author: Seemuth, David P.   **962**
Series: GroupBuilder Resources
Title: *How Dynamic is Your Small Group?*
Publisher: Victor Books, 1991

Num. Sess.	Group Time	Num. Pgs.	Avg. Qst.	Price	Audience	Format	Bible Study
11	-	156	6	7.99		Book	

Features: Charts

Personal Application   Preparation Time: ISBN: 0-89693-880-8
Relationship Building   Ldr. Guide Avail.:   Size: 6.0 x 9.0

Subjects: Commitments, Small Group Resource

Comments: This book allows leaders to evaluate their small groups according to seven criteria, including communication, acceptance, commitment, standards, purpose, recognition of people and their backgrounds, and cohesion. Forms provided include a sample covenant and guidelines for developing neighborhood groups. Questions at the close of each chapter aid in review and reflection on the text. Sections may be used effectively in ongoing small group leadership training.

Author: Sekowsky, JoAnne   **963**
Series: Workbook Series
Title: *Art of Being Single, The: How to Get the Best out of Life*
Publisher: Aglow, 1987

Num. Sess.	Group Time	Num. Pgs.	Avg. Qst.	Price	Audience	Format	Bible Study
9	60-75	93	30	5.95	Mature Chrstn	Workbk	Topical

Features: Intro to Study, Prayer Helps, Scrpt Memory Helps, Follow Up, Drawings, Persnl Study Quest

★★★ Personal Application   Preparation Time: Med   ISBN: 0-932305-41-5
★★★ Relationship Building   Ldr. Guide Avail.: No   Size: 8.50 x 10.0

Subjects: Singles Issues, Victorious Living, Women's Issues

Comments: This nine-week study shows single participants how to live fulfilled single lives. Using Jesus' relationships with single people during His life on earth, and His own experiences as evidence, the author paints a picture of a God vitally concerned about singles of every age. In an age in which women were looked down upon, Christ broke all tradition, using them in His ministry and the spreading of the gospel. He wants to do the same today.

Author: Sekowsky, JoAnne   **964**
Series: Workbook Series
Title: *Spiritual Warfare: Strategy for Winning*
Publisher: Aglow, 1983

Num. Sess.	Group Time	Num. Pgs.	Avg. Qst.	Price	Audience	Format	Bible Study
11	60-75	80	Vry	5.95	Mature Chrstn	Workbk	Topical

Features: Intro to Study, Scrpt Memory Helps, Follow Up, Drawings, Persnl Study Quest

★★★★ Personal Application   Preparation Time: Med   ISBN: 0-930756-74-6
★★★ Relationship Building   Ldr. Guide Avail.: No   Size: 8.50 x 10.0

Subjects: Charismatic Interest, Prayer, Satan

Comments: This eleven-week study prepares participants to use their spiritual authority in prayer and intercession. It concerns the history of the war between the forces of good and evil and the two opposing commanders in chief, Jesus Christ and Satan. It explains believers' assignments and the weapons they have been issued. It teaches four principles of warfare strategy, and shows the dangerous Fifth Column (an enemy from within a person) in operation. The final lesson describes how believers achieve victory.

Author: Sethre, Peter A.   **965**
Series: Friendship Bible Study
Title: *James*
Publisher: Augsburg Publishing House, 1987

Num. Sess.	Group Time	Num. Pgs.	Avg. Qst.	Price	Audience	Format	Bible Study
8	60-75	48	13	3.0	New Christian	Workbk	Book

Features: Intro to Study, Prayer Helps, Study Overview

★★★★ Personal Application   Preparation Time: Low   ISBN:
★★★★ Relationship Building   Ldr. Guide Avail.: Yes   Size: 5.0 x 8.50

Subjects: Faith, James, Joy, Relationships, Suffering

Comments: This eight-lesson study stresses to those who profess faith in Christ that they are called to let that faith govern their actions and relationships. Participants learn what it means to count various trials and circumstances as "all joy" (James 1:2), and receive practical guidelines for their walk in Christian faith. The lesson format includes an overview, an opening, a responsive reading, Bible background, questions for reflection, a key verse, prayer response, and more.

Author: Shaw, Jean   **966**
Series: Woman's Workshop Series
Title: *Greater Love: Studies on Friendship*
Publisher: Zondervan, 1983

Num. Sess.	Group Time	Num. Pgs.	Avg. Qst.	Price	Audience	Format	Bible Study
12	60-90	100	Vry	4.95	Beginner	Workbk	Topical

Features: Intro to Study, Prayer Helps, Ldr's Notes, Drawings

★★★ Personal Application   Preparation Time: Low   ISBN: 0-310-43531-5
★★★ Relationship Building   Ldr. Guide Avail.: No   Size: 5.25 x 8.0

Subjects: Friendships, Love, Marriage, Relationships, Women's Issues

Comments: This study on friendship, rewarding and life changing, helps participants see friendship as a potential force for spiritual growth, evangelism, and discipleship. It will deepen existing friendships and help develop others. A biblical basis for friendship and practical applications is offered. Above all, it helps participants realize that "above and beyond human relationships is the divine friendship of Christ, our Creator, Savior, and Lord."

Author: Shaw, Luci   **967**
Series: Fisherman Bible Studyguide
Title: *Colossians: Focus on Christ*
Publisher: Shaw, 1982

Num. Sess.	Group Time	Num. Pgs.	Avg. Qst.	Price	Audience	Format	Bible Study
9	45-60	56	12	3.95	Mature Chrstn	Workbk	Book

Features: Intro to Leading a Study, Intro to Study, Prayer Helps
  ★★ Personal Application   Preparation Time: Low   ISBN: 0-87788-132-4
  ★★ Relationship Building   Ldr. Guide Avail.: No   Size: 5.0 x 8.25
Subjects: Church Life, Colossians/Philemon, False Teachers, Forgiveness, Hope, Occult, Prison Epistles, Service
Comments: In this verse-by-verse study of Colossians, Paul provides a defense-warning, teaching, and encouraging growth and maturity in Christ. Also dealt with are the same heresies of the young Asian church—threat of legalism and Gnosticism—that are still active today. Eager to investigate other power sources—occult mysticism, astrology, horoscopes, and more—the Colossians allowed false emphases to erode and falsify their view of Jesus Christ.

Author: Shelton, Chuck   **968**
Series: Global Issues
Title: *Voiceless People*
Publisher: InterVarsity, 1990

Num. Sess.	Group Time	Num. Pgs.	Avg. Qst.	Price	Audience	Format	Bible Study
6	45-60	48	10	4.95	Beginner	Workbk	Topical

Features: Intro to Leading a Study, Intro to Study, Bibliography, Prayer Helps, Follow Up
  ★★ Personal Application   Preparation Time: Low   ISBN: 0-8308-4912-2
  ★★ Relationship Building   Ldr. Guide Avail.: No   Size: 5.50 x 8.25
Subjects: Medical Issues, Social Issues
Comments: This six-week study describes the homeless, minorities, the illiterate, terminally ill, and those who live under oppressive governments, among others. It poses questions such as: "How have they become so helpless?" "What can we do to improve life for these people?" and "What does God want us to do?" Participants are challenged to help the world's voiceless people. Leaders should read the study first, to determine appropriateness for their group.

Author: Shields, Ann   **969**
Series: Catholic Bible Study Guide
Title: *Intercession: A Guide to Effective Prayer*
Publisher: Servant Publications, 1988

Num. Sess.	Group Time	Num. Pgs.	Avg. Qst.	Price	Audience	Format	Bible Study
9	60-75	76	10	4.95	Beginner	Workbk	Topical

Features: Intro to Study, Scrpt Memory Helps, Charts
  ★★★ Personal Application   Preparation Time: Low   ISBN: 0-89283-397-1
  ★ Relationship Building   Ldr. Guide Avail.: No   Size: 5.0 x 8.0
Subjects: Prayer
Comments: This nine-lesson study on intercessory prayer is designed to prepare students for effective prayer. It offers practical, Scripture-based teaching that will enable the student to pray for family, friends, relatives, neighbors, and his or her church. Structurally, it is divided into three topical areas and features scripture texts, commentary on the scripture, questions and exercises, and tips for practical application.

Author: Sibley, Larry   **970**
Series: Fisherman Bible Studyguide
Title: *Matthew: People of the Kingdom*
Publisher: Shaw, 1988

Num. Sess.	Group Time	Num. Pgs.	Avg. Qst.	Price	Audience	Format	Bible Study
14	45-60	60	10	3.95	Beginner	Workbk	Book

Features: Intro to Leading a Study, Intro to Study, Prayer Helps, Ldr's Notes, Charts, Maps
  ★★ Personal Application   Preparation Time: None   ISBN: 0-87788-537-0
  ★★ Relationship Building   Ldr. Guide Avail.: No   Size: 5.0 x 8.25
Subjects: Jesus: Life/Teaching, Matthew, Obedience
Comments: This chapter-by-chapter study of Matthew will help participants discover how to submit to Jesus Christ, the Father, and the Holy Spirit. It defines what it means to be a citizen of the Kingdom of God; it defines submission to human authority, a point of tension or confusion for many; it defines what human life and community look like when they come under the gracious rule of God.

Author: Simundson, Daniel J.   **971**
Series: Friendship Bible Study
Title: *Esther*
Publisher: Augsburg Publishing House, 1987

Num. Sess.	Group Time	Num. Pgs.	Avg. Qst.	Price	Audience	Format	Bible Study
8	60-75	48	8	3.0	New Christian	Workbk	Book

Features: Intro to Study, Prayer Helps, Study Overview
  ★★★★ Personal Application   Preparation Time: Low   ISBN:
  ★★★★ Relationship Building   Ldr. Guide Avail.: Yes   Size: 5.50 x 8.50
Subjects: Bible Personalities, Esther, God's Promises, Women's Issues
Comments: This eight-lesson study of Esther raises questions about how Christians and Jews relate to one another, how governments are often hostile to religious people, how (directly or indirectly) God works in the world to keep promises, and how God chooses women as well as men for important tasks. The lesson format includes an overview, an opening, a responsive reading, Bible background, questions for reflection, a key verse, a prayer response, and an "our faith" response.

Author: Sire, James W.   **972**
Series: Fisherman Bible Studyguide
Title: *Meeting Jesus*
Publisher: Shaw, 1988

Num. Sess.	Group Time	Num. Pgs.	Avg. Qst.	Price	Audience	Format	Bible Study
13	45-60	77	11	3.95	Beginner	Workbk	Charctr

Features: Intro to Leading a Study, Intro to Study, Bibliography, Prayer Helps, Ldr's Notes
  ★★ Personal Application   Preparation Time: None   ISBN: 0-87788-542-7
  ★★ Relationship Building   Ldr. Guide Avail.: No   Size: 5.0 x 8.25
Subjects: Evangelism, Jesus: Life/Teaching
Comments: From Mark and Luke thirteen passages of Scripture are explored which highlight Jesus' character and are helpful in presenting the Lord to those who know little about Him. They are used to introduce Jesus in such a way that people cannot mistake the claims He makes. Jesus provides His own best case for Who He is. This study is designed to help seekers "come and see" who this Jesus is.

Author: Smalley, Gary & John Trent, Ph.D. **973**
Series:
Title: *Blessing, The: A Study Guide for Small Groups*
Publisher: NavPress, 1988

Num. Sess.	Group Time	Num. Pgs.	Avg. Qst.	Price	Audience	Format	Bible Study
12	60-90	102	Vry	5.95	Beginner	Workbk	Topical

Features: Intro to Study, Digging Deeper Quest
★★★ Personal Application   Preparation Time: Med   ISBN: 0-89109-275-7
★★★ Relationship Building   Ldr. Guide Avail.: No   Size: 5.50 x 8.50
Subjects: Emotions, Relationships
Comments: This study's message, that everyone has a God-given need to feel blessed, helps participants find emotional healing and experience restored relationships with God, family, and friends. A companion book is optional; however, key principles from the companion book are presented. The format includes excerpts from the book, paraphrased stories, self-tests, and application-oriented exercises. Designed for group study, it is also suited for personal study.

Author: Smalley, Gary & Norma **974**
Series:
Title: *Decide to Love*
Publisher: Zondervan, 1985

Num. Sess.	Group Time	Num. Pgs.	Avg. Qst.	Price	Audience	Format	Bible Study
12	60-90	109	Vry	29.95	Beginner	Audio	Topical

Features: Intro to Study, Drawings, Charts, Book Incl
★★★★ Personal Application   Preparation Time: Med   ISBN: 0-310-44861-1
★★★★ Relationship Building   Ldr. Guide Avail.: Yes   Size: 7.25 x 10.0
Subjects: Marriage
Comments: This twelve-week video study addresses major frustrations in marriage and offers biblical principles on how to remain open with each other, how to become vulnerable again after years of hurt, and other topics. The kit includes a leader's manual, a student's manual, and two audio tapes (with ten- to fifteen-minute segments). Each lesson contains a Bible study, a segment on practical application, and a group-discussion section based on the audio tape. Reading assignments are given.

Author: Smalley, Gary & Norma **975**
Series:
Title: *Decide to Love: A Couple's Workshop*
Publisher: Zondervan, 1985

Num. Sess.	Group Time	Num. Pgs.	Avg. Qst.	Price	Audience	Format	Bible Study
12	90-120	109	Vry	4.95	New Christian	Workbk	Topical

Features: Intro to Study, Scrpt Memory Helps, Follow Up, Drawings, Charts, Cassette Avail
★★★★ Personal Application   Preparation Time: Med   ISBN: 0-310-44331-8
★★★★ Relationship Building   Ldr. Guide Avail.: Yes   Size: 5.25 x 8.0
Subjects: Accountability, Love, Marriage, Relationships
Comments: This study addresses major frustrations in marriage and offers biblical principles for establishing and maintaining solid, lasting relationships. It covers topics such as: "How to Remain Open with Each Other," "How to Get Your Mate's Attention—And Keep It," and more. For best results, three to five couples should work through the study together. They will gain insights from sharing and assuming mutual accountability. Audio tapes are required.

Author: Smalley, Gary **976**
Series: Proven Word
Title: *Key to Your Child's Heart, The*
Publisher: Word, 1984

Num. Sess.	Group Time	Num. Pgs.	Avg. Qst.	Price	Audience	Format	Bible Study
7	45-60	176	7	8.99	Beginner	Book	Topical

Features: Intro to Study, Ldr's Notes, Cartoons
★★★ Personal Application   Preparation Time: Low   ISBN: 0-8499-3071-5
★★★ Relationship Building   Ldr. Guide Avail.: No   Size: 5.50 x 8.0
Subjects: Family, Parenting
Comments: Children need discipline and restraints; but how can parents keep them from being sullen and erecting barriers? An experienced family counselor shows it takes understanding, respect for a child's point of view, and openness to parents' capacity to make mistakes. This study discusses characteristics of a close-knit family, which shares life's experiences, and deals positively with difficulties. It also offers practical ways that family sharing can open children's hearts.

Author: Smalley, Gary **977**
Series: Video Curriculum Resource
Title: *Love Is A Decision*
Publisher: Word, 1991

Num. Sess.	Group Time	Num. Pgs.	Avg. Qst.	Price	Audience	Format	Bible Study
6	60-90	N/A	7	129.99	Begi nner	Video	Topical

Features: Book Incl, Video Study Guide
★★★★ Personal Application   Preparation Time: None   ISBN: 0-8499-8004-6
★★★ Relationship Building   Ldr. Guide Avail.: No   Size: 10.0 x 12.50
Subjects: Love, Marriage, Relationships, Singles Issues, Young Marrieds
Comments: This six-part Bible-centered video series outlines a clear action plan that points the way to vital, healthy, growing relationships for engaged couples, newlyweds, and veteran marrieds. The thirty-five-to-fifty-minute sessions include: "The Incredible Worth of a Woman," "How to Energize Your Mate in 60 Seconds," "The Tremendous Value of a Man," and more. The video format incorporates lecture to a live audience into situational drama. The brief study guide is reproducible.

Author: Smith, Conrad **978**
Series:
Title: *Best Friends*
Publisher: NavPress, 1989

Num. Sess.	Group Time	Num. Pgs.	Avg. Qst.	Price	Audience	Format	Bible Study
10	60-90	250	Vry	7.95	Beginner	Workbk	Topical

Features: Bibliography, Charts
★★★★ Personal Application   Preparation Time: Med   ISBN: 0-89109-271-4
★★★★ Relationship Building   Ldr. Guide Avail.: No   Size: 6.0 x 9.0
Subjects: Friendships, Marriage, Relationships
Comments: This study is for couples who want to strengthen friendship in their marriages. Among its features are insights into the principles of friendship; Bible studies on "friendship in marriage"; communication and relational exercises to complete as couples; a Myers-Briggs Type Indicator to help couples understand, accept, and affirm each other; and practical suggestions on how to make God the center of their relationships.

Author: Smith, Harold Ivan   **979**
Series:
Title: *One Is a Whole Number*
Publisher: Gospel Films, 1990

Num. Sess.	Group Time	Num. Pgs.	Avg. Qst.	Price	Audience	Format	Bible Study
4	75-90	19	13	129.95	Begi nner	Video	Topical

Features: Bibliography, Follow Up, Photos, Video Study Guide
★★★ Personal Application Preparation Time: None ISBN: 1-555-68112-3
★★ Relationship Building Ldr. Guide Avail.: No Size: 8.50 x 11.0
Subjects: Commitments, Divorce, Marriage, Sexual Issues, Singles Issues
Comments: This four-part video series presents Christ as the prime example of the single adult lifestyle. There are four forty-minute episodes that present biblical truths about singleness, marriage, divorce, and sexuality through lecture and drama. The study guide includes a key quote, scripture, and question; something to talk about, and think about; and an activity for each video segment. Participants are invited to either live redeemed lives in relationship to Jesus Christ, or to renew their commitment.

Author: Smith, Joseph E.   **980**
Series:
Title: *How to Win in Spiritual Warfare (Volume 2)*
Publisher: Maranatha Publications, 1988

Num. Sess.	Group Time	Num. Pgs.	Avg. Qst.	Price	Audience	Format	Bible Study
13	60-90	172	Vry	7.95	Beginner	Workbk	Topical

Features: Intro to Study
★★★ Personal Application Preparation Time: Med ISBN: 0-918923-02-6
★★ Relationship Building Ldr. Guide Avail.: No Size: 8.50 x 11.0
Subjects: Emotions, Relationships, Satan
Comments: This is the second volume in a three-part study on winning in spiritual warfare. It points out that Satan often succeeds because Christians don't know their authority and how to use it. This study examines principles and concepts for developing and using that authority. Topics include the invisible war, long-suffering, anger, resentment, impatience, gentleness, judgment, goodness, rejection, and more. Each of the thirteen lessons ends with a series of fill-in-the-blank questions, followed by the answers.

Author: Smith, Joseph E.   **981**
Series:
Title: *How to Win in Spiritual Warfare (Volume 1)*
Publisher: Maranatha Publications, 1984

Num. Sess.	Group Time	Num. Pgs.	Avg. Qst.	Price	Audience	Format	Bible Study
13	60-90	98	Vry	6.95	Beginner	Workbk	Topical

Features: Intro to Study
★★★ Personal Application Preparation Time: Med ISBN: 0-918923-01-8
★★ Relationship Building Ldr. Guide Avail.: No Size: 8.50 x 11.0
Subjects: Emotions, Grief, Joy, Love, Marriage, Relationships, Satan
Comments: This is the first volume in a three-part study on winning in spiritual warfare. It points out that Satan often succeeds because Christians don't know their authority and how to use it. This study examines principles and concepts for developing and using that authority. Topics include how the war began and ended, love, envy, fear, covetousness, joy, depression, grief, worry, and more. Each of the thirteen lessons ends with a series of fill-in-the-blank questions, followed by answers.

Author: Smith, Joyce Marie   **982**
Series: Good Life Bible Studies
Title: *Becoming God's Woman*
Publisher: Tyndale House, 1979

Num. Sess.	Group Time	Num. Pgs.	Avg. Qst.	Price	Audience	Format	Bible Study
12	45-60	63	9	2.95	Beginner	Workbk	Topical

Features: Intro to Leading a Study, Prayer Helps, Ldr's Notes
★★ Personal Application Preparation Time: None ISBN: 0-8423-0130-5
★★ Relationship Building Ldr. Guide Avail.: No Size: 5.0 x 7.50
Subjects: Teens: Emotions, Teens: Family, Teens: Junior High, Teens: Peer Pressure, Teens: Relationships, Teens: Sexuality, Teens: Youth Life
Comments: This study examines what the Bible says to contemporary girls ages twelve to sixteen about acceptance of self; understanding sexuality; knowing God personally; belonging to God's family; growing spiritually; handling peer pressure; and friendship with other girls, parents, and boys. Geared for girls in a transition period that can produce extreme trauma and insecurity, the study is designed to be an adventuresome and happy experience.

Author: Smith, Joyce Marie   **983**
Series: New Life Bible Studies
Title: *Becoming the Parent Your Child Needs*
Publisher: Tyndale House, 1980

Num. Sess.	Group Time	Num. Pgs.	Avg. Qst.	Price	Audience	Format	Bible Study
12	45-60	61	12	2.95	New Christian	Workbk	Topical

Features: Intro to Study, Bibliography, Prayer Helps
★★★ Personal Application Preparation Time: Low ISBN: 0-8423-0133-X
★★ Relationship Building Ldr. Guide Avail.: No Size: 5.0 x 7.50
Subjects: God's Promises, Parenting, Prayer, Relationships
Comments: This study focuses on God's promises and directions for believing parents and reminds participants that God is Father of parents as well as children. Included are basic principles as well as vivid Old and New Testament examples of parent-child relationships. A lesson on "Parental Prayers" closes the study.

Author: Smith, Joyce Marie   **984**
Series: New Life Bible Studies
Title: *Celebration of Womanhood*
Publisher: Tyndale House, 1985

Num. Sess.	Group Time	Num. Pgs.	Avg. Qst.	Price	Audience	Format	Bible Study
12	45-60	64	12	3.95	New Christian	Workbk	Topical

Features: Intro to Study, Prayer Helps
★★ Personal Application Preparation Time: Low ISBN: 0-8423-0254-9
★★ Relationship Building Ldr. Guide Avail.: No Size: 5.0 x 7.50
Subjects: Failure, Family, Friendships, Relationships, Sexual Issues, Success, Suffering, Women's Issues, Work
Comments: This study of woman, as portrayed in Proverbs and other books of the Bible, brings new insights into the celebration of womanhood. It portrays modern woman as required to play more roles than ever, and shows that juggling them can either lead to frustration or to opportunity to discover the rich potential God intends. Other subjects include personal fulfillment, family relationships, work outside the home, sexuality, friendship, and suffering.

Author: Smith, Joyce Marie   **985**
Series: New Life Bible Studies
Title: *Coping with Life and Its Problems*
Publisher: Tyndale House, 1976

Num. Sess.	Group Time	Num. Pgs.	Avg. Qst.	Price	Audience	Format	Bible Study
12	45-60	64	10	3.95	New Christian	Workbk	Topical

Features: Intro to Leading a Study, Intro to Study, Bibliography, Prayer Helps, Summary
  ★★★ Personal Application   Preparation Time: Low   ISBN: 0-8423-0434-7
  ★★ Relationship Building   Ldr. Guide Avail.: No   Size: 5.0 x 7.50
Subjects: Christian Living, Emotions, Failure, Grief, Hope, Loneliness, Relationships, Stress, Victorious Living
Comments: This study, for believers who want to improve their abilities to cope with life's problems, uses examples of Bible men and women who struggle with those same problems and trials. Trials covered include disappointments and hurts, bitterness and resentment, broken relationships, tragedy and sorrow, death and pain, loneliness, and hopelessness. The final lesson deals with how to experience an abundant life in Christ.

Author: Smith, Joyce Marie   **986**
Series: Good Life Bible Studies
Title: *Dating, Love, & Sex*
Publisher: Tyndale House, 1986

Num. Sess.	Group Time	Num. Pgs.	Avg. Qst.	Price	Audience	Format	Bible Study
12	45-60	76	10	2.95	Beginner	Workbk	Topical

Features: Intro to Study, Scrpt Memory Helps, Glossary
  ★★ Personal Application   Preparation Time: None ISBN: 0-8423-0516-5
  ★★ Relationship Building   Ldr. Guide Avail.: No   Size: 5.0 x 7.50
Subjects: Teens: Decisions, Teens: Senior High, Teens: Sexuality, Teens: Youth Life, Youth Life
Comments: This study on dating, love, and sex, designed for fourteen-to-twenty year-old young people, helps teens discover God's plan for their sexual life. The lessons respond to questions such as: "As a teenager, how can I control sexual energy?" "What guidelines should I use to make sexual choices?" "How will my future be affected by my behavior today?" The study is based on relevant and highly practical principles from God's Word.

Author: Smith, Joyce Marie   **987**
Series: New Life Bible Studies
Title: *Esther: A Woman of Courage*
Publisher: Tyndale House, 1981

Num. Sess.	Group Time	Num. Pgs.	Avg. Qst.	Price	Audience	Format	Bible Study
12	45-60	57	12	3.95	Beginner	Workbk	Charctr

Features: Intro to Leading a Study, Intro to Study, Prayer Helps, Study Overview
  ★★ Personal Application   Preparation Time: Low   ISBN: 0-8423-0729-X
  ★★ Relationship Building   Ldr. Guide Avail.: No   Size: 5.0 x 7.50
Subjects: Bible Personalities, Esther, Obedience, Women's Issues
Comments: In this in-depth study of Esther, several types of investigation are used: topical study, character study, verse or chapter analysis, and book analysis. Esther is the historical story of a Jewish orphan girl in exile who married a Gentile king. It is a gripping story of intrigue, romance, and courage. Most of all, it is a demonstration that God is sovereign and in control.

Author: Smith, Joyce Marie   **988**
Series: New Life Bible Studies
Title: *Fulfillment*
Publisher: Tyndale House, 1975

Num. Sess.	Group Time	Num. Pgs.	Avg. Qst.	Price	Audience	Format	Bible Study
16	45-60	62	9	2.95	New Christian	Workbk	Topical

Features: Intro to Leading a Study, Intro to Study, Persnl Study Quest
  ★★★ Personal Application   Preparation Time: Low   ISBN: 0-8423-0980-2
  ★★ Relationship Building   Ldr. Guide Avail.: No   Size: 5.0 x 7.50
Subjects: Emotions, Marriage, Relationships, Singles Issues, Women's Issues
Comments: This study is designed to build pride in womanhood for female participants. It enables them to find total fulfillment in their relationship with God, as wives and mothers or as single women. Each lesson systematically reviews five aspects of a godly life for a woman: fulfilled as a person, fulfilled spiritually, fulfilled in marriage, fulfilled in singleness, and fulfilled as a mother.

Author: Smith, Joyce Marie   **989**
Series: Good Life Bible Studies
Title: *Giants, Lions, & Fire*
Publisher: Tyndale House, 1981

Num. Sess.	Group Time	Num. Pgs.	Avg. Qst.	Price	Audience	Format	Bible Study
12	45-60	75	10	2.95	New Christian	Workbk	Charctr

Features: Intro to Leading a Study, Intro to Study, Scrpt Memory Helps, Full Scrpt Printed
  ★★ Personal Application   Preparation Time: None ISBN: 0-8423-1022-3
  ★★ Relationship Building   Ldr. Guide Avail.: No   Size: 5.0 x 7.50
Subjects: Teens: Bible/Pers., Teens: Christian Liv, Teens: Ethics, Teens: Junior High
Comments: This study, for young people between ten and fourteen, examines the lives of David, Daniel, Joshua, Solomon, Noah, and others. It helps teens discover moral values and spiritual standards that make these Bible heroes stand tall. The study encourages young Christians to lead pure, moral lives in the adverse environment of contemporary society.

Author: Smith, Joyce Marie   **990**
Series: New Life Bible Studies
Title: *Growing in Faith*
Publisher: Tyndale House, 1982

Num. Sess.	Group Time	Num. Pgs.	Avg. Qst.	Price	Audience	Format	Bible Study
12	45-60	61	12	2.95	New Christian	Workbk	Topical

Features: Intro to Study
  ★★ Personal Application   Preparation Time: Low   ISBN: 0-8423-1227-7
  ★★ Relationship Building   Ldr. Guide Avail.: No   Size: 5.0 x 7.50
Subjects: Bible Personalities, Discipleship, Faith, God, Leadership, Obedience
Comments: This study of twelve biblical characters helps illustrate how growth in faith can become a modern reality. Hebrews 11 and other scripture offer a practical look into the kind of daily application of faith that can be supportive during times of testing. The study explores many aspects of faith, including obedience to God, God's nature and work, development and leadership, God's power, and more.

Author: Smith, Joyce Marie   **991**
Series: New Life Bible Studies
Title: *Growing Through Life's Challenges: Studies in 2 Corinthians*
Publisher: Tyndale House, 1988

Num. Sess.	Group Time	Num. Pgs.	Avg. Qst.	Price	Audience	Format	Bible Study
12	45-60	66	12	3.95	New Christian	Workbk	Book

Features: Intro to Study, Prayer Helps
  ★★Personal Application   Preparation Time: Low   ISBN: 0-8423-1235-8
  ★★Relationship Building Ldr. Guide Avail.: No   Size: 5.0 x 7.50
Subjects: Church Life, Grace, Hope, Integrity, Leadership, Repentance, Service, Suffering, 2 Corinthians
Comments: This study of 2 Corinthians, dealing with aspects of Christian life and service, helps participants tap into God's grace, comfort, power to forgive, perseverance, and eternal perspective. It offers encouragement and concern for Christians who face such emotional or physical suffering that they would give up. God reminds, "My grace is sufficient for you" (2 Corinthians 12:9). Christians grow by trusting God, regardless of life's challenges.

Author: Smith, Joyce Marie   **992**
Series: New Life Bible Studies
Title: *Learning to Talk with God*
Publisher: Tyndale House, 1976

Num. Sess.	Group Time	Num. Pgs.	Avg. Qst.	Price	Audience	Format	Bible Study
12	45-60	62	10	2.95	New Christian	Workbk	Topical

Features: Intro to Leading a Study, Intro to Study, Bibliography, Prayer Helps
  ★★★Personal Application   Preparation Time: Low   ISBN: 0-8423-2140-3
  ★★Relationship Building Ldr. Guide Avail.: No   Size: 5.0 x 7.50
Subjects: Prayer, Women's Issues
Comments: This twelve-lesson study on prayer is especially designed for Christian women. In total, it will help students grow spiritually and experience prayer at work in their lives. It is recommended for groups of ten to twelve. The structure of each lesson includes Scripture reading, definitions, discussion questions, and group interaction. Study subject matter includes the importance of prayer, the elements of prayer, praise in prayer, hindrances to prayer, Old and New Testament prayer examples, and more.

Author: Smith, Joyce Marie   **993**
Series: New Life Bible Studies
Title: *Ruth, A Woman of Worth*
Publisher: Tyndale House, 1979

Num. Sess.	Group Time	Num. Pgs.	Avg. Qst.	Price	Audience	Format	Bible Study
12	45-60	57	12	3.95	Beginner	Workbk	Charctr

Features: Intro to Study, Prayer Helps, Study Overview
  ★★Personal Application   Preparation Time: Low   ISBN: 0-8423-5810-2
  ★★Relationship Building Ldr. Guide Avail.: No   Size: 5.0 x 7.50
Subjects: Bible Personalities, Church Life, God, Love, Marriage, Ruth, Women's Issues
Comments: This study of Ruth addresses two questions: "What characterizes a woman of worth?" and "How can one become such a woman?" Participants learn how Ruth's choices and decisions affected the direction of her life, and resulted in her godly character. The Church's relationship to Jesus Christ is pictured through Ruth and Boaz, and the study, more than a love story, reveals the relationship all women can have with God.

Author: Smith, Joyce Marie   **994**
Series: New Life Bible Studies
Title: *Significance of Jesus, The*
Publisher: Tyndale House, 1976

Num. Sess.	Group Time	Num. Pgs.	Avg. Qst.	Price	Audience	Format	Bible Study
13	45-60	61	10	2.95	New Christian	Workbk	Charctr

Features: Intro to Leading a Study, Intro to Study, Prayer Helps, Summary
  ★★Personal Application   Preparation Time: Low   ISBN: 0-8423-5887-0
  ★★Relationship Building Ldr. Guide Avail.: No   Size: 5.0 x 7.50
Subjects: Emotions, God's Promises, Jesus: Life/Teaching
Comments: This in-depth study of Jesus Christ describes who He is and what He can do in the life of a believer. It presents Him as Creator, God, God-Man, Savior, Miracle Worker, Shepherd, Friend, Teacher, and King. It further shows how problems, hang-ups, and insecurities can become nonexistent through knowing Jesus and believing His promises will come to pass.

Author: Smith, Joyce Marie   **995**
Series: New Life Bible Studies
Title: *Spiritual Living*
Publisher: Tyndale House, 1978

Num. Sess.	Group Time	Num. Pgs.	Avg. Qst.	Price	Audience	Format	Bible Study
12	45-60	63	10	3.95	New Christian	Workbk	Topical

Features: Intro to Leading a Study, Intro to Study, Prayer Helps
  ★★★Personal Application   Preparation Time: Low   ISBN: 0-8423-6410-2
  ★★Relationship Building Ldr. Guide Avail.: No   Size: 5.0 x 7.50
Subjects: Christian Living, Discipleship, God, Women's Issues
Comments: This systematic word-study designed to develop spiritual maturity explores subjects like entrance into the presence of God, experiencing His fellowship, and exercising God's power. This study is for women who are not satisfied with their Christian lives, are hungry for more of God in their lives, or desire to experience more of the reality of His presence and power. The lessons should be studied in sequence.

Author: Smith, Joyce Marie   **996**
Series: New Life Bible Studies
Title: *Understanding Your Emotions*
Publisher: Tyndale House, 1977

Num. Sess.	Group Time	Num. Pgs.	Avg. Qst.	Price	Audience	Format	Bible Study
12	45-60	60	10	3.95	New Christian	Workbk	Topical

Features: Intro to Leading a Study, Intro to Study, Bibliography, Prayer Helps
  ★★★Personal Application   Preparation Time: Low   ISBN: 0-8423-7770-0
  ★★Relationship Building Ldr. Guide Avail.: No   Size: 5.0 x 7.50
Subjects: Emotions, Women's Issues
Comments: This study, a comprehensive guide to freedom from the negative side effects of emotions, is a liberating look at how God deals with His people when their hearts are right before Him. It explores emotions such as worry, anxiety, fear, anger, guilt, jealousy, pride, criticism, and gossip. Also included are prayers to help people commit one emotion each week to God.

Author: Smith, Joyce Marie **997**
Series: New Life Bible Studies
Title: *Walking in the Light*
Publisher: Tyndale House, 1981

Num. Sess.	Group Time	Num. Pgs.	Avg. Qst.	Price	Audience	Format	Bible Study
12	45-60	59	12	2.95	New Christian	Workbk	Topical

Features: Intro to Study, Bibliography, Persnl Study Quest
★★ Personal Application Preparation Time: Low ISBN: 0-8423-7813-8
★★ Relationship Building Ldr. Guide Avail.: No Size: 5.0 x 7.50
Subjects: Christian Living, Ephesians, Fruit of the Spirit, Grace, Love, Marriage, Relationships, Victorious Living
Comments: This study of Ephesians looks at many aspects of the Christian walk, including walking in one's inheritance, peace, grace, love, harmony, and in the Spirit. Participants find the keys to exciting, challenging, victorious Christian life in knowing what they possess in Christ and how to lay hold of the inheritance and apply the knowledge. The study helps participants walk in the light of Christ in marriage, parental relationships, employment, ministry, and church life.

Author: Smith, Joyce Marie **998**
Series: New Life Bible Studies
Title: *Woman's Priorities, A*
Publisher: Tyndale House, 1976

Num. Sess.	Group Time	Num. Pgs.	Avg. Qst.	Price	Audience	Format	Bible Study
12	45-60	63	10	3.95	Beginner	Workbk	Charctr

Features: Intro to Leading a Study, Intro to Study, Bibliography, Summary
★★ Personal Application Preparation Time: Low ISBN: 0-8423-8380-8
★★ Relationship Building Ldr. Guide Avail.: No Size: 5.0 x 7.50
Subjects: Bible Personalities, Failure, Success, Women's Issues
Comments: This study uses the lives of eleven women in the Bible—Rahab, Ruth, Sarah, Hannah, Priscilla, and others—to lead to a description of the "ideal woman" of Proverbs 31. The study portrays the Bible examples honestly, without glossing over their weaknesses or exaggerating their virtues.

Author: Snyder, Linda **999**
Series: Group's Active Bible Curriculum
Title: *School Struggles*
Publisher: Group Publishing, 1990

Num. Sess.	Group Time	Num. Pgs.	Avg. Qst.	Price	Audience	Format	Bible Study
4	35-60	46	Vry	6.95	Beginner	Workbk	Topical

Features: Intro to Leading a Study, Intro to Study, Objectives, Study Overview, Ldr's Notes, Handouts, Agenda, Publicity Ideas
★★★ Personal Application Preparation Time: None ISBN: 1-559-45201-3
★★★ Relationship Building Ldr. Guide Avail.: No Size: 8.50 x 11.0
Subjects: Teens: Decisions, Teens: Senior High, Teens: Youth Life
Comments: This study will help teenagers discover practical tips on studying more effectively, improving grades, resisting cheating, and balancing their active schedules. It also helps teenagers set school and extracurricular priorities and attainable goals. The course can be adapted for use in a Bible class or youth meeting. Activities and Bible studies are included as separate sheets that can be reproduced. The instructions are easy to follow and provide multiple options for teachers.

Author: Southern, Randy **1000**
Series:
Title: *It Came from the Media (Student Book)*
Publisher: Victor Books, 1989

Num. Sess.	Group Time	Num. Pgs.	Avg. Qst.	Price	Audience	Format	Bible Study
12	75-90	96	Vry	2.50	New Christian	Book	Topical

Features: Drawings
★★★★ Personal Application Preparation Time: Low ISBN: 0-89693-740-2
★★★★ Relationship Building Ldr. Guide Avail.: Yes Size: 3.50 x 6.0
Subjects: Teens: Junior High, Teens: Music
Comments: This study examines the role of rock music, movies, television, and magazines in modern Christian young people's lives. Unlike other studies on the subject, this is not a list of what is and isn't acceptable. It is designed to help teens understand, with the help of a trained leader, how biblical principles are involved in media habits. A leader's guide ($12.99) offers three four-week studies with reproducible student sheets. Sessions are easy to organize. Activities are included.

Author: Spradley, Ruth **1001**
Series: Women's Bible Studies
Title: *Colossians*
Publisher: Standard Publishing, 1987

Num. Sess.	Group Time	Num. Pgs.	Avg. Qst.	Price	Audience	Format	Bible Study
10	60-75	144	Vry	4.99	New Christian	Book	Book

Features: Intro to Leading a Study, Intro to Study, Cross Ref
★★ Personal Application Preparation Time: Med ISBN: 0-87403-232-6
★★ Relationship Building Ldr. Guide Avail.: No Size: 5.25 x 8.50
Subjects: Church Life, Colossians/Philemon, False Teachers, Prison Epistles, Women's Issues
Comments: This study of Colossians, part of a three-book series, takes participants through a verse-by-verse examination of the book, and helps them know God better and develop better relationships with Him. Each of the ten lessons is divided into five parts to encourage daily devotion/study. Each begins with a reading of from ten to twelve verses, which is followed by questions. The study is ideal for individuals or small groups, and leader guidelines are included.

Author: Spradley, Ruth **1002**
Series: Women's Bible Studies
Title: *Philippians*
Publisher: Standard Publishing, 1987

Num. Sess.	Group Time	Num. Pgs.	Avg. Qst.	Price	Audience	Format	Bible Study
12	60-75	144	Vry	4.99	New Christian	Book	Book

Features: Intro to Leading a Study, Intro to Study, Cross Ref
★★ Personal Application Preparation Time: Med ISBN: 0-87403-231-8
★★ Relationship Building Ldr. Guide Avail.: No Size: 8.25 x 8.50
Subjects: Joy, Philippians, Prison Epistles, Service, Suffering, Victorious Living, Women's Issues
Comments: This verse-by-verse examination of Philippians, part of a three-book series, will help participants know God better and develop better relationships with Him. Each of the twelve lessons is divided into five parts to encourage daily devotion/study and begins with a reading of from ten to twelve verses, which is followed by questions. The study is ideal for individuals or small groups, and leader guidelines are included.

Author: Spradley, Ruth   **1003**
Series: Women's Bible Studies
Title: *2 Corinthians*
Publisher: Standard Publishing, 1988

Num. Sess.	Group Time	Num. Pgs.	Avg. Qst.	Price	Audience	Format	Bible Study
15	60-75	176	Vry	4.99	New Christian	Book	Book

Features: Intro to Leading a Study, Intro to Study, Scrpt Memory Helps, Cross Ref

★★ Personal Application Preparation Time: Med ISBN: 0-87403-479-5
  ★★ Relationship Building Ldr. Guide Avail.: No Size: 5.25 x 8.50

Subjects: Integrity, Reconciliation, Service, Suffering, Victorious Living, Women's Issues, 2 Corinthians
Comments: This study of 2 Corinthians, part of a three-book series, takes participants through a verse-by-verse examination of the book, to help them know God better and develop better relationships with Him. Each of the fifteen lessons is divided into five parts to encourage daily devotion/study. Each begins with a reading of from ten to twelve verses, which is followed by questions. The study is ideal for individuals or small groups, and leader guidelines are included.

Author: Sproul, R. C.   **1004**
Series:
Title: *Abortion: A Rational Look at an Emotional Issue*
Publisher: NavPress, 1990

Num. Sess.	Group Time	Num. Pgs.	Avg. Qst.	Price	Audience	Format	Bible Study
7	60-90	94	21	3.95	Beginner	Workbk	Topical

Features: Intro to Leading a Study, Bibliography, Follow Up, Appendix

★★★ Personal Application Preparation Time: Med ISBN: 0-89109-347-8
  ★★★ Relationship Building Ldr. Guide Avail.: No Size: 5.50 x 8.0

Subjects: Abortion, Emotions, Ethics, Medical Issues, Social Issues, Women's Issues
Comments: This study guide, a companion to a book, audio, and video of the same title by R. C. Sproul, helps participants explore in great depth and breadth the implications of abortion. Emotional response is minimized through examination of both sides of the debate in light of biblical law, civil law, and natural law. The series builds an intelligent biblical position on abortion. Tape outlines for each session are included. Unfamiliar words are given with their definitions.

Author: Sproul, R. C.   **1005**
Series: Ligonier Ministries
Title: *Abortion: A Rational Look at an Emotional Issue*
Publisher: NavPress, 1990

Num. Sess.	Group Time	Num. Pgs.	Avg. Qst.	Price	Audience	Format	Bible Study
7	90-120	N/A	21	95.0	Beginner	Video	Topical

Features: Intro to Study, Bibliography, Follow Up, Summary, Appendix, Cassette Avail, Book Incl, Video Study Guide

★★★ Personal Application Preparation Time: Low ISBN: 9-900738-36-5
  ★★ Relationship Building Ldr. Guide Avail.: No Size: 4.0 x 7.50

Subjects: Abortion, Emotions, Ethics, Medical Issues, Social Issues, Women's Issues
Comments: This six-session video study examines the ethical implications of abortion from the perspectives of biblical law, natural law, and positive judicial law. The thirty-minute segments cover topics such as: "What Are the Key Issues?" "How Sacred Is Human Life?" "When Does Life Begin?" and "What Is Your Verdict?" The study guide encourages an intelligent biblical-based discussion, reflection, and application of lessons.

Author: Sproul, R. C.   **1006**
Series:
Title: *Born Again*
Publisher: Ligonier Ministries, 1988

Num. Sess.	Group Time	Num. Pgs.	Avg. Qst.	Price	Audience	Format	Bible Study
6	90-105	56	24	4.0	New Christian	Workbk	Topical

Features: Intro to Study, Bibliography, Digging Deeper Quest, Cassette Avail

★★★ Personal Application Preparation Time: Low ISBN:
  ★★ Relationship Building Ldr. Guide Avail.: Yes Size: 5.50 x 8.50

Subjects: God, Theology
Comments: This study responds to questions like "Must we be born again?" "What is spiritual rebirth?" and "How do I know that I am born again?" Participants will explore the sovereignty of God in regeneration, the work of the Holy Spirit, and one's own faith and the part it plays in the whole subject of salvation. The audio and video tapes have six thirty-minute messages.

Author: Sproul, R. C.   **1007**
Series: Ligonier Ministries
Title: *Chosen by God*
Publisher: Ligonier Ministries, 1989

Num. Sess.	Group Time	Num. Pgs.	Avg. Qst.	Price	Audience	Format	Bible Study
6	90-105	N/A	18	89.0	New Christian	Video	Topical

Features: Intro to Study, Follow Up, Cassette Avail, Video Study Guide

★★★ Personal Application Preparation Time: Low ISBN:
  ★★ Relationship Building Ldr. Guide Avail.: No Size: 4.0 x 7.50

Subjects: God, Theology
Comments: This six-session video study deals with the classical doctrine of predestination. It begins with a portrait of a loving Father who offers redemption to radically corrupt humanity. It then explains God's sovereignty in election, which affirms without destroying individual freedom and dignity. Topics include: "What Is Free Will?" "Man's Radical Fallenness," "The Divine Initiative," and more. The study guide encourages discussion, reflection, and application of lessons.

Author: Sproul, R. C.   **1008**
Series:
Title: *Christian Marriage*
Publisher: Ligonier Ministries, 1987

Num. Sess.	Group Time	Num. Pgs.	Avg. Qst.	Price	Audience	Format	Bible Study
7	90-105	59	18	4.0	Beginner	Workbk	Topical

Features: Intro to Study, Bibliography, Digging Deeper Quest, Cassette Avail

★★★ Personal Application Preparation Time: Low ISBN:
  ★★ Relationship Building Ldr. Guide Avail.: Yes Size: 5.50 x 8.50

Subjects: Emotions, Marriage, Sexual Issues
Comments: This study presents a biblical view of marriage: a relationship ordained by God and regulated by His commands. It also explores the ingredients of successful marriage: trust, open communication, sacrificial love, honesty, edifying speech, and a proper understanding of the different God-given roles of husbands and wives. It deals with major pitfalls, such as lack of sexual intimacy, guilt, fears, and criticism. Application of the principles will enrich marriages and glorify God.

Author: Sproul, R. C.　　　　　　　　　　　　**1009**
Series: Ligonier Ministries
Title: *Cross of Christ, The*
Publisher: Ligonier Ministries, 1989

Num. Sess.	Group Time	Num. Pgs.	Avg. Qst.	Price	Audience	Format	Bible Study
6	75-90	N/A	Vry	89.0	New Christian	Video	Topical

Features: Intro to Study, Bibliography, Cassette Avail, Video Study Guide

★★★ Personal Application　Preparation Time: Low　ISBN:
★★ Relationship Building　Ldr. Guide Avail.: No　Size: 4.0 x 7.50

Subjects: Faith, Jesus: Life/Teaching, Theology
Comments: This six-session video study reveals the drama of salvation by examining the biblical revelation of the nature and necessity of the Cross. Lessons include: "The Need for an Atonement," "The Drama of Redemption," "Christ Our Ransom," "Justification by Faith," "Blessing or Curse?" and "Securing Our Faith." The study guide encourages discussion, reflection, and application of the lessons.

Author: Sproul, R. C.　　　　　　　　　　　　**1010**
Series: Ligonier Ministries
Title: *Developing Christian Character*
Publisher: Ligonier Ministries, 1988

Num. Sess.	Group Time	Num. Pgs.	Avg. Qst.	Price	Audience	Format	Bible Study
13	45-60	N/A	Vry	89.0	New Christian	Video	Topical

Features: Intro to Study, Bibliography, Summary, Cassette Avail, Video Study Guide

★★★ Personal Application　Preparation Time: Low　ISBN:
★★ Relationship Building　Ldr. Guide Avail.: No　Size: 4.0 x 7.50

Subjects: Discipleship, Fruit of the Spirit, Marriage
Comments: This 13-session video study encourages the difficult, lifelong pursuit of godliness through fruit of the Spirit. Character-building lectures focus on practical steps toward a goal of becoming more Christlike. Topics include: "The Struggle for Spiritual Growth," "The God of Spiritual Growth," "The Priorities of Righteousness," "The Assurance of Salvation," "The Indwelling Power of Love," "The Practice of Love," and more. The study guide encourages discussion, reflection, and application of lessons.

Author: Sproul, R. C.　　　　　　　　　　　　**1011**
Series:
Title: *Holiness of God, The*
Publisher: Ligonier Ministries, 1988

Num. Sess.	Group Time	Num. Pgs.	Avg. Qst.	Price	Audience	Format	Bible Study
7	90-105	96	17	4.0	Beginner	Workbk	Topical

Features: Intro to Study, Objectives, Bibliography, Digging Deeper Quest, Agenda, Cassette Avail, Video Study Guide

★★★ Personal Application　Preparation Time: Low　ISBN:
★★ Relationship Building　Ldr. Guide Avail.: No　Size: 5.50 x 8.50

Subjects: God, Grace, Holiness, Theology
Comments: This study examines what holiness means and why people are both fascinated and terrified by a holy God. It closely explores God's character, leading to new insights on sin, justice, and grace. Participants will develop a new awareness of their dependence on God's mercy and discover the awesomeness of His majestic holiness. The two-tape video series features six thirty-minute messages. The interactive study guide includes quotations, tape outline, application suggestions, and more.

Author: Sproul, R. C.　　　　　　　　　　　　**1012**
Series: Ligonier Ministries
Title: *Holiness of God, The*
Publisher: Ligonier Ministries, 1988

Num. Sess.	Group Time	Num. Pgs.	Avg. Qst.	Price	Audience	Format	Bible Study
7	75-90	N/A	17	89.0	New Christian	Video	Topical

Features: Intro to Study, Bibliography, Follow Up, Cassette Avail, Video Study Guide

★★★ Personal Application　Preparation Time: Low　ISBN:
★★ Relationship Building　Ldr. Guide Avail.: No　Size: 4.0 x 7.50

Subjects: God, Grace, Holiness, Theology
Comments: This seven-session video study examines the meaning of holiness and why people are both fascinated and terrified by a holy God. By investigating God's character participants gain a fresh understanding of sin, justice, and grace. Topics include: "The Importance of Holiness," "The Trauma of Holiness," "Holiness and Justice," "The Insanity of Luther," "The Meaning of Holiness," and "The Holiness of Christ." The study encourages discussion, reflection, and application of lessons.

Author: Sproul, R. C.　　　　　　　　　　　　**1013**
Series:
Title: *Holy Spirit, The*
Publisher: Ligonier Ministries, 1988

Num. Sess.	Group Time	Num. Pgs.	Avg. Qst.	Price	Audience	Format	Bible Study
7	90-105	68	20	4.0	New Christian	Workbk	Topical

Features: Intro to Study, Bibliography, Digging Deeper Quest, Cassette Avail

★★★ Personal Application　Preparation Time: Low　ISBN:
★★ Relationship Building　Ldr. Guide Avail.: Yes　Size: 5.50 x 8.50

Subjects: Beliefs, God, Holy Spirit, Theology
Comments: This is an in-depth study of the nature and work of the Holy Spirit in the contemporary world. God has not left believers orphaned, but in the person of the Holy Spirit He has set up residence in their hearts. This study leads to the recapturing of a sense of living totally in the presence of the Holy Spirit, and helps correct an imbalance in Christian beliefs and practices. The audio and video each have six thirty-minute messages.

Author: Sproul, R. C.　　　　　　　　　　　　**1014**
Series:
Title: *Knowing Scripture*
Publisher: Ligonier Ministries, 1987

Num. Sess.	Group Time	Num. Pgs.	Avg. Qst.	Price	Audience	Format	Bible Study
13	90-105	75	14	4.0	New Christian	Workbk	Topical

Features: Bibliography

★★★ Personal Application　Preparation Time: Low　ISBN:
★★ Relationship Building　Ldr. Guide Avail.: Yes　Size: 5.50 x 8.50

Subjects: Bible Study
Comments: This study helps participants understand God's Word. It details the basic tools of biblical interpretation and stimulates personal involvement in the drama found in the Word. Lessons include twelve thirty-minute messages: "Why Study the Bible?" "Private Interpretation," "Parallelisms," "Scripture and Culture," and more. The concluding lesson offers an opportunity to put together all the series' principles. Its goal is complete exegesis of a particular passage of the Bible.

Author: Sproul, R. C.   **1015**
Series:
Title: *Majesty of Christ, The*
Publisher: Ligonier Ministries, 1991

Num. Sess.	Group Time	Num. Pgs.	Avg. Qst.	Price	Audience	Format	Bible Study
7	90-105	N/A	N/A	4.0	New Christian	Workbk	Charctr

Features: Intro to Study, Cassette Avail
  ★★★ Personal Application   Preparation Time: Low   ISBN:
  ★★ Relationship Building   Ldr. Guide Avail.: Yes   Size: 5.50 x 8.50
Subjects: Jesus: Life/Teaching
Comments: This study explores Christ's majesty, and seeks to enlarge participants' understanding of His biblical portrait. The richness and variety of Christ's scriptural names offer a glimpse of His incomparable majesty. Those include: the Messiah, the Logos, Son of God, Son of Man, son of David, Lion of Judah, the Alpha and the Omega, the Prince of Peace, and the only begotten of the Father. A video series containing six 30-minute messages on two tapes is available.

Author: Sproul, R. C.   **1016**
Series: Ligonier Ministries
Title: *Objections Answered*
Publisher: Ligonier Ministries, 1987

Num. Sess.	Group Time	Num. Pgs.	Avg. Qst.	Price	Audience	Format	Bible Study
13	45-60	N/A	Vry	89.0	New Christian	Video	Topical

Features: Intro to Study, Bibliography, Appendix, Cassette Avail, Video Study Guide
  ★★★ Personal Application   Preparation Time: Low   ISBN:
  ★★ Relationship Building   Ldr. Guide Avail.: No   Size: 4.0 x 7.50
Subjects: Apologetics, Faith, God
Comments: This thirteen-session video study discusses six prevalent, tough questions about Christian faith—asked by nonbelievers and believers alike—and offers biblical answers. Topics include: "The Innocent Native in Africa," "Why Is Christ the Only Way?" "Why Is God So Narrow-minded?" "Does God Exist?" "The Church Is Full of Hypocrites!" and "Is There Life After Death?" The study guide encourages discussion, reflection, and application of lessons.

Author: Sproul, R. C.   **1017**
Series: Ligonier Ministries
Title: *One Holy Passion*
Publisher: Ligonier Ministries, 1989

Num. Sess.	Group Time	Num. Pgs.	Avg. Qst.	Price	Audience	Format	Bible Study
13	45-60	N/A	Vry	89.0	New Christian	Video	Topical

Features: Intro to Study, Bibliography, Follow Up
  ★★★ Personal Application   Preparation Time: Low   ISBN:
  ★★ Relationship Building   Ldr. Guide Avail.: No   Size: 4.0 x 7.50
Subjects: Faith, God, Theology
Comments: This thirteen-session video study examines God's attributes. Participants will draw closer to Him in love and faithfulness as they understand His magnificence. Topics include: "Can God Die?" "Where Is God When I Need Him?" "Does God Have a Body?" "God and Truth," "Does God Have a Withered Arm?" and "Is God in a Rut?" The study guide encourages discussion, reflection, and application of lessons.

Author: Sproul, R. C.   **1018**
Series: Ligonier Ministries
Title: *Pleasing God*
Publisher: Ligonier Ministries, 1989

Num. Sess.	Group Time	Num. Pgs.	Avg. Qst.	Price	Audience	Format	Bible Study
13	45-60	N/A	Vry	89.0	New Christian	Video	Topical

Features: Intro to Study, Follow Up, Cassette Avail, Video Study Guide
  ★★★ Personal Application   Preparation Time: Low   ISBN:
  ★★ Relationship Building   Ldr. Guide Avail.: No   Size: 4.0 x 7.50
Subjects: Christian Living, Forgiveness, Satan, Theology
Comments: This thirteen-session video study clearly identifies the struggles Christians face in pleasing God, then offers insights on how to overcome them. Using practical terms it addresses the doctrine of sanctification. Topics include: "The Goal of Christian Living," "Beware of the Leaven of the Pharisees," "The Battle with the World," "The Battle with the Flesh," "The Battle with the Devil," and "Guilt and Forgiveness." The study guide encourages discussion, reflection, and application of lessons.

Author: Sproul, R. C.   **1019**
Series: Ligonier Ministries
Title: *Providence of God, The*
Publisher: Ligonier Ministries, 1990

Num. Sess.	Group Time	Num. Pgs.	Avg. Qst.	Price	Audience	Format	Bible Study
13	45-60	N/A	Vry	89.0	New Christian	Video	Topical

Features: Intro to Study, Bibliography, Cassette Avail, Video Study Guide
  ★★★ Personal Application   Preparation Time: Low   ISBN:
  ★★ Relationship Building   Ldr. Guide Avail.: No   Size: 4.0 x 7.50
Subjects: God, Prayer, Theology
Comments: This thirteen-session video study explains the doctrine of providence, God's sovereign government of the universe and intimate involvement in all aspects of life. Topics include: "What Is Providence?" "God Makes It All Happen," "God or Chance?" "Is God Responsible for Human Wickedness?" "What About Human Freedom?" "If God Knows Our Needs, Why Pray?" and "The Providence of God and Christian Growth." The study guide encourages discussion, reflection, and application of lessons.

Author: Sproul, R. C.   **1020**
Series: Ligonier Ministries
Title: *Surprised by Suffering*
Publisher: Ligonier Ministries, 1989

Num. Sess.	Group Time	Num. Pgs.	Avg. Qst.	Price	Audience	Format	Bible Study
12	45-60	N/A	Vry	89.0	New Christian	Video	Topical

Features: Intro to Study, Appendix, Cassette Avail, Video Study Guide
  ★★★ Personal Application   Preparation Time: Low   ISBN:
  ★★ Relationship Building   Ldr. Guide Avail.: No   Size: 4.0 x 7.50
Subjects: Counseling, Faith, Heaven/Hell, Suffering
Comments: This twelve-session video study offers insights regarding the question, Why do people suffer? It also offers hope for those struggling to piece together broken lives. Topics include: "Suffering: A Case Study," "Suffering: A Divine Vocation," "Dying in Faith," "Life After Death?" "The Resurrection of Christ," and "What Is Heaven Like?" The study guide encourages discussion, reflection, and application of lessons.

Author: Stanley, Charles F.　　　　　　**1021**
Series:
Title: *Handle with Prayer*
Publisher: Victor Books, 1982

Num. Sess.	Group Time	Num. Pgs.	Avg. Qst.	Price	Audience	Format	Bible Study
13	60-75	120	N/A	6.99	New Christian	Book	Topical

Features:
★★★★ Personal Application　Preparation Time: Low　ISBN: 0-88207-309-5
★★★★ Relationship Building　Ldr. Guide Avail.: Yes　Size: 5.50 x 8.0
Subjects: Prayer, Time
Comments: In this thirteen-week study, participants will realize that prayer and waiting go hand in hand. Lesson titles include "Praying with Authority"; "Answered Prayer"; "How to Pray in the Will of God"; "A Time to Wait, a Time to Act"; "Praying for Others"; "The Warfare of Prayer"; and more. A leader's guide includes many helps and reproducible transparency masters.

Author: Stark, Tom & Joan　　　　　　**1022**
Series: Fisherman Bible Studyguide
Title: *Guidance & God's Will*
Publisher: Shaw, 1978

Num. Sess.	Group Time	Num. Pgs.	Avg. Qst.	Price	Audience	Format	Bible Study
12	45-60	59	9	3.95	Beginner	Workbk	Topical

Features: Intro to Leading a Study, Intro to Study, Follow Up, Full Scrpt Printed
★★ Personal Application　Preparation Time: None　ISBN: 0-87788-324-6
★ Relationship Building　Ldr. Guide Avail.: No　Size: 5.0 x 8.25
Subjects: Christian Living, God, Holy Spirit
Comments: This study addresses two basic questions: does God really guide His children, and how do we balance His will for us with daily circumstances, personal inclinations, and the advice of friends? Searching the life of Paul, the study exposes principles which apply to daily life. The first three segments deal with God's will; 4-5, the Holy Spirit's guidance; studies 6-10, God's guidance and personal preference, good sense, circumstances, counsel, and sovereignty; 11-12 trusting God for guidance.

Author: St. Clair, Barry　　　　　　**1023**
Series: Moving Toward Maturity
Title: *Following Jesus (Book 1)*
Publisher: Victor Books, 1983

Num. Sess.	Group Time	Num. Pgs.	Avg. Qst.	Price	Audience	Format	Bible Study
10	60-90	132	Vry	5.95	Beginner	Workbk	Topical

Features: Objectives, Scrpt Memory Helps, Drawings, Cartoons
★★★ Personal Application　Preparation Time: Low　ISBN: 0-88207-301-X
★★★ Relationship Building　Ldr. Guide Avail.: Yes　Size: 5.25 x 8.0
Subjects: Teens: Bible Study, Teens: Discipleship, Teens: Junior High, Teens: New Testament
Comments: This study introduces participants to the basics of discipleship: becoming children of God; developing relationships with Christ; discovering God's purposes, love, and will; learning Bible study and prayer; and putting God first. It contains ten Bible studies, ten memory verse cards, and a "Bible Response Sheet" for use in a daily study of 1 John. A leader's guide gives an overview and outlines things to do before, during, and after meetings.

Author: St. Clair, Barry　　　　　　**1024**
Series: Moving Toward Maturity
Title: *Spending Time Alone with God (Book 2)*
Publisher: Victor Books, 1984

Num. Sess.	Group Time	Num. Pgs.	Avg. Qst.	Price	Audience	Format	Bible Study
10	60-90	144	Vry	5.99	New Christian	Workbk	Topical

Features: Intro to Study, Prayer Helps, Scrpt Memory Helps, Drawings, Cartoons, Appendix
★★★ Personal Application　Preparation Time: Low　ISBN: 0-88207-302-8
★★★ Relationship Building　Ldr. Guide Avail.: Yes　Size: 5.25 x 8.0
Subjects: Teens: Bible Study, Teens: Junior High, Teens: Prayer
Comments: This study helps participants discover the value of time alone with God, what it can do in their lives, and how to achieve it. It is a workable plan for developing personal Bible study, and covers communicating with God through praise, thanksgiving, confession, petition, and intercession. It also covers scripture memory. A leader's guide is available, as well as notebook inserts which provide a ten-week supply of devotionals.

Author: Steele, Sharon A.　　　　　　**1025**
Series: Enrichment Series
Title: *Choosing to Change: How to Acquire the Mind of Christ*
Publisher: Aglow, 1989

Num. Sess.	Group Time	Num. Pgs.	Avg. Qst.	Price	Audience	Format	Bible Study
9	60-75	56	23	2.95	New Christian	Workbk	Topical

Features: Intro to Study, Prayer Helps, Scrpt Memory Helps, Persnl Study Quest
★★★★ Personal Application　Preparation Time: Med　ISBN: 0-932305-72-5
★★★★ Relationship Building　Ldr. Guide Avail.: No　Size: 5.25 x 8.25
Subjects: Charismatic Interest, Emotions, Prayer, Stress, Victorious Living
Comments: This nine-week study uses key scriptures to help participants learn how to renew their minds and acquire the mind of Christ. Four essential steps include the following: connecting to the power source through prayer; studying God's Word; changing focus by thinking on good things; and changing one's negative thoughts. Other lessons teach participants how to apply the four steps to difficult circumstances.

Author: Steele, Sharon A.　　　　　　**1026**
Series: Basic Bible Study Series
Title: *Keys to Contentment: A Study of Philippians*
Publisher: Aglow, 1981

Num. Sess.	Group Time	Num. Pgs.	Avg. Qst.	Price	Audience	Format	Bible Study
9	75-90	80	41	2.95	New Christian	Workbk	Book

Features: Intro to Study, Prayer Helps, Scrpt Memory Helps, Persnl Study Quest
★★★ Personal Application　Preparation Time: Med　ISBN: 0-930756-65-7
★★★ Relationship Building　Ldr. Guide Avail.: No　Size: 5.25 x 8.25
Subjects: Charismatic Interest, Obedience, Philippians, Stress, Victorious Living
Comments: This nine-week study of Philippians shares the keys to contentment and abundant life. Lesson titles include: "Trust in Jesus," "Praise and Rejoice," "Overcome Worry," "Renew the Mind," "Appropriate Christ's Righteousness," "Forget the Past," "Obey God," "Set Proper Priorities," and "Develop Your Ministry." Participants will see characteristics in Paul's life and principles in his teachings that can lead to this full, rich, contented life.

Author: Steele, Sharon A.   **1027**
Series: Basic Bible Study Series
Title: *New Commandment, A: Loving As Jesus Loved*
Publisher: Aglow, 1986

Num. Sess.	Group Time	Num. Pgs.	Avg. Qst.	Price	Audience	Format	Bible Study
8	75-90	64	25	2.95	New Christian	Workbk	Topical

Features: Intro to Study, Prayer Helps, Scrpt Memory Helps, Persnl Study Quest
  ★★★ Personal Application   Preparation Time: Med   ISBN: 0-932305-21-0
  ★★★ Relationship Building   Ldr. Guide Avail.: No   Size: 5.25 x 8.25
Subjects: Charismatic Interest, Forgiveness, Love, Marriage, Relationships, Service
Comments: This nine-week study teaches that people must learn to love others with Jesus' kind of love. Lessons demonstrate that we are commanded to love; that love reveals our relationship to God; that it is accepting, forgiving, sacrificing, serving, kind, and edifying to others. Participants realize that God is both love and the source of love.

Author: Sterk, Andrea & Peter Scazzero   **1028**
Series: LifeGuide Bible Study
Title: *Christian Character*
Publisher: InterVarsity, 1985

Num. Sess.	Group Time	Num. Pgs.	Avg. Qst.	Price	Audience	Format	Bible Study
12	45-60	64	12	3.95	New Christian	Workbk	Topical

Features: Intro to Leading a Study, Intro to Study, Ldr's Notes
  ★ Personal Application   Preparation Time: Low   ISBN: 0-8308-1054-4
  ★ Relationship Building   Ldr. Guide Avail.: No   Size: 5.50 x 8.25
Subjects: Christian Living, Discipleship, Holiness, Holy Spirit, Jesus: Life/Teaching, Obedience, Service
Comments: This study of Christian character involves an understanding and application of certain qualities which lead one to become the person God wants him or her to be. Such character comes as the Spirit of God transforms through the Word of God. It discusses justification—the meaning of the Cross—establishes the lordship of Jesus Christ, issues a challenge to consider and understand temptation, holiness, compassion, servanthood, self-image, perseverance, and more, all of which lead to godly living.

Author: Sterk, Andrea & Peter Scazzero   **1029**
Series: LifeGuide Bible Study
Title: *Christian Disciplines*
Publisher: InterVarsity, 1985

Num. Sess.	Group Time	Num. Pgs.	Avg. Qst.	Price	Audience	Format	Bible Study
12	45-60	64	13	3.95	New Christian	Workbk	Topical

Features: Intro to Leading a Study, Intro to Study, Ldr's Notes
  ★ Personal Application   Preparation Time: Low   ISBN: 0-8308-1055-2
  ★ Relationship Building   Ldr. Guide Avail.: No   Size: 5.50 x 8.25
Subjects: Accountability, Bible Study, Discipleship, Missions, Prayer, Social Issues, Stewardship, Time, Worship
Comments: This is a discussion of the discipline required to achieve spiritual depth. Strengthening character and deepening one's relationship with Christ in the areas of prayer, Bible study, quiet time, evangelism, social justice, the church, missions, managing time and gifts, guidance, worship, giving, and discipling all help build depth, strength, wisdom, and maturity. Biblical examples and models are used to clarify the disciplines.

Author: Stevens, Paul   **1030**
Series: LifeGuide Bible Study
Title: *Revelation: The Triumph of God*
Publisher: InterVarsity, 1987

Num. Sess.	Group Time	Num. Pgs.	Avg. Qst.	Price	Audience	Format	Bible Study
12	45-60	64	12	3.95	New Christian	Workbk	Book

Features: Intro to Leading a Study, Intro to Study, Ldr's Notes
  ★ Personal Application   Preparation Time: Low   ISBN: 0-8308-1021-8
  ★ Relationship Building   Ldr. Guide Avail.: No   Size: 5.50 x 8.25
Subjects: Church Life, God, Hope, Revelation
Comments: This study of Revelation is divided into three parts. Part 1 includes five studies on Christ and the seven churches (Rev. 1-5). In part 2, four studies focus on key themes (Rev. 6-18); while part 3 contains three studies on the concluding visions (Rev. 19-22). Jesus gave John the vision he recorded in the Book of Revelation, to offer hope. Revelation, which touches at the point of despair, world-weariness, future shock, fear of persecution, and collaboration with a sick society, is relevant today.

Author: Stevens, Paul & Gerry Schoberg   **1031**
Series: Fisherman Bible Studyguide
Title: *Satisfying Work: Christian Living from Nine to Five*
Publisher: Shaw, 1989

Num. Sess.	Group Time	Num. Pgs.	Avg. Qst.	Price	Audience	Format	Bible Study
13	45-60	85	10	3.95	Beginner	Workbk	Topical

Features: Intro to Leading a Study, Intro to Study, Prayer Helps, Ldr's Notes
  ★★★ Personal Application   Preparation Time: None   ISBN: 0-87788-752-7
  ★★ Relationship Building   Ldr. Guide Avail.: No   Size: 5.0 x 8.25
Subjects: Christian Living, Ethics, Success, Women's Issues, Work
Comments: This study from Genesis to Revelation will help answer the question, What is a Christian view of work? It explores issues such as ethics, success and prosperity, creative rest, the value of homemaking, and meaningful ministry. Discovering God's design for modern-day work in the Scriptures is not simple because a new set of satisfactions exists today. Today jobs must be meaningful, appropriate to a person's talents, continuously challenging, and adequately remunerated.

Author: Stevens, Paul & Dan Williams   **1032**
Series: LifeGuide Bible Study
Title: *1 Corinthians: The Challenges of Life Together*
Publisher: InterVarsity, 1988

Num. Sess.	Group Time	Num. Pgs.	Avg. Qst.	Price	Audience	Format	Bible Study
13	45-60	80	12	3.95	New Christian	Workbk	Book

Features: Intro to Leading a Study, Intro to Study, Ldr's Notes
  ★ Personal Application   Preparation Time: Low   ISBN: 0-8308-1009-9
  ★ Relationship Building   Ldr. Guide Avail.: No   Size: 5.50 x 8.25
Subjects: Marriage, Relationships, Singles Issues, Spiritual Gifts, 1 Corinthians
Comments: Paul's advice to the Corinthians is practical for people today who seek fellowship with others in and out of a church setting. Paul deals with issues such as cliques and power struggles, people who think they are spiritually or intellectually superior, immorality, exercising one's rights, marriage, singleness, and spiritual gifts as theological principles which are current today. Paul specifically addresses matters which distress the church at Corinth, including the Resurrection.

Author: Stevens, Paul   **1033**
Series: LifeGuide Bible Study
Title: *2 Corinthians: Finding Strength in Weakness*
Publisher: InterVarsity, 1990

Num. Sess.	Group Time	Num. Pgs.	Avg. Qst.	Price	Audience	Format	Bible Study
12	45-60	75	10	3.95	New Christian	Workbk	Topical

Features: Intro to Leading a Study, Intro to Study, Ldr's Notes
★★★ Personal Application   Preparation Time: Low   ISBN: 0-8308-1010-2
★★★ Relationship Building   Ldr. Guide Avail.: No   Size: 5.50 x 8.25
Subjects: God's Promises, Grace, Hope, Leadership, Relationships, Repentance, Service, Suffering, 2 Corinthians
Comments: This study on finding strength in weakness concerns real relationships, not perfect ones. The Apostle Paul delighted in his weaknesses, welcomed hardships and difficulties, and thanked God for obstacles that provided opportunities for experiencing His power. In Second Corinthians, Paul turns many contemporary values upside down and teaches that in all circumstances Christians can rely on God's promise ("My grace is sufficient for you").

Author: Stevens, R. Paul & Gerry Schoberg   **1034**
Series: NetWork Discussion Guide
Title: *Fulfilling Work*
Publisher: Shaw, 1991

Num. Sess.	Group Time	Num. Pgs.	Avg. Qst.	Price	Audience	Format	Bible Study
8	30-45	48	5	3.50	Beginner	Workbk	Topical

Features: Intro to Leading a Study, Intro to Study, Bibliography, Follow Up, Ldr's Notes
★★★★ Personal Application   Preparation Time: Low   ISBN: 0-87788-271-1
★★★ Relationship Building   Ldr. Guide Avail.: No   Size: 5.25 x 8.25
Subjects: Ethics, Success, Work
Comments: Eight short lessons help participants answer questions that focus on issues like workplace ethics, creative rest, the value of homemaking, and meaningful ministry. Questions include: What is a Christian's view of work? What is success and prosperity? What makes work fulfilling?

Author: Stevens, R. Paul & Gail   **1035**
Series: Fisherman Bible Studyguide
Title: *Marriage: Learning from Couples in Scripture*
Publisher: Shaw, 1991

Num. Sess.	Group Time	Num. Pgs.	Avg. Qst.	Price	Audience	Format	Bible Study
12	45-60	80	12	3.95	New Christian	Workbk	Topical

Features: Intro to Leading a Study, Intro to Study, Prayer Helps, Follow Up
Personal Application   Preparation Time: None   ISBN: 0-87788-533-8
Relationship Building   Ldr. Guide Avail.: No   Size: 5.0 x 8.25
Subjects: Bible Personalities, Marriage
Comments: These lessons explore stories of couples in the Bible, people whose life experiences are amazingly similar to those of contemporary couples face. It shows examples of both good and bad relationships. Participants will gain deeper understanding of the marriage covenant, and strengthen the spiritual dimension of their lives together.

Author: Stewart, Ruth Goring   **1036**
Series: Global Issues
Title: *Environmental Stewardship*
Publisher: InterVarsity, 1990

Num. Sess.	Group Time	Num. Pgs.	Avg. Qst.	Price	Audience	Format	Bible Study
6	45-60	48	12	4.95	Beginner	Workbk	Topical

Features: Intro to Leading a Study, Intro to Study, Bibliography
★ Personal Application   Preparation Time: Low   ISBN: 0-8308-4903-3
★ Relationship Building   Ldr. Guide Avail.: No   Size: 5.50 x 8.25
Subjects: Social Issues
Comments: This six-week study helps participants examine from a biblical perspective, crucial issues involved in caring for the environment. It helps them become responsible leaders in restoring God's creation to wholeness. Subjects discussed include oil spills, dangerous pesticides, unsanitary sewage dumps, toxic landfills, and nuclear waste. Two important questions explored are "What attitudes and values have led to the poisoning of our planet?" and "What does this have to do with Christianity?"

Author: Stokes, Penelope J.   **1037**
Series: Fisherman Bible Studyguide
Title: *Ruth & Daniel: God's People in an Alien Society*
Publisher: Shaw, 1986

Num. Sess.	Group Time	Num. Pgs.	Avg. Qst.	Price	Audience	Format	Bible Study
11	45-60	61	10	3.95	New Christian	Workbk	Charctr

Features: Intro to Leading a Study, Intro to Study, Prayer Helps, Follow Up
★★★ Personal Application   Preparation Time: Low   ISBN: 0-87788-735-7
★★ Relationship Building   Ldr. Guide Avail.: No   Size: 5.0 x 8.25
Subjects: Bible Personalities, Daniel, Faith, God, Integrity, Major Prophets, Obedience, Ruth
Comments: This is a character study of Ruth and Daniel. Part 1 portrays Ruth as a woman of faithfulness, humility, obedience, and fruitfulness. Part 2 shows Daniel to be a man of integrity, prayer, witness, submission, trust, and reputation. Part 3 shows participants how to follow the examples, learning from Ruth and Daniel. These studies offer clear examples of God's provision for His people in adverse circumstances. They show how people can receive both reassurance and a challenge to live out their faith.

Author: Stokes, Penelope J.   **1038**
Series: Crisispoints for Women
Title: *So What If You've Failed*
Publisher: NavPress, 1990

Num. Sess.	Group Time	Num. Pgs.	Avg. Qst.	Price	Audience	Format	Bible Study
5	45-60	91	11	3.95	New Christian	Workbk	Topical

Features: Intro to Study, Bibliography, Prayer Helps, Pre-discussion Quest, Follow Up, Persnl Study Quest
★★★★ Personal Application   Preparation Time: Med   ISBN: 0-89109-326-5
★★ Relationship Building   Ldr. Guide Avail.: No   Size: 4.25 x 7.0
Subjects: Emotions, Failure, God, Women's Issues
Comments: This five-lesson study—part of an eight-book series for women in crises—helps participants put failure in perspective. By being realistic and honest, they can learn to be introspective about failures, mistakes, needing to "look good," and taking risks by trusting God. In the lessons, a magazine article format is followed by Bible study or discussion questions. Due to added sections on evaluation, journaling, and activities, six or seven sessions are recommended. The series is nonthreatening.

Author: Stolpe, Norman D.   **1039**
Series: Group's Active Bible Curriculum
Title: *Genesis: The Beginnings*
Publisher: Group Publishing, 1991

Num. Sess.	Group Time	Num. Pgs.	Avg. Qst.	Price	Audience	Format	Bible Study
4	35-60	47	Vry	6.95	Beginner	Workbk	Book

Features: Intro to Leading a Study, Intro to Study, Objectives, Study Overview, Ldr's Notes, Drawings, Handouts, Agenda, Publicity Ideas
★★★★ Personal Application   Preparation Time: None   ISBN: 1-559-45111-4
★★★★ Relationship Building   Ldr. Guide Avail.: No   Size: 8.50 x 11.0
Subjects: Teens: Christian Liv, Teens: Junior High, Teens: Old Testament, Teens: Self-esteem
Comments: This four-lesson study helps junior high youth learn powerful lessons from familiar stories in Genesis. Students will build self-esteem, as they uncover what it means to be created in God's image, grow in faith as they discover how to overcome temptation, discover what it means to give their best to God, and learn hope even when things aren't going well. Instructions are easy to follow and provide multiple options for teachers. No student books are required.

Author: Stott, John   **1040**
Series: LifeGuide Bible Study
Title: *Sermon on the Mount*
Publisher: InterVarsity, 1987

Num. Sess.	Group Time	Num. Pgs.	Avg. Qst.	Price	Audience	Format	Bible Study
13	45-60	80	12	3.95	New Christian	Workbk	Topical

Features: Intro to Leading a Study, Intro to Study, Ldr's Notes
★ Personal Application   Preparation Time: Low   ISBN: 0-8308-1036-6
★ Relationship Building   Ldr. Guide Avail.: No   Size: 5.50 x 8.25
Subjects: Ethics, Jesus: Life/Teaching, Matthew, Money, Relationships, Sermon on the Mount
Comments: Matthew's gospel recounts Jesus' greatest sermon, preached near the beginning of His public ministry. In this study, a contrast is drawn between the standards of Christians and non-Christians. Christian values, ethical standards, religious devotion, attitudes about money, ambition, lifestyles, and relationships are all discussed. It calls for students to be challenged by this great sermon, and respond to what Jesus wants His followers to be and do.

Author: Stowell, Joseph M.   **1041**
Series:
Title: *Tongue in Check*
Publisher: Victor Books, 1983

Num. Sess.	Group Time	Num. Pgs.	Avg. Qst.	Price	Audience	Format	Bible Study
13	60-75	132	N/A	6.99	New Christian	Book	Topical

Features: Intro to Study
★★★★ Personal Application   Preparation Time: Low   ISBN: 0-88207-293-5
★★★ Relationship Building   Ldr. Guide Avail.: Yes   Size: 5.50 x 8.0
Subjects: Christian Living, Holy Spirit
Comments: This thirteen-week study helps participants take control of their tongues, especially if they're accustomed to living by the motto, "Speak first—think later." That philosophy leads to lying, deceit, gossip, slander, boasting and murmuring. The lessons help create speech patterns that will heal, help, warm, and encourage others—but only under the Spirit's control.

Author: Strauss, Richard L.   **1042**
Series: Living Studies
Title: *Famous Couples of the Bible*
Publisher: Tyndale House, 1978

Num. Sess.	Group Time	Num. Pgs.	Avg. Qst.	Price	Audience	Format	Bible Study
13	45-60	141	7	5.95	Beginner	Book	Charctr

Features:
★★ Personal Application   Preparation Time: None   ISBN: 0-8423-0836-9
★ Relationship Building   Ldr. Guide Avail.: No   Size: 5.0 x 8.0
Subjects: Bible Personalities, Christian Living, Marriage
Comments: This study, an in-depth review of successful Bible marriages, points out problems contemporary couples should avoid. Each lesson adds a personal touch and application for a marriage. Famous couples including Adam and Eve, Abraham and Sarah, Joseph and Mary, Aquila and Priscilla, and others provide memorable examples of the possibilities and pitfalls of marriage and add enrichment and instruction as well.

Author: Strauss, Richard L.   **1043**
Series: Living Studies
Title: *Marriage Is for Love*
Publisher: Tyndale House, 1973

Num. Sess.	Group Time	Num. Pgs.	Avg. Qst.	Price	Audience	Format	Bible Study
13	60-90	116	N/A	5.95	New Christian	Book	Topical

Features: No Grp Discussion Quest
★★ Personal Application   Preparation Time: Low   ISBN: 0-8423-4178-1
★★ Relationship Building   Ldr. Guide Avail.: No   Size: 5.0 x 8.0
Subjects: Love, Marriage, Money
Comments: This book, for Christians who face marital problems, sets forth God's principles for making marriage work. It's appropriate for couples planning a wedding as well as those celebrating twenty-five years of marriage. Understanding and applying lessons such as "Speaking the Truth in Love," "Solving Marital Conflicts," "Money, Money, Money," and more will strengthen the fabric of any marriage relationship. Small group study questions are not included.

Author: Strom, Kay Marshall   **1044**
Series: Woman's Workshop Series
Title: *Perfect in His Eyes: Studies on Self-esteem*
Publisher: Zondervan, 1988

Num. Sess.	Group Time	Num. Pgs.	Avg. Qst.	Price	Audience	Format	Bible Study
13	60-90	112	Vry	4.95	Beginner	Workbk	Topical

Features: Intro to Leading a Study, Intro to Study, Ldr's Notes, Drawings, Charts
★★★ Personal Application   Preparation Time: None   ISBN: 0-310-33691-0
★★ Relationship Building   Ldr. Guide Avail.: No   Size: 5.25 x 8.0
Subjects: Christian Living, Self-esteem, Women's Issues
Comments: This study shows that the solution to low self-esteem is understanding how precious each person is to God, who creates and molds him or her into His own likeness. It defines self-esteem, identifies true values, promotes learning about oneself and shedding guilt, and outlines steps for attaining healthy self-esteem.

Author: Swaby-Ellis, E. Dawn   **1045**
Series: Global Issues
Title: *Sanctity of Life*
Publisher: InterVarsity, 1990

Num. Sess.	Group Time	Num. Pgs.	Avg. Qst.	Price	Audience	Format	Bible Study
6	45-60	48	11	4.95	Beginner	Workbk	Topical

Features: Intro to Leading a Study, Intro to Study, Bibliography, Follow Up
  ★★ Personal Application Preparation Time: Low ISBN: 0-8308-4911-4
  ★★ Relationship Building Ldr. Guide Avail.: No Size: 5.50 x 8.25
Subjects: Abortion, Ethics, Social Issues
Comments: This six-week study exposes participants to tough questions on abortion, war, and capital punishment, to guide them to a biblical view of life. Questions explored include: "Does being created in God's image suggest anything to us about capital punishment for murderers?" "What if the person in question is a serial killer?" "What about a drug kingpin?" and "What biblical principles would Christians base their decision on?" Leaders should read first, to determine appropriateness for their group.

Author: Swanson, Sandi   **1046**
Series: Woman's Workshop Series
Title: *Fruit of the Spirit, The: Studies on Galatians 5:22-23*
Publisher: Zondervan, 1989

Num. Sess.	Group Time	Num. Pgs.	Avg. Qst.	Price	Audience	Format	Bible Study
12	60-90	156	Vry	6.95	New Christian	Workbk	Book

Features: Intro to Leading a Study, Intro to Study, Scrpt Memory Helps, Study Overview, Ldr's Notes, Charts, Word Study
  ★★★ Personal Application Preparation Time: Med ISBN: 0-310-52241-2
  ★★★ Relationship Building Ldr. Guide Avail.: No Size: 5.25 x 8.0
Subjects: Faith, Fruit of the Spirit, Galatians, Women's Issues
Comments: This is a study on the fruit of the Spirit: love, joy, goodness, kindness, patience, faithfulness, gentleness, peace, and self-control. In his letter to the Galatians, Paul paints a picture of faithful Christians' potential under the New Covenant; and the study reveals how such pictures are to be interpreted. A comparison is made between works of the flesh and the fruit of the Spirit.

Author: Sweeting, George   **1047**
Series:
Title: *No-Guilt Guide to Witnessing, The*
Publisher: Victor Books, 1991

Num. Sess.	Group Time	Num. Pgs.	Avg. Qst.	Price	Audience	Format	Bible Study
14	45-60	127	Vry	6.99	New Christian	Book	No

Features:
  ★★★★ Personal Application Preparation Time: Low ISBN: 0-89693-400-4
  ★★★★ Relationship Building Ldr. Guide Avail.: Yes Size: 5.50 x 8.0
Subjects: Commitments, Discipleship, Evangelism, Obedience, Small Group Resource
Comments: This book is for those who fail to witness because of fear or lack of know-how. It shows how to prepare to witness, present an effective witness, seek commitment, and follow up. Readers gain confidence as they brush up on proven "how-to's" of witnessing, and gain assurance that as they are faithful to the task they can trust the Lord with the results. This book could be used to train leaders.

Author: Swindoll, Charles R.   **1048**
Series: Insight for Living
Title: *Abraham: The Friend of God*
Publisher: Word, 1986

Num. Sess.	Group Time	Num. Pgs.	Avg. Qst.	Price	Audience	Format	Bible Study
25	45-60	174	2	4.99	Mature Chrstn	Workbk	Charctr

Features: Intro to Study, Bibliography, Digging Deeper Quest, Charts, Cassette Avail
  ★★ Personal Application Preparation Time: Med ISBN: 0-8499-8329-0
  ★★ Relationship Building Ldr. Guide Avail.: No Size: 5.50 x 8.50
Subjects: Bible Personalities, Faith, God
Comments: This study motivates participants to replace theoretical talk about God with practical, daily walks with God. The story of Abraham, "father of a multitude," is a story of faith in action. Even though he lived in ancient times, he modeled an enviable walk with his Lord. Far from perfect, he still demonstrated faith and sincerity seldom found today. A two-page chart depicts Abraham's life from Genesis 12-25.

Author: Swindoll, Charles R.   **1049**
Series: Insight for Living
Title: *Behold Christ the Lamb of God: A Study of John 15-21*
Publisher: Word, 1975

Num. Sess.	Group Time	Num. Pgs.	Avg. Qst.	Price	Audience	Format	Bible Study
16	45-60	130	2	4.99	New Christian	Workbk	Book

Features: Intro to Study, Bibliography, Charts, Cassette Avail
  ★★ Personal Application Preparation Time: Med ISBN: 0-8499-8297-9
  ★★ Relationship Building Ldr. Guide Avail.: No Size: 5.50 x 8.50
Subjects: Jesus: Life/Teaching, John
Comments: This study of John's gospel chapters 15-21, covers the Lamb—Jesus Christ—on display. After an intimate last supper with His disciples, He faces the horrors of illegal trials, scourging, crucifixion, and death. The Lamb is slain—but He is later raised! Participants' attention is focused on the Christ who bore humankind's sin. A chart depicting six trials of Jesus lists the pertinent scripture, the officiating authority, accusation, legality, type, and result.

Author: Swindoll, Charles R.   **1050**
Series: Insight for Living
Title: *Calm Answers for a Confused Church: A Study of 1 Corinthians*
Publisher: Word, 1973

Num. Sess.	Group Time	Num. Pgs.	Avg. Qst.	Price	Audience	Format	Bible Study
16	45-60	114	2	3.99	Mature Chrstn	Workbk	Book

Features: Intro to Study, Bibliography, Charts, Cassette Avail
  ★★ Personal Application Preparation Time: Med ISBN: 0-8499-8400-9
  ★★ Relationship Building Ldr. Guide Avail.: No Size: 5.50 x 8.50
Subjects: Church Life, Hope, Love, Marriage, 1 Corinthians
Comments: This study is Paul's response to Corinthian Christians who were confused over spiritual issues. Their disagreements led to cliques and splinter groups, each going in a different direction and listening to a different leader. Interwoven through this final segment in a three-part study of 1 Corinthians are the themes of unity, assurance, hope, and love.

Author: Swindoll, Charles R.   **1051**
Series: Insight for Living
Title: *Christ's Agony and Ecstacy*
Publisher: Word, 1982

Num. Sess.	Group Time	Num. Pgs.	Avg. Qst.	Price	Audience	Format	Bible Study
16	45-60	49	1	3.99	New Christian	Book	Charctr

Features: Intro to Study, Cassette Avail
  ★★ Personal Application   Preparation Time: Med   ISBN: 0-8499-8205-7
  ★★ Relationship Building   Ldr. Guide Avail.: No   Size: 5.50 x 8.50
Subjects: Jesus: Life/Teaching, Miracles, Suffering
Comments: This study covers eighteen passages from the Old and New Testaments which pertain to the agonies and ecstasies of Jesus Christ. Each passage takes participants through an in-depth view of Christ's sufferings and the miracle of His resurrection. These messages, which encourage worship through quiet meditation, are meant to enable participants to relive those moments in history, observing each one through the lens of Scripture.

Author: Swindoll, Charles R.   **1052**
Series: Insight for Living
Title: *Coming to Terms with Sin: A Study of Romans 1-5*
Publisher: Word, 1977

Num. Sess.	Group Time	Num. Pgs.	Avg. Qst.	Price	Audience	Format	Bible Study
12	45-60	67	2	3.99	New Christian	Book	Book

Features: Intro to Study, Bibliography, Digging Deeper Quest, Charts, Cassette Avail
  ★★★ Personal Application   Preparation Time: Med   ISBN: 0-8499-8214-6
  ★★ Relationship Building   Ldr. Guide Avail.: No   Size: 5.50 x 8.50
Subjects: Hope, Repentance, Romans, Theology
Comments: This verse-by-verse study of the first five chapters of Romans, which contrasts bright rays of relief with the black backdrop of human despair, offers sound doctrine mixed with modern practicality. Romans presents a vivid description of sin and its consequences, then offers hope, a "gift of God." Through twelve segments, participants are led to come to terms with sin.

Author: Swindoll, Charles R.   **1053**
Series: Insight for Living
Title: *Contagious Christianity: A Study of First Thessalonians*
Publisher: Word, 1985

Num. Sess.	Group Time	Num. Pgs.	Avg. Qst.	Price	Audience	Format	Bible Study
12	45-60	75	2	3.99	New Christian	Book	Book

Features: Intro to Study, Bibliography, Digging Deeper Quest, Charts, Cassette Avail
  ★★ Personal Application   Preparation Time: Med   ISBN: 0-8499-8211-1
  ★★ Relationship Building   Ldr. Guide Avail.: No   Size: 5.50 x 8.50
Subjects: Christian Living, Church Life, Joy, Work, 1 & 2 Thessalonians
Comments: This study, drawn from Paul's first letter to the Thessalonians, has a remarkably twentieth-century ring to it. The first of Paul's letters, it establishes his style of ministry, provides insights into the Rapture of the Church, offers needed balance regarding the Lord's imminent return, and emphasizes vocational diligence. Paul discusses a pastor's heart and burden. A chart breaks down 1 Thessalonians chapter by chapter.

Author: Swindoll, Charles R.   **1054**
Series: Insight for Living
Title: *Daniel: God's Pattern For The Future*
Publisher: Word, 1986

Num. Sess.	Group Time	Num. Pgs.	Avg. Qst.	Price	Audience	Format	Bible Study
18	45-60	123	2	3.99	Mature Chrstn	Book	Charctr

Features: Intro to Study, Bibliography, Digging Deeper Quest, Charts, Cassette Avail
  ★★ Personal Application   Preparation Time: Med   ISBN: 0-8499-8219-7
  ★★ Relationship Building   Ldr. Guide Avail.: No   Size: 5.50 x 8.50
Subjects: Bible Personalities, Daniel, Integrity, Major Prophets, Prophecy
Comments: This study allows participants to gain a deeper understanding of Daniel, a true biblical model of integrity. It takes the reader from the pit of peer pressure to the pinnacle of prophecy, as Daniel endures the rigors of "boot camp" in Babylon and emerges as premier counselor to the king. In addition to dealing with Daniel, the study exposes some of the most significant prophetic themes found in Scripture.

Author: Swindoll, Charles R.   **1055**
Series: Insight for Living
Title: *David: A Man After God's Own Heart*
Publisher: Word, 1988

Num. Sess.	Group Time	Num. Pgs.	Avg. Qst.	Price	Audience	Format	Bible Study
24	45-60	167	2	4.99	New Christian	Workbk	Charctr

Features: Intro to Study, Bibliography, Charts, Cassette Avail
  ★★ Personal Application   Preparation Time: Med   ISBN: 0-8499-8328-2
  ★★ Relationship Building   Ldr. Guide Avail.: No   Size: 5.50 x 8.50
Subjects: Bible Personalities, Leadership, 1 & 2 Samuel
Comments: This study helps participants apply biblical facts about David in concrete, personal ways. It helps build the realization that devotion—not perfection—is the secret of living a life that pleases God. Perhaps the most popular Old Testament character, David is a study in contrasts: an unknown shepherd lad who became the king; a rugged warrior who wrote tender psalms; a strong leader who was weak at home; a man of God with a rebellious son.

Author: Swindoll, Charles R.   **1056**
Series: Insight for Living
Title: *Dropping Your Guard: The Value of Open Relationships*
Publisher: Word, 1981

Num. Sess.	Group Time	Num. Pgs.	Avg. Qst.	Price	Audience	Format	Bible Study
13	45-60	79	2	3.99	New Christian	Book	Topical

Features: Intro to Study, Bibliography, Digging Deeper Quest, Charts, Cassette Avail
  ★★ Personal Application   Preparation Time: Med   ISBN: 0-8499-8210-3
  ★★ Relationship Building   Ldr. Guide Avail.: No   Size: 5.50 x 8.50
Subjects: Accountability, Christian Living, Love, Marriage, Relationships
Comments: These twelve studies show participants how to achieve authentic and meaningful involvement in others' lives through open, unguarded relationships. The lessons cover loosening the mask, risking change, getting closer, growing stronger, and authentic love and accountability. Based on the Hebrews' Exodus from Egyptian bondage and their journey to the Promised Land, these messages will motivate participants to seek better relationships.

Author: Swindoll, Charles R. **1057**
Series: Insight for Living
Title: *Exalting Christ the Son of God: A Study of John 1-5*
Publisher: Word, 1975

Num. Sess.	Group Time	Num. Pgs.	Avg. Qst.	Price	Audience	Format	Bible Study
12	45-60	97	2	3.99	New Christian	Book	Book

Features: Intro to Study, Bibliography, Charts, Cassette Avail
★★ Personal Application Preparation Time: Med ISBN: 0-8499-8295-2
★★ Relationship Building Ldr. Guide Avail.: No Size: 5.50 x 8.50
Subjects: Jesus: Life/Teaching, John
Comments: This study of John 1-5 is designed to take participants back to the first century, to clear away the debris of traditional opinion and personal feelings, so the evidence of the deity of the Son of God can be examined. The evidence strongly suggests that Jesus of Nazareth is, in fact, truly God. Background information, an overview, and a chart of John's gospel enhances the study's clarity and understanding.

Author: Swindoll, Charles R. **1058**
Series: Insight for Living
Title: *Following Christ the Man of God: A Study of John 6-14*
Publisher: Word, 1975

Num. Sess.	Group Time	Num. Pgs.	Avg. Qst.	Price	Audience	Format	Bible Study
14	45-60	110	2	3.99	New Christian	Workbk	Book

Features: Intro to Study, Bibliography, Charts, Cassette Avail
★★ Personal Application Preparation Time: Med ISBN: 0-8499-8296-0
★★ Relationship Building Ldr. Guide Avail.: No Size: 5.50 x 8.25
Subjects: Jesus: Life/Teaching, John
Comments: This study of John 6-14 follows Christ through numerous scenes, facing criticism, defending a helpless woman, giving sight to the blind, teaching His disciples, raising the dead, and modeling humility by washing the feet of His closest friends. The more participants know about the Lord, the more they will want to emulate Him. Godly qualities are contagious.

Author: Swindoll, Charles R. **1059**
Series: Insight for Living
Title: *Galatians: Letter of Liberation*
Publisher: Word, 1987

Num. Sess.	Group Time	Num. Pgs.	Avg. Qst.	Price	Audience	Format	Bible Study
20	45-60	157	2	4.99	New Christian	Book	Book

Features: Intro to Study, Bibliography, Charts, Cassette Avail
★★ Personal Application Preparation Time: Med ISBN: 0-8499-8294-4
★★ Relationship Building Ldr. Guide Avail.: No Size: 5.50 x 8.50
Subjects: Galatians, Grace, Holiness
Comments: This study of Galatians promotes rejoicing for freedom in Christ. It is a bold statement of liberation, pointing away from a "gospel" of works and toward the grace Christ provides His own. Grace is the way to life and the way of life. This study also discusses the experience of being delivered from legalism. A chart divides Galatians into three sections: issues of truth, the nature of salvation, and principles of holiness.

Author: Swindoll, Charles R. **1060**
Series: Insight for Living
Title: *Growing Pains*
Publisher: Word, 1989

Num. Sess.	Group Time	Num. Pgs.	Avg. Qst.	Price	Audience	Format	Bible Study
8	45-60	63	2	4.99	New Christian	Workbk	Topical

Features: Intro to Study, Bibliography, Cassette Avail
★★ Personal Application Preparation Time: Med ISBN: 0-8499-8409-2
★★ Relationship Building Ldr. Guide Avail.: No Size: 5.50 x 8.50
Subjects: Christian Living, Emotions, Failure, Hope
Comments: This study elaborates on eight of life's more difficult and frustrating experiences. It contains neither clichés nor empty promises; rather it offers keys to help Christians through life's more difficult times. Subject matter covered includes growth through waiting, failure, misunderstanding, loss, mistakes, weakness, monotony, and fear. Each lesson brings reassurance and renewed determination to "hang in."

Author: Swindoll, Charles R. **1061**
Series: Insight for Living
Title: *Growing Up in God's Family*
Publisher: Word, 1985

Num. Sess.	Group Time	Num. Pgs.	Avg. Qst.	Price	Audience	Format	Bible Study
16	45-60	84	2	3.99	New Christian	Book	Topical

Features: Intro to Study, Bibliography, Digging Deeper Quest, Charts, Cassette Avail
★★ Personal Application Preparation Time: Med ISBN: 0-8499-8218-9
★★ Relationship Building Ldr. Guide Avail.: No Size: 5.50 x 8.50
Subjects: Christian Living, Discipleship, Faith
Comments: This study offers participants a penetrating and enlightening look at the importance of maturity in their spiritual lives. Using selected scriptures, Swindoll explores how to become strong and healthy adults in walks of faith, rather than remaining childish and immature. The insights are relevant to people's contemporary needs.

Author: Swindoll, Charles R. **1062**
Series: Insight for Living
Title: *Improving Your Serve: The Art of Unselfish Living*
Publisher: Word, 1979

Num. Sess.	Group Time	Num. Pgs.	Avg. Qst.	Price	Audience	Format	Bible Study
15	45-60	84	2	3.99	New Christian	Book	Topical

Features: Intro to Study, Bibliography, Charts, Cassette Avail
★★ Personal Application Preparation Time: Med ISBN: 0-8499-8209-X
★★ Relationship Building Ldr. Guide Avail.: No Size: 5.50 x 8.50
Subjects: Christian Living, Service
Comments: This study offers straight talk and biblical answers on how to live an unselfish life, how to serve rather than be served, and how to give rather than receive and keep. It addresses a "me-first" generation which finds itself in a confused tailspin, smug and preoccupied with its own needs, yet desperately lonely, isolated, and cold. The study will encourage participants to "improve their serve."

Author: Swindoll, Charles R.   **1063**
Series: Insight for Living
Title: *Jesus, Our Lord*
Publisher: Word, 1981

Num. Sess.	Group Time	Num. Pgs.	Avg. Qst.	Price	Audience	Format	Bible Study
8	45-60	60	2	3.99	New Christian	Book	Charctr

Features: Intro to Study, Charts, Cassette Avail
  ★★ Personal Application Preparation Time: Med ISBN: 0-8499-8292-8
  ★★ Relationship Building Ldr. Guide Avail.: No   Size: 5.50 x 8.50
Subjects: Jesus: Life/Teaching, New Testament
Comments: This study, responding to the question "Who is Jesus?" can be easily understood by anyone interested in the most unique life ever lived on earth. The study traces Christ's life in chronological order. The journey goes through the New Testament, from His preexistence with the Father to His return to Heaven as the ascended Christ. The stories, both interesting and convincing, leave no doubt that Jesus is Lord!

Author: Swindoll, Charles R.   **1064**
Series: Insight for Living
Title: *Joseph: From Pit to Pinnacle*
Publisher: Word, 1982

Num. Sess.	Group Time	Num. Pgs.	Avg. Qst.	Price	Audience	Format	Bible Study
12	45-60	44	2	3.99	New Christian	Book	Charctr

Features: Intro to Study, Charts, Cassette Avail
  ★★ Personal Application Preparation Time: Med ISBN: 0-8499-8206-5
  ★★ Relationship Building Ldr. Guide Avail.: No   Size: 5.50 x 8.50
Subjects: Bible Personalities, Failure, Forgiveness, Obedience, Success
Comments: In twelve segments, this study portrays Joseph's response to broken dreams and impossible circumstances as he rose from the pit of slavery to the pinnacle of respect. In Genesis 37-50, Joseph embodies some of Scripture's most significant truths. He perseveres through mistreatment, false accusations, undeserved punishment, and gross misunderstanding. He exemplifies forgiveness, freedom from bitterness, and a positive attitude toward those who had done him harm.

Author: Swindoll, Charles R.   **1065**
Series: Insight for Living
Title: *Koinonia: Authentic Fellowship*
Publisher: Word, 1972

Num. Sess.	Group Time	Num. Pgs.	Avg. Qst.	Price	Audience	Format	Bible Study
8	45-60	52	2	3.99	New Christian	Workbk	Topical

Features: Intro to Study, Bibliography, Charts, Cassette Avail
  ★★ Personal Application Preparation Time: Med ISBN: 0-8499-8220-0
  ★★ Relationship Building Ldr. Guide Avail.: No   Size: 5.50 x 8.50
Subjects: Caring, Christian Living, Forgiveness, Love, Marriage, Relationships
Comments: This study of biblical expositions spells out particulars involved in changing relationships from superficial and shallow to compassionate and caring. The principles studied are helpful in breaking down walls of prejudice that keep people from knowing and loving one another. The Bible calls this "koinonia." It means an authentic display of love and acceptance, care and compassion, support and forgiveness—which Jesus Christ modeled when He walked on earth.

Author: Swindoll, Charles R.   **1066**
Series: Insight for Living
Title: *Lamentations of Jeremiah, The*
Publisher: Word, 1977

Num. Sess.	Group Time	Num. Pgs.	Avg. Qst.	Price	Audience	Format	Bible Study
8	45-60	52	2	3.99	New Christian	Book	Book

Features: Intro to Study, Bibliography, Charts, Cassette Avail
  ★★ Personal Application Preparation Time: Med ISBN: 0-8499-8284-7
  ★★ Relationship Building Ldr. Guide Avail.: No   Size: 5.50 x 8.50
Subjects: Bible Personalities, Grief, Lamentations, Obedience
Comments: This is a verse-by-verse study of one of the lesser-known books of the Bible—The Lamentations of Jeremiah. In this brief journal, the prophet describes his beloved city in ruins and his own people in sorrow, grief, misery, barrenness, and pain because of sin. The overriding theme is that "whatever we sow, we reap." In this book, Jeremiah makes his grim, bold announcement that a holy God will not remain silent forever when His people disobey Him.

Author: Swindoll, Charles R.   **1067**
Series: Insight for Living
Title: *Learning to Walk by Grace: A Study of Romans 6-11*
Publisher: Word, 1985

Num. Sess.	Group Time	Num. Pgs.	Avg. Qst.	Price	Audience	Format	Bible Study
16	45-60	87	2	3.99	New Christian	Book	Book

Features: Intro to Study, Bibliography, Charts, Cassette Avail
  ★★ Personal Application Preparation Time: Med ISBN: 0-8499-8215-4
  ★★ Relationship Building Ldr. Guide Avail.: No   Size: 5.50 x 8.50
Subjects: Grace, Romans, Theology, Victorious Living
Comments: This study of Romans 6-11 is actually a short course in theology, designed for a believer learning to walk by grace. Doctrinal studies provide the basis for triumphant living. Paul provides insights into God's sovereignty, humanity's responsibility, and Israel's destiny. This is important Scripture for Christians to examine, understand, and apply.

Author: Swindoll, Charles R.   **1068**
Series: Insight for Living
Title: *Letters to Churches . . . Then and Now*
Publisher: Word, 1980

Num. Sess.	Group Time	Num. Pgs.	Avg. Qst.	Price	Audience	Format	Bible Study
10	45-60	64	2	3.99	Mature Chrstn	Book	Book

Features: Intro to Study, Bibliography, Charts, Maps, Cassette Avail
  ★★ Personal Application Preparation Time: Med ISBN: 0-8499-8290-1
  ★★ Relationship Building Ldr. Guide Avail.: No   Size: 5.50 x 8.50
Subjects: Church Life, Leadership, Revelation
Comments: This study examines seven letters from Revelation 2-3 addressed to first-century churches. The letters are practical and helpful, and as applicable today as in the first century. Through them, God counsels, warns, and reproves. Modern Christians are called to respond and be sensitive to His voice. The lesson on Exodus 18 is a thoughtful look at leadership in the church, while the closing lesson—"Will You Lead or Lag?"—is taken from 1 Corinthians 14.

Author: Swindoll, Charles R. **1069**
Series: Insight for Living
Title: *Living Above the Level of Mediocrity: A Commitment to Excellence*
Publisher: Word, 1987

Num. Sess.	Group Time	Num. Pgs.	Avg. Qst.	Price	Audience	Format	Bible Study
20	45-60	145	2	4.99	Mature Chrstn	Workbk	Topical

Features: Intro to Study, Bibliography, Charts, Cassette Avail
★★ Personal Application Preparation Time: Med ISBN: 0-8499-8293-6
★★ Relationship Building Ldr. Guide Avail.: No Size: 5.50 x 8.50
Subjects: Accountability, Christian Living, Joy, Obedience, Success
Comments: This study of excellence serves as a powerful motivator to stretch participants' potential and offer new perspectives leading to joy and freedom. Breaking out of the rut of mediocrity involves looking at one's mind and the costs, vision, determination, priorities, and accountability involved in living in God's Kingdom; becoming a model of unselfishness; and standing strong when tempted.

Author: Swindoll, Charles R. **1070**
Series: Insight for Living
Title: *Living on the Ragged Edge: Coming to Terms with Reality*
Publisher: Word, 1983

Num. Sess.	Group Time	Num. Pgs.	Avg. Qst.	Price	Audience	Format	Bible Study
24	45-60	134	2	3.99	Mature Chrstn	Book	Topical

Features: Intro to Study, Bibliography, Digging Deeper Quest, Charts, Cassette Avail
★★ Personal Application Preparation Time: Med ISBN: 0-8499-8212-X
★★ Relationship Building Ldr. Guide Avail.: No Size: 5.50 x 8.50
Subjects: Christian Living, Ecclesiastes, Stress
Comments: This study reveals how empty, disillusioning, and downright depressing life can be. It points out that Solomon, with all his under-the-sun counsel, finally came back to the most foundational of all realities, the living God. As participants study the pages of Ecclesiastes, they will feel as though someone has been looking through their journals. Finally, they will realize that satisfaction doesn't come from living on the ragged edge, but only through a vital relationship with the Son.

Author: Swindoll, Charles R. **1071**
Series: Insight for Living
Title: *Minister Everyone Would Respect, A: A Study of 2 Corinthians 8-13*
Publisher: Word, 1989

Num. Sess.	Group Time	Num. Pgs.	Avg. Qst.	Price	Audience	Format	Bible Study
14	45-60	113	2	4.99	Mature Chrstn	Book	Book

Features: Intro to Study, Bibliography, Charts, Cassette Avail
★★ Personal Application Preparation Time: Med ISBN: 0-8499-8404-1
★★ Relationship Building Ldr. Guide Avail.: No Size: 5.50 x 8.50
Subjects: Bible Personalities, Church Life, Hope, Integrity, Leadership, Service, Suffering, 2 Corinthians
Comments: In this study of the latter half of his second letter to the Corinthian Christians, Paul spells out the crucial importance of ministering in a way that fosters trust. And by using his own life as an example, the apostle gives participants more than an unforgettable autobiography; he offers a model worth emulating. Paul reminds that confidence in ministry hinges on respect for the minister. A chart of Paul's ministry is helpful.

Author: Swindoll, Charles R. **1072**
Series: Insight for Living
Title: *Ministry Anyone Could Trust, A: A Study of 2 Corinthians 1-7*
Publisher: Word, 1989

Num. Sess.	Group Time	Num. Pgs.	Avg. Qst.	Price	Audience	Format	Bible Study
16	45-60	127	2	4.99	Mature Chrstn	Book	Book

Features: Intro to Study, Bibliography, Charts, Cassette Avail
★★ Personal Application Preparation Time: Med ISBN: 0-8499-8403-3
★★ Relationship Building Ldr. Guide Avail.: No Size: 5.50 x 8.50
Subjects: Church Life, Hope, Integrity, Leadership, Repentance, Service, Suffering, 2 Corinthians
Comments: This study addresses the disappointment and disillusionment found in human ministries, and directs participants to the Word of God for a trustworthy ministry model. The first seven chapters of 2 Corinthians offer the necessary ingredients: integrity, compassion, dedication, servanthood, realism, hope, and other qualities worth emulating. The study focuses on a renewed perspective of ministry at a time when many Christian leaders have failed personally and deviated from doctrine.

Author: Swindoll, Charles R. **1073**
Series: Insight for Living
Title: *Moses: God's Man For a Crisis*
Publisher: Word, 1985

Num. Sess.	Group Time	Num. Pgs.	Avg. Qst.	Price	Audience	Format	Bible Study
20	45-60	110	2	3.99	New Christian	Book	Charctr

Features: Intro to Study, Bibliography, Charts, Cassette Avail
★★ Personal Application Preparation Time: Med ISBN: 0-8499-8217-0
★★ Relationship Building Ldr. Guide Avail.: No Size: 5.50 x 8.50
Subjects: Bible Personalities, Faith, God, Service
Comments: This study uses the books of Exodus, Numbers, and Deuteronomy to present a living portrait of Moses, whose life is traced through three forty-year segments: from Egyptian Pharaoh-in-the-making, to obscure, forgotten shepherd, to leader of the Exodus. It centers on a man many Christians have never examined in-depth. The study also shows how God prepares people to be used through trust in Him alone.

Author: Swindoll, Charles R. **1074**
Series: Insight for Living
Title: *New Testament Postcards*
Publisher: Word, 1977

Num. Sess.	Group Time	Num. Pgs.	Avg. Qst.	Price	Audience	Format	Bible Study
6	45-60	46	2	3.99	New Christian	Book	Book

Features: Intro to Study, Bibliography, Digging Deeper Quest, Cassette Avail
★★★ Personal Application Preparation Time: Med ISBN: 0-8499-8287-1
★★ Relationship Building Ldr. Guide Avail.: No Size: 5.50 x 8.50
Subjects: Colossians/Philemon, Faith, Love, Marriage, New Testament, 1, 2 & 3 John/Jude
Comments: This six-lesson study features six "postcard" segments on Philemon, 2 John, 3 John, and Jude-(in three parts). The postcard to Philemon has a present-day postmark, with modern names on the forwarding address. In 2 John, hospitality is misplaced; it is missing completely in 3 John. Both carry the theme: balance love and truth. The theme of Jude is found in the admonition to "contend earnestly for the faith," and it makes it clear that apostasy is diametrically opposed to Christ.

Author: Swindoll, Charles R.   **1075**
Series: Insight for Living
Title: *Old Testament Characters*
Publisher: Word, 1973

Num. Sess.	Group Time	Num. Pgs.	Avg. Qst.	Price	Audience	Format	Bible Study
12	45-60	86	2	3.99	New Christian	Book	Charctr

Features: Intro to Study, Bibliography, Charts, Cassette Avail
  ★★ Personal Application Preparation Time: Med ISBN: 0-8499-8288-X
  ★★ Relationship Building Ldr. Guide Avail.: No Size: 5.50 x 8.50
Subjects: Bible Personalities, Emotions, Faith, Wisdom
Comments: This study, introducing ten Old Testament personalities, is encouraging because it shows God's truth reflected in the most obsure and unorthodox lives. This collection of Old Testament characters reveals the full range of human emotions, from tragedy to triumph. Each sketch will reaffirm faith, reveal helpful perspectives, and provide wisdom that will result in greater spiritual stability.

Author: Swindoll, Charles R.   **1076**
Series: Insight for Living
Title: *Practical Helps for a Hurting Church: A Study of 1 Corinthians*
Publisher: Word, 1973

Num. Sess.	Group Time	Num. Pgs.	Avg. Qst.	Price	Audience	Format	Bible Study
12	45-60	94	2	3.99	Mature Chrstn	Workbk	Book

Features: Intro to Study, Bibliography, Charts, Cassette Avail
  ★★ Personal Application Preparation Time: Med ISBN: 0-8499-8299-5
  ★★ Relationship Building Ldr. Guide Avail.: No Size: 5.50 x 8.50
Subjects: Church Life, Marriage, Sexual Issues, Singles Issues, 1 Corinthians
Comments: This study of 1 Corinthians 6:12-11:34 addresses some controversial issues. Paul offers principles inspired by the Holy Spirit that modern Christians should adopt. The study addresses practical problems, such as: "How should I handle my sexual desires?" "Is it OK to remain single?" "How can I handle an unhappy marriage?" "Are there taboos we should shun?" "Does observance of the Lord's Table have certain requirements?"

Author: Swindoll, Charles R.   **1077**
Series: Insight for Living
Title: *Preeminent Person of Christ, The: A Study of Hebrews 1-10*
Publisher: Word, 1989

Num. Sess.	Group Time	Num. Pgs.	Avg. Qst.	Price	Audience	Format	Bible Study
24	45-60	177	2	4.99	Mature Chrstn	Book	Book

Features: Intro to Study, Bibliography, Charts, Cassette Avail
  ★★ Personal Application Preparation Time: Med ISBN: 0-8499-8410-6
  ★★ Relationship Building Ldr. Guide Avail.: No Size: 5.50 x 8.50
Subjects: Faith, Hebrews, Victorious Living
Comments: This study of the first ten chapters of Hebrews magnifies the significance of Jesus Christ. He is presented as the Preeminent One, clearly superior to all others—created beings, including men and women in authority. As such, He deserves both highest praise and deepest devotion. This advanced study requires mental energy and spiritual motivation on the part of the participant.

Author: Swindoll, Charles R.   **1078**
Series: Insight for Living
Title: *Prophecy*
Publisher: Word, 1983

Num. Sess.	Group Time	Num. Pgs.	Avg. Qst.	Price	Audience	Format	Bible Study
10	45-60	44	2	3.99	Mature Chrstn	Book	Topical

Features: Intro to Study, Charts, Cassette Avail
  ★★ Personal Application Preparation Time: Med ISBN: 0-8499-8197-2
  ★★ Relationship Building Ldr. Guide Avail.: No Size: 5.50 x 8.50
Subjects: Christian Living, Heaven/Hell, Prophecy
Comments: This study includes ten balanced segments on how Bible prophecy relates to important future events, and how modern participants should live. God's prophetic plan is made clear, believable, and easy to understand. Each study is directly linked to specific passages in the Bible. The final study, titled "A Place Prepared for You," is a look at the characteristics of Heaven as found in Revelation 21-22.

Author: Swindoll, Charles R.   **1079**
Series: Insight for Living
Title: *Questions Christians Ask*
Publisher: Word, 1989

Num. Sess.	Group Time	Num. Pgs.	Avg. Qst.	Price	Audience	Format	Bible Study
12	45-60	109	2	3.99	New Christian	Book	Topical

Features: Intro to Study, Bibliography, Digging Deeper Quest, Charts, Cassette Avail
  ★★ Personal Application Preparation Time: Med ISBN: 0-8499-8405-X
  ★★ Relationship Building Ldr. Guide Avail.: No Size: 5.50 x 8.50
Subjects: Discipleship, Emotions, God, Relationships
Comments: This study examines a dozen crucial questions basic to the foundation of a relationship with God. The more we live, the deeper our level of curiosity. Who is this Jesus? Christ is raised, but what about me? How can I win over worry? Can "ordinary people" make a contribution? Why do we throw rocks at each other? This study uses Scripture to lead to answers that will strengthen participants' walk with, and closeness to, God.

Author: Swindoll, Charles R.   **1080**
Series: Insight for Living
Title: *Relating to Others in Love: A Study of Romans 12-16*
Publisher: Word, 1977

Num. Sess.	Group Time	Num. Pgs.	Avg. Qst.	Price	Audience	Format	Bible Study
16	45-60	84	2	3.99	New Christian	Book	Book

Features: Intro to Study, Bibliography, Digging Deeper Quest, Charts, Cassette Avail
  ★★ Personal Application Preparation Time: Med ISBN: 0-8499-8216-2
  ★★ Relationship Building Ldr. Guide Avail.: No Size: 5.50 x 8.50
Subjects: Faith, Love, Marriage, Relationships, Romans
Comments: This study of the final five chapters of Romans makes the Christian aware of the role of authentic demonstrative love, the kind of love that can draw people to Christianity. It focuses on relationships with those inside and outside the family, and includes guidelines for applying the Christian faith. Helpful chapters include: "You and Your Enemy," "Competent Christians," "When Trouble Is Brewing" and "Unseen Evil and Uplifting Good."

Author: Swindoll, Charles R. **1081**
Series: Insight for Living
Title: *Solomon*
Publisher: Word, 1978

Num. Sess.	Group Time	Num. Pgs.	Avg. Qst.	Price	Audience	Format	Bible Study
8	45-60	62	2	3.99	New Christian	Workbk	Charctr

Features: Intro to Study, Bibliography, Charts, Cassette Avail
★★ Personal Application Preparation Time: Med ISBN: 0-8499-8289-8
★★ Relationship Building Ldr. Guide Avail.: No Size: 5.50 x 8.50
Subjects: Bible Personalities, Morals, New Testament, Wisdom
Comments: The first six lessons in this study thoroughly examine King Solomon, his rich-and-famous lifestyle and his subsequent moral bankruptcy. The last two lessons, from 1 Peter, Ephesians, and 1 Corinthians, drive home the relevancy of this man's life. For modern believers, there are "soul conservation projects" from the New Testament, designed to prevent moral erosion from taking place. There is straight talk about temptation, sensuality, defiance, and cynicism.

Author: Swindoll, Charles R. **1082**
Series: Insight for Living
Title: *Spiritual Gifts*
Publisher: Word, 1972

Num. Sess.	Group Time	Num. Pgs.	Avg. Qst.	Price	Audience	Format	Bible Study
6	45-60	44	2	3.99	Mature Chrstn	Book	Topical

Features: Intro to Study, Bibliography, Charts, Cassette Avail
★★★ Personal Application Preparation Time: Med ISBN: 0-8499-8291-X
★★ Relationship Building Ldr. Guide Avail.: No Size: 5.50 x 8.50
Subjects: Church Life, Spiritual Gifts
Comments: This study describes spiritual gifts and discusses why God has given them and how to know which gift or gifts a Christian possesses. Understanding and applying gifts will enhance participants' walk with Christ as well as their involvement in a local church. Two helpful charts, one listing spiritual gifts found in Corinthians, Romans, and Ephesians and another listing categories—support, service, and sign—enhance the study. The final chapter provides guidelines for using spiritual gifts.

Author: Swindoll, Charles R. **1083**
Series: Insight for Living
Title: *Steadfast Christianity: A Study of Second Thessalonians*
Publisher: Word, 1986

Num. Sess.	Group Time	Num. Pgs.	Avg. Qst.	Price	Audience	Format	Bible Study
8	45-60	58	2	3.99	New Christian	Book	Book

Features: Intro to Study, Bibliography, Charts, Cassette Avail
★★ Personal Application Preparation Time: Med ISBN: 0-8499-8286-3
★★ Relationship Building Ldr. Guide Avail.: No Size: 5.50 x 8.50
Subjects: Hope, Obedience, 1 & 2 Thessalonians
Comments: This study on 2 Thessalonians, a powerful three-chapter letter, is packed full of affirmations and encouragement, in spite of hard times endured by Thessalonian Christians. It provides hope for modern Christians who feel persecuted, misunderstood, and "on trial" by others. Through consistency, readiness, determination, and perseverance, participants can find strength and encouragement.

Author: Swindoll, Charles R. **1084**
Series: Insight for Living
Title: *Stones of Remembrance*
Publisher: Word, 1987

Num. Sess.	Group Time	Num. Pgs.	Avg. Qst.	Price	Audience	Format	Bible Study
4	45-60	30	2	3.99	New Christian	Workbk	Charctr

Features: Intro to Study, Cassette Avail
★★ Personal Application Preparation Time: Med ISBN: 0-8499-8402-5
★★ Relationship Building Ldr. Guide Avail.: No Size: 5.50 x 8.50
Subjects: God, Holiness, Theology
Comments: This study recounts God's instructions to Joshua, to leave twelve stones from the Jordan River bed as a remembrance for future generations. When children yet to be born would ask their parents, "What do these stones mean?" they would be told of God's mighty acts and be encouraged to reverence Him forever. The stones stand to remind modern participants of the Lord's sovereignty, mercy, faithfulness, and holiness.

Author: Swindoll, Charles R. **1085**
Series: Insight for Living
Title: *Strengthening Your Grip: Essentials in an Aimless World*
Publisher: Word, 1980

Num. Sess.	Group Time	Num. Pgs.	Avg. Qst.	Price	Audience	Format	Bible Study
16	45-60	127	2	4.99	New Christian	Workbk	Topical

Features: Intro to Study, Bibliography, Cassette Avail
★★ Personal Application Preparation Time: Med ISBN: 0-8499-8407-6
★★ Relationship Building Ldr. Guide Avail.: No Size: 5.50 x 8.50
Subjects: Christian Living, Ethics, Family, Integrity, Morals, Obedience
Comments: This study focuses on certain essentials: keeping priorities straight, staying involved with others, striving for purity of life, maintaining integrity, and cherishing family life. These principles, based on eternal truths, form fixed points that keep the study on track. In order for Christians to live by moral and spiritual absolutes and renew their vigor, they need to "strengthen their grip" on timeless biblical truths.

Author: Swindoll, Charles R. **1086**
Series: Video Curriculum Resource
Title: *Strengthening Your Grip*
Publisher: Word, 1988

Num. Sess.	Group Time	Num. Pgs.	Avg. Qst.	Price	Audience	Format	Bible Study
6	75-105	N/A	Vry	179.99	New Christian	Video	Topical

Features: Intro to Leading a Study, Intro to Study, Scrpt Memory Helps, Follow Up, Cassette Avail, Video Study Guide, Book Avail
★★★★ Personal Application Preparation Time: None ISBN: 8-01-920079-7
★★★ Relationship Building Ldr. Guide Avail.: No Size: 11.0 x 12.0
Subjects: Christian Living, Ethics, Family, Integrity, Morals, Obedience
Comments: This three-part video study is divided into six sessions. Each session has three parts: "Losing Your Grip" considers questions about the film; "Catching Hold Again" emphasizes biblical concepts and guidelines needed for a firm grip; and "Strengthening Your Grip" reviews the film and suggests application. Lessons cover priorities, aging, leisure, godliness, attitudes, and authority. Participants are challenged to strengthen their grip on biblical truths necessary for living amid modern pessimism and apathy.

Author: Swindoll, Charles R.　　　　　　**1087**
Series: Insight for Living
Title: *Strong Reproofs for a Scandalous Church: A Study of 1 Corinthians*
Publisher: Word, 1973

Num. Sess.	Group Time	Num. Pgs.	Avg. Qst.	Price	Audience	Format	Bible Study
12	45-60	96	2	3.99	Mature Chrstn	Workbk	Book

Features: Intro to Study, Bibliography, Charts, Cassette Avail
　★★ Personal Application　Preparation Time: Med　ISBN: 0-8499-8298-7
　★★ Relationship Building　Ldr. Guide Avail.: No　　Size: 5.50 x 8.50
Subjects: Christian Living, Church Life, Money, Morals, 1 Corinthians
Comments: This study of 1 Corinthians 1:1-6:11 is based on the first part of Paul's first letter to the Corinthian church. Paul's strong words to the Corinthians, a stubborn body of carnal saints, are timely reproofs for Christians living in any modern society. Moral, legal, and carnal disorders are addressed in the study, including Paul's specific comments on domestic, social, ecclesiastical, practical, doctrinal, and financial issues.

Author: Swindoll, Charles R.　　　　　　**1088**
Series: Insight for Living
Title: *You and Your Child*
Publisher: Word, 1973

Num. Sess.	Group Time	Num. Pgs.	Avg. Qst.	Price	Audience	Format	Bible Study
14	45-60	89	2	3.99	Beginner	Book	Topical

Features: Intro to Study, Bibliography, Charts, Cassette Avail
　★★★ Personal Application　Preparation Time: Med　ISBN: 0-8499-8285-5
　★★ Relationship Building　Ldr. Guide Avail.: No　　Size: 5.50 x 8.50
Subjects: Parenting, Self-esteem
Comments: This study applies truths preserved in the Old and New Testaments to the task of raising children. It deals with parents' struggles: understanding a little one, dealing with his or her low self-esteem or strong will, proper discipline, cultivating a spiritual hunger for God, and sibling rivalry. The lessons demonstrate wisdom, sensitivity, and underlying principles.

Author: Swindoll, Charles R.　　　　　　**1089**
Series: Insight for Living
Title: *You and Your Problems*
Publisher: Word, 1989

Num. Sess.	Group Time	Num. Pgs.	Avg. Qst.	Price	Audience	Format	Bible Study
16	45-60	127	2	4.99	New Christian	Book	Topical

Features: Intro to Study, Bibliography, Charts, Cassette Avail
　★★ Personal Application　Preparation Time: Med　ISBN: 0-8499-8408-4
　★★ Relationship Building　Ldr. Guide Avail.: No　　Size: 5.50 x 8.50
Subjects: Christian Living, Emotions, Grief, Self-esteem, Victorious Living
Comments: This study deals with ideas on how to handle life's challenges. It offers practical advice based on Scripture and aimed directly at problems Christians face, including inferiority, temptation, depression, worry, anger, loneliness, death, resentment, and discouragement. These problems breed worry, ill health, and even more problems. The study points out that Christians are not different because they are free from problems, but because they have a power within them the world cannot claim.

Author: Swindoll, Luci　　　　　　**1090**
Series:
Title: *Celebrating Life: Catching the Thieves That Steal Your Joy*
Publisher: NavPress, 1989

Num. Sess.	Group Time	Num. Pgs.	Avg. Qst.	Price	Audience	Format	Bible Study
8	60-90	106	20	5.95	Beginner	Workbk	Topical

Features: Intro to Leading a Study
　★★★ Personal Application　Preparation Time: Med　ISBN: 0-89109-547-0
　★★ Relationship Building　Ldr. Guide Avail.: No　　Size: 5.25 x 8.50
Subjects: Emotions, Failure, Joy, Relationships, Stress
Comments: This study is for people who struggle with regret, resentment, disappointment, failure, discontentment, unpleasant relationships, and pressure. It focuses on harnessing these joy-stealers, dwelling on the positive instead of the negative, and counting blessings. Each lesson is divided into six sections: an opening quote, identification of joy-stealers, a Bible Study, quotations and comments from the author, a personal inventory, and putting the new discoveries to work.

Author: Synder, Linda　　　　　　**1091**
Series: Group's Active Bible Curriculum
Title: *Guys & Girls: Understanding Each Other*
Publisher: Group Publishing, 1991

Num. Sess.	Group Time	Num. Pgs.	Avg. Qst.	Price	Audience	Format	Bible Study
4	35-60	48	Vry	6.95	Beginner	Workbk	Topical

Features: Intro to Leading a Study, Intro to Study, Objectives, Study Overview, Ldr's Notes, Drawings, Handouts, Agenda, Publicity Ideas
　★★★★ Personal Application　Preparation Time: None　ISBN: 1-559-45110-6
　★★★★ Relationship Building　Ldr. Guide Avail.: No　　Size: 8.50 x 11.0
Subjects: Teens: Junior High, Teens: Relationships, Teens: Sexuality
Comments: This study helps junior high students unravel the mystery of the opposite sex. Its four lessons help them understand physical and emotional changes, examine how members of the opposite sex express their feelings, explore traditional sex roles and how they're changing, and learn how to relate in a positive way to the opposite sex. Instructions are easy to follow and provide multiple options for teachers. No student books are required.

Author: Taylor, Linda Chaffee, et al.　　　　　　**1092**
Series: Life Application
Title: *Ruth & Esther*
Publisher: Tyndale House, 1989

Num. Sess.	Group Time	Num. Pgs.	Avg. Qst.	Price	Audience	Format	Bible Study
13	60-90	82	11	4.95	New Christian	Workbk	Book

Features: Intro to Leading a Study, Intro to Study, Study Overview, Digging Deeper Quest, Full Scrpt Printed, Drawings, Charts, Maps, Cross Ref
　★★★ Personal Application　Preparation Time: Med　ISBN: 0-8423-2716-9
　★★★ Relationship Building　Ldr. Guide Avail.: No　　Size: 6.50 x 9.0
Subjects: Esther, Faith, God, Obedience, Ruth
Comments: This study, contains the complete texts of Ruth and Esther. Ruth shows how she, Naomi, and Boaz remained strong in character and true to God. Ruth, an encouraging study, shows that God is at work in the world and wants to use His people. Esther, the second of only two books named for women, demonstrates God's sovereignty and loving care for His people. Participants will realize that any Christian's life can make a difference.

Author: Thatcher, Martha   **1093**
Series:
Title: *When the Squeeze Is On: Growing Through Pressure*
Publisher: NavPress, 1987

Num. Sess.	Group Time	Num. Pgs.	Avg. Qst.	Price	Audience	Format	Bible Study
8	60-90	93	10	4.95	Beginner	Workbk	Topical

Features: Intro to Leading a Study, Intro to Study
★★★ Personal Application   Preparation Time: Med   ISBN: 0-89109-182-3
★★ Relationship Building   Ldr. Guide Avail.: No   Size: 5.50 x 8.50
Subjects: Bible Personalities, Christian Living, Decision Making, Money, Relationships, Time
Comments: This practical study on pressure offers scriptural reinforcement for making the best choices when facing life's pressures. Questions offer new insights about Bible characters like Moses, Samson, David, Daniel, and Peter. Time, relationships, responsibilities, and financial pressures are among topics covered. Participants learn to apply the principles to real-life situations. The study is effective for individuals and groups.

Author: Thompson, David A.   **1094**
Series:
Title: *Premarital Guide for Couples and Their Counselors, A*
Publisher: Bethany House, 1979

Num. Sess.	Group Time	Num. Pgs.	Avg. Qst.	Price	Audience	Format	Bible Study
6	45-60	80	Vry	5.95	Beginner	Workbk	Topical

Features: Intro to Study, Bibliography
★★★ Personal Application   Preparation Time: Med   ISBN: 0-87123-465-3
★★★ Relationship Building   Ldr. Guide Avail.: No   Size: 8.50 x 11.0
Subjects: Counseling, Ethics, Marriage, Money, Relationships, Sexual Issues
Comments: This premarital guide can be used by couples by themselves or with the assistance of a counselor or clergy. Its format is a detailed six-section fill-in-the-blank questionnaire on every facet of personal history and the current situation. Subject matter for both prospective bride and groom includes family and dating history; ideas on communication, sex, children, in-laws; values; finances; future employment, home, and friends; and the wedding.

Author: Timmons, Tim   **1095**
Series: Video Curriculum Resource
Title: *Maximum Marriage*
Publisher: Word, 1986

Num. Sess.	Group Time	Num. Pgs.	Avg. Qst.	Price	Audience	Format	Bible Study
4	75-105	N/A	Vry	159.99	Begi nner	Video	Topical

Features: Scrpt Memory Helps, Cartoons, Video Study Guide
★★★★ Personal Application   Preparation Time: None   ISBN: 8-01-940079-6
★★★ Relationship Building   Ldr. Guide Avail.: No   Size: 10.25 x 12.50
Subjects: Marriage, Young Marrieds
Comments: This four-session video study is for married people, from newlyweds to "emptynesters," and for those preparing for marriage. Topics include: "Why Marriage When You Can Live Together?" "The Eleven Battlegrounds of Marriage," "Why Are Women So Weird and Men So Strange?" and "How Do You Spell Relief?" The fifty-minute lessons inspire participants to enter a oneness with their mates, to build strong family units, to cherish and respect their spouses, and to communicate openly.

Author: Townsend, John   **1096**
Series:
Title: *Hiding from Love*
Publisher: NavPress, 1991

Num. Sess.	Group Time	Num. Pgs.	Avg. Qst.	Price	Audience	Format	Bible Study
8	60-90	96	12	5.95	New Christian	Workbk	No

Features: Intro to Leading a Study, Prayer Helps, Scrpt Memory Helps, Pre-discussion Quest, Digging Deeper Quest, Follow Up, Ldr's Notes, Persnl Study Quest, Book Avail
★★★★ Personal Application   Preparation Time: None   ISBN: 0-89109-645-0
★★★★ Relationship Building   Ldr. Guide Avail.: No   Size: 5.25 x 8.25
Subjects: Counseling, Emotions, Psychology, Relationships
Comments: This companion guide to Townsend's book by the same name can be used without reading the book. Each session includes an excerpt from the book as a basis for discussion. Topics include what hiding is and why we hide (we hide from relationships to protect our wounded parts), helpful versus harmful hiding, how to identify ways we hide, and how to come out of harmful hiding. Application questions help group members support each other in understanding and applying insights.

Author: Traina, Robert A.   **1097**
Series:
Title: *Methodical Bible Study*
Publisher: Zondervan, 1952

Num. Sess.	Group Time	Num. Pgs.	Avg. Qst.	Price	Audience	Format	Bible Study
4	-	270	N/A	15.95	Mature Chrstn	Book	No

Features: Intro to Study, Bibliography, No Grp Discussion Quest, Summary, Charts, Appendix
     Personal Application   Preparation Time: ISBN: 0-310-31230-2
     Relationship Building   Ldr. Guide Avail.:   Size: 5.75 x 8.75
Subjects: Bible Study, Small Group Resource
Comments: This guide to inductive Bible study, which involves comparing related Bible texts in order to let the Bible interpret itself—rather than approaching Scripture with predetermined notions of what it means. The study is divided into four parts: "Observation," "Interpretation," "Evaluation and Application," and "Correlation." Added inductive charts, a word study, outlines, and a teaching manual make this a helpful study aid.

Author: Travilla, Carol   **1098**
Series:
Title: *Caring Without Wearing*
Publisher: NavPress, 1990

Num. Sess.	Group Time	Num. Pgs.	Avg. Qst.	Price	Audience	Format	Bible Study
8	90-120	87	11	4.95	Beginner	Workbk	Topical

Features: Intro to Leading a Study, Prayer Helps, Ldr's Notes, Charts
★★★★ Personal Application   Preparation Time: None   ISBN: 0-89109-369-9
★★★★ Relationship Building   Ldr. Guide Avail.: No   Size: 5.50 x 8.50
Subjects: Caring, Christian Living, Support
Comments: This study hones skills that help Christians give quality care and comfort to the weary and burdened around them without wearing themselves out in the process. Lessons deal with ways to express understanding and acceptance and to listen to hurting people. Self-care to avoid burnout is covered and burnout warning signs are outlined. A case history used in the final lesson reviews the whole study. A list of "feeling words" and openers for active listening is helpful.

Author: Trenner, Rev. Ed., et al. **1099**
Series: Life Application
Title: *John*
Publisher: Tyndale House, 1989

Num. Sess.	Group Time	Num. Pgs.	Avg. Qst.	Price	Audience	Format	Bible Study
13	60-90	120	13	4.95	New Christian	Workbk	Book

Features: Intro to Leading a Study, Intro to Study, Study Overview, Digging Deeper Quest, Full Scrpt Printed, Drawings, Charts, Maps, Cross Ref
  ★★★ Personal Application Preparation Time: Med ISBN: 0-8423-2717-7
  ★★★ Relationship Building Ldr. Guide Avail.: No Size: 6.50 x 9.0
Subjects: Jesus: Life/Teaching, John
Comments: This study contains the complete text of John's Gospel, which is not a life of Christ but a powerful argument for the Incarnation, a conclusive demonstration that Jesus is the Heaven-sent Son of God and the only source of eternal life. The study has three main divisions: Jesus' birth and preparation; Jesus' message and ministry; and Jesus' death and resurrection. Questions lead to application of biblical truth and action plans.

Author: Truman, Bryan **1100**
Series: Global Issues
Title: *Basic Human Needs*
Publisher: InterVarsity, 1990

Num. Sess.	Group Time	Num. Pgs.	Avg. Qst.	Price	Audience	Format	Bible Study
6	45-60	48	12	4.95	Beginner	Workbk	Topical

Features: Intro to Leading a Study, Intro to Study, Bibliography, Follow Up
  ★ Personal Application Preparation Time: Low ISBN: 0-8308-4907-6
  ★ Relationship Building Ldr. Guide Avail.: No Size: 5.50 x 8.25
Subjects: Medical Issues, Social Issues
Comments: This six-week study discusses the magnitude of unhealthy world living conditions, and identifies ways in which participants can help see that people's needs are met. It describes the following: poverty; poor sanitation; shortage of food, water, and medical supplies; increases in preventable diseases; inadequate housing; illiteracy; population explosion; and insufficient educational facilities. Participants are challenged to effect change in these conditions.

Author: Ulland, Rose Mary **1101**
Series: Small Group Bible Studies
Title: *Only in Christ*
Publisher: Augsburg Publishing House, 1976

Num. Sess.	Group Time	Num. Pgs.	Avg. Qst.	Price	Audience	Format	Bible Study
4	60-75	16	21	0.95	New Christian	Book	Book

Features: Intro to Study, Bibliography, Prayer Helps
  ★★★ Personal Application Preparation Time: None ISBN:
  ★★★ Relationship Building Ldr. Guide Avail.: No Size: 8.50 x 5.50
Subjects: Church Life, Colossians/Philemon, False Teachers, Hope, Service, Suffering, Victorious Living
Comments: This short study teaches four lessons from Colossians. Paul wrote to the Christians at Colosse, a church primarily made up of Gentiles, because he had heard both good and bad news. Some reports gave reason for rejoicing; but there was also news of false teaching that posed a threat to the young church. The sufficiency and supremacy of Christ were being challenged, calling forth Paul's most decisive arguments to establish that completeness exists only in Christ.

Author: Underwood, Daniel R. **1102**
Series: Standard Bible Studies
Title: *Acts*
Publisher: Standard Publishing, 1987

Num. Sess.	Group Time	Num. Pgs.	Avg. Qst.	Price	Audience	Format	Bible Study
13	60-80	80	Vry	3.50	New Christian	Workbk	Book

Features: Intro to Leading a Study, Objectives, Digging Deeper Quest, Maps
  ★★ Personal Application Preparation Time: Low ISBN: 0-87403-185-0
  ★★ Relationship Building Ldr. Guide Avail.: Yes Size: 8.50 x 11.0
Subjects: Acts, Church Life, Holy Spirit
Comments: This thirteen-lesson workbook, companion to John W. Wade's study of Acts, focuses on main Scripture ideas, and is comprehensive. Each lesson features learning goals, lesson aims, and key ideas. Lessons begin with introductory activities—suggested as homework—followed by Bible study, and "Digging Deeper" and "What do you think?" questions. Only the leader in a small group setting needs this companion book.

Author: Underwood, David A. **1103**
Series: Standard Bible Studies
Title: *Luke*
Publisher: Standard Publishing, 1986

Num. Sess.	Group Time	Num. Pgs.	Avg. Qst.	Price	Audience	Format	Bible Study
13	60-80	80	Vry	3.50	New Christian	Workbk	Book

Features: Intro to Leading a Study, Objectives, Digging Deeper Quest
  ★★ Personal Application Preparation Time: Low ISBN: 0-87403-183-4
  ★★ Relationship Building Ldr. Guide Avail.: Yes Size: 8.50 x 11.0
Subjects: Jesus: Life/Teaching, Luke
Comments: This thirteen-lesson workbook, a companion to Lewis Foster's study of Luke, focuses on four parts of Jesus' life: the beginning, Christ's ministry in Galilee, the way to Jerusalem, and the final week and Christ's resurrection. Each lesson includes an outline, Bible study, and summary and application questions. Only the leader in a small group setting needs this companion book.

Author: Underwood, Jonathan **1104**
Series: Standard Bible Studies
Title: *First Corinthians*
Publisher: Standard Publishing, 1987

Num. Sess.	Group Time	Num. Pgs.	Avg. Qst.	Price	Audience	Format	Bible Study
13	60-80	76	Vry	3.50	New Christian	Workbk	Book

Features: Intro to Leading a Study, Objectives, Digging Deeper Quest
  ★★ Personal Application Preparation Time: Low ISBN: 0-87403-187-7
  ★★ Relationship Building Ldr. Guide Avail.: Yes Size: 8.50 x 11.0
Subjects: Church Life, Relationships, Worship, 1 Corinthians
Comments: This thirteen-lesson workbook, companion to the author's study of 1 Corinthians, focuses on problems of church unity, relationships, Christian liberty, worship assembly, and more. Each lesson features learning goals, lesson aims, and key ideas. Lessons begin with introductory activities, followed by Bible study, and "Digging Deeper" and "What do you think?" questions. Only the leader in a small group setting needs this companion guide.

Author: Underwood, Jonathan   **1105**
Series: Standard Bible Studies
Title: *Matthew*
Publisher: Standard Publishing, 1986

Num. Sess.	Group Time	Num. Pgs.	Avg. Qst.	Price	Audience	Format	Bible Study
26	60-80	96	Vry	3.50	New Christian	Workbk	Book

Features: Intro to Leading a Study, Objectives, Digging Deeper Quest, Charts
  ★★ Personal Application Preparation Time: Low ISBN: 0-87403-181-8
  ★★ Relationship Building Ldr. Guide Avail.: Yes Size: 8.50 x 11.0
Subjects: Faith, Jesus: Life/Teaching, Matthew
Comments: This twenty-six lesson workbook, a companion to LeRoy Lawson's study of Matthew, focuses on main Scripture ideas, such as the authority of the Lord, signs of true faith, and biblical questions. Each lesson features learning goals, lesson aims, and key ideas and begins with introductory activities, which are followed by Bible study, "Digging Deeper" questions, and "What do you think?" questions. Only the leader in a small group setting needs this companion book.

Author: Vaughn, Joe & Loren L. Nielsen   **1106**
Series: Small Group Bible Studies
Title: *Issues That Still Matter*
Publisher: Augsburg Publishing House, 1980

Num. Sess.	Group Time	Num. Pgs.	Avg. Qst.	Price	Audience	Format	Bible Study
6	60-75	24	14	1.15	New Christian	Book	Book

Features: Intro to Study, Prayer Helps
  ★★★★ Personal Application Preparation Time: None ISBN:
  ★★★★ Relationship Building Ldr. Guide Avail.: No Size: 8.50 x 5.50
Subjects: Relationships, 1 Corinthians
Comments: This small pamphlet includes six sessions on 1 Corinthians, reviewing advice Paul gave to traveling missionaries who were developing factions among themselves. They were allowing old, ugly problems from their former pagan lives to continue to manifest themselves. He wrote a very practical letter that deals with issues that still matter today.

Author: Veerman, David R.   **1107**
Series: Any Old Time
Title: *Any Old Time (Book 2)*
Publisher: Victor Books, 1984

Num. Sess.	Group Time	Num. Pgs.	Avg. Qst.	Price	Audience	Format	Bible Study
15	30-45	80	Vry	9.99	Beginner	Book	Topical

Features: Intro to Study, Objectives, Bibliography, Prayer Helps, Study Overview, Digging Deeper Quest, Ldr's Notes
  ★★★★ Personal Application Preparation Time: None ISBN: 0-88207-596-9
  ★★★★ Relationship Building Ldr. Guide Avail.: No Size: 8.50 x 11.0
Subjects: Teens: Christian Liv, Teens: Decisions, Teens: Discipleship, Teens: Junior High, Teens: Senior High
Comments: This second book in the "Any Old Time" series contains an assortment of topical sessions in four general categories: Christian living, Christian growth, basic doctrine, and relationships. Each session is relevant, easy to prepare, and written to get group members involved. Topics include moral choices, loneliness, security and values, anger and hostility, self-acceptance, quiet time, mediocrity, spiritual self-examination, misconception about God, purpose of the Christian life, prayer, parents, and more.

Author: Veerman, David R.   **1108**
Series: Any Old Time
Title: *Any Old Time (Book 1)*
Publisher: Victor Books, 1984

Num. Sess.	Group Time	Num. Pgs.	Avg. Qst.	Price	Audience	Format	Bible Study
15	30-45	80	Vry	9.99	Beginner	Book	Topical

Features: Intro to Study, Objectives, Bibliography, Prayer Helps, Study Overview, Digging Deeper Quest, Summary, Ldr's Notes
  ★★★★ Personal Application Preparation Time: None ISBN: 0-88207-595-0
  ★★★★ Relationship Building Ldr. Guide Avail.: No Size: 8.50 x 11.0
Subjects: Teens: Christian Liv, Teens: Discipleship, Teens:Drugs/Drinking, Teens: Junior High, Teens: Peer Pressure, Teens: Senior High, Teens: Sexuality
Comments: These fifteen creative lessons for youth are short on preparation time and long on content. Each contains opening games, warm-up activities, biblical application, and a wrap-up section to help teens remember what they have learned. Topics include drinking, guidelines on sex, family and parents, dating, witnessing, finding God's will, temptation, peer pressure, cheating, obedience and discipleship, the Incarnation, faith, honesty and openness, self-awareness, and priorities.

Author: Veerman, David R.   **1109**
Series: Any Old Time
Title: *Any Old Time (Book 12)*
Publisher: Victor Books, 1989

Num. Sess.	Group Time	Num. Pgs.	Avg. Qst.	Price	Audience	Format	Bible Study
15	30-45	80	Vry	9.99	New Christian	Book	Topical

Features: Intro to Study, Objectives, Bibliography, Prayer Helps, Study Overview, Digging Deeper Quest, Ldr's Notes
  ★★★★ Personal Application Preparation Time: None ISBN: 0-89693-722-4
  ★★★★ Relationship Building Ldr. Guide Avail.: No Size: 8.50 x 11.0
Subjects: Teens: Christian Liv, Teens: Discipleship, Teens: Junior High, Teens: Senior High
Comments: These fifteen creative lessons for youth are short on preparation time and long on content. Each contains opening games, warm-up activities, biblical application, and a wrap-up section to help teens remember what they have learned. Topics include Jesus, the Bible, grace, Satan, witnessing, selfishness, conflict, worship, stewardship, commitment, learning to listen, fellowship, and old age.

Author: Veerman, David R.   **1110**
Series: Any Old Time
Title: *Any Old Time (Book 10)*
Publisher: Victor Books, 1988

Num. Sess.	Group Time	Num. Pgs.	Avg. Qst.	Price	Audience	Format	Bible Study
15	30-45	79	Vry	9.99	New Christian	Book	Topical

Features: Intro to Study, Objectives, Bibliography, Prayer Helps, Study Overview, Digging Deeper Quest, Ldr's Notes, Charts
  ★★★★ Personal Application Preparation Time: None ISBN: 0-89693-454-3
  ★★★★ Relationship Building Ldr. Guide Avail.: No Size: 8.50 x 11.0
Subjects: Teens: Christian Liv, Teens: Discipleship, Teens: Junior High, Teens: Prayer, Teens: Senior High
Comments: These fifteen creative youth-meeting lessons are short on preparation time and long on content. Each contains opening games, warm-up activities, biblical application, and a wrap-up section to help teens remember what they have learned. Topics include conversion, effective prayer, consistent faith, values and priorities, ways to witness, enduring trials, facing the future, true spirituality, real commitment, apologetics, goals in life, and social concern.

Author: Veerman, David R.   **1111**
Series: Any Old Time
Title: *Any Old Time (Book 6)*
Publisher: Victor Books, 1986

Num. Sess.	Group Time	Num. Pgs.	Avg. Qst.	Price	Audience	Format	Bible Study
15	30-45	80	Vry	9.99	New Christian	Book	Topical

Features: Intro to Study, Objectives, Bibliography, Prayer Helps, Study Overview, Digging Deeper Quest, Ldr's Notes, Charts
★★★★ Personal Application   Preparation Time: None   ISBN: 0-89693-510-8
★★★★ Relationship Building   Ldr. Guide Avail.: No   Size: 8.50 x 11.0
Subjects: Teens: Christian Liv, Teens: Discipleship, Teens: Friends, Teens: Junior High, Teens: Senior High
Comments: These fifteen sessions help young people dig into the following issues: the truth of God's Word, evil, love, and life. Each session contains opening games, warm-up activities, biblical application, and a wrap-up section to help teens remember what they have learned. Topics include the Incarnation, Satan, the Church, identity, hope, conflict, lordship of Christ, witnessing, guilt and forgiveness, death, convictions, friends, and dating.

Author: Veerman, David R.   **1112**
Series: Any Old Time
Title: *Any Old Time (Book 11)*
Publisher: Victor Books, 1989

Num. Sess.	Group Time	Num. Pgs.	Avg. Qst.	Price	Audience	Format	Bible Study
15	30-45	80	Vry	9.99	New Christian	Book	Topical

Features: Intro to Study, Objectives, Bibliography, Prayer Helps, Study Overview, Digging Deeper Quest, Ldr's Notes
★★★★ Personal Application   Preparation Time: None   ISBN: 0-89693-673-2
★★★★ Relationship Building   Ldr. Guide Avail.: No   Size: 8.50 x 11.0
Subjects: Teens: Christian Liv, Teens: Discipleship, Teens: Junior High, Teens: Peer Pressure, Teens: Senior High
Comments: This book provides fifteen fun and informative studies on subjects vital to modern young people: knowing God's will, the Holy Spirit, the Second Coming, handling frustrations, self-image, obedience, depression, foundations for growth, change, honesty, discipleship, love, family relationships, peer pressure, and competition. Each session contains opening games, warm-up activities, biblical application, and a wrap-up section.

Author: Veerman, David R.   **1113**
Series: Any Old Time
Title: *Any Old Time (Book 7)*
Publisher: Victor Books, 1987

Num. Sess.	Group Time	Num. Pgs.	Avg. Qst.	Price	Audience	Format	Bible Study
15	30-45	80	Vry	9.99	New Christian	Book	Topical

Features: Intro to Study, Objectives, Bibliography, Prayer Helps, Study Overview, Digging Deeper Quest, Ldr's Notes, Charts
★★★★ Personal Application   Preparation Time: None   ISBN: 0-89693-560-4
★★★★ Relationship Building   Ldr. Guide Avail.: No   Size: 8.50 x 11.0
Subjects: Teens: Christian Liv, Teens: Discipleship, Teens: Junior High, Teens: Senior High
Comments: This book can be used at anytime, in any-sized group, and in a variety of settings. Features include creative warm-up activities, ice-breakers, brainteasers, role playing activities, games, and methods to involve youth. Fifteen sessions on getting young people caught up in God's Word deal with topics like belief, the Resurrection, the Second Coming, self-acceptance, trusting God, resisting temptation, loving others, parents, Christian fellowship, having right motives, and putting faith to work.

Author: Veerman, Rev. David R., et al.   **1114**
Series: Life Application
Title: *Acts*
Publisher: Tyndale House, 1989

Num. Sess.	Group Time	Num. Pgs.	Avg. Qst.	Price	Audience	Format	Bible Study
13	60-90	136	14	4.95	New Christian	Workbk	Book

Features: Intro to Leading a Study, Intro to Study, Study Overview, Digging Deeper Quest, Full Scrpt Printed, Drawings, Charts, Maps, Cross Ref
★★★ Personal Application   Preparation Time: Med   ISBN: 0-8423-2730-4
★★★ Relationship Building   Ldr. Guide Avail.: No   Size: 6.50 x 9.0
Subjects: Acts, Bible Personalities, Church Life
Comments: This study contains the complete text of Acts, which provides an accurate account of the birth and growth of the early Christian Church. It is divided into two main sections: Peter's ministry (1:1—12:25), including the establishment and expansion of the Church; and Paul's ministry (13:1—28:31), including the first missionary journey, meeting of the church council, second and third missionary journeys, and Paul himself on trial. Questions lead to application of biblical truth and action plans.

Author: Vinger, Theodore J.   **1115**
Series: Small Group Bible Studies
Title: *Free to Be Responsible*
Publisher: Augsburg Publishing House, 1975

Num. Sess.	Group Time	Num. Pgs.	Avg. Qst.	Price	Audience	Format	Bible Study
4	60-75	16	18	0.95	New Christian	Book	Book

Features: Intro to Study, Bibliography, Prayer Helps, Digging Deeper Quest
★★★ Personal Application   Preparation Time: None   ISBN:
★★★ Relationship Building   Ldr. Guide Avail.: No   Size: 8.50 x 5.50
Subjects: Church Life, Pastoral Epistles, 1 & 2 Timothy/Titus
Comments: This small pamphlet includes four sessions on 1 Timothy. The three Pastoral Epistles in the New Testament, 1 and 2 Timothy and Titus, are concerned with spiritual care and guidance for the congregation and its individual members. First Timothy was written to those who would be responsible Christians in a time of dizzying conflicts. This study is a chapter-by-chapter presentation. The questions marked with a star are suggested for use in group discussion.

Author: Vinger, Theodore J.   **1116**
Series: Small Group Bible Studies
Title: *No Longer a Stranger*
Publisher: Augsburg Publishing House, 1975

Num. Sess.	Group Time	Num. Pgs.	Avg. Qst.	Price	Audience	Format	Bible Study
4	60-75	16	13	0.95	New Christian	Book	Book

Features: Intro to Study, Prayer Helps, Digging Deeper Quest
★★ Personal Application   Preparation Time: None   ISBN:
★★ Relationship Building   Ldr. Guide Avail.: No   Size: 8.50 x 5.50
Subjects: Bible Personalities, Ruth
Comments: This small pamphlet includes four sessions on Ruth, an Old Testament book that provides an important link in the ancestry of Jesus Christ. The four chapters of the book, which become the four sessions, cover the Israelites' return to Judah, the meeting of Ruth and Boaz, the next of kin claim, and the birth of Obed. A story of simple, everyday occurrences, as a foreigner is welcomed among God's people; it helps remind participants that Jesus Christ is for all people everywhere.

Author: Wald, Oletta   **1117**
Series: Small Group Bible Studies
Title: *Ask*
Publisher: Augsburg Publishing House, 1978

Num. Sess.	Group Time	Num. Pgs.	Avg. Qst.	Price	Audience	Format	Bible Study
4	60-75	16	17	0.95	New Christian	Book	Topical

Features: Intro to Study, Prayer Helps
  ★★★ Personal Application Preparation Time: None ISBN:
  ★★★ Relationship Building Ldr. Guide Avail.: No   Size: 8.50 x 5.50
Subjects: Forgiveness, Prayer
Comments: This small pamphlet includes four sessions on prayer. Session 1, "What Shall I Say?" considers prayers of thanksgiving and praise. Session 2, "What Shall I Say When I Have Needs?" considers prayers of petition, or asking for something. Session 3, "What Shall I Say When Others Have Needs?" considers prayers of intercession. Session 4, "What Shall I Say When I Have Done Wrong?" Considers prayers of confession and forgiveness. This is a practical short study for small groups.

Author: Walker, Catherine B.   **1118**
Series:
Title: *Bible Workbook: Volume 2 (New Testament)*
Publisher: Moody Press, 1943

Num. Sess.	Group Time	Num. Pgs.	Avg. Qst.	Price	Audience	Format	Bible Study
26	60-75	72	Vry	5.95	Beginner	Workbk	Topical

Features: Intro to Study, Ldr's Notes, Maps
  ★★★ Personal Application Preparation Time: Med ISBN: 0-8024-0752-8
  ★★ Relationship Building Ldr. Guide Avail.: No Size: 8.0 x 10.50
Subjects: Bible Study, New Testament
Comments: This study, second of a two-volume series, covers the entire New Testament. It's a systematic, individual study in which participants learn by doing—information is given and questions test their understanding. An introductory section gives a good review of the Bible and how the study is developed, and it shows students how to make the most of the study. Each lesson comprises a series of questions based on Bible study. The study is appropriate for individuals, or groups of any size.

Author: Walker, Catherine B.   **1119**
Series:
Title: *Bible Workbook: Volume 1—Old Testament*
Publisher: Moody Press, 1943

Num. Sess.	Group Time	Num. Pgs.	Avg. Qst.	Price	Audience	Format	Bible Study
26	60-75	72	Vry	5.95	Beginner	Workbk	Topical

Features: Intro to Study, Scrpt Memory Helps, Maps
  ★★★ Personal Application Preparation Time: Med ISBN: 0-8024-0751-X
  ★★ Relationship Building Ldr. Guide Avail.: No Size: 8.0 x 10.50
Subjects: Bible Study, Old Testament
Comments: This study, first of a two-volume series, covers the entire Old Testament. It's a systematic, individual study in which participants learn by doing—information is given and questions test their understanding. An introductory section gives a good review of the Bible and how the study is developed, and it shows students how to make the most of the study. Each lesson comprises a series of questions based on Bible study. The study is appropriate for individuals or groups of any size.

Author: Walter, Donna   **1120**
Series: Discover Your Bible
Title: *Discover: Prayer*
Publisher: Church Development Resources, 1986

Num. Sess.	Group Time	Num. Pgs.	Avg. Qst.	Price	Audience	Format	Bible Study
8	60-75	56	7	1.35	Beginner	Workbk	Book

Features: Intro to Study, Summary, Full Scrpt Printed
  ★★★ Personal Application Preparation Time: None ISBN:
  ★★ Relationship Building Ldr. Guide Avail.: Yes Size: 5.50 x 8.50
Subjects: Faith, God, Obedience, Prayer
Comments: This inductive study on prayer helps participants discover who God is and why it is important to pray to Him. The prayers of Jesus and other Bible characters serve as models. Attitudes and faithfulness in prayer are stressed as well as content. In addition to learning prayer, participants will come to know God, His identity and His relationship with people. A comprehensive leader's guide is available.

Author: Wamberg, Steve & Annie   **1121**
Series: Group's Active Bible Curriculum
Title: *Drugs & Drinking*
Publisher: Group Publishing, 1990

Num. Sess.	Group Time	Num. Pgs.	Avg. Qst.	Price	Audience	Format	Bible Study
4	35-60	48	Vry	6.95	Beginner	Workbk	Topical

Features: Intro to Leading a Study, Intro to Study, Objectives, Study Overview, Ldr's Notes, Drawings, Handouts, Agenda, Publicity Ideas
  ★★★★ Personal Application Preparation Time: None ISBN: 1-559-45118-1
  ★★★★ Relationship Building Ldr. Guide Avail.: No Size: 8.50 x 11.0
Subjects: Teens:Drugs/Drinking, Teens: Junior High
Comments: This four-lesson study helps young people learn to make Christian decisions about drugs and drinking. Participants will explore the lure of drugs and drinking, weigh the options of having just one drink, and learn to avoid drugs and beat the temptation. The studies can be used in a Bible class or youth meeting. Activities and Bible studies are included as separate reproducible sheets. Instructions are easy to follow and provide multiple options for teachers. No student books are required.

Author: Wamberg, Steve   **1122**
Series: Group's Active Bible Curriculum
Title: *Is God Unfair?*
Publisher: Group Publishing, 1990

Num. Sess.	Group Time	Num. Pgs.	Avg. Qst.	Price	Audience	Format	Bible Study
4	35-60	48	Vry	6.95	New Christian	Workbk	Charctr

Features: Intro to Leading a Study, Intro to Study, Objectives, Study Overview, Ldr's Notes, Drawings, Handouts, Agenda, Publicity Ideas
  ★★★★ Personal Application Preparation Time: None ISBN: 1-559-45108-4
  ★★★★ Relationship Building Ldr. Guide Avail.: No Size: 8.50 x 11.0
Subjects: Teens: Emotions, Teens: Junior High, Teens: Theology
Comments: This study prepares junior high youth to answer tough questions about God. The four lessons help students grapple with the question: Does God care? They will understand that God loves them no matter how unlovable they feel; learn how to find God's love in the midst of tragedy and suffering; and discover how to turn anger at God into trust in Him. Instructions are easy to follow and provide multiple options for teachers. No student books are required.

Author: Ward, Ted　　　　　　　　　　　　**1123**
Series:
Title: *Values Begin at Home*
Publisher: Victor Books, 1979

Num. Sess.	Group Time	Num. Pgs.	Avg. Qst.	Price	Audience	Format	Bible Study
13	60-75	144	N/A	7.99	New Christian	Book	Topical

Features: Intro to Study, Bibliography, Charts, Glossary
★★★★ Personal Application　Preparation Time: Med　ISBN: 0-89693-646-5
★★★ Relationship Building　Ldr. Guide Avail.: Yes　Size: 5.50 x 8.0
Subjects: Parenting, Teens: Decisions, Teens: Ethics
Comments: This study concerns the enormous responsibility facing Christian parents of helping their children learn to make positive moral choices. Moral character does not result from building fences around children, but from supervising their interaction with parents, adults, and other children. Participants review children's built-in capability to make decisions about right and wrong, their need for encouragement, discipline, and a well-furnished foundation of responsible moral conduct.

Author: Warren, Richard　　　　　　　　　　**1124**
Series:
Title: *Answers to Life's Difficult Questions*
Publisher: Victor Books, 1985

Num. Sess.	Group Time	Num. Pgs.	Avg. Qst.	Price	Audience	Format	Bible Study
13	60-75	130	N/A	6.99	Beginner	Book	Topical

Features: Intro to Study
★★★ Personal Application　Preparation Time: Low　ISBN: 0-89693-395-4
★★★ Relationship Building　Ldr. Guide Avail.: Yes　Size: 5.50 x 8.0
Subjects: Bible Personalities, Christian Living, Emotions, Friendships, Loneliness, Relationships, Stress, Success, Victorious Living
Comments: This study uses the lives of Bible characters to show how to make the most of difficult circumstances. Difficult questions facing both Christians and nonChristians include stress, discouragement, depression, and loneliness. Relationships with spouses, children, friends, and business associates are often discouraging. This study can produce two results: learning God's principles for successful living; and believing God can use anyone in a significant way.

Author: Warren, Richard & William A. Shell　**1125**
Series:
Title: *12 Dynamic Bible Study Methods*
Publisher: Victor Books, 1981

Num. Sess.	Group Time	Num. Pgs.	Avg. Qst.	Price	Audience	Format	Bible Study
12	-	250	N/A	8.99		Book	No

Features: Intro to Study, Bibliography, Digging Deeper Quest, Charts, Appendix
　　Personal Application　Preparation Time:　　ISBN: 0-88207-815-1
　　Relationship Building　Ldr. Guide Avail.:　　Size: 5.50 x 8.0
Subjects: Small Group Resource
Comments: This book describes twelve tested ways to study and personally apply the Word of God. Each chapter covers a method in the same basic format: a condensed outline of the method, a definition, a rationale, the procedure for each method, an example, and suggestions for beginning. Methods covered include: devotional, chapter summary, character quality, thematic, biographical, topical, word study, book background, book survey, and more. Each chapter stands alone.

Author: Webb, Jana L.　　　　　　　　　　**1126**
Series: Global Issues
Title: *Economic Justice*
Publisher: InterVarsity, 1990

Num. Sess.	Group Time	Num. Pgs.	Avg. Qst.	Price	Audience	Format	Bible Study
6	45-60	48	11	4.95	Beginner	Workbk	Topical

Features: Intro to Leading a Study, Intro to Study, Bibliography, Follow Up
★★ Personal Application　Preparation Time: Low　ISBN: 0-8308-4906-8
★★ Relationship Building　Ldr. Guide Avail.: No　Size: 5.50 x 8.25
Subjects: Money, Social Issues
Comments: This six-week study focuses on global economic injustice. The introduction reinforces its point of reference with statistics, information on "haves" and "have nots," and a recommended response from God's people. Lesson titles include: "An Unjust World," "Money and God's Servants," "The Global Community," "Christians Mobilize," and more. Group leaders should read the introduction before selection, to determine its appropriateness for their group.

Author: Weiner, Bob & Rose　　　　　　　　**1127**
Series:
Title: *Bible Studies for a Firm Foundation*
Publisher: Maranatha Publications, 1980

Num. Sess.	Group Time	Num. Pgs.	Avg. Qst.	Price	Audience	Format	Bible Study
22	60-90	128	Vry	6.95	New Christian	Workbk	Topical

Features:
★★ Personal Application　Preparation Time: Med　ISBN: 0-938558-00-5
★★ Relationship Building　Ldr. Guide Avail.: No　Size: 8.50 x 11.0
Subjects: Baptism, Beliefs, Faith, Holy Spirit, Jesus: Life/Teaching, Repentance
Comments: This study deals with the basics—the foundation of Christian belief and faith—and prepares participants for growth once these fundamental issues are dealt with. Beginning with Atonement, the study covers repentance, baptism in water and the Holy Spirit, God's provision for healing, the Great Commision, the last days and Christ's return, and more. It closes with a lesson on God's predetermined purpose versus man's free will. Each lesson includes a series of questions and answers.

Author: Weiner, Bob & Rose　　　　　　　　**1128**
Series:
Title: *Bible Studies for the Life of Excellence: A Study of James*
Publisher: Maranatha Publications, 1981

Num. Sess.	Group Time	Num. Pgs.	Avg. Qst.	Price	Audience	Format	Bible Study
12	60-75	60	20	4.95	New Christian	Workbk	Book

Features: Intro to Study
★★ Personal Application　Preparation Time: Med　ISBN: 0-938558-04-8
★★ Relationship Building　Ldr. Guide Avail.: No　Size: 8.50 x 11.0
Subjects: Faith, Hope, James, Service
Comments: This twelve-lesson study of James, a verse-by-verse exposition, deals with the essence of Christianity—faith, hope, and love. It exhorts, comforts, and encourages participants; and it warns and reproofs as well. It challenges Christians to action, to be "doers" and not just "hearers" of the Word. It demonstrates God's love, and it ends with the hope we share for eternity. Each lesson is composed of a series of questions, and all answers are together in the back of the book.

Author: Weiner, Bob & Rose   **1129**
Series:
Title: *Bible Studies on the Overcoming Life*
Publisher: Maranatha Publications, 1981

Num. Sess.	Group Time	Num. Pgs.	Avg. Qst.	Price	Audience	Format	Bible Study
20	60-90	113	Vry	6.95	New Christian	Workbk	Topical

Features:
  ★★ Personal Application Preparation Time: Med ISBN: 0-938558-01-3
  ★★ Relationship Building Ldr. Guide Avail.: No Size: 8.50 x 11.0
Subjects: Christian Living, Holy Spirit, Suffering, Victorious Living
Comments: In twenty lessons, this study effectively leads participants through the whole Christian experience. Four series take them from the cross to good works. The first series—"Brokenness"—deals with the path of the cross, personal trial, suffering for others, living in the Spirit, and walking in the resurrection. The second, "Righteousness," deals with becoming new creations and taking on the nature of God. The third and fourth series deal with practical Christian living and good works. Answers given.

Author: Weiner, Bob & Rose   **1130**
Series:
Title: *Bible Studies for the Lovers of God: A Study of Philippians*
Publisher: Maranatha Publications, 1980

Num. Sess.	Group Time	Num. Pgs.	Avg. Qst.	Price	Audience	Format	Bible Study
5	60-90	44	Vry	4.95	New Christian	Workbk	Topical

Features: Intro to Study, Summary
  ★★ Personal Application Preparation Time: Med ISBN: 0-938558-03-X
  ★★ Relationship Building Ldr. Guide Avail.: No Size: 8.50 x 11.0
Subjects: God, Joy, Philippians, Prison Epistles, Relationships, Service, Suffering
Comments: This five-lesson study of Philippians covers four basic areas of the Christian experience. This experience is full of Christ, joy, holy-mindedness, and fellowship. The lesson titles include: "The All-Sufficiency of Christ," "The True Servants of God," "The High Calling of God," and "Our Christian Responsibility." Each lesson comprises a series of questions, and all answers are together in the back of the book.

Author: Weiner, Bob & Rose   **1131**
Series:
Title: *Bible Studies for the Preparation of the Bride*
Publisher: Maranatha Publications, 1980

Num. Sess.	Group Time	Num. Pgs.	Avg. Qst.	Price	Audience	Format	Bible Study
34	60-90	230	Vry	7.95	New Christian	Workbk	Book

Features: Intro to Study
  ★★ Personal Application Preparation Time: Med ISBN: 0-88270-471-0
  ★★ Relationship Building Ldr. Guide Avail.: No Size: 8.50 x 11.0
Subjects: Love, Marriage, Song of Solomon
Comments: This study, in an effective workbook format, takes participants through the Song of Solomon. It begins with good instructions on how to read the Song of Solomon, then follows with an introduction explaining the book. Thirty-four lessons complete a verse-by-verse, exhaustive study of the entire work, from the initial song of love to the bride making herself ready. Each lesson comprises a series of questions, and all answers are listed together in the back of the book.

Author: Weiner, Bob & Rose   **1132**
Series:
Title: *Jesus Brings New Life*
Publisher: Maranatha Publications, 1989

Num. Sess.	Group Time	Num. Pgs.	Avg. Qst.	Price	Audience	Format	Bible Study
7	90-120	31	23	2.0	Beginner	Workbk	Charctr

Features: Intro to Study, Scrpt Memory Helps, Appendix
  ★★ Personal Application Preparation Time: Med ISBN: 0-938558-24-2
  ★★ Relationship Building Ldr. Guide Avail.: No Size: 5.50 x 8.50
Subjects: Baptism, Commitments, Evangelism, Faith, Holy Spirit, Repentance, Youth Life
Comments: This study introduces the Christian faith to college-age adults. A lesson on the authority of God's Word is followed by lessons covering atonement, faith toward God, repentance, baptism in water, baptism in the Holy Spirit, and commitment to Christ. This study can be used either one-on-one or in a group. If used in a group, homework will help facilitate group interaction.

Author: Weising, Gwen   **1133**
Series: Enrichment Series
Title: *First John: A Pattern for Christian Living*
Publisher: Aglow, 1988

Num. Sess.	Group Time	Num. Pgs.	Avg. Qst.	Price	Audience	Format	Bible Study
8	60-75	62	Vry	2.95	New Christian	Workbk	Book

Features: Intro to Study, Prayer Helps, Scrpt Memory Helps, Persnl Study Quest
  ★★★★ Personal Application Preparation Time: Low ISBN: 0-932305-58-X
  ★★★★ Relationship Building Ldr. Guide Avail.: No Size: 5.25 x 8.25
Subjects: Charismatic Interest, Christian Living, Discipleship, Joy, 1, 2 & 3 John/Jude
Comments: This eight-week study concerns 1 John, a letter of both encouragement and warning to first-century and modern Christians. It covers important concepts, such as fellowship, light, joy, righteousness, and love. John encourages believers to have fellowship with God, Jesus Christ, the Holy Spirit, and other believers. He urges Christians to protect God's light, to share abiding joy, and protect the righteousness received at the time of new birth from all false doctrine.

Author: Welch, Reuben R.   **1134**
Series: Francis Asbury Press
Title: *Faith for the Journey*
Publisher: Zondervan, 1988

Num. Sess.	Group Time	Num. Pgs.	Avg. Qst.	Price	Audience	Format	Bible Study
13	60-90	154	8	5.95	New Christian	Book	Book

Features: Intro to Study, Full Scrpt Printed
  ★★ Personal Application Preparation Time: Med ISBN: 0-310-75311-2
  ★★ Relationship Building Ldr. Guide Avail.: No Size: 5.25 x 8.0
Subjects: Faith, Hebrews, Theology
Comments: This study of Hebrews is divided into thirteen lessons, each beginning with scripture passages, followed by commentary on the given text, and concluding with discussion questions. A notebook is needed for responding to questions. Of the many themes in Hebrews, foremost is the vivid portrayal of Jesus as the Christian's high priest.

Author: Welch, Reuben R.   **1135**
Series: Francis Asbury Press
Title: *Let's Listen to Jesus*
Publisher: Zondervan, 1978

Num. Sess.	Group Time	Num. Pgs.	Avg. Qst.	Price	Audience	Format	Bible Study
13	60-90	112	7	5.95	New Christian	Book	Book

Features: Prayer Helps, Full Scrpt Printed
  ★★ Personal Application   Preparation Time: Med   ISBN: 0-310-75271-X
  ★★ Relationship Building   Ldr. Guide Avail.: No   Size: 5.25 x 8.0
Subjects: Jesus: Life/Teaching, John, Prayer
Comments: This study on John 13-17 is divided into thirteen lessons, each beginning with scripture passages, followed by commentary, and concluding with discussion questions. A notebook is needed for responding to questions. Jesus prayed in the Garden of Gethsemane for those He would leave behind. His words deserve careful study as His last will and testament to believers.

Author: Welch, Reuben R.   **1136**
Series: Francis Asbury Press
Title: *Open Secret of Strength, The*
Publisher: Zondervan, 1988

Num. Sess.	Group Time	Num. Pgs.	Avg. Qst.	Price	Audience	Format	Bible Study
13	60-90	143	10	5.95	New Christian	Book	Book

Features: Full Scrpt Printed
  ★★ Personal Application   Preparation Time: Med   ISBN: 0-310-75281-7
  ★★ Relationship Building   Ldr. Guide Avail.: No   Size: 5.25 x 8.0
Subjects: Hope, Joy, Philippians, Prison Epistles, Service, Suffering, Victorious Living
Comments: This study of Philippians is divided into thirteen lessons, each beginning with scripture passages, followed by commentary on the given text, and concluding with discussion questions. A notebook is needed for responding to questions. The great theme of strength, or total dependence on Christ, is developed in this study.

Author: Welch, Reuben R.   **1137**
Series: Francis Asbury Press
Title: *Our Freedom in Christ*
Publisher: Zondervan, 1988

Num. Sess.	Group Time	Num. Pgs.	Avg. Qst.	Price	Audience	Format	Bible Study
13	60-90	144	7	5.95	New Christian	Book	Book

Features: Full Scrpt Printed
  ★★ Personal Application   Preparation Time: Med   ISBN: 0-310-75251-5
  ★★ Relationship Building   Ldr. Guide Avail.: No   Size: 5.25 x 8.0
Subjects: Faith, Grace, Romans
Comments: This study on Romans is divided into thirteen lessons, each beginning with scripture passages, followed by commentary on the given text, and concluding with discussion questions. A notebook is needed for responding to questions. The theme of freedom is developed in this study—freedom from guilt, alienation, ourselves, the law, and the power of sin and death.

Author: Wengert, Timothy J.   **1138**
Series: Men's Bible Study Series
Title: *Revelation*
Publisher: Augsburg Publishing House, 1988

Num. Sess.	Group Time	Num. Pgs.	Avg. Qst.	Price	Audience	Format	Bible Study
10	30-45	48	8	3.0	New Christian	Workbk	Book

Features: Intro to Study, Prayer Helps, Summary
  ★★★★ Personal Application   Preparation Time: None   ISBN:
  ★★★★ Relationship Building   Ldr. Guide Avail.: Yes   Size: 4.50 x 9.50
Subjects: Eschatology, Jesus: Life/Teaching, Men's Issues, Revelation
Comments: This ten-lesson study provides helpful insight into the final book of the Bible. Revelation often creates controversy when studied. This study is attentive to all themes and cognizant of the main point—the gospel of Jesus Christ. It may be used at prayer breakfasts, men's Bible study groups, or any other men's meetings.

Author: West, W. Peter   **1139**
Series: Men's Bible Study Series
Title: *Men of Faith*
Publisher: Augsburg Publishing House, 1988

Num. Sess.	Group Time	Num. Pgs.	Avg. Qst.	Price	Audience	Format	Bible Study
10	30-45	48	10	3.0	New Christian	Workbk	Topical

Features: Intro to Study, Prayer Helps, Summary
  ★★★★ Personal Application   Preparation Time: None   ISBN:
  ★★★★ Relationship Building   Ldr. Guide Avail.: Yes   Size: 4.50 x 9.50
Subjects: Bible Personalities, Faith, Forgiveness, Integrity, Men's Issues, Obedience
Comments: This ten-lesson study examines the life and faith of ten key men in the Bible and history of the Church. Included are the following: Peter, for his eagerness; Onesimus, an example of true Christian forgiveness; Abraham, for his pioneer spirit; Joseph, for his model of integrity; Jonah, for his disobedience; Paul, for his vision which spread the gospel; and more. It may be used at prayer breakfasts, men's Bible study groups, or any other men's meetings.

Author: White, Jerry & Mary   **1140**
Series:
Title: *Friends & Friendship: The Secrets of Drawing Closer*
Publisher: NavPress, 1982

Num. Sess.	Group Time	Num. Pgs.	Avg. Qst.	Price	Audience	Format	Bible Study
10	60-75	250	13	8.95	New Christian	Book	Topical

Features: Scrpt Memory Helps, Follow Up, Summary, Charts, Appendix
  ★★★ Personal Application   Preparation Time: Med   ISBN: 0-89109-500-4
  ★★ Relationship Building   Ldr. Guide Avail.: No   Size: 5.0 x 8.0
Subjects: Christian Living, Family, Friendships, Relationships
Comments: This book discusses friendships, why friends are needed, individual capacities for friendship, right ways to make and keep them, how to heal wounded friendships, closer friendships within the family, and friendships with nonChristians. The book includes a personal test of a participant's friendship potential and Bible study questions for individuals or groups. No leader "helps" are included.

Author: White, Jerry   **1141**
Series:
Title: *Honesty, Morality & Conscience*
Publisher: NavPress, 1979

Num. Sess.	Group Time	Num. Pgs.	Avg. Qst.	Price	Audience	Format	Bible Study
12	60-90	300	9	8.95	Mature Chrstn	Book	Topical

Features: Intro to Leading a Study, Intro to Study, Scrpt Memory Helps, Follow Up
★★★★ Personal Application   Preparation Time: Med   ISBN: 0-89109-431-8
★★★★ Relationship Building   Ldr. Guide Avail.: No   Size: 5.50 x 8.50
Subjects: Christian Living, Decision Making, Ethics, Holy Spirit, Morals, Relationships, Work
Comments: This study explores topics such as questionable business practices, lying, declining morals, sexual temptation, superficial relationships, and deceit. The author relates how Scripture, the Holy Spirit, and one's conscience will lead ultimately to right convictions and right decisions. In the back of the book, an entirely separate Bible study is included.

Author: White, Jerry   **1142**
Series:
Title: *Power of Commitment, The*
Publisher: NavPress, 1985

Num. Sess.	Group Time	Num. Pgs.	Avg. Qst.	Price	Audience	Format	Bible Study
12	60-90	250	12	8.95	New Christian	Book	Topical

Features: Scrpt Memory Helps, Follow Up, Appendix, Word Study
★★★ Personal Application   Preparation Time: Med   ISBN: 0-89109-178-5
★★ Relationship Building   Ldr. Guide Avail.: No   Size: 5.25 x 8.0
Subjects: Christian Living, Commitments, Relationships
Comments: This study offers participants sound, biblical counsel for making commitments in their spiritual lives, personal discipline, relationships, and lifestyles. They will discover how to make realistic commitments, distinguish short-term commitments from lifelong ones, defeat the enemy of commitments, and refuse commitments without guilt. A twenty-two chapter book precedes the twelve-lesson study. Each lesson includes a stated goal, reading assignment, and study questions.

Author: White, John   **1143**
Series: NetWork Discussion Guide
Title: *Lifestyle Priorities*
Publisher: Shaw, 1990

Num. Sess.	Group Time	Num. Pgs.	Avg. Qst.	Price	Audience	Format	Bible Study
8	30-45	47	5	3.50	Beginner	Workbk	Topical

Features: Intro to Leading a Study, Intro to Study, Bibliography, Follow Up, Ldr's Notes
★★★★ Personal Application   Preparation Time: Low   ISBN: 0-87788-501-X
★★★ Relationship Building   Ldr. Guide Avail.: No   Size: 5.25 x 8.25
Subjects: Christian Living, God, Obedience
Comments: These eight short studies on worldliness and obedience are designed for people on the move. The course will challenge participants to look beyond traditional "do's and don'ts" that define worldliness for many Christians. Christians are called to radical obedience that will restore priorities and make people stop, take notice, and turn to the living God. Change exacts a high cost, but its value to God, to the world, and to participants is incalculable.

Author: White, John   **1144**
Series:
Title: *Magnificent Obsession: The Joy of Christian Commitment*
Publisher: InterVarsity, 1976

Num. Sess.	Group Time	Num. Pgs.	Avg. Qst.	Price	Audience	Format	Bible Study
10	45-60	142	8	6.95	New Christian	Book	Topical

Features:
★★★ Personal Application   Preparation Time: Low   ISBN: 0-8308-1274-1
★★★ Relationship Building   Ldr. Guide Avail.: No   Size: 5.50 x 8.25
Subjects: Christian Life, Commitments, Discipleship, Joy, Service
Comments: This book is a powerful call to Christian discipleship. Commitment to Christ was never intended to be a dreary duty of self-denial. Rather it is like finding a pearl of such beauty, color, weight, and value that a person would gladly sell everything just to own it. Whatever the cost, the benefits of sacrifice are worth it. This expanded edition includes new chapters, and each chapter is followed by a set of discussion questions for group use.

Author: White, John   **1145**
Series: LifeGuide Bible Study
Title: *Parables: The Greatest Stories Ever Told*
Publisher: InterVarsity, 1988

Num. Sess.	Group Time	Num. Pgs.	Avg. Qst.	Price	Audience	Format	Bible Study
12	45-60	64	11	3.95	Beginner	Workbk	Topical

Features: Intro to Leading a Study, Intro to Study, Ldr's Notes
★ Personal Application   Preparation Time: Low   ISBN: 0-8308-1037-4
★ Relationship Building   Ldr. Guide Avail.: No   Size: 5.50 x 8.25
Subjects: Jesus: Life/Teaching, New Testament, Parables
Comments: In this study, twelve parables in Matthew and Luke are introduced, each with a central point, revealing standards and values of the Kingdom that contrast sharply with values in contemporary society. The parables illustrate truths about Christ's Kingdom that demand a response. Included are the parables of the sower, the lost sheep, the lost coin, the lost son, the good Samaritan, the unforgiving servant, the widow and the judge, the wheat and the weeds, the vineyard workers, and others.

Author: White, William A.   **1146**
Series:
Title: *Single: Understanding and Accepting the Reality of It All*
Publisher: Warner Press, 1990

Num. Sess.	Group Time	Num. Pgs.	Avg. Qst.	Price	Audience	Format	Bible Study
13	60-75	170	Vry	4.95	Beginner	Book	Topical

Features: Intro to Study, Bibliography
★★★ Personal Application   Preparation Time: Low   ISBN: 0-87162-513-X
★★★★ Relationship Building   Ldr. Guide Avail.: Yes   Size: 4.25 x 7.0
Subjects: Singles Issues
Comments: This thirteen-week study on being single addresses topics like: the reality of being single, freedom, wholeness, too little self-esteem, loneliness and aloneness, friendship, dating, intimacy, breaking-up, future marriage, single parenting, and growing spiritually. The study is designed to produce in-depth interaction with the text material and achieve informational and behavioral goals. The study doesn't include much scripture.

Author: Wichern, Ed & Bo Hoskins **1147**
Series:
Title: *Explore the Word*
Publisher: Roper Press, 1988

Num. Sess.	Group Time	Num. Pgs.	Avg. Qst.	Price	Audience	Format	Bible Study
26	45-60	210	Vry	6.95	New Christian	Book	Book

Features: Intro to Study, Bibliography, Summary, Charts, Maps, Appendix
★★★ Personal Application Preparation Time: Med ISBN: 0-86606-260-2
★★ Relationship Building Ldr. Guide Avail.: Yes Size: 5.50 x 8.50
Subjects: Bible Study, Small Group Resource, Teens: Bible Study
Comments: This book is for those who want to study the Bible but don't have much time. It chronologically takes a reader through the entire Bible and provides a concise grasp of what the Bible says. It features inspirational daily Bible readings, in-depth study of key passages, background material, a summary of each book of the Bible, and practical values for today. This doesn't take the place of Bible study, but it can provide a solid foundation.

Author: Wiersbe, Warren W. **1148**
Series: The "Be" Series
Title: *Be Alert*
Publisher: Victor Books, 1984

Num. Sess.	Group Time	Num. Pgs.	Avg. Qst.	Price	Audience	Format	Bible Study
13	45-60	168	N/A	7.99	New Christian	Book	Book

Features: Intro to Study
★★ Personal Application Preparation Time: Low ISBN: 0-89693-380-6
★★ Relationship Building Ldr. Guide Avail.: Yes Size: 5.50 x 8.0
Subjects: Church Life, False Teachers, 1 & 2 Peter, 1, 2 & 3 John/Jude
Comments: This study will help Christians recognize false teachers and know how to fight them. It can also help participants recognize the false doctrines these apostates teach, doctrines that today sometimes pass for Christian truth. The study of the letters of Peter, John, and Jude outline the problems and solutions and sharpen spiritual discernment. A leader's guide, which includes transparency masters, is available.

Author: Wiersbe, Warren W. **1149**
Series: The "Be" Series
Title: *Be Alive*
Publisher: Victor Books, 1986

Num. Sess.	Group Time	Num. Pgs.	Avg. Qst.	Price	Audience	Format	Bible Study
13	45-60	156	N/A	7.99	Beginner	Book	Book

Features: Intro to Study
★★ Personal Application Preparation Time: Low ISBN: 0-89693-359-8
★★ Relationship Building Ldr. Guide Avail.: Yes Size: 5.50 x 8.0
Subjects: Faith, Jesus: Life/Teaching, John, Miracles
Comments: This study of the first twelve chapters of John focuses on Christ's public ministry, especially His miracles and the messages that grew out of them. The climax of His public ministry was official rejection by the religious rulers of Israel. This is an excellent study for helping Christians strengthen their faith, but is also a good study for those interested in Jesus but not yet committed to Him. A leader's guide, which includes transparency masters, is available.

Author: Wiersbe, Warren W. **1150**
Series: The "Be" Series
Title: *Be Compassionate*
Publisher: Victor Books, 1988

Num. Sess.	Group Time	Num. Pgs.	Avg. Qst.	Price	Audience	Format	Bible Study
13	45-60	156	N/A	7.99	New Christian	Book	Book

Features: Intro to Study
★★ Personal Application Preparation Time: Low ISBN: 0-89693-591-4
★★ Relationship Building Ldr. Guide Avail.: Yes Size: 5.50 x 8.0
Subjects: Caring, Jesus: Life/Teaching, Luke
Comments: In this study of Dr. Luke's record of Christ, the Great Physician, participants will understand God's compassion. They will be motivated to show more loving concern for others and, with God's power, help others in distress. Jesus showed compassion to all kinds of people: the sinful, rejected, brokenhearted, men, women, and children. Luke exhorts Christians to be more like the Christ, to "be compassionate." A leader's guide, which includes transparency masters, is available.

Author: Wiersbe, Warren W. **1151**
Series: The "Be" Series
Title: *Be Complete*
Publisher: Victor Books, 1981

Num. Sess.	Group Time	Num. Pgs.	Avg. Qst.	Price	Audience	Format	Bible Study
13	45-60	159	N/A	7.99	New Christian	Book	Book

Features: Intro to Study
★★ Personal Application Preparation Time: Low ISBN: 0-89693-726-7
★★ Relationship Building Ldr. Guide Avail.: Yes Size: 5.50 x 8.0
Subjects: Christian Living, Church Life, Colossians/Philemon, False Teachers, Hope, Integrity, Prison Epistles
Comments: This study shows participants how to put Christ first in their lives. Too often, Christians confuse man-made philosophies and legalistic rules with gospel truth; the Colossians faced that, just as do contemporary believers. Paul corrects erring ways and warns against the temptation to look for spiritual fulfillment from sources other than God. He calls Christians to "be complete" in Christ. A leader's guide, which includes transparency masters, is available.

Author: Wiersbe, Warren W. **1152**
Series: The "Be" Series
Title: *Be Confident*
Publisher: Victor Books, 1982

Num. Sess.	Group Time	Num. Pgs.	Avg. Qst.	Price	Audience	Format	Bible Study
13	45-60	157	N/A	7.99	New Christian	Book	Book

Features: Intro to Study
★★ Personal Application Preparation Time: Low ISBN: 0-89693-728-3
★★ Relationship Building Ldr. Guide Avail.: Yes Size: 5.50 x 8.0
Subjects: Christian Living, Faith, Hebrews
Comments: This study of Hebrews reflects a time when the ages were colliding and everything in society seemed to be shaking. Christians wondered what was going on and what they could do about it. Old stability was passing away, and their faith was wavering. Hebrews' major message is "be confident." God shakes up things so that believers can learn to live by faith, not by sight. A leader's guide, including transparency masters, is available.

Author: Wiersbe, Warren W.   **1153**
Series: The "Be" Series
Title: *Be Courageous: Take Heart from Christ's Example*
Publisher: Victor Books, 1989

Num. Sess.	Group Time	Num. Pgs.	Avg. Qst.	Price	Audience	Format	Bible Study
13	45-60	151	N/A	7.99	New Christian	Book	Topical

Features: Intro to Study, Study Overview
  ★★★ Personal Application   Preparation Time: Low   ISBN: 0-89693-665-1
  ★★★ Relationship Building   Ldr. Guide Avail.: Yes   Size: 5.50 x 8.0
Subjects: Accountability, Christian Living, Discipleship, Jesus: Life/Teaching, Luke, Money, Victorious Living
Comments: This is a study of Luke's account of the Lord's journey to Jerusalem. It reminds participants that the major message for contemporary Christians today is "Be Courageous!" Topics covered include discipleship—its cost and compensation; daily living—wasting, spending, or investing your life; the right and wrong of riches; facing up to Christ's authority; and the power of a joyful life. A leader's guide with reproducible student response sheets is available.

Author: Wiersbe, Warren W.   **1154**
Series: The "Be" Series
Title: *Be Daring*
Publisher: Victor Books, 1988

Num. Sess.	Group Time	Num. Pgs.	Avg. Qst.	Price	Audience	Format	Bible Study
13	45-60	152	N/A	7.99	New Christian	Book	Book

Features: Intro to Study
  ★★ Personal Application   Preparation Time: Low   ISBN: 0-89693-447-0
  ★★ Relationship Building   Ldr. Guide Avail.: Yes   Size: 5.50 x 8.0
Subjects: Acts, Caring, Evangelism, Service
Comments: This practical study of Acts 13-28 explains how God equips and calls ordinary people to perform extraordinary tasks. It deals with questions such as: "What is a call to service?" "How does God equip His servants?" "How can I determine His will for my life?" and "What is God's program for world outreach?" The sin of being a "spectator" is exposed, and Christians are challenged to reach out to others.

Author: Wiersbe, Warren W.   **1155**
Series: The "Be" Series
Title: *Be Diligent*
Publisher: Victor Books, 1987

Num. Sess.	Group Time	Num. Pgs.	Avg. Qst.	Price	Audience	Format	Bible Study
13	45-60	156	N/A	7.99	New Christian	Book	Book

Features: Intro to Study
  ★★ Personal Application   Preparation Time: Low   ISBN: 0-89693-356-3
  ★★ Relationship Building   Ldr. Guide Avail.: Yes   Size: 5.50 x 8.0
Subjects: Caring, Jesus: Life/Teaching, Mark, Service
Comments: This study of Mark is ideal for busy people who want to use every opportunity to serve God. It presents a Lord "on the move," meeting people's physical and spiritual needs. Mark depicts Christ as God's "suffering servant" who came not to be ministered to, but to minister. The study motivates and encourages believers to reach out to a world filled with hurting people. A leader's guide, which includes transparency masters, is available.

Author: Wiersbe, Warren W.   **1156**
Series: The "Be" Series
Title: *Be Dynamic*
Publisher: Victor Books, 1987

Num. Sess.	Group Time	Num. Pgs.	Avg. Qst.	Price	Audience	Format	Bible Study
13	45-60	155	N/A	7.99	New Christian	Book	Book

Features: Intro to Study
  ★★ Personal Application   Preparation Time: Low   ISBN: 0-89693-358-X
  ★★ Relationship Building   Ldr. Guide Avail.: Yes   Size: 5.50 x 8.0
Subjects: Acts, Church Life, Holy Spirit
Comments: This exposition of the first twelve chapters of Acts shows how early church history is directly relevant to the modern church. Topics participants cover include: the ministry of the Spirit in the church; how to be an effective witness for Christ; how to turn persecution into blessing; and how to understand and solve church problems. The challenge is for contemporary Christians to claim the power in Acts, to "be dynamic!" A leader's guide, which includes transparency masters, is available.

Author: Wiersbe, Warren W.   **1157**
Series: The "Be" Series
Title: *Be Encouraged*
Publisher: Victor Books, 1984

Num. Sess.	Group Time	Num. Pgs.	Avg. Qst.	Price	Audience	Format	Bible Study
13	45-60	153	N/A	7.99	Mature Chrstn	Book	Book

Features: Intro to Study
  ★★ Personal Application   Preparation Time: Med   ISBN: 0-88207-620-5
  ★★ Relationship Building   Ldr. Guide Avail.: Yes   Size: 5.50 x 8.0
Subjects: Church Life, Hope, Integrity, Leadership, Repentance, Service, Suffering, 2 Corinthians
Comments: This study of 2 Corinthians shows how God can turn trials into truimphs and sufferings into service. The spiritually young Corinthian church dealt with difficult obstacles; they were confused, defiant, and discouraged. Paul's God-centered perspective serves as the only effective antidote to discouragement, then and now. Participants should read 2 Corinthians twice before beginning the study. A leader's guide, which includes transparency masters, is available.

Author: Wiersbe, Warren W.   **1158**
Series: The "Be" Series
Title: *Be Faithful*
Publisher: Victor Books, 1981

Num. Sess.	Group Time	Num. Pgs.	Avg. Qst.	Price	Audience	Format	Bible Study
13	45-60	175	N/A	7.99	New Christian	Book	Topical

Features: Intro to Study, Study Overview
  ★★★ Personal Application   Preparation Time: Low   ISBN: 0-89693-685-6
  ★★ Relationship Building   Ldr. Guide Avail.: Yes   Size: 5.50 x 8.0
Subjects: Church Life, Colossians/Philemon, Leadership, Service, 1 & 2 Timothy/Titus
Comments: This study helps participants understand a local church's ministry, how to stick with it and be faithful to the Word, their tasks, and other people. If people are faithful to God-given tasks, then His work will prosper and His name will be glorified. A leader's guide with transparency masters is available.

Author: Wiersbe, Warren W.   **1159**
Series: The "Be" Series
Title: *Be Free*
Publisher: Victor Books, 1975

Num. Sess.	Group Time	Num. Pgs.	Avg. Qst.	Price	Audience	Format	Bible Study
13	45-60	160	N/A	7.99	New Christian	Book	Book

Features: Intro to Study
  ★★ Personal Application   Preparation Time: Low   ISBN: 0-89693-733-X
  ★★ Relationship Building   Ldr. Guide Avail.: Yes   Size: 5.50 x 8.0
Subjects: Christian Living, Church Life, Galatians, Holy Spirit
Comments: This expository study of Galatians helps participants deal with the problem "If I want to be a 'really' good Christian, I must. . . ." It clearly describes one wrong way to do so, as Paul exposes the most popular substitute for spiritual living in churches then and now—legalism. Many people believe themselves "spiritual" because of what they don't do, because of a leader they follow, or a group to which they belong. The correct answer: let the Holy Spirit take over; be free.

Author: Wiersbe, Warren W.   **1160**
Series: The "Be" Series
Title: *Be Hopeful*
Publisher: Victor Books, 1982

Num. Sess.	Group Time	Num. Pgs.	Avg. Qst.	Price	Audience	Format	Bible Study
13	45-60	143	N/A	6.99	New Christian	Book	Book

Features: Intro to Study
  ★★ Personal Application   Preparation Time: Low   ISBN: 0-89693-737-2
  ★★ Relationship Building   Ldr. Guide Avail.: Yes   Size: 5.50 x 8.0
Subjects: Grace, Hope, Suffering, 1 & 2 Peter
Comments: This study reviews the people who first read Peter's epistle, people who experienced suffering and persecution because of their loyalty to Christ. Peter warned of a "fiery trial" of persecution; his goal was to prepare believers to be triumphant. Today there is suffering for faith too, but believers should "be hopeful" because God's grace is present for the asking. Participants will prepare for, rather than fear, hatred. A leader's guide, which includes transparency masters, is available.

Author: Wiersbe, Warren W.   **1161**
Series: The "Be" Series
Title: *Be Joyful*
Publisher: Victor Books, 1974

Num. Sess.	Group Time	Num. Pgs.	Avg. Qst.	Price	Audience	Format	Bible Study
13	45-60	143	N/A	7.99	New Christian	Book	Book

Features: Intro to Study
  ★★ Personal Application   Preparation Time: Low   ISBN: 0-89693-739-9
  ★★ Relationship Building   Ldr. Guide Avail.: Yes   Size: 5.50 x 8.0
Subjects: Joy, Obedience, Philippians, Prison Epistles, Suffering, Victorious Living
Comments: Through this study of the joy of Philippians, participants can enjoy a happy Christian life. The lessons identify joy-stealers, put worry in perspective, and outline and define contentment. The four chapters of Philippians identify four attitudes that assist in maintaining joy: the single mind, the submissive mind, the spiritual mind, and the secure mind. They show that joy can be achieved in spite of circumstances, people, things, and worry. A leader's guide, with transparency masters, is available.

Author: Wiersbe, Warren W.   **1162**
Series: The "Be" Series
Title: *Be Loyal*
Publisher: Victor Books, 1980

Num. Sess.	Group Time	Num. Pgs.	Avg. Qst.	Price	Audience	Format	Bible Study
26	45-60	220	N/A	7.99	New Christian	Book	Book

Features: Intro to Study
  ★★ Personal Application   Preparation Time: Low   ISBN: 0-89693-313-X
  ★★ Relationship Building   Ldr. Guide Avail.: Yes   Size: 5.50 x 8.0
Subjects: Jesus: Life/Teaching, Matthew
Comments: This expository survey of Matthew presents Christ as King and emphasizes Matthew's message to Christians about Christ and His ministry. It leads to a deeper love for, and loyalty to, Christ. Its outline follows the revelation of the King, the rebellion against the King, the retirement of the King, the rejection of the King, and the resurrection of the King. Matthew's material is presented in topical rather than chronological order.

Author: Wiersbe, Warren W.   **1163**
Series: The "Be" Series
Title: *Be Mature*
Publisher: Victor Books, 1978

Num. Sess.	Group Time	Num. Pgs.	Avg. Qst.	Price	Audience	Format	Bible Study
13	45-60	176	N/A	7.99	New Christian	Book	Book

Features: Intro to Study
  ★★ Personal Application   Preparation Time: Low   ISBN: 0-89693-754-2
  ★★ Relationship Building   Ldr. Guide Avail.: Yes   Size: 5.50 x 8.0
Subjects: Christian Living, Discipleship, Faith, James, Prayer
Comments: The Epistle of James was written to help first-century Christians understand and attain spiritual maturity. This study covers areas of growth such as learning to be patient, overcoming temptation, practicing what the Bible teaches, learning to control the tongue, making peace rather than trouble, and praying and getting results. Many Christian problems are caused by spiritual immaturity. God wants believers to grow up, not just grow old. A leader's guide, which includes transparency masters, is available.

Author: Wiersbe, Warren W.   **1164**
Series: The "Be" Series
Title: *Be Ready*
Publisher: Victor Books, 1979

Num. Sess.	Group Time	Num. Pgs.	Avg. Qst.	Price	Audience	Format	Bible Study
13	45-60	178	N/A	7.99	New Christian	Book	Book

Features: Intro to Study
  ★★ Personal Application   Preparation Time: Low   ISBN: 0-89693-773-9
  ★★ Relationship Building   Ldr. Guide Avail.: Yes   Size: 5.50 x 8.0
Subjects: Church Life, Holiness, Hope, Suffering, 1 & 2 Thessalonians
Comments: This study focuces on two major themes: the return of Christ and the ministry of the local church. Strong emphasis is placed on Christians' need to "be ready," with prepared lives and churches. Utilizing 1 Thessalonians, the study discusses how to walk in holiness, harmony, honesty, hope, and helpfulness. From 2 Thessalonians comes encouragement in suffering, enlightenment in teaching, and enablement in living. A leader's guide, which includes transparency masters, is available.

Author: Wiersbe, Warren W.   **1165**
Series: The "Be" Series
Title: *Be Real*
Publisher: Victor Books, 1972

Num. Sess.	Group Time	Num. Pgs.	Avg. Qst.	Price	Audience	Format	Bible Study
12	45-60	190	N/A	7.99	New Christian	Book	Book

Features: Intro to Study
   ★★ Personal Application   Preparation Time: Low   ISBN: 0-89693-774-7
   ★★ Relationship Building Ldr. Guide Avail.: Yes   Size: 5.50 x 8.0
Subjects: Christian Living, Obedience, 1, 2 & 3 John/Jude
Comments: This study of 1 John emphasizes the truth that "real" living is Christian living as God intended. More than simply being "in" the family of God, it is growing in the Lord, in truth, in obedience, and in love. This through-the-book study deals with a number of subjects. Similar ideas are grouped and only given casual reference when they occur elsewhere. Leaders should be familiar with the entire book prior to beginning the first session.

Author: Wiersbe, Warren W.   **1166**
Series: The "Be" Series
Title: *Be Rich*
Publisher: Victor Books, 1976

Num. Sess.	Group Time	Num. Pgs.	Avg. Qst.	Price	Audience	Format	Bible Study
13	45-60	175	N/A	7.99	New Christian	Book	Book

Features: Intro to Study
   ★★ Personal Application   Preparation Time: Low   ISBN: 0-89693-775-5
   ★★ Relationship Building Ldr. Guide Avail.: Yes   Size: 5.50 x 8.0
Subjects: Christian Living, Ephesians, Holy Spirit, Satan, Victorious Living
Comments: This study of Ephesians exhorts participants to stop living like paupers when Christ has made them rich. Three points are covered: the Christian home as it relates to the work of the Holy Spirit; Satan's strategy and how Christians can be victorious over him; and each Christian's responsibility in light of his or her great wealth in Christ. A leader's guide, which includes transparency masters, is available.

Author: Wiersbe, Warren W.   **1167**
Series: The "Be" Series
Title: *Be Right*
Publisher: Victor Books, 1977

Num. Sess.	Group Time	Num. Pgs.	Avg. Qst.	Price	Audience	Format	Bible Study
13	45-60	178	N/A	6.99	New Christian	Book	Book

Features: Intro to Study
   ★★ Personal Application   Preparation Time: Low   ISBN: 0-89693-778-X
   ★★ Relationship Building Ldr. Guide Avail.: Yes   Size: 5.50 x 8.0
Subjects: Christian Living, Relationships, Romans, Success
Comments: This study of Romans is not a detailed expository. Rather, it is a survey which helps participants understand the letter's main message and how it applies to their lives today. If participants will commit to concentration as they study this letter, they will better understand the rest of the Bible and the secrets of successful Christian living. Christians can "be right" in the world, with God, and with others. A leader's guide, which includes transparency masters, is available.

Author: Wiersbe, Warren W.   **1168**
Series: The "Be" Series
Title: *Be Transformed*
Publisher: Victor Books, 1986

Num. Sess.	Group Time	Num. Pgs.	Avg. Qst.	Price	Audience	Format	Bible Study
13	45-60	151	N/A	7.99	New Christian	Book	Book

Features: Intro to Study
   ★★ Personal Application   Preparation Time: Low   ISBN: 0-89693-352-0
   ★★ Relationship Building Ldr. Guide Avail.: Yes   Size: 5.50 x 8.0
Subjects: Holy Spirit, John, Prayer, Relationships, Stress
Comments: This study of John 13-21 covers the private ministry of Christ to His own disciples. He prepared them for future service, when the Holy Spirit would empower them. Just as the disciples were transformed, participants will be transformed through lessons with titles like "How Does the Holy Spirit Work in My Life?" "What Are the Secrets of Answered Prayer?" "Why Is Christian Fellowship So Important?" and "How Can I Overcome the Pressures of the World?"

Author: Wiersbe, Warren W.   **1169**
Series: The "Be" Series
Title: *Be Victorious*
Publisher: Victor Books, 1985

Num. Sess.	Group Time	Num. Pgs.	Avg. Qst.	Price	Audience	Format	Bible Study
13	45-60	156	N/A	7.99	New Christian	Book	Book

Features: Intro to Study
   ★★ Personal Application   Preparation Time: Low   ISBN: 0-89693-547-7
   ★★ Relationship Building Ldr. Guide Avail.: Yes   Size: 5.50 x 8.0
Subjects: Hope, Revelation, Suffering
Comments: This study of Revelation contains the message of the glorious victory of Christ over all enemies. More than prophecy, Revelation reveals the truth that in Christ all believers can overcome. John wrote this book to encourage first-century Christians who were experiencing great suffering. In every age of the church, Revelation brings comfort and hope. Its symbols are timeless and can be understood by believers at any point in history. A leader's guide, with transparency masters, is available.

Author: Wiersbe, Warren W.   **1170**
Series: The "Be" Series
Title: *Be Wise*
Publisher: Victor Books, 1983

Num. Sess.	Group Time	Num. Pgs.	Avg. Qst.	Price	Audience	Format	Bible Study
13	45-60	172	N/A	6.99	New Christian	Book	Book

Features: Intro to Study
   ★★ Personal Application   Preparation Time: Low   ISBN: 0-89693-304-0
   ★★ Relationship Building Ldr. Guide Avail.: Yes   Size: 5.50 x 8.0
Subjects: Church Life, Repentance, Wisdom, 1 Corinthians
Comments: This chapter-by-chapter study of 1 Corinthians explores Paul's letter that confronts Corinthians with their sins and urges them to repent. Christians then and now share problems: overpopulation, pride, and pollution. Church leaders compete with one another. Christians live immorally, and appear proud of it, and so on. Where humankind's knowledge produces problems, God's wisdom provides answers. A leader's guide, which includes transparency masters, is available.

Author: Wiersbe, Warren W.   **1171**
Series: Living Studies
Title: *His Name Is Wonderful*
Publisher: Tyndale House, 1976

Num. Sess.	Group Time	Num. Pgs.	Avg. Qst.	Price	Audience	Format	Bible Study
12	60-75	152	N/A	7.95	New Christian	Book	Charctr

Features: Intro to Study, No Grp Discussion Quest
★★ Personal Application   Preparation Time: Low   ISBN: 0-8423-1447-4
★★ Relationship Building   Ldr. Guide Avail.: No   Size: 5.0 x 8.0
Subjects: God, Isaiah/Jeremiah, Jesus: Life/Teaching, Major Prophets
Comments: This book brings to life the names of Christ used in the book of Isaiah, including: "Wonderful," takes care of life's dullness; "Mighty God," takes care of life's demands; "Everlasting Father," takes care of life's dimensions; and "Prince of Peace," takes care of life's disturbances. Each name He bears indicates a blessing He shares.

Author: Wiersbe, Warren W   **1172**
Series:
Title: *Meet Yourself in the Psalms*
Publisher: Victor Books, 1983

Num. Sess.	Group Time	Num. Pgs.	Avg. Qst.	Price	Audience	Format	Bible Study
13	60-75	140	N/A	7.99	New Christian	Book	Book

Features: Intro to Study, Full Scrpt Printed
★★★★ Personal Application   Preparation Time: Low   ISBN: 0-88207-740-6
★★★ Relationship Building   Ldr. Guide Avail.: Yes   Size: 5.50 x 8.0
Subjects: Failure, Forgiveness, Psalms, Service, Stress
Comments: This thirteen-week study of selected psalms helps participants find themselves in the Psalms. They will also find the Lord, who waits to give new vision and strength for life and service. The study responds to people who ask why good things happen to bad people, who look for God when the bottom drops out, who face midlife crises with expectations of God's best, and who receive forgiveness and begin again after failure. A leader's guide includes reproducible transparency masters.

Author: Wiersbe, Warren W   **1173**
Series:
Title: *Window on the Parables*
Publisher: Victor Books, 1979

Num. Sess.	Group Time	Num. Pgs.	Avg. Qst.	Price	Audience	Format	Bible Study
13	60-75	154	N/A	7.99	New Christian	Book	Topical

Features: Intro to Study
★★★★ Personal Application   Preparation Time: Low   ISBN: 0-89693-682-1
★★★ Relationship Building   Ldr. Guide Avail.: Yes   Size: 5.50 x 8.0
Subjects: Forgiveness, Money, Parables, Prayer, Service
Comments: This study offers insights into thirteen of Jesus' most beloved parables. In them, Jesus deals with subjects no Christian can afford to treat lightly: salvation, forgiveness of others, love for minorities, right and wrong use of money, prayer, and motives for service. Participants will see themselves in ancient parables, and see light shed in their modern lives. The leader's guide includes reproducible response sheets.

Author: Wilcox, Anne   **1174**
Series: Building Books
Title: *Building Bible Study Skills*
Publisher: Bethany House, 1985

Num. Sess.	Group Time	Num. Pgs.	Avg. Qst.	Price	Audience	Format	Bible Study
34	45-60	70	Vry	4.95	New Christian	Workbk	Topical

Features: Intro to Leading a Study, Intro to Study, Scrpt Memory Helps, Charts, Maps
★★★ Personal Application   Preparation Time: Low   ISBN: 0-87123-821-7
★★ Relationship Building   Ldr. Guide Avail.: Yes   Size: 8.50 x 11.0
Subjects: Teens: Bible Study, Teens: Discipleship
Comments: This thirty-four-lesson study, which gives young adults hands-on experience studying, interpreting, and applying the Scripture to daily life, is divided into five sections. Part 1 explores the inspiration of Scripture and the results of careless interpretation. Part 2 is an introduction to Bible reference books. Part 3 gives instructions for using six different Bible study methods. Part 4 applies the six methods to one book of the Bible. Part 5 teaches remembering.

Author: Wilde, Gary A.   **1175**
Series: Group's Active Bible Curriculum
Title: *Dealing with Death*
Publisher: Group Publishing, 1991

Num. Sess.	Group Time	Num. Pgs.	Avg. Qst.	Price	Audience	Format	Bible Study
4	35-60	48	Vry	6.95	Beginner	Workbk	Topical

Features: Intro to Leading a Study, Intro to Study, Objectives, Study Overview, Ldr's Notes, Drawings, Handouts, Agenda, Publicity Ideas
★★★★ Personal Application   Preparation Time: None   ISBN: 1-559-45112-2
★★★★ Relationship Building   Ldr. Guide Avail.: No   Size: 8.50 x 11.0
Subjects: Teens: Emotions, Teens: Friends, Teens: Junior High
Comments: This study helps junior high students answer questions about death. In the four lessons participants will explore the Christian response to the idea of reincarnation, learn healthy ways to express feelings when a loved one dies, discover practical ways to help a friend who's mourning, and learn how to reach out to people with terminal illnesses. Instructions are easy to follow and provide multiple options for teachers. No student books are required.

Author: Wilde, Gary A.   **1176**
Series: Lay Action Ministry
Title: *Your Ministry of Prayer*
Publisher: Lay Action Ministry Program, 1990

Num. Sess.	Group Time	Num. Pgs.	Avg. Qst.	Price	Audience	Format	Bible Study
12	60-90	143	Vry	5.95	New Christian	Workbk	Topical

Features: Prayer Helps, Ldr's Notes
★★★ Personal Application   Preparation Time: Low   ISBN: 0-89191-490-0
★★★ Relationship Building   Ldr. Guide Avail.: Yes   Size: 5.25 x 8.25
Subjects: God, Prayer
Comments: This practical study helps participants grow in understanding and practicing prayer, while showing them how to organize with others in the church an ongoing prayer ministry. They will become familiar with the names and attributes of God, deal with the tough questions concerning God's will, and grapple with what it means to truly worship God in prayer. Examples of Jesus and other biblical pray-ers provide insights to apply to one's own prayer life. Homework is required.

Author: Williams, Michael **1177**
Series: Bible Study for Christian
Title: *Acts (Volumes 1 & 2)*
Publisher: Cokesbury, 1990

Num. Sess.	Group Time	Num. Pgs.	Avg. Qst.	Price	Audience	Format	Bible Study
7	45-60	N/A	Vry	29.95	New Christian	Video	Book

Features: Intro to Leading a Study, Intro to Study, Summary, Video Study Guide

★★★ Personal Application Preparation Time: Low ISBN: 0-687-76155-7
★★★ Relationship Building Ldr. Guide Avail.: Yes Size: 4.75 x 8.0
Subjects: Acts, Bible Personalities, Church Life, Faith
Comments: This two-volume video lecture series on Acts includes seven twenty-minute lessons. It concerns what happened to the apostles after Christ left them. It introduces participants to early Church members, shows them growing in faith and understanding, and follows them as they begin to carry out the Great Commission. Lessons cover "The New Community," "Pentecost," "Stephen," "Paul," "Peter and Cornelius," "Barnabas," and "The Acts." A comprehensive leader's guide helps those leading group study.

Author: Williamson, David **1178**
Series: Serendipity Support Group
Title: *Unemployed Unfulfilled: Down but Not Out*
Publisher: Serendipity House, 1990

Num. Sess.	Group Time	Num. Pgs.	Avg. Qst.	Price	Audience	Format	Bible Study
7	60-90	80	Vry	5.45	Beginner	Workbk	Topical

Features: Intro to Leading a Study, Objectives, Bibliography, Prayer Helps, Full Scrpt Printed, Cartoons, Agenda

★★★★ Personal Application Preparation Time: None ISBN:
★★★★ Relationship Building Ldr. Guide Avail.: No Size: 6.50 x 9.25
Subjects: Emotions, Hope, Support, Work
Comments: This study, for the unemployed and underemployed, surveys interests and career options, and helps participants focus on the "right" job. Lessons are entitled "The Toughest Job," "Emotion Control," "Discovering the Real You," "The Meaning of Work," "The Hunt Begins," "Coming Up Empty," and "Keeping Hope Alive." The format includes icebreakers, Bible study, and prayer. Timelines are provided for each lesson.

Author: Wilson, Rev. Neil S., et al. **1179**
Series: Life Application
Title: *Genesis*
Publisher: Tyndale House, 1989

Num. Sess.	Group Time	Num. Pgs.	Avg. Qst.	Price	Audience	Format	Bible Study
13	60-90	146	13	4.95	New Christian	Workbk	Book

Features: Intro to Leading a Study, Intro to Study, Study Overview, Digging Deeper Quest, Full Scrpt Printed, Drawings, Charts, Maps, Cross Ref

★★★ Personal Application Preparation Time: Med ISBN: 0-8423-2714-2
★★★ Relationship Building Ldr. Guide Avail.: No Size: 6.50 x 9.0
Subjects: Bible Personalities, Faith, Genesis, God, God's Promises, Obedience, Success
Comments: This study, which contains the complete text of Genesis, covers God's creation of the world and His desire to have a people set apart to worship Him. Key people include Adam, Eve, Noah, Isaac, Jacob, and Joseph, all of whom emphasize the promises of God and proof that He is faithful. Themes include: beginnings, disobedience, sin, promises, obedience, prosperity, and Israel. Questions lead to application of biblical truth and action plans.

Author: Wilson, Rev. Neil S., et al. **1180**
Series: Life Application
Title: *Hosea & Jonah*
Publisher: Tyndale House, 1989

Num. Sess.	Group Time	Num. Pgs.	Avg. Qst.	Price	Audience	Format	Bible Study
13	60-90	82	13	4.95	New Christian	Workbk	Book

Features: Intro to Leading a Study, Intro to Study, Study Overview, Digging Deeper Quest, Full Scrpt Printed, Drawings, Charts, Maps, Cross Ref

★★★ Personal Application Preparation Time: Med ISBN: 0-8423-2724-X
★★★ Relationship Building Ldr. Guide Avail.: No Size: 6.50 x 9.0
Subjects: Commitments, God, Minor Prophets, Obedience, Prophecy
Comments: This study contains the complete texts of Hosea and Jonah. Hosea portrays God's constant and persistent love. As the book progresses, the prophet submits himself willingly to his Lord's direction. Participants will grieve with him over the unfaithfulness of his wife and people; they should hear the clear warning of judgment and reaffirm their commitments to God. Jonah provides a full picture of God's love and compassion, and proves that no one is beyond redemption.

Author: Wilson, Rev. Neil S., et al. **1181**
Series: Life Application
Title: *Joshua*
Publisher: Tyndale House, 1989

Num. Sess.	Group Time	Num. Pgs.	Avg. Qst.	Price	Audience	Format	Bible Study
13	60-90	96	15	4.95	New Christian	Workbk	Book

Features: Intro to Leading a Study, Intro to Study, Study Overview, Digging Deeper Quest, Full Scrpt Printed, Drawings, Charts, Maps, Cross Ref

★★★ Personal Application Preparation Time: Med ISBN: 0-8423-2723-1
★★★ Relationship Building Ldr. Guide Avail.: No Size: 6.50 x 9.0
Subjects: Failure, Joshua, Leadership, Obedience, Success
Comments: In this study, complete with the full text of the book, Joshua outlines the history of Israel's conquest of the Promised Land. It is presented in three parts: entering the Promised Land, conquering the Promised Land, and dividing the Promised Land. Themes include success, faith, guidance, leadership, and conquest. Joshua was committed to obeying God, and this study concerns obedience. Questions lead to application of biblical truth and action plans.

Author: Wise, Janice **1182**
Series: Enrichment Series
Title: *Walk Out of Worry: The Way to an Anxiety-Free Life*
Publisher: Aglow, 1988

Num. Sess.	Group Time	Num. Pgs.	Avg. Qst.	Price	Audience	Format	Bible Study
8	60-75	59	14	2.95	New Christian	Workbk	Book

Features: Intro to Study, Prayer Helps, Scrpt Memory Helps, Persnl Study Quest

★★★★ Personal Application Preparation Time: Med ISBN: 0-932305-49-0
★★★★ Relationship Building Ldr. Guide Avail.: No Size: 5.25 x 8.25
Subjects: Charismatic Interest, Faith, Stress
Comments: This eight-week study provides participants with practical steps to overcome worry. Worry comes with a high price tag; it damages health, depletes energy and creativity, and robs joy. This study points out that throughout the New Testament, Jesus' constant admonition to His listeners was to not worry, to stop being afraid. In God's eyes worry is a sin, because the bottom line is always lack of trust in Him. Participants go beyond theory and are forced to admit the real motives behind their worries.

Author: Wold, Margaret   **1183**
Series: Small Group Bible Studies
Title: *Miracles*
Publisher: Augsburg Publishing House, 1980

Num. Sess.	Group Time	Num. Pgs.	Avg. Qst.	Price	Audience	Format	Bible Study
6	60-75	16	6	1.15	New Christian	Book	Topical

Features: Intro to Study, Prayer Helps
   ★★★Personal Application   Preparation Time: None   ISBN:
   ★★Relationship Building   Ldr. Guide Avail.: No   Size: 8.50 x 5.50
Subjects: Faith, Jesus: Life/Teaching, Miracles
Comments: This small pamphlet includes six sessions on miracles. It is not designed to argue whether or not the miracles actually occurred. That is a matter of faith. However, throughout history many different ways of interpreting miracles have developed, all worthy of discussion. Sessions discuss Jesus' miracles of healing, of feeding, of casting out demons, of faith, and of challenging nature.

Author: Woods, Paul   **1184**
Series: Group's Active Bible Curriculum
Title: *Applying the Bible to Life*
Publisher: Group Publishing, 1991

Num. Sess.	Group Time	Num. Pgs.	Avg. Qst.	Price	Audience	Format	Bible Study
4	35-60	48	Vry	6.95	New Christian	Workbk	Topical

Features: Intro to Leading a Study, Intro to Study, Objectives, Study Overview, Ldr's Notes, Drawings, Handouts, Agenda, Publicity Ideas
   ★★★★Personal Application   Preparation Time: None   ISBN: 1-559-45116-5
   ★★★★Relationship Building   Ldr. Guide Avail.: No   Size: 8.50 x 11.0
Subjects: Teens: Bible Study, Teens: Junior High
Comments: This study helps junior high students get excited about reading the Bible. Its four lessons allow students to see how the Bible helps them overcome everyday problems and worries; learn an easy-to-use method for personal Bible study; discover how study tools can make reading the Bible fun; examine how Bible study is critical to knowing God; and show how the Bible is a guide to life. Instructions are easy to follow and provide multiple options for teachers. No student books are required.

Author: Woods, Paul   **1185**
Series: Group's Active Bible Curriculum
Title: *What's a Christian?*
Publisher: Group Publishing, 1990

Num. Sess.	Group Time	Num. Pgs.	Avg. Qst.	Price	Audience	Format	Bible Study
4	35-60	46	Vry	6.95	Beginner	Workbk	Topical

Features: Intro to Leading a Study, Intro to Study, Objectives, Study Overview, Ldr's Notes, Handouts, Agenda, Publicity Ideas
   ★★★Personal Application   Preparation Time: None   ISBN: 1-559-45105-X
   ★★★Relationship Building   Ldr. Guide Avail.: No   Size: 8.50 x 11.0
Subjects: Teens: Evangelism, Teens: Junior High
Comments: In this study, the basics of Christianity are taught to help teenagers learn to live out their faith in Christ. Four lessons cover the rich history of Christian faith, the meaning and significance of salvation, putting faith into action, and building faith on true hope in Jesus Christ. It can be adapted for use in a Bible class or youth meeting. Activities and Bible studies are included as separate sheets that can be reproduced. The instructions are easy to follow.

Author: Worley, Mike   **1186**
Series:
Title: *Brand Name Christians: A Bible-Study Devotional for Junior Highers*
Publisher: Zondervan, 1988

Num. Sess.	Group Time	Num. Pgs.	Avg. Qst.	Price	Audience	Format	Bible Study
75	30-45	133	Vry	6.95	Beginner	Book	No

Features: Cartoons
   ★★Personal Application   Preparation Time: Low   ISBN: 0-310-30291-9
   ★★Relationship Building   Ldr. Guide Avail.: No   Size: 5.50 x 8.0
Subjects: Teens: Bible Study, Teens: Devotionals, Teens: Junior High, Teens: New Testament
Comments: This collection of devotions includes selected verses from Philippians, Galatians, Ephesians, and Colossians, paired with stories and questions related to their themes. While intended for personal study, it could easily be adapted to a pre-Sunday school class small group. Each day's ten-to-fifteen minutes of study include prayer, Bible verse reading, a story, and "fill in the blanks." A calendar of the seventy-five lessons allows participants to checkoff completed lessons.

Author: Wright, David   **1187**
Series:
Title: *Finding Freedom from Fear*
Publisher: Zondervan, 1990

Num. Sess.	Group Time	Num. Pgs.	Avg. Qst.	Price	Audience	Format	Bible Study
9	60-90	180	12	7.95	New Christian	Book	Topical

Features: Intro to Study, Ldr's Notes
   ★★★Personal Application   Preparation Time: Med   ISBN: 0-310-44351-2
   ★★Relationship Building   Ldr. Guide Avail.: No   Size: 5.25 x 8.0
Subjects: Christian Living, Emotions, Faith, Psalms, Stress
Comments: This study outlines Christians' unique spiritual resources for facing and conquering fear. It provides helpful explanations of what fear is, where it comes from, how it affects lives, and how it can be coped with successfully. King David's life, selected psalms, and popular psychological material are used to illustrate and explore fear, stress, and faith. Study guides at the end of the book paraphrase and review each chapter.

Author: Wright, David   **1188**
Series:
Title: *Wisdom as a Lifestyle: Building Biblical Life-Codes*
Publisher: Zondervan, 1987

Num. Sess.	Group Time	Num. Pgs.	Avg. Qst.	Price	Audience	Format	Bible Study
10	60-90	151	N/A	7.95	New Christian	Book	Topical

Features: Intro to Study, No Grp Discussion Quest, Full Scrpt Printed
   ★★Personal Application   Preparation Time: None   ISBN: 0-310-44311-3
   ★★Relationship Building   Ldr. Guide Avail.: No   Size: 5.25 x 8.0
Subjects: Christian Life, Money, Proverbs, Relationships, Wisdom
Comments: This study uses Solomon's book of Proverbs to construct a life-code built on wisdom. It covers topics such as the key to true identity, drawing strength from personal relationships, handling wealth or the lack of it, and making sound judgments. The lack of group questions requires a seasoned leader to construct questions and facilitate a group study.

Author: Wright, H. Norman **1189**
Series:
Title: *More Communication Keys for Your Marriage*
Publisher: Regal Books, 1983

Num. Sess.	Group Time	Num. Pgs.	Avg. Qst.	Price	Audience	Format	Bible Study
11	60-90	200	Vry	7.95	Beginner	Workbk	Topical

Features:
★★★★ Personal Application Preparation Time: Low ISBN: 0-8307-0904-5
★★★★ Relationship Building Ldr. Guide Avail.: Yes Size: 5.0 x 8.0
Subjects: Emotions, Marriage, Relationships
Comments: Personal involvement is the key feature of eleven sessions designed to involve couples in thinking, interacting, and communicating to build successful marriage relationships. Areas covered include: mutual servanthood, self-talk and how it affects one's emotions, the significance of the past, passive and active coping, and more. The leader's guide includes preparation notes, session guidelines, recommended books, time frames for activities, and overhead transparencies. A video is available.

Author: Yagel, Bobbie **1190**
Series: Workbook Series
Title: *Building Better Relationships: How to Put Love into Action*
Publisher: Aglow, 1988

Num. Sess.	Group Time	Num. Pgs.	Avg. Qst.	Price	Audience	Format	Bible Study
8	60-75	74	12	5.95	New Christian	Workbk	Topical

Features: Intro to Study, Prayer Helps, Scrpt Memory Helps, Follow Up, Drawings, Persnl Study Quest
★★★★ Personal Application Preparation Time: Med ISBN: 0-932305-51-2
★★★★ Relationship Building Ldr. Guide Avail.: No Size: 8.50 x 10.0
Subjects: Emotions, Forgiveness, Grace, Love, Marriage, Relationships
Comments: This eight-week study provides biblical counsel on human relationships, covering topics like building right relationships, loving neighbors, honoring and encouraging one another, handling confrontation, seeking forgiveness, and controlling emotions. It also provides tools needed to continue to grow in grace. This study will lead to an improved relationship with friends, family, coworkers, pastor, next-door neighbor, plumber, and mechanic.

Author: Yancey, Philip & Tim Stafford **1191**
Series:
Title: *Students Guide to the Bible, The*
Publisher: Zondervan, 1988

Num. Sess.	Group Time	Num. Pgs.	Avg. Qst.	Price	Audience	Format	Bible Study
	-	96	N/A	4.95	Beginner	Workbk	No

Features: Intro to Study, Study Overview
 Personal Application Preparation Time: ISBN: 0-310-58961-4
 Relationship Building Ldr. Guide Avail.: Size: 7.0 x 9.0
Subjects: Bible Study, Teens: Bible Study
Comments: This guide for students introduces each Bible book, giving keen insight into the story line, eliminating much of the mystery, and enhancing its wonderment and sense of adventure. Written in magazine style, the guide is especially helpful for those reading the Bible for the first time. Blanks for taking notes follow the introduction to each lesson, and enhance the guide's use in study groups.

Author: Yohn, Rick **1192**
Series: Living Studies
Title: *Discover Your Spiritual Gift and Use It*
Publisher: Tyndale House, 1974

Num. Sess.	Group Time	Num. Pgs.	Avg. Qst.	Price	Audience	Format	Bible Study
13	60-90	154	N/A	5.95	Mature Chrstn	Book	Topical

Features: Bibliography, No Grp Discussion Quest
★★ Personal Application Preparation Time: Low ISBN: 0-8423-0626-9
★★ Relationship Building Ldr. Guide Avail.: No Size: 5.0 x 8.0
Subjects: Discipleship, Spiritual Gifts
Comments: This book argues that God gives every believer gifts for maximum service, and examines the relevancy and necessity of spiritual gifts for contemporary Christians. It outlines New Testament gifts, discusses their biblical meaning, and describes contemporary ways they can be used. It makes the case that these gifts are not to be exercised only within church walls, but wherever there is need. Study questions are not provided.

Author: Yount, Christine **1193**
Series: Group's Active Bible Curriculum
Title: *Responding to Injustice*
Publisher: Group Publishing, 1991

Num. Sess.	Group Time	Num. Pgs.	Avg. Qst.	Price	Audience	Format	Bible Study
4	35-60	48	Vry	6.95	New Christian	Workbk	Topical

Features: Intro to Leading a Study, Intro to Study, Objectives, Study Overview, Ldr's Notes, Drawings, Handouts, Agenda, Publicity Ideas
★★★★ Personal Application Preparation Time: None ISBN: 1-559-45214-5
★★★★ Relationship Building Ldr. Guide Avail.: No Size: 8.50 x 11.0
Subjects: Teens: Ethics, Teens: Relationships, Teens: Senior High
Comments: This four-lesson study helps senior high students understand and develop Christian responses to injustice. Participants will learn to recognize injustice and respond with Christian love, commit themselves toward eliminating prejudice, examine what the Bible says about personal rights, discover why some people play favorites and learn practical ways to confront favoritism, and learn how they can make a positive difference in the world. Instructions are easy to follow and provide many options.

Author: Yount, Christine **1194**
Series: Group's Active Bible Curriculum
Title: *Telling Your Friends About Christ*
Publisher: Group Publishing, 1991

Num. Sess.	Group Time	Num. Pgs.	Avg. Qst.	Price	Audience	Format	Bible Study
4	35-60	48	Vry	6.95	New Christian	Workbk	Topical

Features: Intro to Leading a Study, Intro to Study, Objectives, Study Overview, Ldr's Notes, Drawings, Handouts, Agenda, Publicity Ideas
★★★★ Personal Application Preparation Time: None ISBN: 1-559-45114-9
★★★★ Relationship Building Ldr. Guide Avail.: No Size: 8.50 x 11.0
Subjects: Teens: Evangelism, Teens: Junior High
Comments: This four-lesson study helps youth learn practical skills for sharing their faith. Teens will understand their friends' need for Christ, how to reach out, how to tell others, and how to develop their own method for telling others about their relationship with God. They can be used in a Bible class or youth meeting. Instructions are easy to follow and provide multiple options for teachers. No student books are required.

Author: Youssef, Michael   **1195**
Series:
Title: *Leadership Style of Jesus, The: How to Develop Leadership Qualities*
Publisher: Victor Books, 1986

Num. Sess.	Group Time	Num. Pgs.	Avg. Qst.	Price	Audience	Format	Bible Study
13	60-90	168	N/A	7.99	New Christian	Book	Topical

Features:
  ★★★ Personal Application   Preparation Time: Med   ISBN: 0-89693-168-4
  ★★★ Relationship Building Ldr. Guide Avail.: Yes   Size: 5.50 x 8.0
Subjects: Gospels, Leadership, Loneliness, Stress
Comments: This study outlines Jesus' style of leadership, as derived from the gospel accounts. It uses eighteen principles to suggest Christlike qualities every leader needs. It also considers how to deal with the temptations and pressures leaders face, including ego, anger, loneliness, doubters, criticism, the use of power, and passing the leadership torch to others. A leader's guide with transparency masters is available.